STRUCTURE OF ARITHMETIC

JOHN H. Harrison MINNICK, 1877-

and

RAYMOND C. STRAUSS

Department of Mathematics, Foothill College, California

HARPER & ROW, Publishers   New York

STRUCTURE OF ARITHMETIC

LIBRARY OF CONGRESS CATALOG CARD NUMBER: 66-10840

CONTENTS

PREFACE

STRUCTURE OF ARITHMETIC was written not only for those who wish to strengthen their computational skill, but also for those who want to gain a deeper understanding of the nature of "number" and "operation." Many of the modern techniques for teaching mathematics are employed, and the book may serve as an introduction to the "new math." It may be used as the text for a one semester course in general mathematics either for those who plan to do no further study in mathematics or for those who need a refresher course for subsequent study of algebra.

While the book presumes the reader can perform the fundamental operations of addition, subtraction, multiplication, and division with natural numbers, there are ample opportunities, through applications, for drill. No such assumption, however, is made about computations with simple and decimal fractions. Operations with these forms of numbers are carefully defined and explained.

The unifying concept of the book is that of "set." Sets are used to define natural numbers and the addition of natural numbers. From these the rational numbers and other operations are carefully developed. Without overemphasizing the axiomatic approach, there is enough attention given to this to give the reader a flavor of the logical structure of mathematics as the real numbers and the real number line are gradually developed.

The book is in the form of a linear program, both easy to read and effective as a learning device. It makes independent study practical, but the book can also be used as the text in classes taught traditionally. The present edition is the outcome of a year's successful use in such classes. Each of the thirty chapters will require from one to one and a half hours to read, and each is followed by two sets of problems. Answers to the first set are included in the book, and answers to the second are available in an instructor's manual. Included also are a glossary of important definitions and an index.

The authors are indebted to the administration and staff of Foothill College for making it possible to use a preliminary edition of the book to carry out an effective testing program, and to the college's faculty and students for their help in making the revisions and modifications included in this edition.

J. H. M.
R. C. S.

INTRODUCTION

1. Since this is a programmed text, you must actively participate while studying it. At intervals a word is omitted, and it is your responsibility to supply the missing word. Then you should have a pencil handy, and whenever a blank appears, fill in the missing _____ .

WORD

2. After filling in the blank, you should check your answer by comparing it with the correct response, which is provided at the end of the frame. Each frame tries to convey a particular idea, and you can best learn that idea by responding whenever a blank appears, and comparing that response with the correct one, which is found at the _____ of the frame.

END

3. It is important that you understand clearly the idea presented in each frame before proceeding to the next. If your response to the blank does not exactly match the answer given at the end of the frame, you have probably misunderstood something and should re-read the frame to see why your response was incorrect. Do not go on to the next frame until you are certain that you have learned the _____ which was presented.

IDEA

4. If your answer to the frame exactly matches the one given at the end, you have probably understood the idea completely and should feel ready to go on to the next frame. It is your active response to a missing word and the immediate reinforcement of the response by comparing it with the _____ one given at the end of the frame which best insures that you will learn.

CORRECT

5. Naturally, you will want to avoid reading the correct response until after you have made your own. It will be a good idea for you to hold a small card over the correct response while reading the frame, so that you will not accidently read the answer before making your _____ .

RESPONSE

6. Remember, you will learn more if you make your response _____ reading the correct one given at the end.

BEFORE

7. And be certain that your response is either exactly like the correct one or that you understand completely where you made your mistake, before proceeding to the next frame. If you have not already done so, stop now and get a pencil to make your responses and a small card to cover the _____ response.

CORRECT

8. If you prefer not to write in your book, you may instead write your response on a separate sheet of paper, but be certain that you do not read the correct answer until after you have written down your response. Remember it is this active participation that contributes most to your learning. You will probably not learn as much if you just read the text without _____ to the blanks which appear.

RESPONDING

9. Since this is a text in arithmetic, many of the blanks will require that you supply a missing number. For example, the number of this frame is _____ .

9

10. Often you will be required to make a computation before knowing what the missing number is. If you multiply the number of this frame by the number of the preceding one, the result is _____ .

90

11. It will frequently happen that you may have to do considerable computation before finding the correct number. You may use the margin of the text or a separate sheet of paper for such computations. When 518 is divided by 14, the result is _____ .

$$14\overline{)518} \quad \begin{array}{r} 37 \\ \hline \end{array}$$
$$\begin{array}{r} 42 \\ \hline 98 \\ 98 \end{array}$$

12. The answer portion of the last frame showed not only the correct response, but also how that answer was obtained. When this is done you will want to compare not only your final result, but also your method of obtaining that result. Be certain that your _____ as well as your result agrees with the correct one given.

METHOD

13. Sometimes a frame will contain more than one blank. After making your response to the first blank, check your answer before going to the next. You should be especially careful when checking your_____ response to avoid accidentally reading the answer to the following blank. Respond to each blank separately and check your response _____ continuing to the next blank.

FIRST;   BEFORE

14. This becomes especially important when more than one arithmetic computation is required in one frame. In the problem below it is essential to have the correct response to the first blank before continuing to the second.

$3 + 5 + 2 =$ _____ $+ 2 =$ _____ .

8;   10

15. But in the preceding frame it is equally important to _____ reading the second response while checking the first.

AVOID

16. Sometimes the answer portion to a frame will indicate that two blanks could be interchanged without affecting the meaning of the frame. For example, since a programmed text requires that the reader actively participate while studying, then he must certainly be able to both _____ and _____ in order to use such a text properly.

READ;   WRITE   (either order)

17. But in most frames with more than one blank it is important not to change the order of the responses. For best results with a programmed text you should first _____ the answer and then _____ the correct response.

WRITE;   READ

18. Occasionally a frame will contain no blank at all, and it will not be necessary for you to make any response. Be sure to read such frames just as carefully as you would any other frame, and go on to the next one.

19. If you are reading carefully and thinking about your response before writing it down, you should make a mistake very seldom. There is always some hint given in the frame, and if you do not immediately think of the answer, re-read the frame and look for the _____.

HINT

20. As you read each chapter keep a count of the number of frames missed. A careful reader should not miss more than six or eight frames out of a hundred. If you miss more than that, you are probably reading carelessly or not giving enough thought before making your response. You are more likely to learn when you seldom make an _____ response to a frame.

INCORRECT

21. Sometimes a word will be written in all capital letters. These words are especially important, and you should learn exactly what they mean. At the end of the book there is a GLOSSARY of important words and their meanings. The most important word in this frame is _____.

GLOSSARY

22. Frequently the capitalized words are ones that have a special meaning when used in mathematics. Even though you may know the meaning of the word when used in another context, it will be essential that you understand its meaning as used in this text. When in doubt about the meaning of a word, you should consult the _____ found at the end of the text.

GLOSSARY

23. The text also contains an INDEX, which gives the page number and frame number where important words are first used in the text. If the glossary does not explain the meaning of a key word to your satisfaction, you may want to consult the _____ to see where you may find a more complete explanation of the word.

INDEX

24. By all means be careful to learn exactly the meanings given in this text for all words which are written in _____ letters.

CAPITAL

25. If your understanding of these key words is in error or is incomplete, it will be impossible for you to continue reading with comprehension. Don't depend on your previous knowledge or try to guess the meanings of these words. You must fully understand the exact meaning as given in the text. Both the _____ and the _____ will be an aid in helping you to remember these key words.

GLOSSARY; INDEX (either order)

26. The text is divided into thirty chapters, each of which contains approximately 100-150 frames. It will probably be to your advantage to read an entire chapter without interruption, since each chapter contains a group of related ideas, and these will be best understood if taken together. Then if this advice is followed, you must plan to read at least one _____ each time you begin reading.

CHAPTER

27. Reading time for the chapters will vary greatly from person to person, but the average reader will require approximately one hour per chapter. Your rate may differ significantly from that depending on your reading skill and your previous training in arithmetic. Keep a record of your time spent reading so that you may allow yourself enough time to read an entire _____ at one sitting.

CHAPTER

28. At the end of each chapter you will find two sets of problems. In addition to reading the text, it is important that you work enough of the problems to be certain that you learn completely all of the ideas presented in the chapter. If you have an instructor, he may want to assign certain problems. If you are reading without the benefit of an instructor, you should work all of the problems in each chapter designated "Problems A." Those marked "Problems B" may also be worked if you feel that you need additional practice. But as a minimum plan to work at least all of the problems labeled _____.

A

29. At the end of the book you will find answers to the A problems. Be certain to check your answers against the correct ones given and try to understand them fully, if you made any mistakes. If you miss many of the problems, you may want to re-read portions of the chapter. You will learn the ideas in the text best if you plan not only to _____ the chapters, but also to work the _____ at the end of the chapters.

READ; PROBLEMS

30. If you are tired or bored after reading an entire chapter, you may want to rest before attempting the problems. But do not begin the next chapter until you have worked at least those problems marked _____ and have checked all your answers.

A

31. If you work the problems on the day following your reading of the chapter, this will serve as an excellent review of the chapter. By working most of the problems correctly, you can be certain that you are ready to proceed to the following _____.

CHAPTER

32. You are now ready to begin the first chapter, which follows.

CHAPTER 1

SETS

1. In this chapter we shall develop the concept of a SET. To begin we will examine some examples of sets.

2. The collection of symbols below is a _____ of road signs.

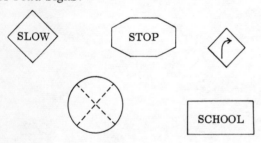

> ### SET

3. The collection of names below is a _____ of words.

> Mary   Bill
>
> Ed
>
> Carol   Dale

> ### SET

4. The symbols shown below also form a _____ .

> ### SET

5. One kind of set we shall want to consider is illustrated by

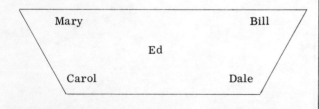

It is a set whose MEMBERS are _____ symbols.

> ### NUMBER

6. Another set whose members are _____ symbols is

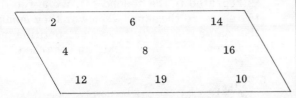

7. Some sets include dissimilar members. The assembly below is another example of a _____ .

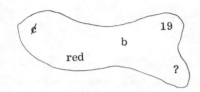

8. We are less likely to be concerned with sets whose _____ are not related in some manner, but such sets can certainly be considered.

9. The set of color names below has green as one of its _____ .

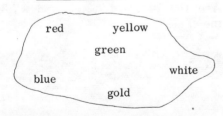

10. Sometimes it is easier to describe a set by listing its _____ in a horizontal line. Thus the set in frame 9 can be represented:

{red, yellow, blue, green, gold, white}

11. The BRACES are needed to show that the objects are to be considered as members of a _____ .

12. Use braces to represent the set whose members are 1, 2, 3, and 4. _____ .

13. Use braces to represent the set

cat

monkey

dog

bird

_____

14. Another possible representation of the set in frame 13 is

{bird, cat, monkey, _____}

15. A set is described only by the members it contains and not the _____ in which they are listed.

16. Are the following two sets the same?

$\{4, 5, 2, 19\}$ $\{4, 2, 19, 5\}$ _____

YES

17. The set

$\{$Blue, Red, White$\}$

is the same as the set

$\{$Red, White, _____$\}$

BLUE

18. Are the following two sets the same?

$\{a, b, c, d\}$ $\{\alpha, \beta, \gamma, \delta\}$ _____

NO

19. Are the sets $\{\Delta, \odot, *, \perp\}$ and $\{\odot, *, \Delta, \perp\}$ the same? _____

YES

20. Are the sets below the same set?

$\{\square, \top, \vdash, \otimes\}$ $\{\boxtimes, \bigcirc, \top, \vdash\}$ _____

NO

21. Are the following sets the same?

$\{1, 2, 3\}$ $\{1, 2, 3, 1\}$ _____

YES!   (see next frame)

22. The sets in frame 21 contain exactly the same members, even though the member 1 is repeated in the second set. We agree that two sets are the same whenever they contain the same _____. Repetition and order of _____ is disregarded.

MEMBERS;   MEMBERS

23. Are the following pairs of sets the same?

$\{\%, \%, *\}$ $\{\%, *\}$ _____

$\{4, 10, 5\}$ $\{5, 10, 4\}$ _____

$\{\nabla, \square, \perp\}$ $\{\Delta, \square, \perp\}$ _____

YES;   YES;   NO

24. Then the only consideration which need be given to answer the question, "Are these two sets the same?" is whether the sets have the same _____ without regard to _____ or repetition.

MEMBERS;   ORDER

25. Are the following two sets the same?

$\{a, b, c, a\}$ $\{c, b, c, a, c\}$ _____.

YES

26. Are the sets $\{4, 7, 2, 9\}$ and $\{7, 2, 4, 9, 9, 2\}$ the same? _____.

YES

27. Whenever two sets contain exactly the same members they are, in fact, the same set. We shall call such sets EQUAL. Thus sets $\{5, 6, 7\}$ and $\{6, 5, 7\}$ are _____.

EQUAL

28. Then two sets are equal whenever they contain the same _____ .

29. Are the following sets equal?

$\{14, 16, 18, 19, 20\}$

$\{14, 18, 20, 16, 19\}$ _____

30. Are the following sets equal?

$\{*, *, *\}$ $\{*\}$ _____

31. Are sets $\{x, y, z, x\}$ and $\{x, y, z, w\}$ equal? _____

32. Are sets $\{*, \boxminus, !, *\}$ and $\{!, *, \boxminus\}$ equal? _____

33. We will use the symbol = in place of the word _____ .

34. Then we can write

$\{1, 2, 3\} = \{3, 2, 1\}$

since the two sets are _____ .

35. Does

$\{2, 4, 6, 8\} = \{2, 4, 6\}$? _____

36. Does

$\{1, 2, 1, 3\} = \{3, 3, 1, 2\}$? _____

37. In fact, we can write

$\{*, 1, *, y\}$ _____ $\{1, *, y\}$

38. Sometimes we use capital or upper-case letters to name a set. We might call the set containing 1, 2, 3 by the name A, and write

$A = \{1, 2, 3\}$

What are the members of A? _____

39. If $B = \{\&, \%, \$, !\}$, what are the members of B? _____

40. If $C = \{2, 3, 4\}$

and $D = \{4, 3, 2\}$

does $C = D$? _____

41. If $E = \{*, \#, \ddagger\}$

and $F = \{\#, *, \$\}$

does $E = F$? _____

NO

42. Set $\{*, \#, \ddagger\}$ is not equal to set $\{\#, *, \$\}$ because it does not contain exactly the same members.
If $G = \{\alpha, \alpha, \beta, \beta, \gamma, \gamma, \delta\}$ and $H = \{\alpha, \beta, \gamma, \delta, \epsilon, \pi, \theta\}$, does $G = H$? _____

NO

43. Set $\{\alpha, \alpha, \beta, \beta, \gamma, \gamma, \delta\}$ and set $\{\alpha, \beta, \gamma, \delta, \epsilon, \pi, \theta\}$ are not equal since they do not contain exactly the _____ members.

SAME

44. When two sets, such as $J = \{1, 2, 3\}$ and $K = \{1, 2, 3, 4\}$, do not contain the same members, they are not equal. We sometimes use the symbol $\neq$ to indicate this and write $J \neq K$.

45. $\{x, y, z\}$ ___ $\{z, y, x\}$

$\{p, q, p, r\} \neq \{p, q, r, s\}$

$\{5, 7, 9, 11\}$ _____ $\{6, 8, 10, 12\}$

$\{4, 4, 4, 4\}$ _____ $\{4\}$

$\{5, *, !\}$ _____ $\{!, *, !\}$

$\neq$; $=$; $\neq$

46. We shall sometimes use the letters A, B, C, D, E, F, G, H, J, and K to represent sets different from those in the preceding frames. In fact, any letter or other suitable symbol may be used to represent a set so long as it is clear which set is being represented.

47. Some sets contain many members. Consider the set

$A = \{1, 2, 3, 4, 5, 6, 7, 8, 9, 10, 11, 12, 13, 14, 15, 16, 17, 18, 19, 20, 21, 22, 23, 24, 25\}$

A more convenient way to represent A would be to write

$A = \{1, 2, 3, ..., 25\}$

48. The three dots following the member 3 indicate that the remaining members are understood to be in the set, but are not actually listed.

If $B = \{1, 2, 3, ..., 10\}$

then the three dots here represent the members _____.

4, 5, 6, 7, 8, 9

49. If $C = \{2, 4, 6, 8, ..., 20\}$

then the three dots represent the members _____.

10, 12, 14, 16, and 18

50. If $D = \{$Sunday, Monday, Tuesday, ..., Saturday$\}$

then the three dots here represent _____.

WEDNESDAY, THURSDAY, FRIDAY

51. Let $E = \{$January, February, March, April, ..., December$\}$

Here the three dots represent _____.

MAY, JUNE, JULY, AUGUST, SEPTEMBER, OCTOBER, NOVEMBER

52. When a set contains too many members to list all of them conveniently, we shall list only a few and use three _____ to represent those understood but not actually listed.

DOTS

53. Notice that

$$\{1, 2, 3, \ldots, 10\}$$

and

$$\{1, 2, 3, 4, \ldots, 10\}$$

contain exactly the same members and hence are _____ .

EQUAL

54. If $A = \{2, 4, 6, \ldots, 30\}$

and $B = \{2, 4, 6, 8, \ldots, 30\}$

does $A = B$?   _____

YES

55. If $C = \{1, 2, 3, 4, \ldots, 20\}$

and $D = \{1, 2, 3, 4, \ldots, 30\}$

does $C = D$?   _____

NO

56. We use dots to represent members in a set only when it is clear what members the dots represent. Is it clear what the dots represent in

$$\{5, 9, 2, 8, \ldots, 51\}?$$ _____

NO

57. Use dots to represent the set containing all the letters of the alphabet.

$$\{a, b, c, \ldots, z\}$$

58. It is important to actually list the member, z, in the set above to indicate that all of the letters are in the set.

Does the set

$$\{a, b, c, d, \ldots, t\}$$

contain all the letters of the alphabet?   _____

NO

59. Let $D = \{a, b, c, \ldots, p\}$

Is k a member of D?   _____

Is s a member of D?   _____

YES;   NO

60. Use dots to represent the set of all letters from a to m.   _____

$$\{a, b, c, \ldots, m\}$$

61. Use dots to represent the set containing all the letters of the alphabet from n to z.

_____ .

$$\{n, o, p, q, \ldots, z\}$$

62. Let A be the set containing the names of all men who have been president of the United States.

Is Abraham Lincoln a member of A?   _____

Is Winston Churchill a member of A?   _____

YES;   NO

63. Let B be the set containing the names of all women who have been president of the United States.

Is George Washington a member of B?

_____

Is Queen Elizabeth a member of B? _____

Is Eleanor Roosevelt a member of B? _____

NO;   NO;   NO

64. Does the set B in frame 63 contain any members at all? _____

NO

65. A set which contains no members is called the EMPTY SET. Then set B above is an example of the _____ set.

EMPTY

66. The set of all airplane pilots who lived before 1492 contains no members and is an example of the _____ _____.

EMPTY SET

67. We use the special symbol, ϕ, to represent the empty set, or the set which contains no _____.

MEMBERS

68. The symbol used to represent the empty set is _____.

ϕ

69. The set of all men over ten feet tall is an example of the _____ _____, and can be represented by the symbol _____.

EMPTY SET; ϕ

70. The symbol ϕ will be used only to represent the _____ _____, which is the set that contains no _____.

EMPTY SET;   MEMBERS

71. Does $\phi = \{1, 2, 3\}$? _____

Is 5 a member of ϕ? _____

NO;   NO

72. If $A = \{5, 6, 7, ..., 50\}$, does $A = \phi$? _____

Is 15 a member of A? _____

Is 3 a member of A? _____

Is 10 a member of ϕ? _____

NO;   YES;   NO;   NO

73. Let $A = \{1, 2, 3\}$

$B = \{4, 5\}$

We can form a new set,

$\{1, 2, 3, 4, 5\}$

called the UNION of A and B.

74. $A = \{a, b\}$

$B = \{c, d, e, f\}$

The union of sets A and B is _____.

$\{a, b, c, d, e, f\}$

75.   A = {1, 2, 3}

        B = {3, 4, 5}

And the union of sets A and B is _____

_____ .

{1, 2, 3, 4, 5}   (there is no need to re-peat 3)

76.   A = {1, 2, 3, 4, 5}

        B = {2, 4, 6, 8, 10}

Form the union of sets A and B.

_____

{1, 2, 3, 4, 5, 6, 8, 10}

77.   A = {1, 2, 3, 4}

        B = {2, 3}

What is the union of A and B? _____

{1, 2, 3, 4}   or   A

78. If   A = {5, 6, 7}

    and   B = {2, 3, 4}

    then   {2, 3, 4, 5, 6, 7}

    is called the _____ of A and B.

UNION

79. A set which contains all the members in either of two original sets, or in both sets, is called their _____ .

UNION

80. When convenient, we shall use the symbol ∪ to represent "union." Thus, A ∪ B will represent the union of sets A and B and will be read "A _____ B."

UNION

81. If   A = {@, *, 0}

    and   B = {%, ¢},

    then A ∪ B is the set _____ .

{@, *, 0, %, ¢}

82. Find

    {5, 8, 9} ∪ {1, 6, 7}   _____

    {a, c, d, e} ∪ {b, c, d}   _____

    {cat, dog} ∪ {rabbit, monkey} _____

{1, 5, 6, 7, 8, 9};   {a, b, c, d, e};
{cat, dog, rabbit, monkey}

83. The union of sets A and B can be represented by the symbols _____ . It is the set which contains all the members found either in A or in B or in both.

A ∪ B

84. Let   A = {1, 2, 3, 4}

    and   B = {3, 4, 5}

Notice that 3 and 4 are members of both A and B. The set

{3, 4}

is called the INTERSECTION of A and B.

85.   C = {a, b, c, d}

        D = {b, d, e, f}

The intersection of C and D is _____

{b, d}

86. $E = \{\not c, \$, !, ?\}$
        $F = \{@, \$, \#, \&\}$

What is the intersection of E and F?

_____

$\{\$\}$

87. $A = \{1, 2, 3, 4\}$
        $B = \{3, 2, 1\}$

Find the intersection of A and B.

_____

$\{1, 2, 3\}$ or   B

88. $C = \{a, c, d\}$
        $D = \{b, d, e\}$

The union of C and D is _____ .

$\{a, b, c, d, e\}$ (This is the union of D and C.)

89. When convenient, we shall use the symbol ∩ to represent "intersection." Thus, A ∩ B will represent the intersection of sets A and B and will be read " _____ _____ _____ ."

A   INTERSECTION   B

90. If $P = \{a, b, d\}$
          $Q = \{b, c, d\}$

then P ∩ Q = _____ .

$\{b, d\}$

91. We can represent the intersection of A and B in symbols by writing _____ . This is the set which contains exactly those members found in A and at the same time in B.

A ∩ B

92. If $A = \{1, 3, 5, 6\}$
          $B = \{2, 5, 6, 7\}$

then A ∪ B = _____
      A ∩ B = _____ .

$\{1, 2, 3, 5, 6, 7\}$; $\{5, 6\}$

93. The symbol ∪ means _____ , while the symbol ∩ means _____ .

UNION;   INTERSECTION

94. Find each of the following:

$\{1, 2, 3, 4, 5\} \cap \{2, 4, 6, 8, 10\}$ _____
$\{a, d, e\} \cup \{b, c, d\}$ _____
$\{12, 8, 6, 4\} \cap \{4, 5, 9, 11\}$ _____

$\{2, 4\}$; $\{a, b, c, d, e\}$; $\{4\}$

95. If $A = \{1, 2, 3\}$
          $B = \{4, 5\}$

then A ∩ B = _____ .

φ   (There are no members both in A and in B.)

96. We say that sets A and B in frame 95 are DISJOINT, since their intersection is the _____ _____.

EMPTY SET

97. Are $\{a, c, f\}$ and $\{d, f, g\}$ disjoint? _____

NO

98. Are $\{1, 3, 5\}$ and $\{2, 4, 6\}$ disjoint? _____

YES

99. If $A \cap B = \phi$, that is, if the intersection of A and B is the _____ _____, then we say that A and B are _____.

EMPTY SET; DISJOINT

100. If $A = \{a, c, e, f\}$
        $B = \{b, d\}$
    then $A \cap B =$ _____
        $A \cup B =$ _____.
    Are A and B disjoint? _____

ϕ; $\{a, b, c, d, e, f\}$;   YES

101. Let $A = \{1, 2, 3, 4, 5\}$. Consider the sets
        $B = \{1, 2, 3, 4\}$
        $C = \{2, 4, 5\}$
        $D = \{1, 3, 4, 5\}$.

Since every member of sets B, C, and D is also a member of set A, these sets are SUBSETS of A.

102. Since set B contains only members which are also in set A, we say that B is a _____ of A.

SUBSET

103. If $A = \{1, 4, 6, 8\}$
    and $B = \{2, 4, 6\}$
    is B a subset of A? _____

NO

104. If $A = \{1, 4, 6, 8\}$
    and $B = \{4, 6, 8\}$
    is B a subset of A? _____

YES

105. Let $A = \{2, 5, 6, 7, 9, 11\}$.
    Which of the following subsets are of A?
        $B = \{2, 7, 11\}$
        $C = \{5, 6, 9\}$
        $D = \{6, 7, 8, 9\}$

B and C

106. If $E = \{a, b, c, d\}$, then $\{b, c\}$ is an example a _____ of E.

SUBSET

107. Let   A = {1, 2, 3, 4, 5}
           B = {2, 3, 4}
    Is B a subset of A?   _____
    Is A a subset of B?   _____
    Are A and B disjoint?   _____

    YES;   NO;   NO

108. Let   C = {4, 5, 6}
           D = {6, 5, 4}
    Is C a subset of D?   _____

    YES   (Every member of C is also a
    member of D.)

109.   A = {a, b, c}
       B = {c, b, a}
    Is A a subset of B?   _____
    Is B a subset of A?   _____

    YES;   YES

110.   A = {1, 2, 3, 4}
       B = {1, 2, 3, 4}
    Is A a subset of B?   _____
    Is B a subset of A?   _____
    Is A equal to B?   _____

    YES;   YES;   YES

111. If two sets are equal, each is a _____
    of the other.

    SUBSET

112. In fact, every set is a _____ of itself.

    SUBSET

113. Remember if B contains only members which
    are also in A, then B is a _____ of A.

    SUBSET

114. Consider φ and A = {1, 2, 3}.
    Does φ contain any members which are not
    also in A?   _____

    NO   (In fact φ contains no members at all)

115.   A = {1, 2, 3}
    Since φ, the empty set, contains no members
    which are not also in A, we say that φ is a
    _____ of A.

    SUBSET

116. Suppose S is any set. Since φ contains no
    members at all, and hence no members which
    are not also in S, we can say that φ is a
    _____ of S.

    SUBSET

117. Then _____ is a subset of every set.

    φ

118. Hence every set has two rather special sub-sets. For if S is any set, then both _____ and _____ are subsets of S.

S; φ (either order)

119. Consider the sets

A = {1, 3, 4, 7}

B = {c, d, e, f}

C = {a, b}

D = {g, h, 5, 6}

One of these sets is different from the others. The set which is different is _____.

C

120. Set C in frame 119 is different from the others because it has fewer _____ than the others.

MEMBERS

121. Examine sets

A = {1, 3, 4, 7} and B = {c, d, e, f}.

Notice that it is possible to exactly "pair off" the members of A with the members of B.

Thus, 1 3 4 7 is such a pairing.

↕ ↕ ↕ ↕
c d e f

Here we have associated each member of set A with a member of set B in such a way that no two members of A are paired with the same member of B.

122. B = {c, d, e, f}

C = {a, b}

Is an association or pairing like that described in frame 121 possible with sets B and C? _____

NO (B has too many members.)

123. B = {c, d, e, f}

D = {%, *, &, !}

Is it possible to pair the members of B with the members of D? _____

YES

124. E = {cat, dog, tree}

F = {*, 1, a}

Can the members of E and F be paired? _____

YES

125. Whenever two sets have the property that each member of the first set can be associated or paired exactly with a member of the second set, the two sets are said to have the SAME SIZE.

126. A = {1, 4, a, b}

B = {cat, dog, blue, green}

Do A and B have the same size? _____

YES

127. A = {a, 1, 4, c}

B = {tree, girl, dog}

C = {$, *, #}

D = {2, 3, 4, 5}

A and _____ have the same size.

B and _____ have the same size.

D; C

128. Whenever the members of one set can be paired exactly with the members of another set, the two sets are said to have the same _____ .

SIZE

129. Remember that

$\{1, 2, 3, 1\} = \{1, 2, 3\}$

A = $\{1, 2, 3, 1\}$

B = $\{a, b, c\}$

Do A and B have the same size?

YES   (Since A = $\{1, 2, 3\}$, B = $\{a, b, c\}$)

130.   C = $\{a, b, a, c, b\}$

D = $\{\#, \#, !, *\}$

Do sets C and D have the same size? _____

YES   (C = $\{a, b, c\}$, D = $\{\#, !, *\}$)

131. When comparing sets to determine whether they have the same size, we will first want to eliminate any members which are repeated in either set.

132. Let us review. Any collection of things is called a _____ .

SET

133. Two sets are equal if they contain exactly the same _____ .

MEMBERS

134. The set which contains no members is called the _____ _____ , and is represented by the symbol _____ .

EMPTY SET; ϕ

135. If we begin with two sets and form a third set which contains all those members found in either or both of the original sets, then such a third set is called the _____ of the first two.

UNION

136. If we begin with two sets and form a third set which contains exactly those members of the first which are also members of the second, then such a third set is called the _____ of the first two.

INTERSECTION

137.   A = $\{1, 3, 4, 6\}$

B = $\{2, 4, 5, 6\}$

A $\cap$ B = _____ .

A $\cup$ B = _____ .

$\{4, 6\}$; $\{1, 2, 3, 4, 5, 6\}$

138. If the intersection of two sets is the empty set, then the sets are said to be _____ .

DISJOINT

139. If we begin with a set and form a second set which contains only members found in the first, then the second set is said to be a _____ of the first.

SUBSET

140. A = {1, 4, 5, 7}

Which of the following are subsets of A?

_____

B = {1, 4}

C = {4, 5, 8}

D = {5}

E = {7, 5, 4, 1}

F = φ

All except C are subsets of A.

141. If each member of one set can be paired exactly with a different member of a second set, then the two sets are said to have the same _____ .

SIZE

142. A = {a, d, e, g}

B = {1, 2, 3, 4}

Are A and B equal? _____

Do A and B have the same size? _____

Are A and B disjoint? _____

Is A a subset of B? _____

NO;   YES;   YES;   NO

Chapter 1

Problems A (Answers on page 506)

Between each of the pairs of sets below, insert either the symbol = or the symbol ≠ so as to form a true statement.

Examples: {p, q} _____ {q, p}   Answer: =

{4, 5, 4} _____ {5, 4, 6}
Answer: ≠

1. {□, △, ⊥} _____ {△, □, ⊥}

2. {4, 4, 4} _____ {3, 3, 3}

3. {α, β, γ, δ, ε} _____ {a, b, c, d}

4. {α, β, γ, δ, ε} _____ {a, b, c, d, e}

5. {⊥} _____ {⊥, ⊥, ⊥, ⊥}

For each pair of sets below, state whether the sets do or do not have the same size.

Examples: {p, q}; {q, p}   Answer: DO

{4, 5, 6}; {5, 6, 7}   Answer: DO

6. {1, 2, 3, 4}; {4, 5, 6, 7}

7. {*, #, ♭}; {x, y, z}

8. {□, ⊠, ■}; {○, ⊗, ●}

9. {red, white, blue}; {orange, yellow, green, black}

10. {1, 4, 7, 10, 13}; {3, 3, 3, 3, 3}

Consider the following sets:

A = {1, 2, 3, 4, 5}

B = {2, 3, 5}

C = {1, 4}

D = {4, 5, 6, 7}

E = {2, 5, 6}

F = {5, 4, 1, 3, 4, 2}

11. Which of the sets is a subset of A?

12. Form the set A ∪ D.

13. Form the set B ∪ E.

14. Form the set A ∪ B.

15. Form the set D ∩ E.

16. Form the set B ∩ C.

17. Form the set A ∩ F.

18. Which pairs of sets are disjoint?

19. Which pairs of sets are equal?

20. Which pairs of sets have the same size?

Let S be the set of states in the United States. Tell whether each statement below is true or false.

Examples: {Alabama, Alaska, Arizona} is a subset of S.   Answer: True

George Washington is a member of S.   Answer: False

21. The set of Pacific coast states, {California, Oregon, Washington}, is a subset of S.

22. φ is a subset of S.

23. Mexico is a member of S.

24. New Orleans is a member of S.

25. Massachusetts is a member of S.

Describe each of the following sets.

Example: The union of the set of all male students at a college and the set of all female students at that college.

Answer: The set of all students at the college.

26. The intersection of the set of all persons living in the United States west of the Mississippi River and the set of people living in the states of New York and California.

27. The union of the set of all males living in Cincinnati and the set of all females living in Cincinnati.

28. The intersection of the set of all living females less than six feet tall and the set of all living persons under five years of age.

29. The intersection of the set of all male students at a college and the set of all female students at that college.

30. The union of the set of all persons whose income last year was under $5,000 and the set of all persons whose income last year was $5,000 or more, but less than $10,000.

Problems B

Between each of the pairs of sets below, insert either the symbol = or the symbol ≠ so as to form a true statement.

1. {△, □, △, □} _____ {△, □, △}
2. {3, 5, 7, 9, 11} _____ {11, 9, 7, 5, 3}
3. {□, ⊠, ■} _____ {◯ ⊗, ●}
4. {1, 2, 1, 3, 1, 4} _____ {2, 1, 2, 3, 2, 4}
5. φ _____ {0}

For each pair of sets below, state whether the sets do or do not have the same size.

6. {α, β, γ, δ}; {ρ, θ, φ}
7. {4, 5, 4}; {4, 5}
8. {*, #, ♭, ♮}; {1, 1, 1, 1}
9. {▽, ▽, ▽}; {□, □, □, □, □}
10. {1, 3, 5, 7, 9}; {2, 4, 6, 8, 10}

Let S = {1, 2, 3}

11. Form the set S ∪ φ.
12. Form the set S ∩ φ.
13. Form the set S ∪ S.
14. Form the set S ∩ S.
15. Form the set φ ∪ φ.
16. Form the set φ ∩ φ.
17. List all the subsets of S. (There are eight of them.)
18. Are S and φ disjoint sets?
19. Are φ and φ disjoint sets?
20. Are S and S disjoint sets?

Let S be the set of states in the United States. Tell whether each statement below is true or false.

21. S is a subset of {Massachusetts, Maine, Missouri}.
22. Boston is a subset of S.
23. Louisiana is a member of S.
24. {Louisiana} is a subset of S.
25. {Louisiana} is a member of S.

Describe each of the following sets.

26. The intersection of the set consisting of interstate highways 40 and 50, and the set consisting of interstate highways 50 and 60.
27. The intersection of the set of all automobile mechanics living in Chicago and the set of all stamp collectors living in Chicago.
28. The union of the set of all male United States citizens living in Florida and the set of all female United States citizens living in Florida.
29. The intersection of the set of all animals that lay eggs and the set of all animals that do not lay eggs.
30. The union of the set of all living persons over one thousand years old and the set of all living horses that can fly.

Suppose P and Q are any two sets, not necessarily different sets, and that P is a subset of Q.

31. What is P ∪ Q?
32. What is P ∩ Q?
33. Could P and Q be equal?
34. Could P and Q have the same size?
35. Could P and Q be disjoint?

CHAPTER 2

NATURAL NUMBERS AND ADDITION

1. Any collection of things is called a _____.

> **SET**

2. If A = {1, yellow, ?, Bill}
   then yellow is one of the _____ of A.

> **MEMBERS**

3. A set which contains all the members which are either in set A, or in set B, or in both sets, is called the _____ of A and B.

> **UNION**

4. If   A = {a, b, c}
      B = {b, d, e, f}
   then   A ∪ B = _____.

> **{a, b, c, d, e, f}**

5. A set which contains all the members of set A which are also members of set B is called the _____ of A and B.

> **INTERSECTION**

6. If   A = {a, b, c}
      B = {b, c, d}
   then   A ∩ B = _____.

> **{b, c}**

7. If   C = {1, 3, 5, 7}
      D = {2, 4, 6}
   then   C ∪ D = _____.
      C ∩ D = _____.

> **{1, 2, 3, 4, 5, 6, 7};   φ**

8. If C ∩ D = φ, then sets C and D are said to be _____.

> **DISJOINT**

9. A = {a, b, c}

Which of the following have the same size as A? _____

B = {1, 2, 3}

C = {x, y, z}

D = {cat, dog, rat}

E = {%, #, *}

ALL DO

10. E = {red, white, blue}

F = {Tom, Dick, Harry}

E and F are not equal sets, but they have the same _____.

SIZE

11. Are there other sets of the same size as {a, b, c}? _____

YES

12. In fact there is no limit to the list of sets all of which have the same size as {a, b, c}. The sets in this list might contain different kinds of members, but there is one thing all these sets have in common, their size. We could call this common property threeness.

13. Which of these sets have the property of threeness? _____

F = {Mary, Ruth, Jane}

G = {101, 102, 103}

H = {Utah, Arizona, Montana}

I = {+, −, ×}

ALL DO

14. The property shared by the sets in frame 13 has been called _____.

THREENESS

15. But this is only a name for the property. These sets would have the property even if we used a different name for it. We admit that san, drei, trois, III, and 3 are other possible names for it. Is three a possible name? _____

YES

16. Does A = {a, b, c, d, e} have the threeness property? _____

NO

17. B = {2, 4, 6, 8, 10}

C = {red, orange, yellow, green, blue}

D = {Ford, Rambler, Dodge, Pontiac, Dobbin}

E = {%, *, @, 0, !}

These sets are not equal, but they all have the same _____ as A = {a, b, c, d, e}.

SIZE

18. The property shared by all sets of the same size as

    A = {a, b, c, d, e}

    may be called fiveness. Which of these sets possess fiveness?

    F = {6, 5, 4, 3, 2}

    G = {r, s, t, u, v}

    H = {up, down, left, right, back}

    _____

    ALL DO

19. The property shared by all sets which have the same size as

    A = {a, b, c, d, e}

    has been called _____.

    FIVENESS

20. Other _____ for the property we have called fiveness might be sanc, cinco, V, or 5.

    NAMES

21. Which of these sets possess twoness?
    _____

    A = {a, b}

    B = {3, 4}

    C = {Ed, George}

    D = {&, @}

    E = {blue, black}

    ALL DO

22. A = {a}   E = {George}

    B = {*}   F = {cat}

    C = {1}   G = {Z}

    D = {$}

    These sets all possess a property that we might call _____.

    ONENESS

23. However, we prefer to call this property the NATURAL NUMBER ONE.

24. Then the property shared by all sets which have the same size as {a} is called the natural _____ one.

    NUMBER

25. Many symbols, both verbal and nonverbal, represent the _____ number one.

    NATURAL

26. The symbols 1, 3 − 2, 6/6, 1/2 + 1/2, all represent the _____ _____ one.

    NATURAL NUMBER

27. Any symbol used to represent the natural number one will be called a NUMERAL. Thus

    $1, \quad 3-2, \quad \frac{6}{6}, \quad$ and $\quad \frac{1}{2} + \frac{1}{2}$

    are all N_____ representing the natural number one.

    NUMERALS

28. Of all the possible numerals which might be used to represent the natural number one, let us agree that the SIMPLEST FORM shall be the symbol 1.

29. Then the symbol 1 is the simplest form of the _____ _____ _____.

NATURAL NUMBER ONE

30. And the natural number one is the property shared by all _____ which have the same _____ as {a}.

SETS;   SIZE

31. Similarly, we call that property shared by all sets of the same size as {a, b} the natural number _____.

TWO

32. And many different symbols could be used to represent the natural number two. Thus, 1 + 1, 6 – 4, 6/3, II, and 2 are all numerals representing the _____ _____ two.

NATURAL NUMBER

33. Let us agree that the numeral 2 will be called the _____ form of the natural number two. It is the symbol we shall most commonly use.

SIMPLEST

34. We could define the _____ _____ _____ as that property shared by all sets of the same size as {a, b, c}.

NATURAL NUMBER THREE

35. Possible symbols used to represent the natural number three might be 3, 1 + _____, and 4 – _____.

2;   1

36. Each of the symbols 3, 1 + 2, and 4 – 1 is a _____ which represents the natural number three.

NUMERAL

37. But we agree that the numeral 3 is the _____ _____ of the natural number three.

SIMPLEST FORM

38. And the natural number three is that property shared by all _____ of the same _____ as {a, b, c}.

SETS;   SIZE

39. That property shared by all sets of the same size as {a, b, c, d} is called the _____ _____ _____.

NATURAL NUMBER FOUR

40. And the simplest form of the natural number four is the numeral _____ .

4

41. In a similar way we can define other _____ numbers.

NATURAL

42. Sets of the same size as {a, b, c, d, e} share a property we call the natural _____ _____ .

NUMBER FIVE

43. The symbol 7 is the simplest form of the _____ _____ _____ .

NATURAL NUMBER SEVEN

44. Other numerals which represent 7 are 3 + _____ , 8 – _____ , and 14/2.

4;   1

45. We could go on, indefinitely, defining other natural numbers. Each is a property shared by _____ of the same _____ .

SETS;   SIZE

46. The symbols used to represent natural numbers are called _____ .

NUMERALS

47. Which of the following are numerals?

12, 63, 100/2, 30 + 75, 15 – 9

_____

ALL ARE

48. The numerals most commonly used to represent natural numbers are 1, 2, 3, 4, 5, ... Each of these symbols is the _____ _____ of the natural number it represents.

SIMPLEST FORM

49. The symbol 8 is a numeral which represents the natural number eight. While 8 is only a symbol representing a natural number, we shall often speak of "the natural number 8" or even shorten this to simply "the number 8." This is done for convenience only.

50. Similarly, the symbols 1, 2, 3, 4, ... will often be called "natural numbers" whereas, in fact, they are only N_____ which represent natural numbers.

NUMERALS

51. Indeed, we shall even refer to these symbols as, simply, "numbers." However, whenever there is a possibility of misunderstanding, or whenever the distinction between a natural number and a numeral which represents it must be made, we shall be careful to use the correct term.

52. Associated with every set there is a number. For the set {x, y, z} there is the number 3; for the set {5} the number 1. What number is associated with these sets?

{a, b}   _____

{red, blue, green, yellow}   _____

{1, 2, 3, 4, 5, 6, 7, 8, 9, 10}   _____

2;   4;   10

53. The number associated with each set is the name of the property shared by that set and all other sets of the same _____.

> SIZE

54. We call the number associated with each set the SIZE OF THE SET.

55. Thus the size of {a, b} is 2; the size of {3} is 1; the size of {cat, dog, red} is _____.

> 3

56. What is the size of each of these sets?

{a, b, c, d}   _____

{2, 4}   _____

{5}   _____

> 4;   2;   1

57. Let us consider the ADDITION of natural numbers. The result of adding 4 to 7 is _____.

> 11

58. The result of an addition is called a SUM. Thus 11 is the sum of 4 and 7. What is the sum of 16 and 21? _____

> 37

59. The result of an addition is called a _____.

> SUM

60. The sum of 9 and 6 is 15. The numbers 9 and 6 are called the TERMS of this sum. Since 12 is the sum of 3 and 9, we call _____ and _____ the terms of this sum.

> 3;   9

61. The symbol +, called a PLUS SIGN, is used to indicate a sum. Thus, 3+4 represents the _____ of 3 and 4.

> SUM

62. In the sum 5 + 7, we call 5 and 7 the _____.

> TERMS

63. The symbol 4 + 5 and the symbol 9 both represent the natural number nine. Let us agree to call two numerals which represent the same natural number EQUAL and indicate this by using the symbol =. Thus, we shall write

$4 + 5$ _____ 9

> =

64. Since 4 + 5 = 9, we shall use either expression to represent the sum of 4 and 5. Hence, the expression 4 + 5 may itself be referred to as a _____.

> SUM

65. $9 + 2 = 11$

We call 9 + 2 a _____, while _____ and _____ are called the terms of this _____.

> SUM;   9;   2;   SUM

66. Perform the indicated addition.

$$3 + 8 \ = \ \rule{2cm}{0.4pt}$$

$$23 + 12 \ = \ \rule{2cm}{0.4pt}$$

$$846 + 295 \ = \ \rule{2cm}{0.4pt}$$

11;   35;   1141

67. You are already familiar with the addition facts needed to perform any problem in addition of natural numbers. Let us see what it actually _means_ to add two natural numbers.

68. A = {a, b}   B = {c, d, e}

C = {a, b, c, d, e}

The size of A is 2.
The size of B is _____.
The size of C is _____.

3;   5

69. A = {a, b}   B = {c, d, e}

C = {a, b, c, d, e}

It is interesting to note that

A _____ B = C

2 _____ 3 = 5

∪;   +

70. R = {x}   S = {y, z}

R ∪ S = _____

The size of R is 1.

The size of S is 2.

The size of R ∪ S is _____.

{x, y, z};   3

71. P = {a, b, c, d}   Q = {1, 2, 3}

What is the size of P? _____

What is the size of Q? _____

What is the size of P ∪ Q? _____

4;   3;   7

72. G = {a, b}   H = {x, y}

Does the size of G ∪ H equal the size of G plus the size of H? _____

YES

73. G = {1, 2, 3, 4, 5}   H = {6, 7, 8, 9, 10, 11}

The size of G ∪ H equals the size of G _____ the size of H.

PLUS   or   +

74. A = {2}   B = {x, y}

Does the size of A ∪ B equal the size of A plus the size of B? _____

YES

75. If A and B are _any_ two sets, will the size of A ∪ B equal the size of A plus the size of B? _____

NO!   (see next frame)

76. Suppose   A = {a, b, c}   B = {c, d}

Then A ∪ B = _____.

{a, b, c, d}

77.　　A = {a, b, c}　　B = {c, d}

　　　　A ∪ B = {a, b, c, d}

The size of A is 3, the size of B is 2, but the size of A ∪ B is _____, not 5.

> 4

78.　　A = {a, b, c}　　B = {c, d}　　C = {x, y}

Does the size of A ∪ B equal the size of A plus the size of B?_____

Does the size of A ∪ C equal the size of A plus the size of C?_____

> NO;　　YES

79.　　A = {a, b, c}　　B = {c, d}　　C = {x, y}

Notice that

　　　　A ∩ B = {c}

while A ∩ C = _____.

> φ

80.　　A = {a, b, c}　　B = {c, d}　　C = {x, y}

Since A ∩ C = φ, we say that A and C are _____ sets.

> DISJOINT

81.　　A = {a, b, c}　　B = {c, d}　　C = {x, y}

A and C are disjoint, and the size of A ∪ C equals the size of A plus the size of C.

A and B are not disjoint, and the size of A ∪ B does not equal the size of A plus the size of B.

82.　　R = {1, 2, 3}　　S = {2, 4, 5, 6}

Are R and S disjoint? _____

Does the size of R ∪ S equal the size of R plus the size of S? _____

> NO;　　NO

83.　　P = {1, 3, 5}　　Q = {2, 4, 6, 8}

Are P and Q disjoint? _____

Does the size of P ∪ Q equal the size of P plus the size of Q? _____

> YES;　　YES

84.　The size of A ∪ B equals the size of A plus the size of B only when A and B are _____ sets.

> DISJOINT

85.　In fact, we define the sum of two natural numbers to be the size of the union of two disjoint sets whose sizes are the given natural numbers.

86.　Hence the sum of 2 and 4 is the size of the _____ of two disjoint sets which have sizes 2 and 4.

> UNION

87.　And the sum of 4 and 7 is the size of the union of two _____ sets which have sizes 4 and 7.

> DISJOINT

88. The sum of 12 and 3 is the _____ of the union of two disjoint sets which have _____ 12 and 3.

> SIZE;   SIZES

89. Which of these sets could be used to find the sum of 3 and 2?

A = {a, b, c}

B = {c, d}

C = {d, e, f, g}

D = {d, e}   _____

> ONLY A AND D

90. A = {a, b}

B = {b, c, d}

C = {a, b, c, d}

D = {x, y, z}

Using the letters A, B, C, and D, represent a set whose size is the sum of 3 and 4.

_____.

> D ∪ C   or   C ∪ D

91. The sum of two natural numbers is the _____ of the _____ of two disjoint sets whose sizes are the given natural numbers.

> SIZE;   UNION

92. Does

{1, 2, 3, 4} = {3, 4, 1, 2} ?   _____

> YES

93. A = {1, 2}   B = {3, 4}

Does A ∪ B = {1, 2, 3, 4} ?   _____

Does A ∪ B = {3, 4, 1, 2} ?   _____

And A ∪ B = {4, 3, _____, 1}.

> YES;   YES;   2

94. C = {1, 2}   D = {3, 4, 5}

Does C ∪ D = {3, 1, 5, 2, 4} ?   _____

Does D ∪ C = {3, 1, 5, 2, 4} ?   _____

> YES;   YES

95. G = {a, b}   H = {x, y, z}

Does G ∪ H = {a, b, x, y, z} ?   _____

Does H ∪ G = {a, b, x, y, z} ?   _____

Does G ∪ H = H ∪ G?   _____

> YES;   YES;   YES

96. R = {a, b, c}   S = {x, y}

Does R ∪ S = S ∪ R?   _____

> YES

97. Does {1, 2} ∪ {3, 4, 5} = {3, 4, 5} ∪ {1, 2} ?

_____

Does {a} ∪ {b, c, d} = {b, c, d} ∪ {a} ?   _____

> YES;   YES

98. {a, b} ∪ {c, d, e} = {c, d, e} ∪ _____.

> {a, b}

99.   A = {x, y}   B = {a, b, c}

      A ∪ B = B ∪ _____

> A

100.   P = {1, 2, 3}   Q = {2, 3, 4}

Does P ∪ Q = Q ∪ P?   _____

Are P and Q disjoint?   _____

> YES;   NO

101.   S = {1, 3, 5}   T = {2, 4}

Does S ∪ T = T ∪ S?   _____

Are S and T disjoint?   _____

> YES;   YES

102.   Whether or not S and T are disjoint sets, we see that

      S ∪ T = T ∪ _____

> S

103.   In fact, if A and B are any sets at all, then

      A ∪ B = _____

> B ∪ A

104.   Then in forming the union of two sets it makes no difference in which order the sets are taken. We say that forming a union of two sets is a COMMUTATIVE process.

105.   The fact that

      A ∪ B = B ∪ A

is described by saying that forming a union of two sets is a C_____ process.

> COMMUTATIVE

106.   A = {1, 2, 3}   B = {2, 3, 4}

A ∩ B = {2, 3}

B ∩ A = _____

> {2, 3}

107.   C = {a, b, c, d}   D = {b, c, d, e}

Does C ∩ D = D ∩ C?   _____

> YES

108.   A = {1, 2}   B = {x, 4}

A ∩ B = _____

Are A and B disjoint?   _____

> φ;   YES

109.   A = {1, 2}   B = {x, y}

A ∩ B = φ

B ∩ A = _____

Does A ∩ B = B ∩ A?   _____

> φ;   YES

110. In fact, if A and B are any two sets

A ∩ B = _____

B ∩ A

111. Since A ∩ B = B ∩ A

we say that forming the intersection of two sets is a C_____ process.

COMMUTATIVE

112. Both set union and set intersection are said to be _____ processes.

COMMUTATIVE

113. Consider the sum 3 + 5. By definition, this is the size of the _____ of two disjoint sets whose sizes are 3 and 5.

UNION

114. We are considering 3 + 5. Let A = {a, b, c} and B = {p, q, r, s, t}. Then

A ∩ B = _____

A ∪ B = _____

φ;   {a, b, c, p, q, r, s, t}

115.   A ∩ B = φ   A ∪ B = {a, b, c, p, q, r, s, t}

The size of A ∪ B is _____ and so

3 + 5 = _____

8;   8

116. We have shown that 3 + 5 = 8.

Let us now consider the sum 5 + 3. By definition, this is the _____ of the _____ of two disjoint sets whose sizes are 5 and 3.

SIZE;   UNION

117. Again, let B = {p, q, r, s, t} and A {a, b, c}.

Since B and A are disjoint sets, the sum 5 + 3 is the size of _____.

B ∪ A

118.   A = {a, b, c}   B = {p, q, r, s, t}

The sum 3 + 5 is the size of _____.

The sum 5 + 3 is the size of _____.

A ∪ B;   B ∪ A

119.   A = {a, b, c}   B = {p, q, r, s, t}

3 + 5 is the size of A ∪ B.

5 + 3 is the size of B ∪ A.

But we have already seen that set union is a commutative process, and so A ∪ B = _____.

B ∪ A

120.   A = {a, b, c}   B = {p, q, r, s, t}

Since A ∪ B = B ∪ A, the size of A ∪ B and the size of B ∪ A must both be the number _____.

8

121. Hence we have shown that $3 + 5 = 5 + 3$, since both sums equal 8. The sum, 8, does not depend on the order of the _____, 3 and 5.

TERMS

122. This is an example of a general result. If a and b represent any two natural numbers, the sum $a + b$ is the size of the _____ of two _____ sets whose sizes are a and b.

UNION;   DISJOINT

123. And the sum $b + a$ is the size of the union of two disjoint sets whose sizes are _____ and _____.

b;   a

124. But the sum $b + a$ can be found using the same two disjoint sets, and their union does not depend on the order in which the sets are considered since set union is a _____ process.

COMMUTATIVE

125. Hence the size of the union remains unchanged.

$b + a =$ _____.

a + b

126. $b + a = a + b$

Thus, addition of natural numbers is also a _____ process.

COMMUTATIVE

127. The fact that

$a + b = b + a$

for any natural numbers a and b, is called the COMMUTATIVE PROPERTY OF ADDITION.

128. Let us review what we have learned.

A natural number is a property shared by _____ of the same size.

SETS

129. The words one, two, three, . . ., and the symbols 1, 2, 3, . . . are used to represent or name the natural numbers. If two such numerals represent the same natural number, we say that the symbols are _____.

EQUAL

130. Two different natural numbers are not equal, and it is incorrect to say that they are. But two numerals, even though they may be different, which represent the _____ natural number are said to be equal.

SAME

131. Then when we write

$3 + 4 = 7$

we mean that both $3 + 4$ and 7 represent the same _____ _____.

NATURAL NUMBER

132. If A and B are sets, then to write $A = B$ means that A and B have the same _____, but $2 + 3 = 5$ means that the expression $2 + 3$ and 5 both represent the same _____ _____.

MEMBERS;   NATURAL NUMBER

133. An expression of the form 3 + 4 is called a
_____, and 3 and 4 are the _____
in that _____.

> SUM;   TERMS;   SUM

134. The sum of two natural numbers is the
_____ of a set which is the
_____ of two disjoint sets whose
sizes are the two natural numbers.

> SIZE;   UNION

135. Set union, set intersection, and addition of
natural numbers are all
_____ processes.

> COMMUTATIVE

136. The fact that

   $a + b = b + a$

for all natural numbers a and b is called
the _____ property of
_____.

> COMMUTATIVE;   ADDITION

Chapter 2

Problems A (Answers on page 506)

1. What do the following sets have in common?

   {x, y}; {5, 2}; {cat, rug}; {π, √}; {0, Θ}; {many, 4}; {8246, a}; {α, *}

2. Define "the natural number three."

3. Which of the following sets share a property we call the natural number four?

   A = {a, b, c, d}; B = {four}; C = {4}; D = {4, 4, 4, 4}; E = {1, 2, 3, 4}; F = {5, 6, 7, 8}

What is the size of each of the following sets?

4. A = {a, b, c}

5. B = {2, 4}

6. C = {1, 2, 3, 5}

7. D = {x}

8. E = {7, 6, 5, 4, 3}

9. F = {1, 2, 4, 1, 5}

10. G = {three}

To show that 4 + 3 = 7, we could consider the union of set A = {a, b, c, d} and some other suitable set, B. In each of the following, tell whether or not the given set could be used for set B. Explain the reasons for your answers.

11. {a, b, c}

12. {x, y, z}

13. {e, f, g, h}

14. {e, f, e}

15. {three}

16. {red, white, blue}

17. Let A and B be any two sets. Express, symbolically, the fact that set union and set intersection are commutative processes.

18. Which of the following statements illustrate the commutative property of addition?
    a) 3 + 4 = 5 + 2
    b) 3 + 4 = 2 + 5
    c) 5 + 6 = 5 + 6
    d) 3 + 9 = 9 + 3
    e) 16 + 3 = 91

19. What is the size of the set whose members form a playing basketball team?

20. What is the size of the set of people who form the Supreme Court of the United States?

21. What property is shared by the set containing a pair of dice, the set containing the states of Alaska and Hawaii, and the set containing the President and Vice-President of the United States?

22. Which of the following are commutative processes?

    a) Adding sugar to coffee, and pouring coffee on sugar.

    b) The crossing of the finish line by runner A followed by runner B, and the crossing of the finish line by runner B followed by runner A.

    c) Mixing red paint with yellow to form orange paint, and mixing yellow paint with red to form orange paint.

23. What is the size of the union of the set of members of a school's "first string" football team, and the set of members of the same school's "first string" basketball team? Explain your answer.

24. What is the size of the intersection of the set of states whose name begins with the letter A, and the set of states which are east of the Mississippi River?

Problems B

1. What do the following sets have in common?

$\{x, y, z, \omega\}$; $\{$red, orange, yellow, green$\}$;
$\{\pi, \theta, \alpha, \pi, \varphi\}$; $\{*, \square, \otimes, *, \square, \otimes, !\}$

2. Define "the natural number seven."

3. Which of the following sets share a property we call the natural number three?

$A = \{3\}$; $B = \{III\}$; $C = \{3, 3, 3\}$; $D = \phi$;
$E = \{\alpha, \beta, \gamma\}$; $F = \{x, y, z, x, y, z, x, y, z\}$

What is the size of each of the following sets?

4. $A = \{6, 6, 6, 6, 6, 6\}$

5. $B = \{\square, \boxtimes, \bigcirc, \otimes, \square, \bigcirc\}$

6. $C = \{$six, six$\}$

7. $D = \{1, 2, 3, 1, 2, 6\}$

8. $E = \{4/2\}$

9. $F = \{2, 4, 6, 8, 10, 12\}$

10. $G = \{$empty$\}$

To show that $5 + 4 = 9$, we could consider the union of set $C = \{1, 2, 3, 4, 5\}$ and some other suitable set, D. In each of the following, tell whether or not the given set could be used for set D.

11. $\{a, b, c, d\}$

12. $\{1, 2, 3, 4\}$

13. $\{a, a, a, a\}$

14. $\{1, 1, 1, 1\}$

15. $\{w, x, y, z\}$

16. $\{\triangle, 6, \text{red}, p\}$

17. What is the size of the set of days in the calendar year 1966?

18. What is the size of the set which contains all present United States Senators?

19. What property is shared by the set of all playing members of a hockey team, the set of all playing members of a basketball team, the set of all toes on one foot, and the set of all tires normally carried on or in an automobile?

20. Which of the following are commutative processes?

a) The compression of gas (in the cylinder of an internal combustion engine) followed by the firing of the spark, and the firing of the spark followed by the compression of the gas. (Ask your service station attendant.)

b) Adding water to concentrated sulfuric acid, and adding concentrated sulfuric acid to water. (Ask your chemistry instructor.)

c) Writing a large check and then making a deposit to cover the amount, and making a large deposit and then writing a check for the amount of the deposit.

21. There are 30 students in a 9 o'clock English class and 35 students in a 10 o'clock history class. What is the size of the union of the two classes?

22. Explain why the sum of two natural numbers can always be found, and why it is always a natural number. The following questions may help you with this problem.

a) How is it possible to associate a natural number with every non-empty set?

b) Given any natural number, can we always find a set whose size is this natural number?

c) Given any two natural numbers, is it always possible to find two disjoint sets whose sizes are the two given natural numbers?

PROPERTIES OF ADDITION

1. We have been considering the addition of _____ numbers. Let us review this concept.

   NATURAL

2. A natural number is that property common to all _____ of the same size.

   SETS

3. We represent natural numbers by symbols and agree that these symbols are _____ only if they represent the same natural numbers.

   EQUAL

4. We have defined the operation of addition for natural numbers. The result of applying this operation to two such numbers is called their _____.

   SUM

5. The sum of two natural numbers is the size of a set which is the _____ of two _____ sets.

   UNION; DISJOINT

6. Since the process of union of sets is commutative, there is a _____ _____ of addition for natural numbers.

   COMMUTATIVE PROPERTY

7. That is, for any two natural numbers a and b,

   a + b = _____

   b + a

8. In Chapter 1 we considered the set which had no members. We called this the _____ set and represented it by the symbol _____.

   EMPTY; φ

9. We have also agreed that two sets will be equal only when they contain exactly the _____ members.

SAME

10. Could any set equal the empty set? To do so it would have to contain exactly those _____ that the empty set does.

MEMBERS

11. But the empty set contains _____ members.

NO

12. Hence for a set to equal the empty set it must contain no members and so itself must be an _____ set.

EMPTY

13. We shall not distinguish among empty sets. If a set has no members it is empty, and we shall call it the empty set. But then no set can have the same size as the empty set, other than the empty set itself.

14. Every non-empty set has some size. This will be a _____ number which it shares with all other sets of the same size.

NATURAL

15. Thus, the size of {a, b, c, d} is 4, the size of {*, Δ, □} is _____, and the size of {4, 5, 6, 7, 10} is _____.

3;   5

16. But no other set has the same size as the empty set, and so there is no property shared by the empty set and all others of the same size. Hence the empty set does not have any _____ _____ for its size.

NATURAL NUMBER

17. Let us introduce a new number for the size of the empty set. It will be called ZERO. Note that zero is _____ a natural number.

NOT

18. The size of the empty set is the number _____.

ZERO

19. We use the symbol 0 to represent the number _____, and we use the symbol _____ to represent the empty set.

ZERO; ϕ

20. Be careful to distinguish between the two symbols 0 and ϕ! 0 is a symbol for a _____, and ϕ is a symbol for a _____.

NUMBER;   SET

21. Of course the number zero must be remembered as that number which is the size of the _____ set, and a symbol for the number zero is _____.

EMPTY;   0

22. Other names for the number zero are possible. All of the following numerals represent the number zero:

$$12 - 12 \qquad 4 - \rule{2cm}{0.4pt} \qquad 0/3$$

4

23. But only one symbol will be used to represent the empty set. It is _____.

φ

24. The number zero is the _____ of the _____ set.

SIZE;   EMPTY

25. And a symbol that will be used to designate the size of the empty set is _____.

0   (not φ)

26. The size of _____ is 0.

φ   (not 0)

27. And any natural number, a, is the property shared by all sets of _____ a.

SIZE

28. A natural number is the property shared by all sets of the same size. Zero is not a natural number but, rather, the size of the empty set. Let us use the name WHOLE NUMBER to describe either zero or a natural number.

Then 4, 7, 19, 0, and 1 are all _____ numbers.

WHOLE

29. Consider the problem 0 + 4.

As in the case when both terms are natural numbers, let us define the sum to be that number which is the size of the union of two _____ sets.

DISJOINT

30. We are considering the problem 0 + 4.

The set of size 0 is the _____ _____, and a set of size 4 is the set {*, #, @, ¢}.

EMPTY SET

31. We are considering the problem 0 + 4.

The set of size 0 is the empty set, φ.

A set of size 4 is the set {*, #, @, ¢}.

What is $\phi \cap \{*, \#, @, ¢\}$?

_____

THE EMPTY SET   or   φ

32. Because φ has no members, $\phi \cap \{*, \#, @, ¢\} = \phi$ and we say φ and {*, #, @, ¢} are _____ sets.

DISJOINT

33. We are considering the problem 0 + 4.

The size of ϕ is 0.

The size of $\{*, \#, @, ¢\}$ is 4.

And $\phi \cap \{*, \#, @, ¢\} = \phi$, so ϕ and $\{*, \#, @, ¢\}$ are disjoint.

What is $\phi \cup \{*, \#, @, ¢\}$? _____

$\{*, \#, @, ¢\}$

34. We are considering the problem 0 + 4.

We have two disjoint sets, ϕ and $\{*, \#, @, ¢\}$, whose sizes are 0 and 4. Their union is the set $\{*, \#, @, ¢\}$ whose size is _____.

4

35. Hence by our definition of addition

0 + 4 = _____

4

36. Next consider the problem 7 + 0.

To find this sum let us choose the sets

$\{I, II, III, IV, V, VI, VII\}$ and ϕ.

$\{I, II, III, IV, V, VI, VII\} \cap \phi =$ _____

ϕ

37. We are considering the problem 7 + 0.

$\{I, II, III, IV, V, VI, VII\} \cap \phi = \phi$

and so these sets are _____.

Also $\{I, II, III, IV, V, VI, VII\} \cup \phi =$

_____

DISJOINT; $\{I, II, III, IV, V, VI, VII\}$

38. We are considering the problem 7 + 0.

$\{I, II, III, IV, V, VI, VII\}$ and ϕ are disjoint.

$\{I, II, III, IV, V, VI, VII\} \cup \phi = \{I, II, III, IV, V, VI, VII\}$

Furthermore the size of set $\{I, II, III, IV, V, VI, VII\}$ is _____ and the size of ϕ is _____.

7; 0

39. Hence by the definition of addition

7 + 0 = _____

7

40. If A is any set, what is $A \cap \phi$?

_____

THE EMPTY SET or ϕ

41. Since there are no members in the empty set, there can be no members which are in A and also in ϕ. It follows that

$A \cap \phi = \phi$

We also see that

$\phi \cap A =$ _____ $\cap$ _____

since the process of set intersection is commutative.

$A \cap \phi$

42. For any set A its intersection with ϕ is the empty set. Hence any set and the empty set are _____.

DISJOINT

43. What is $A \cup \phi$? _____

> A

44. Since there are no members in ϕ, the union of A and ϕ will contain precisely the members of A, and hence

$A \cup \phi = A$

Also, since set union is commutative, we see that

$\phi \cup A =$ _____ $\cup$ _____

> A; ϕ

45. Hence, for any set A

$\phi \cup A = A \cup \phi =$ _____

That is, the union of any given set and the empty set is the given set.

> A

46. Let us consider the problem of adding any natural number and the number zero. Let us represent the natural number by the symbol n and zero by the symbol _____.

> 0

47. We are considering the problem of adding any natural number, n, and zero, 0. We can represent their sum by

n _____ 0

> +

48. We are considering the sum $n + 0$.

To find this sum we must find the union of two disjoint sets whose sizes are _____ and _____.

> n;   0

49. We are considering the problem $n + 0$.

Let A be some set whose size is n. The only set whose size is 0 is _____.

> ϕ

50. We are considering $n + 0$.

We have sets A and ϕ of sizes n and 0.

What is $A \cap \phi$? _____

> ϕ

51. We are considering $n + 0$.

A has size n, and ϕ has size 0.

$A \cap \phi = \phi$, and so A and ϕ are _____.

What is $A \cup \phi$? _____

> DISJOINT;   A

52. We are considering $n + 0$.

A has size n, and ϕ has size 0.

A and ϕ are disjoint, and $A \cup \phi = A$.

Hence the size of $A \cup \phi$ is _____ and so $n + 0$ = _____.

> n;   n

53. We have shown that n + 0 = n for any natural number n.

Next consider the sum 0 + n.

ϕ has size 0, and A has size n.

What is $\phi \cap A$? _____

> ϕ

54. We are considering the problem 0 + n.

ϕ and A are sets of sizes 0 and n.

Since $\phi \cap A = \phi$, sets ϕ and A are disjoint.

What is $\phi \cup A$? _____

> A

55. We are considering 0 + n.

We have sets ϕ and A whose sizes are 0 and n. ϕ and A are disjoint, and $\phi \cup A = A$.

Hence the size of $\phi \cup A$ is _____, and so 0 + n = _____.

> n;   n

56. We have shown that for any natural number, n,

n + 0 = n   and   0 + n = n

Hence

n + 0 = 0 + _____

> n

57. Since n represents any natural number, we see that addition of a natural number and zero is also a commutative process.

In symbols, n + 0 = _____ + _____

> 0;   n

58. Also note that the sum of any natural number and the number zero is that same natural number. In symbols,

n + 0 = 0 + n = _____

> n

59. What is 0 + 0? _____

> 0

60. We shall not show the reasons for this conclusion here.

We assume 0 + 0 = 0.

We also have shown that n + 0 = n and 0 + n = n.

That is, adding zero to any natural number, or adding zero to zero, produces no "change." The sum is always the term added to zero. For this reason we call zero the ADDITIVE IDENTITY.

61. Since the sum of zero and any number is that same number, we say that zero is the additive _____.

> IDENTITY

62. Perform the following additions:

1) 5 + 0   _____
2) 0 + 19 _____
3) 47 + 0 _____

> 5;   19;   47

63. Find the following sums:

1) $127 + 0$ _____

2) $0 + 44$ _____

3) $16 + 1$ _____

127;   44;   17

64. Find

1) $5,927 + 0$ _____

2) $0 + 0$ _____

3) $0 + 275$ _____

5,927;   0;   275

65. Can you add the numbers 2, 3, and 4 together?

Before you answer this question be sure that you understand what is required of you. You are asked to add T_____ numbers together.

THREE

66. What is the sum of 2, 3, and 4?

This problem has not been defined! We defined the sum of two numbers as the size of the union of _____ disjoint sets.

TWO

67. We can add 2 and 3 or 3 and 4. We can even add 2 and 4. But we cannot add 2, 3, and 4, because addition has been defined only for _____ terms.

TWO

68. Hence it makes no sense to ask for the sum of 2, 3, and 4. This problem illustrates one of the fundamental properties of addition. Addition is defined for only two numbers; their sum is the size of the _____ of two disjoint sets of suitable sizes.

UNION

69. We describe this state of affairs by calling addition a BINARY OPERATION. Addition is a binary operation because, fundamentally, it is defined for only _____ numbers.

TWO

70. It is possible to consider a sum involving the numbers 2, 3, and 4. Let us first find the sum of 2 and 3.

$2 + 3 =$ _____

5

71. We are considering a sum involving 2, 3, and 4.

We see that

$2 + 3 = 5$

Now let us find the sum of 5 and the third number, 4.

$5 + 4 =$ _____

9

72. We began with the numbers 2, 3, and 4.

We see that

2 + 3 = 5

and

5 + 4 = 9

The number 9 is a sum; it was obtained by first adding 2 and 3, and then adding 4 to their _____ .

SUM

73. Let us introduce some mathematical punctuation to describe the previous additions better. We shall use parentheses to indicate "first."

Then

(2 + 3) + 4

shall mean "first" find the sum of 2 and 3, then add _____ to this sum.

4

74. The use of parentheses makes it possible to write

(2 + 3) + 4

This means that 2 and 3 are to be added first, and then 4 is added to the number _____ .

5

75. Hence

(2 + 3) + 4 = 5 + 4

and

5 + 4 = _____

9

76. Note that even though addition is a binary operation, (2 + 3) + 4 is clearly defined.

What is (3 + 4) + 5?

The parentheses indicate that first the sum of _____ and _____ must be found.

3;   4

77. We are considering (3 + 4) + 5.

First we find the sum of 3 and 4:

3 + 4 = _____

Next we must add _____ to this sum.

7;   5

78. We are considering (3 + 4) + 5.

We have 3 + 4 = 7 and must next find

7 + 5 = _____

12

79.   (3 + 4) + 5 = 12

Note that we could abbreviate our previous steps as

(3 + 4) + 5 = 7 + 5 = 12.

Then

(5 + 6) + 3 = 11 + 3 = _____

14

80. Remember that parentheses are used to indicate "first." Then

4 + (7 + 9)

must mean that first the numbers _____ and _____ should be added and then their sum should be added to 4.

7;   9

81. Thus

$4 + (7 + 9) = 4 + 16 =$ _____

20

82. Find each of the following:

1) $5 + (8 + 1) = 5 +$ _____ $=$ _____

2) $(4 + 6) + 11 =$ _____ $+$ _____

$=$ _____

$5 + (8 + 1) = 5 + \underline{9} = \underline{14}$;
$(4 + 6) + 11 = \underline{10} + \underline{11} = \underline{21}$

83. Find each of the following:

1) $(6 + 3) + 6 =$ _____ $+$ _____ $=$ _____

2) $14 + (1 + 8) =$ _____ $+$ _____

$=$ _____

$(6 + 3) + 6 = \underline{9} + \underline{6} = \underline{15}$;
$14 + (1 + 8) = \underline{14} + \underline{9} = \underline{23}$

84. Find each of the following:

1) $7 + (3 + 5) =$ _____ $+$ _____ $=$ _____

2) $(7 + 3) + 5 =$ _____ $+$ _____ $=$ _____

$7 + (3 + 5) = \underline{7} + \underline{8} = \underline{15}$;
$(7 + 3) + 5 = \underline{10} + \underline{5} = \underline{15}$

85. Note that

$7 + (3 + 5) = 15$ and $(7 + 3) + 5 = 15$

The result is 15 in each case. Find each of the following:

1) $6 + (5 + 13) =$ _____ $+$ _____

$=$ _____

2) $(6 + 5) + 13 =$ _____ $+$ _____

$=$ _____

$6 + (5 + 13) = \underline{6} + \underline{18} = \underline{24}$;
$(6 + 5) + 13 = \underline{11} + \underline{13} = \underline{24}$

86. Again the results are the same:

$(6 + 5) + 13 = 24$ and $6 + (5 + 13) = 24$

Is

$(5 + 11) + 10 = 5 + (11 + 10)$? _____

YES

$(5 + 11) + 10 = 16 + 10 = 26$ and
$5 + (11 + 10) = 5 + 21 = 26$

87. In the last three frames we have shown that

$7 + (3 + 5) = (7 + 3) + 5$

$6 + (5 + 13) = (6 + 5) + 13$

$(5 + 11) + 10 = 5 + (11 + 10)$

In each example, the natural numbers involved were the same. The difference was in the sum that was found first. These examples illustrate the ASSOCIATIVE PROPERTY OF ADDITION.

88. We can show that

$(2 + 8) + 6 = 2 + (8 + 6)$

The fact that in each case the result is 16 is another illustration of the _____ property of addition.

ASSOCIATIVE

89. By the associative property of addition

$(16 + 6) + 8 = 16 + ($_____$)$

$6 + 8$

90. The associative property of addition is illustrated by:

1) $(3 + 15) + 6 =$ _____ $+$ _____

2) $12 + (5 + 17) =$ _____ $+$ _____

$3 + (15 + 6)$; $(12 + 5) + 17$

91. The fact that
     1) $(6 + 17) + 21 = 6 + ($ _____ $)$
     2) $5 + (30 + 7) =$ _____ $+ 7$

   illustrates the _____
   _____ of addition.

   (17 + 21);   (5 + 30);
   ASSOCIATIVE PROPERTY

92. Does $(5 + 0) + 6 = 5 + (0 + 6)$? _____

   YES
   $(5 + 0) + 6 = 5 + 6 = 11$ and
   $5 + (0 + 6) = 5 + 6 = 11$

93. As all of these examples illustrate, addition of whole numbers is an associative operation. If a, b, and c represent whole numbers, this associative property can be symbolized by

   $a + (b + c) = (a + b) +$ _____

   c

94. The statement
   $a + (b + c) = (a + b) + c$

   symbolizes the _____
   _____ of _____ .

   ASSOCIATIVE PROPERTY;   ADDITION

95. Which of the following demonstrate the associative property of addition?
     1) $(6 + 6) + 15 = 6 + (6 + 15)$
     2) $(9 + 0) + 21 = 9 + (0 + 21)$
     3) $64 + (17 + 88) = (64 + 17) + 88$

   _____

   ALL DO

96. Which of the following demonstrate the associative property of addition?
     1) $(6 + 22) + 0 = 6 + (22 + 0)$
     2) $4 + 17 = 17 + 4$
     3) $27 + (8 + 3) = (27 + 8) + 3$ _____

   1 AND 3 DO.   (2 demonstrates the commutative property of addition.)

97. Let us return to the problem of adding 2, 3, and 4.

   We know by the binary nature of addition that the expression

   $2 + 3 + 4$

   is not meaningful.

   But we know by the associative property of addition that

   $2 + (3 + 4) =$ _____

   $(2 + 3) + 4$

98. Since
   $2 + (3 + 4) = (2 + 3) + 4$

   let us agree that when we write $2 + 3 + 4$ we shall mean either

   $2 + (3 + 4)$ or $(2 + 3) + 4$

   In either case the result is _____ .

   9

99. Then by convention
   $6 + 7 + 3$ means either $6 + (7 + 3)$
   or _____

   and in either case the result is _____ .

   $(6 + 7) + 3$;   16

100. Similarly

    13 + 8 + 4   means either

    (13 + 8) + 4   or   13 + (8 + 4)   and so

    13 + 8 + 4 = _____

> 25

101. Hence

    5 + 6 + 82 = (5 + 6) + 82 = 5 + (6 + 82)

    = _____

and

    14 + 8 + 5 = (14 + 8) + 5 = 14 + (8 + 5)

    = _____

> 93;   27

102. Find

    1) 16 + 7 + 4 = (16 + 7) + 4   = _____

    2) 5 + 33 + 9 = (5 + 33) + 9   = _____

    3) 100 + 8 + 3 = (100 + 8) + 3 = _____

> 27;   47;   111

103. Consider the problem 3 + 4 + 5.

By our convention, this means either

    (3 + 4) + 5   or   3 + (4 + 5)

In either case, the sum is _____, and the fact that

    (3 + 4) + 5 = 3 + (4 + 5)

is an illustration of the _____ property of addition.

> 12;   ASSOCIATIVE

104. We have established the result 3 + 4 + 5 = 12.

Now consider the problem 3 + 5 + 4.

By our convention, 3 + 5 + 4 means either

    (3 + 5) + 4   or   3 + (5 + 4)

and

    (3 + 5) + 4 = _____ + 4 = _____

    3 + (5 + 4) = _____ + _____ = _____

> (3 + 5) + 4 = 8 + 4 = 12;
> 3 + (5 + 4) = 3 + 9 = 12

105. Then 3 + 4 + 5 = 12 and 3 + 5 + 4 = 12 also.

Next consider 2 + 4 + 6.

By our convention, 2 + 4 + 6 means either

    (2 + 4) + 6   or   2 + (4 + 6)

and by the associative property of addition these expressions are equal. Hence we can use either (2 + 4) + 6 or 2 + (4 + 6) to find 2 + 4 + 6 and 2 + 4 + 6 = _____.

> 12

106.   2 + 4 + 6 = 12

Now consider 2 + 6 + 4.

By our convention, 2 + 6 + 4 means either

    (2 + 6) + 4   or   2 + (6 + 4)

and in either case the result is _____.

> 12

107. So 2 + 4 + 6 = 12 and 2 + 6 + 4 = 12 also.

Find

    3 + 5 + 9 = _____

    3 + 9 + 5 = _____

    9 + 3 + 5 = _____

> 17;   17;   17

108. Find

$$2 + 5 + 7 = \underline{\hspace{1.5cm}}$$

$$7 + 2 + 5 = \underline{\hspace{1.5cm}}$$

$$7 + 5 + 2 = \underline{\hspace{1.5cm}}$$

$$2 + 7 + 5 = \underline{\hspace{1.5cm}}$$

$$5 + 2 + 7 = \underline{\hspace{1.5cm}}$$

> 14;   14;   14;   14;   14

109. It appears that if a sum involves the numbers 2, 5, and 7, the terms can be arranged in any _____.

> ORDER

110. Let us establish the general fact that in a sum of three terms the result does not depend on the order in which they are added. Let a, b, and c represent the numbers and consider the six sums:

$$a + b + c \qquad a + c + b \qquad b + a + c$$

$$b + c + a \qquad c + a + b \qquad \text{and} \underline{\hspace{1.5cm}}$$

> $c + b + a$

111. Let us choose two of these and show they are equal. Consider

$$a + b + c \qquad \text{and} \qquad c + b + a$$

By our convention

$a + b + c$ means either $(a + b) + c$
or _____

and

$c + b + a$ means either $c + (b + a)$
or _____

> $a + (b + c);$ $(c + b) + a$

112. Let us write

$$a + b + c = (a + b) + c$$

and

$$c + b + a = c + (b + a)$$

Now $c + (b + a)$ means that first the sum of b and a is to be found and then this sum is to be added to _____.

> c

113. The commutative property of addition states that the terms in a sum can be arranged in either order. Hence we can just as well add c to the sum of b and a. That is

$$c + (b + a) = (b + a) + \underline{\hspace{1.5cm}}$$

> c

114. $$c + b + a = c + (b + a)$$
$$= (b + a) + c$$

Another use of the commutative property of addition allows us to write

$$b + a = \underline{\hspace{1.5cm}} + \underline{\hspace{1.5cm}}$$

> $\underline{a} + \underline{b}$

115. Hence

$$c + b + a = c + (b + a)$$
$$= (b + a) + c$$
$$= (a + b) + c$$

But $(a + b) + c = a + b + c$ by our notation convention. Hence

$$c + b + a \underline{\hspace{1.5cm}} a + b + c$$

> =

116. Similar appeals to the associative and commutative properties of addition could be used to show that all of the expressions

$$a + b + c \qquad a + c + b \qquad b + a + c$$

$$b + c + a \qquad c + a + b \qquad \text{and} \qquad c + b + a$$

are _____ .

EQUAL

117. Hence, in finding a sum involving three numbers, the numbers can be arranged in any _____ . All that is required is that two numbers be chosen, their sum is determined, and the third number _____ to this sum.

ORDER;   ADDED

118. Find

1) $12 + 20 + 9 =$ _____

2) $6 + 30 + 3 \ =$ _____

3) $15 + 6 + 7 \ =$ _____

41;   39;   28

119. Find

1) $22 + 10 + 8 =$ _____

2) $17 + 5 + 10 =$ _____

3) $3 + 18 + 20 =$ _____

40;   32;   41

120. Now consider the problem

$$2 + 3 + 4 + 5$$

We have no convention regarding the meaning of this expression. Rather than carefully defining its meaning and using the commutative and associative properties to establish the fact, let us agree that this expression represents a sum which can be found by adding pairs of numbers in <u>any</u> order.

121. That is, to find $2 + 3 + 4 + 5$ we can choose any two terms, find their sum, add one of the remaining terms to this sum and, finally, add the last term to the result.

Hence

$$2 + 3 + 4 + 5 =$$ _____

14

122. Find

$$6 + 8 + 10 + 5 =$$ _____

$$2 + 5 + 8 + 10 =$$ _____

29;   25

123. Find

1) $5 + 6 + 7 + 8 \ =$ _____

2) $6 + 9 + 3 + 2 \ =$ _____

3) $12 + 10 + 4 + 0 =$ _____

26;   20;   26

124. When a problem involves three or more terms, we can find the sum by adding the terms, two at a time, in any order, until all terms in the problem have been considered. Hence

$$5 + 7 + 2 + 19 + 1 =$$ _____

and

$$7 + 52 + 93 =$$ _____

34;   152

125.　7 + 52 + 93 = 152

Note that it may be possible to find this sum in several ways, but that if one chooses first to add 7 and 93, the result, _____, is easily added to 52.

100

126.　To review, since addition is defined only for a pair of numbers, we say that addition is a _____ operation.

BINARY

127.　However, we have established a convention for finding the sum of three or more numbers. We can do so by choosing any _____ of numbers, finding their sum, and adding another number to this sum. We continue until all terms have been considered. Certain pairings may be more advantageous than others from a practical standpoint.

PAIR

128.　The number 0 is the size of the _____ set. The symbol _____ represents the empty set.

EMPTY;　ϕ

129.　Zero is the additive identity. This means that the sum of any natural number and zero is that same _____ _____ .

NATURAL NUMBER

130.　The commutative property of addition can be symbolized by writing

a + b = _____ .

b + a

131.　The associative property of addition can be symbolized by writing

(a + b) + c = _____ .

a + (b + c)

Chapter 3

Problems A (Answers on page 506)

Find the following sums.

1. 4 + 9
2. 6 + 5
3. 15 + 7
4. 18 + 34
5. 101 + 15
6. 5212 + 969

Add in the order indicated by the parentheses.

7. (5 + 12) + 6
8. 19 + (25 + 75)
9. 83 + (17 + 39)

Add from left to right.

10. 8 + 5 + 3
11. 3 + 12 + 7
12. 26 + 19 + 10

Find the following sums by adding terms in any order desired.

13. 15 + 5 + 31
14. 214 + 50 + 50
15. 4 + 9 + 6 + 1
16. 45 + 19 + 627 + 5003
17. 444 + 555 + 21 + 6040 + 7
18. 2215 + 78 + 129 + 4377 + 531

Sometimes the terms in a sum are written vertically and the plus signs are omitted. Thus, 45 + 19 is written

$$\begin{array}{r} 45 \\ \underline{19} \end{array}$$

and 602 + 57 + 8 is written

$$\begin{array}{r} 602 \\ 57 \\ \underline{8} \end{array}$$

Find the following sums.

19.
$$\begin{array}{r} 45 \\ \underline{119} \end{array}$$

20.
$$\begin{array}{r} 606 \\ \underline{129} \end{array}$$

21.
$$\begin{array}{r} 52 \\ 77 \\ \underline{83} \end{array}$$

22.
$$\begin{array}{r} 451 \\ 62 \\ \underline{854} \end{array}$$

23.
$$\begin{array}{r} 206 \\ 31 \\ 5117 \end{array}$$

24.
$$\begin{array}{r} 8319 \\ 5280 \\ \underline{701} \end{array}$$

25.
$$\begin{array}{r} 451 \\ 327 \\ 765 \\ \underline{41} \end{array}$$

26.
$$\begin{array}{r} 384 \\ 291 \\ 777 \\ 653 \\ \underline{720} \end{array}$$

Example: Express 26 as the sum of two terms, the first of which is 12. Answer: 12 + 14.

27. Express 14 as the sum of two terms, the first of which is 5.
28. Express 53 as the sum of two terms, the first of which is 26.
29. Express 24 as the sum of two equal terms.
30. Express 0 as the sum of two equal terms.
31. A bowler made a score of 171 on the first game, 129 on the second game, and 193 on the third game. What was his total score for the three-game series?
32. A highway counter was used to measure traffic flow past a certain point. The weekday count of vehicles is given below:

Monday	2287
Tuesday	1943
Wednesday	2080
Thursday	1909
Friday	2316

How many vehicles passed the meter during the five-day period?

33. A student kept a record of the number of hours he devoted to the subject of mathematics.

	Hours in Class	Hours outside of Class
Monday	1	0
Tuesday	0	2
Wednesday	1	1
Thursday	0	3
Friday	1	0
Saturday	0	2
Sunday	0	0

How many hours did this student spend "on" mathematics during the week?

34. The five longest suspension bridges in the United States are:

Verrazano	4260 feet
Golden Gate	4200 feet
Mackinac	3800 feet
George Washington	3500 feet
Tacoma	2800 feet

If the five bridges were connected into a single structure, how far would it extend?

35. For a special showing of old silent films, a theater compiled the following attendance figures:

Wednesday	388
Thursday	291
Friday	774
Saturday	1066

How many persons attended this four-day rerun?

Problems B

Find the following sums.

1. 8 + 7
2. 3 + 8
3. 24 + 12
4. 77 + 42
5. 265 + 347
6. 20003 + 899

And in the order indicated by the parentheses.

7. 5 + (12 + 6)
8. (19 + 25) + 75
9. (83 + 17) + 39

Add from left to right.

10. 5 + 9 + 6
11. 18 + 5 + 4
12. 8 + 4 + 7 + 5

Find the following sums by adding terms in any order desired.

13. 18 + 7 + 3
14. 19 + 1 + 37
15. 25 + 12 + 88 + 75
16. 17 + 306 + 88 + 429
17. 512 + 887 + 1259 + 7078
18. 5721 + 3345 + 29 + 717 + 663

Find the following sums.

19.
$$\begin{array}{r} 55 \\ 248 \end{array}$$

20.
$$\begin{array}{r} 4567 \\ 387 \end{array}$$

21.
$$\begin{array}{r} 57 \\ 75 \\ 83 \end{array}$$

22.
$$\begin{array}{r} 29 \\ 816 \\ 653 \end{array}$$

23.
$$\begin{array}{r} 5 \\ 49 \\ 727 \end{array}$$

24.
$$\begin{array}{r} 53 \\ 417 \\ 2986 \end{array}$$

25.
$$\begin{array}{r} 2073 \\ 456 \\ 822 \\ 1502 \end{array}$$

26.
$$\begin{array}{r} 7754 \\ 206 \\ 3017 \\ 424 \\ 961 \end{array}$$

27. Express 13 as the sum of two terms, the first of which is 0.

28. Express 21 as the sum of two terms, the first of which is 21.

29. Express 12 as the sum of three equal numbers.

30. Express 28 as the sum of four equal numbers.

31. On the first hour examination a student made a score of 29, on the second a score of 33, on the third a score of 22, and on the fourth a score of 38. What was his cumulative score on the four hour examinations?

32. A slightly over-weight young lady decided to "count calories." Her breakfast consisted of:

1 glass juice	105 calories	
1 bowl cereal (with sugar and cream)	308 calories	
2 eggs	220 calories	
4 strips of bacon	190 calories	
2 pieces of toast (plain)	120 calories	
2 cups of coffee (black)	0 calories	

What was her total caloric intake for the meal?

33. In keeping track of his time worked on various jobs, a plumber compiled the following record:

	Hours Regular Time	Hours Overtime
Monday	7	1
Tuesday	8	0
Wednesday	8	2
Thursday	3	5
Friday	6	3
Saturday	2	2
Sunday	0	6

How many hours, in all, did the plumber work during the week?

34. The areas of the six New England states are given at the top of the second column:

Maine	33215 square miles
Massachusetts	10577 square miles
Vermont	9609 square miles
New Hampshire	9304 square miles
Connecticut	5009 square miles
Rhode Island	1214 square miles

What is the area of New England?

35. On a "high country" hiking expedition, the following entries were made in a log:

Tuesday:	12 miles (all up-hill)
Wednesday:	9 miles (blister on left heel)
Thursday:	14 miles (it rained all day)
Friday:	3 miles
Saturday:	11 miles
Sunday:	5 miles (not exactly a day of rest)
Monday:	12 miles (at least the pack is a bit lighter)
Tuesday:	15 miles (and only one small blister)
Wednesday:	7 miles (afternoon thunder-shower)
Thursday:	10 miles (downhill and unloaded)

How many miles were walked on the ten-day trip?

MULTIPLICATION OF NATURAL NUMBERS

CHAPTER 4

1. We have been studying the operation of addition and some of its properties. When two numbers, a and b, are added, the result, a + b, is called their _____ ; a and b are called the _____ of this sum.

SUM;   TERMS

2. One of the properties of addition can be symbolized by

   a + b = b + a

   This statement represents the

   _____ _____ _____
   _____ .

COMMUTATIVE PROPERTY OF ADDITION

3. The commutative property of addition states that two numbers may be added in either order.

   Another property of addition can be represented by the symbolic statement

   a + (b + c) = (a + b) + c

   This is called the _____
   _____ _____ _____ .

ASSOCIATIVE PROPERTY OF ADDITION

4. The associative property of addition is concerned with the addition of three numbers. The third may be added to the _____ of the first two, or the _____ of the last two may be added to the first.

SUM;   SUM

5. Hence   (4 + 3) + 9 = 4 + (3 + 9)

   since   (4 + 3) + 9 = _____ + 9 = _____

   and also   4 + (3 + 9) = 4 + _____ = _____

(4 + 3) + 9 = 7 + 9 = 16;   4 + (3 + 9) = 4 + 12 = 16

6. And since (4 + 3) + 9 = 4 + (3 + 9), we often write 4 + 3 + 9 to represent either.

   In the same way, either (a + b) + c or a + (b + c) could be written _____ .

a + b + c

7. We have agreed that for a sum of three or more numbers, the terms may be added in any _____ .

ORDER

8. Hence

$$7 + 5 + 3 + 1 = \rule{2cm}{0.4pt}$$

$$2 + 4 + 6 + 8 + 10 = \rule{2cm}{0.4pt}$$

$$5 + 5 + 4 + 3 + 2 = \rule{2cm}{0.4pt}$$

16;   30;   19

9. Also

$$6 + 6 + 6 + 3 + 2 = \rule{2cm}{0.4pt}$$

$$4 + 4 + 4 + 4 + 4 + 4 = \rule{2cm}{0.4pt}$$

$$6 + 5 + 4 + 3 + 2 + 1 = \rule{2cm}{0.4pt}$$

23;   24;   21

10. Find

$$3 + 3 + 3 + 3 + 3 + 3 + 3 = \rule{2cm}{0.4pt}$$

$$2 + 2 + 3 + 3 + 5 + 5 + 2 = \rule{2cm}{0.4pt}$$

21;   22

11. We next consider another binary operation with numbers. We call this operation MULTIPLICATION and use a DOT to indicate that two numbers are to be multiplied. Hence the expression

$$4 \cdot 3$$

indicates that the numbers 4 and 3 are to be
\rule{4cm}{0.4pt}.

MULTIPLIED

12. Let us define the multiplication operation by example. We define:

$$1 \cdot 5 = 5$$

$$1 \cdot 9 = 9$$

$$1 \cdot 23 = 23$$

$$1 \cdot 3 = \rule{2cm}{0.4pt}$$

$$1 \cdot 6 = \rule{2cm}{0.4pt}$$

3;   6

13. We define:

$$1 \cdot 37 = 37$$

$$1 \cdot 82 = 82$$

$$1 \cdot 104 = \rule{2cm}{0.4pt}$$

$$1 \cdot 2 = \rule{2cm}{0.4pt}$$

$$1 \cdot 0 = 0$$

104;   2

14. In fact, if a represents any whole number, we define:

$$1 \cdot a = \rule{2cm}{0.4pt}$$

a

15. We next define:

$$2 \cdot 5 = 5 + 5 \quad \text{which equals} \quad 10$$

$$2 \cdot 8 = 8 + 8 \quad \text{which equals} \quad 16$$

$$2 \cdot 12 = \rule{2cm}{0.4pt} + \rule{2cm}{0.4pt} \quad \text{which equals}$$
\rule{2cm}{0.4pt}.

12;   12;   24

16. We define:

$$2 \cdot 3 = 3 + 3 \qquad \text{and} \qquad 3 + 3 = 6$$

$$2 \cdot 21 = 21 + 21 \qquad \text{and} \qquad 21 + 21 = 42$$

$$2 \cdot 7 = \underline{\quad\quad} + \qquad \text{and} \qquad \underline{\quad\quad} +$$

$$\underline{\quad\quad} \quad \underline{\quad\quad} =$$

$$2 \cdot 0 = 0 + 0 \qquad \text{and} \qquad 0 + 0 = \underline{\quad\quad}$$

> 7; 7; 7; 7; 14; 0

17. If a represents any whole number, we define:

$$2 \cdot a = a + a$$

We next define:

$$3 \cdot 1 = 1 + 1 + 1 = 3$$

$$3 \cdot 4 = 4 + 4 + 4 = \underline{\quad\quad}$$

> 12

18. We define:

$$3 \cdot 9 = 9 + 9 + 9 = 27$$

$$3 \cdot 15 = 15 + 15 + 15 = \underline{\quad\quad}$$

$$3 \cdot 2 = \underline{\quad\quad} + \underline{\quad\quad} + \underline{\quad\quad} =$$

$$\underline{\quad\quad}$$

$$3 \cdot 0 = 0 + 0 + 0 = 0$$

> 45; 2; 2; 2; 6

19. In fact, if a is any whole number, we define:

$$3 \cdot a = \underline{\quad\quad} + \underline{\quad\quad} + \underline{\quad\quad}$$

> a; a; a

20. Similarly, we define:

$$4 \cdot 3 = 3 + 3 + 3 + 3 = 12$$

$$4 \cdot 9 = \underline{\quad\quad} + \underline{\quad\quad} + \underline{\quad\quad} +$$

$$\underline{\quad\quad} = \underline{\quad\quad}$$

$$4 \cdot 0 = 0 + 0 + 0 + 0 = 0$$

$$4 \cdot 11 = 11 + 11 + 11 + 11 = \underline{\quad\quad}$$

> 9; 9; 9; 9; 36; 44

21. For any whole number a we define:

$$4 \cdot a = a + a + a + a$$

We also define:

$$5 \cdot a = a + a + a + a + a \qquad \text{and}$$

$$6 \cdot a = \underline{\quad\quad\quad} .$$

> a + a + a + a + a + a

22. In general, if n is any natural number, we define n · a to be the result of writing the number a exactly n times and forming the sum of all terms, where possible.

$$3 \cdot 7 = 7 + 7 + 7 = \underline{\quad\quad}$$

$$5 \cdot 6 = 6 + 6 + 6 + 6 + 6 = \underline{\quad\quad}$$

$$9 \cdot 2 = \underline{\quad\quad\quad\quad\quad}$$

$$= \underline{\quad\quad}$$

> 21;   30;   2 + 2 + 2 + 2 + 2 + 2 + 2 + 2 + 2;
> 18

23. Perform the following multiplications:

$$7 \cdot 8 = 8 + 8 + 8 + 8 + 8 + 8 + 8 = \underline{\quad\quad}$$

$$5 \cdot 0 = 0 + 0 + 0 + 0 + 0 = \underline{\quad\quad}$$

$$3 \cdot 12 = 12 + 12 + 12 = \underline{\quad\quad}$$

$$5 \cdot 20 = 20 + 20 + 20 + 20 + 20 = \underline{\quad\quad}$$

> 56; 0; 36; 100

24. $7 \cdot 3 = 3 + 3 + 3 + 3 + 3 + 3 + 3 = 21$

We call the number 21 the PRODUCT of the numbers 7 and 3. Then the product of 6 and 2 is _____ .

> $6 \cdot 2 = 2 + 2 + 2 + 2 + 2 + 2 = \underline{12}$

25. Find the product of 4 and 8. _____

> $4 \cdot 8 = 8 + 8 + 8 + 8 = \underline{32}$

26. 63 is the _____ of 9 and 7.

55 is the _____ of 5 and 11.

> PRODUCT;   PRODUCT

27. We write $9 \cdot 7 = 63$ since

$9 \cdot 7 = 7 + 7 + 7 + 7 + 7 + 7 + 7 + 7 + 7$

and

$7 + 7 + 7 + 7 + 7 + 7 + 7 + 7 + 7 = 63$

We call 63 the _____ of 9 and 7.

We shall call the numbers 9 and 7 FACTORS of 63.

> PRODUCT

28. Then when we multiply 6 and 8 we get _____ for the product; we call 6 and 8 the _____ of the product.

> 48;   FACTORS

29. In the multiplication problem

$7 \cdot 10 = 70$

7 and 10 are called _____ of 70 while 70 is called the _____ of 7 and 10.

> FACTORS;   PRODUCT

30. $7 \cdot 10 = 10 + 10 + 10 + 10 + 10 + 10 + 10 = 70$

But while the product, 70, can be obtained by this use of the definition, it will not usually be practical to carry out the additions. Consider the difficulties connected with finding $29 \cdot 37$ by recourse to the definition!

31. You already know the basic multiplication facts needed to find the product of any two numbers. Use these facts, or the definition of multiplication, to find

$5 \cdot 3 \ = $ _____

$7 \cdot 11 = $ _____

$9 \cdot 6 \ = $ _____

$7 \cdot 5 \ = $ _____

> 15;   77;   54;   35

32. Find the product of

1) 7 and 3   _____

2) 12 and 4   _____

3) 5 and 12   _____

4) 3 and 8   _____

> 21;   48;   60;   24

33. Multiply

1) 2 and 13   _____

2) 6 and 8   _____

3) 12 and 3   _____

4) 9 and 8   _____

> 26;   48;   36;   72

34. 1) 5 and 8 are factors of _____ .

2) 11 and 4 are factors of _____ .

3) 6 and 12 are factors of _____ .

4) 17 and 2 are factors of _____ .

40;   44;   72;   34

35. By our definition of multiplication:

$$5 \cdot 4 = 4 + 4 + 4 + 4 + 4 = \underline{\qquad}$$

and

$$4 \cdot 5 = 5 + 5 + 5 + 5 = \underline{\qquad}$$

20;   20

36. $5 \cdot 4 = 4 \cdot 5$

since, in each case, 20 is the _____ .
Next consider

$$7 \cdot 2 = 2 + 2 + 2 + 2 + 2 + 2 + 2 = \underline{\qquad}$$

and

$$2 \cdot 7 = 7 + 7 = \underline{\qquad}$$

PRODUCT;   14;   14

37. Hence $7 : 2 = 2 \cdot 7$

since, in each case, the product is _____ .
Also

$$12 \cdot 4 = 4 + 4 + 4 + 4 + 4 + 4 + 4 + 4 + 4 + 4 + 4 + 4 = \underline{\qquad}$$

and

$$4 \cdot 12 = 12 + 12 + 12 + 12 = \underline{\qquad} .$$

14;   48;   48

38. Again, $12 \cdot 4 = 4 \cdot 12$

since each product equals 48.

Find $5 \cdot 9 = \underline{\qquad}$

and $9 \cdot 5 = \underline{\qquad}$

45;   45

39. As these examples show, the product of two factors is the same, regardless of which factor appears _____ . While we cannot verify this for every case, we shall assume that for any natural numbers, a and b,

$$a \cdot b = b \cdot \underline{\qquad} .$$

FIRST;   a

40. We assume that, for any natural numbers a and b,

$$a \cdot b = b \cdot a$$

That is, in a multiplication problem the product of two natural numbers does not depend on the _____ of the _____ .

ORDER;   FACTORS

41. For any natural numbers, a and b, we assume

$$a \cdot b = \underline{\qquad} .$$

We shall call this the COMMUTATIVE PROPERTY OF MULTIPLICATION.

b·a

42. The fact that

$$6 \cdot 5 = 5 \cdot 6$$

illustrates the _____ property of multiplication.

COMMUTATIVE

43. All of the statements

$$4 \cdot 27 = 27 \cdot 4$$
$$16 \cdot 3 = 3 \cdot 16$$
$$24 \cdot 1 = 1 \cdot 24$$
$$32 \cdot 8 = 8 \cdot 32$$

illustrate the commutative property of

_____ .

MULTIPLICATION

44. Our definition of multiplication gives

$$4 \cdot 0 = 0 + 0 + 0 + 0 = 0$$

but it does <u>not</u> define $0 \cdot 4$.

We have also defined

$$6 \cdot 0 = 0 + 0 + 0 + 0 + 0 + 0 = _____ .$$

but we have <u>not</u> defined $0 \cdot 6$.

| 0 |

45. By the definition of multiplication

$$1 \cdot 0 = 0$$
$$2 \cdot 0 = 0 + 0 = 0$$
$$3 \cdot 0 = 0 + 0 + 0 = 0$$
$$10 \cdot 0 = 0 + 0 + 0 + 0 + 0 + 0 + 0 + 0 + 0 + 0$$
$$= 0$$

In fact, for any natural number a,

$$a \cdot 0 = _____ .$$

| 0 |

46. We have <u>determined</u> that, for any natural number a,

$$a \cdot 0 = 0$$

We also have <u>established</u> that, for any natural numbers a and b,

$$a \cdot b = b \cdot a$$

We wish to <u>define</u> the product of 0 and a natural number.

47. Let us define the product of 0 and a natural number in such a way that the commutative property of multiplication,

$$a \cdot b = _____$$

will apply even if the factors include zero.

| $b \cdot a$ |

48. Then since $9 \cdot 0 = 0$, we must define

$$0 \cdot 9 = 0$$

and since $16 \cdot 0 = 0$, we must define

$$0 \cdot 16 = _____$$

| 0 |

49. Since for any natural number a,

$$a \cdot 0 = 0$$

and since we shall require that

$$0 \cdot a = a \cdot 0$$

we must define

$$0 \cdot a = a \cdot 0 = _____ \text{ for all natural numbers, a.}$$

| 0 |

50. Hence

$$0 \cdot 5 = 0$$
$$0 \cdot 17 = _____$$
$$15 \cdot 0 = _____$$
$$0 \cdot 1 = _____$$

| 0;　0;　0 |

51. And

$$6 \cdot 0 = \underline{\qquad}$$
$$12 \cdot 0 = \underline{\qquad}$$
$$5 \cdot 1 = \underline{\qquad}$$
$$0 \cdot 11 = \underline{\qquad}$$
$$0 \cdot 53 = \underline{\qquad}$$

0;   0;   5;   0;   0

52. We have defined multiplication so that, for any natural number a,

$$0 \cdot a = 0$$

Let us complete the definition by defining

$$0 \cdot 0 = 0$$

We can then state that, for any whole number a,

$$a \cdot 0 = 0 \cdot a = \underline{\qquad}.$$

0

53. $0 \cdot a = a \cdot 0 = 0$

for all whole numbers a.

Our definitions have been made so that the commutative property of multiplication applies to all problems in which the factors are either natural numbers or zero.

We can say, for all whole numbers a and b,

$$a \cdot b = \underline{\qquad}$$

b·a

54. $a \cdot b = b \cdot a$

for all whole numbers, a and b.

That is, the product of two numbers does not depend on the _____ of the factors.

ORDER

55. We have introduced parentheses as a notation to indicate "first." Hence, by

$$(2 \cdot 3) \cdot 4$$

we mean that first the product of _____ and _____ is to be found and the result is to be multiplied by _____.

2;   3;   4

56. Then

$$(2 \cdot 3) \cdot 4 = \underline{\qquad} : 4 = \underline{\qquad}$$

$(2 \cdot 3) \cdot 4 = \underline{6} \cdot 4 = \underline{24}$

57. Now consider $2 \cdot (3 \cdot 4)$.

This means that we first find the product of _____ and _____ and then multiply _____ by this result.

3;   4;   2

58. Then

$$2 \cdot (3 \cdot 4) = \underline{\qquad} \cdot \underline{\qquad} = \underline{\qquad}$$

$2 \cdot (3 \cdot 4) = \underline{2} \cdot \underline{12} = \underline{24}$

59. And

$$(2 \cdot 3) \cdot 4 = 6 \cdot 4 = 24$$
$$2 \cdot (3 \cdot 4) = 2 \cdot 12 = 24$$

We see, then, that

$$(2 \cdot 3) \cdot 4 = 2 \cdot (3 \cdot 4)$$

Find

$$(2 \cdot 4) \cdot 7 = \underline{\qquad} \cdot \underline{\qquad} = \underline{\qquad}$$

and

$$2 \cdot (4 \cdot 7) = \underline{\qquad} \cdot \underline{\qquad} = \underline{\qquad}$$

$(2 \cdot 4) \cdot 7 = \underline{8} \cdot \underline{7} = \underline{56}; \qquad 2 \cdot (4 \cdot 7) = \underline{2} \cdot \underline{28} = \underline{56}$

60. $(2 \cdot 4) \cdot 7 = 56$ and $2 \cdot (4 \cdot 7) = 56$

Hence

$(2 \cdot 4) \cdot 7 = 2 \cdot (4 \cdot 7)$

Find

$(3 \cdot 7) \cdot 4 = $ _____ and

$3 \cdot (7 \cdot 4) = $ _____

> $(3 \cdot 7) \cdot 4 = 21 \cdot 4 = \underline{84};$
>
> $3 \cdot (7 \cdot 4) = 3 \cdot 28 = \underline{84}$

61. $(3 \cdot 7) \cdot 4 = 84$ and $3 \cdot (7 \cdot 4) = 84$

and so

$(3 \cdot 7) \cdot 4 = 3 \cdot (7 \cdot 4).$

Does

$(5 \cdot 6) \cdot 8 = 5 \cdot (6 \cdot 8)?$ _____

> YES
>
> $(5 \cdot 6) \cdot 8 = 30 \cdot 8 = 240$ and
>
> $5 \cdot (6 \cdot 8) = 5 \cdot 48 = 240$ also

62. Which of the following statements are true?

$(5 \cdot 4) \cdot 6 = 5 \cdot (4 \cdot 6)$

$(3 \cdot 8) \cdot 3 = 3 \cdot (8 \cdot 3)$

$(7 \cdot 1) \cdot 9 = 7 \cdot (1 \cdot 9)$

$(6 \cdot 5) \cdot 0 = 6 \cdot (5 \cdot 0)$ _____

> ALL ARE TRUE
>
> $(5 \cdot 4) \cdot 6 = 5 \cdot (4 \cdot 6) = 120$
>
> $(3 \cdot 8) \cdot 3 = 3 \cdot (8 \cdot 3) = 72$
>
> $(7 \cdot 1) \cdot 9 = 7 \cdot (1 \cdot 9) = 63$
>
> $(6 \cdot 5) \cdot 0 = 6 \cdot (5 \cdot 0) = 0$

63. While we cannot consider every possible case, it appears that for any whole numbers, a, b, and c,

$(a \cdot b) \cdot c = a \cdot ($ _____ $\cdot$ _____ $).$

We shall assume that this is true and shall call this the ASSOCIATIVE PROPERTY OF MULTIPLICATION.

> b;   c

64. Then the statement

$(a \cdot b) \cdot c = a \cdot (b \cdot c)$

symbolizes the _____ property of multiplication.

> ASSOCIATIVE

65. The statement

$(2 \cdot 5) \cdot 6 = 2 \cdot (5 \cdot 6)$

illustrates the _____

_____ of multiplication.

> ASSOCIATIVE PROPERTY

66. And by the associative property of multiplication we can write

$(5 \cdot 9) \cdot 8 = $ _____

> $5 \cdot (9 \cdot 8)$

67. $(5 \cdot 9) \cdot 8 = 5 \cdot (9 \cdot 8)$

since each represents the same number. Since the expressions are equal let us write

$5 \cdot 9 \cdot 8$

to represent <u>either</u> $(5 \cdot 9) \cdot 8$ <u>or</u> $5 \cdot (9 \cdot 8).$

68. $5 \cdot 9 \cdot 8$ means _____ $(5 \cdot 9) \cdot 8$ or $5 \cdot (9 \cdot 8)$.

by the _____ _____

_____ _____.

EITHER;   ASSOCIATIVE PROPERTY OF MULTIPLICATION

69. Since

$$(6 \cdot 5) \cdot 9 = 6 \cdot (5 \cdot 9)$$

let us represent either by the expression _____.

$6 \cdot 5 \cdot 9$

70. Then

$5 \cdot 9 \cdot 8$

means either _____ or _____.

$(5 \cdot 9) \cdot 8$; $5 \cdot (9 \cdot 8)$ (either order)

71. If a, b, and c represent whole numbers, by the expression

$a \cdot b \cdot c$

we mean either $(a \cdot b) \cdot c$ or _____.

$a \cdot (b \cdot c)$

72. When we introduced the operation of multiplication, we defined the product of two numbers. Hence multiplication is a B _____ operation.

BINARY

73. Multiplication is a binary operation since a product was defined for only _____ factors.

TWO

74. Then, strictly speaking, a product of more then two factors has no meaning.

But consider the expression

$2 \cdot 3 \cdot 4$

We agree that this represents either _____ or _____.

$(2 \cdot 3) \cdot 4$; $2 \cdot (3 \cdot 4)$ (either order)

75. And the associative property of multiplication ensures that

$(2 \cdot 3) \cdot 4$ _____ $2 \cdot (3 \cdot 4)$.

$=$

76. Hence we have given a clear meaning to the expression $2 \cdot 3 \cdot 4$ and shall write

$$2 \cdot 3 \cdot 4 = 24$$

Similarly $5 \cdot 9 \cdot 3$ means either $(5 \cdot 9) \cdot 3$ or $5 \cdot (9 \cdot 3)$ and, in any case,

$5 \cdot 9 \cdot 3 =$ _____

135

77. The expression $a \cdot b \cdot c$ means either $(a \cdot b) \cdot c$ or $a \cdot (b \cdot c)$. But, regardless of which is chosen, the results are equal.

Hence we shall often omit the parentheses.

$6 \cdot 4 \cdot 5 =$ _____

120

$6 \cdot 4 \cdot 5 = \begin{cases} (6 \cdot 4) \cdot 5 = 24 \cdot 5 = 120 \\ \text{or} \\ 6 \cdot (4 \cdot 5) = 6 \cdot 20 = 120 \end{cases}$

78. Find the products

$8 \cdot 4 \cdot 5$ = _____

$3 \cdot 5 \cdot 0$ = _____

$9 \cdot 2 \cdot 8$ = _____

$3 \cdot 1 \cdot 11$ = _____

160;   0;   144;   33

79. Find

$6 \cdot 5 \cdot 8$ = _____

$9 \cdot 9 \cdot 3$ = _____

$14 \cdot 1 \cdot 2$ = _____

$0 \cdot 71 \cdot 4$ = _____

240;   243;   28;   0

80. Consider the problem $3 \cdot 4 \cdot 5$.

By our notation convention this means either

$(3 \cdot 4) \cdot 5$ or $3 \cdot (4 \cdot 5)$

In either case the product is _____ and the fact that

$(3 \cdot 4) \cdot 5 = 3 \cdot (4 \cdot 5)$

is an illustration of the _____ property of multiplication.

60;   ASSOCIATIVE

81. $3 \cdot 4 \cdot 5 = 60$

Now consider the problem $5 \cdot 4 \cdot 3$.

By our convention this means either

$(5 \cdot 4) \cdot 3$ or $5 \cdot (4 \cdot 3)$

and in either case the result is _____.

60

82. Since $3 \cdot 4 \cdot 5 = 60$ and also $5 \cdot 4 \cdot 3 = 60$, we see that

$3 \cdot 4 \cdot 5 = 5 \cdot 4 \cdot 3$

Now consider $5 \cdot 6 \cdot 9$. This represents either $(5 \cdot 6) \cdot 9$ or _____ and, in either case, the result is _____.

$5 \cdot (6 \cdot 9)$;   270

83. $5 \cdot 6 \cdot 9 = 270$

Now consider $6 \cdot 9 \cdot 5$.

This represents either $(6 \cdot 9) \cdot 5$ or $6 \cdot (9 \cdot 5)$ and

$(6 \cdot 9) \cdot 5 = 6 \cdot (9 \cdot 5)$ = _____.

270

84. $5 \cdot 6 \cdot 9 = 270$ and also $6 \cdot 9 \cdot 5 = 270$.

Hence

$5 \cdot 6 \cdot 9 = 6 \cdot 9 \cdot 5$

Find

$3 \cdot 8 \cdot 7$ = _____

$3 \cdot 7 \cdot 8$ = _____

$8 \cdot 3 \cdot 7$ = _____

$7 \cdot 3 \cdot 8$ = _____

168;   168;   168;   168

85. Find

$5 \cdot 4 \cdot 9$ = _____

$5 \cdot 9 \cdot 4$ = _____

$9 \cdot 5 \cdot 4$ = _____

$9 \cdot 4 \cdot 5$ = _____

$4 \cdot 5 \cdot 9$ = _____

$4 \cdot 9 \cdot 5$ = _____

180;   180;   180;   180;   180;   180

86. If a product involves the factors 4, 5 and 9, the result does not depend on how the factors are _____ .

87. This result is generally true. Let a, b, and c represent any whole numbers. Consider the six products

   $a \cdot b \cdot c$ $b \cdot a \cdot c$ $c \cdot a \cdot b$

   $a \cdot c \cdot b$ $b \cdot c \cdot a$ _____

88. Let us choose two of these products and show they are equal. Consider $a \cdot c \cdot b$ and $b \cdot c \cdot a$.

   $a \cdot c \cdot b$ means either $(a \cdot c) \cdot b$ or

   _____

   $b \cdot c \cdot a$ means either $(b \cdot c) \cdot a$ or

   _____

89. Let us use

   $a \cdot c \cdot b = a \cdot (c \cdot b)$

   and

   $b \cdot c \cdot a = (b \cdot c) \cdot a$

   $a \cdot (c \cdot b)$ means that first the product of c and b is to be found and then a is to be _____ by the result.

90. But the commutative property of multiplication allows us to arrange the factors in either _____ . Hence we can write

   $a \cdot (c \cdot b) = a \cdot ($ _____ · _____ $)$

91. $a \cdot (c \cdot b) = a \cdot (b \cdot c)$

   We can again use the commutative property of multiplication, this time on the numbers a and b · c, to write

   $a \cdot (b \cdot c) = (b \cdot c) \cdot$ _____

92. Hence

   $a \cdot c \cdot b = a \cdot (c \cdot b)$
   $\qquad = a \cdot (b \cdot c)$
   $\qquad = (b \cdot c) \cdot a$

   But

   $b \cdot c \cdot a = (b \cdot c) \cdot a$

   and so

   $a \cdot c \cdot b$ _____ $b \cdot c \cdot a$

93. Using the associative as well as the commutative property of multiplication, all of the expressions

   $a \cdot b \cdot c$ $b \cdot a \cdot c$ $c \cdot a \cdot b$

   $a \cdot c \cdot b$ $b \cdot c \cdot a$ $c \cdot b \cdot a$

   could be shown to be _____ .

94. We shall not prove this statement but shall assert that a problem involving three factors can be solved by choosing <u>any</u> two, finding their _____ and multiplying the result by the third number.

95. Find

$$5 \cdot 8 \cdot 2 = \underline{\hspace{2cm}}$$

$$16 \cdot 4 \cdot 0 = \underline{\hspace{2cm}}$$

$$21 \cdot 20 \cdot 5 = \underline{\hspace{2cm}}$$

> 80;   0;   2100

96. Now consider the problem

$$2 \cdot 3 \cdot 4 \cdot 6$$

We have no convention regarding the meaning of this expression. Rather than carefully defining its meaning, let us agree that it represents a product which can be found by multiplying pairs of numbers in any _____ .

> ORDER

97. So, to find $2 \cdot 3 \cdot 4 \cdot 6$ we choose any two factors, find their product, multiply the product by a third factor, and finally multiply the result by the last factor.

Accordingly,

$$2 \cdot 3 \cdot 4 \cdot 6 = \underline{\hspace{2cm}}$$

> 144

98. Find

$$5 \cdot 5 \cdot 4 \cdot 3 = \underline{\hspace{2cm}}$$

$$6 \cdot 2 \cdot 9 \cdot 2 = \underline{\hspace{2cm}}$$

$$7 \cdot 8 \cdot 1 \cdot 3 = \underline{\hspace{2cm}}$$

$$2 \cdot 11 \cdot 13 \cdot 0 = \underline{\hspace{2cm}}$$

> 300;   216;   168;   0

99. In fact, when a problem involves three or more factors, we can find the product by multiplying factors two at a time, in any order, until all factors have been considered.

Find

$$4 \cdot 4 \cdot 3 \cdot 3 = \underline{\hspace{2cm}}$$

$$2 \cdot 2 \cdot 3 \cdot 2 \cdot 4 = \underline{\hspace{2cm}}$$

> 144;   96

100. Two numbers play rather special roles for multiplication. Consider first the number 1.

Find

$$142 \cdot 1 \quad = \underline{\hspace{2cm}}$$

$$1 \cdot 87 \quad = \underline{\hspace{2cm}}$$

$$21 \cdot 1 \quad = \underline{\hspace{2cm}}$$

$$1 \cdot 117 \quad = \underline{\hspace{2cm}}$$

$$1 \cdot 0 \quad = \underline{\hspace{2cm}}$$

> 142;   87;   21;   117;   0

101. These examples and the definition of multiplication show that the product of 1 and any other whole number is, again, that number.

In symbols, if a is any whole number, then

$$1 \cdot a = a \cdot 1 = \underline{\hspace{2cm}}$$

> a

102. Since, if one of two factors is 1, the product is the other factor, and we shall call the number 1 the MULTIPLICATIVE IDENTITY.

Then

$$53 \cdot 1 = \underline{\hspace{2cm}}$$

since 1 is the multiplicative _____ .

> 53;   IDENTITY

103. Then

$$44 \cdot 1 = \underline{\qquad} \quad \text{and} \quad 1 \cdot 103 = \underline{\qquad}$$

since the number 1 is the $\underline{\qquad\qquad\qquad}$
$\underline{\qquad\qquad}$.

44;   103;   MULTIPLICATIVE IDENTITY

104. Multiplying any number by 1 gives a product which is again that number.

Hence if

$$4 \cdot 9 \cdot 7 \cdot 6 = 1512$$

then

$$4 \cdot 9 \cdot 7 \cdot 6 \cdot 1 = \underline{\qquad\qquad}$$

1512

105. Since 1 is the multiplicative $\underline{\qquad\qquad}$, if

$$7 \cdot 7 \cdot 8 \cdot 11 = 4312$$

then

$$1 \cdot 7 \cdot 7 \cdot 8 \cdot 11 = \underline{\qquad\qquad}$$

IDENTITY;   4312

106. If

$$17 \cdot 13 \cdot 11 \cdot 51 = 123981$$

then

$$17 \cdot 13 \cdot 1 \cdot 11 \cdot 51 = \underline{\qquad\qquad}$$

123981

107. Which of the following are true?

$$4 \cdot 19 \cdot 27 \cdot 1 = 4 \cdot 19 \cdot 27$$
$$67 \cdot 1 \cdot 17 \cdot 55 = 67 \cdot 17 \cdot 55$$
$$49 \cdot 88 \cdot 1 \cdot 19 \cdot 99 = 49 \cdot 88 \cdot 19 \cdot 99$$
$\underline{\qquad\qquad}$.

ALL ARE TRUE

108. We can state, then, that if 1 is a factor in any product, the result will not be altered if the factor 1 is removed!

That is,

$$99 \cdot 87 \cdot 75 \cdot 1 \cdot 63$$
$$= \underline{\qquad} \cdot \underline{\qquad} \cdot \underline{\qquad} \cdot \underline{\qquad}$$

99 · 87 · 75 · 63

109. Find the following products:

$$41 \cdot 1 \ = \underline{\qquad}$$
$$32 \cdot 1 \ = \underline{\qquad}$$
$$64 \cdot 0 \ = \underline{\qquad}$$
$$1 \cdot 75 \ = \underline{\qquad}$$

41;   32;   0;   75

110. Find

$$117 \cdot 1 \ = \underline{\qquad}$$
$$1 \cdot 75 \ = \underline{\qquad}$$
$$93 \cdot 0 \ = \underline{\qquad}$$
$$0 \cdot 27 \ = \underline{\qquad}$$

117;   75;   0;   0

111. The number zero also plays a special role in multiplication.

Find

$$15 \cdot 0 \ = \underline{\qquad}$$
$$0 \cdot 921 = \underline{\qquad}$$
$$0 \cdot 447 = \underline{\qquad}$$
$$727 \cdot 0 \ = \underline{\qquad}$$
$$0 \cdot 0$$

0;   0;   0;   0;   0

112. Again, these examples and the definition of multiplication show that the product of 0 and any other whole number is 0.

In symbols, if a is any whole number, then

$$a \cdot 0 = 0 \cdot a = \underline{\hspace{1.5cm}}.$$

0

113. Find

$$176 \cdot 0 \quad = \underline{\hspace{1.5cm}}$$
$$0 \cdot 579 = \underline{\hspace{1.5cm}}$$
$$0 \cdot 1 \quad = \underline{\hspace{1.5cm}}$$
$$900 \cdot 0 \quad = \underline{\hspace{1.5cm}}$$

0;　0;　0;　0

114. Consider the product

$$12 \cdot 8 \cdot 0 \cdot 7 \cdot 14$$

By our convention, the product can be determined by arranging the factors in _____ order.

ANY

115. We are considering

$$12 \cdot 8 \cdot 0 \cdot 7 \cdot 14$$

Let us first find the product $12 \cdot 0 = \underline{\hspace{1.5cm}}.$

But then this result, no matter which factor is chosen next, gives a product with it of _____.

0;　0

116. If this process is continued until all remaining factors have been considered, we arrive at the final result

$$12 \cdot 8 \cdot 0 \cdot 7 \cdot 14 = \underline{\hspace{1.5cm}}.$$

0

117. Consider another example:

$$4 \cdot 19 \cdot 23 \cdot 7 \cdot 0$$

Again, at some stage the number zero must be taken as a factor and from that point on all products must be _____. Hence

$$4 \cdot 19 \cdot 23 \cdot 7 \cdot 0 = \underline{\hspace{1.5cm}}.$$

0;　0

118. Let us observe that if zero occurs as any factor in a multiplication problem, the product is _____.

0

119. As a final topic let us recognize that our symbol for the operation of multiplication is not the only one. In many places a "times sign," $\times$, is found.

Hence $3 \cdot 9$ can also be written _____.

3×9

120. In fact, still another symbol is used to indicate multiplication. We shall consider it in the next chapter.

Let us review.

In this chapter we introduced a new operation, _____.

MULTIPLICATION

121. We indicate multiplication by the symbol ·

Hence $4 \cdot 9 = 36$

We call 36 the _____ of 4 and 9, and we call 4 and 9 _____ of 36.

PRODUCT;   FACTORS

122. Our definitions of the product of whole numbers were made so as to include a commutative property of multiplication.

This law is symbolized by the statement

$a \cdot b =$ _____ .

b · a

123. We can write

$(a \cdot b) \cdot c = a \cdot (b \cdot c)$

This statement symbolizes the _____ _____ of multiplication.

ASSOCIATIVE PROPERTY

124. When three or more numbers are included in a multiplication problem we find the result by choosing two factors at a time in _____ order.

ANY

125. The numbers 0 and 1 play special roles in multiplications. For any whole number, a

$a \cdot 0 =$ _____   and $0 \cdot a =$ _____

0;   0

126. And, for any whole number a,

$a \cdot 1 =$ _____   and $1 \cdot a =$ _____

a;   a

127. Recall that, for any whole number a,

$a + 0 =$ _____   and $0 + a =$ _____

a;   a

128. We call the number 0 the additive identity; the number 1 is called the _____ _____ .

MULTIPLICATIVE IDENTITY

Chapter 4

Problems A (Answers on page 507)

Find the following products.

1. $7 \cdot 9$
2. $6 \cdot 8$
3. $12 \cdot 6$
4. $11 \cdot 11$
5. $9 \cdot 66$
6. $63 \cdot 42$

Multiply in the order indicated by the parentheses.

7. $(7 \cdot 8) \cdot 9$
8. $4 \cdot (20 \cdot 5)$
9. $(6 \cdot 50) \cdot 2$

Multiply from left to right.

10. $7 \cdot 5 \cdot 2$
11. $27 \cdot 25 \cdot 4$
12. $2 \cdot 5 \cdot 8 \cdot 9$

Find the following products by multiplying terms in any order desired.

13. $5 \cdot 72 \cdot 2$
14. $7 \cdot 8 \cdot 5 \cdot 4$
15. $10 \cdot 21 \cdot 35 \cdot 5$

Sometimes the factors in a product are written vertically and the multiplication symbol is omitted. Thus $41 \cdot 239$ is written

$$\begin{array}{r} 239 \\ \underline{41} \end{array}$$

Find the following products

16. $\begin{array}{r} 52 \\ \underline{88} \end{array}$

17. $\begin{array}{r} 409 \\ \underline{37} \end{array}$

18. $\begin{array}{r} 65 \\ \underline{150} \end{array}$

19. $\begin{array}{r} 2017 \\ \underline{35} \end{array}$

20. $\begin{array}{r} 4529 \\ \underline{104} \end{array}$

Example: Express 36 as the product of two factors, the first of which is 4. Answer: $4 \cdot 9$

21. Express 24 as the product of two factors, the first of which is 12.

22. Express 63 as the product of two factors, the second of which is 3.

23. Express 36 as the product of two equal factors.

24. What number is called the additive identity?

25. What number is called the multiplicative identity?

Each of the following true statements illustrates some property of addition or multiplication. Give the complete name of the property for each statement below.

Example: $12 + (3 + 7) = (12 + 3) + 7$. Answer: Associative property of addition

26. $3 \cdot 7 = 7 \cdot 3$
27. $3 \cdot (4 \cdot 2) = (3 \cdot 4) \cdot 2$
28. $7 + (2 + 3) = (7 + 2) + 3$
29. $3 + (4 + 5) = 3 + (5 + 4)$
30. $9 \cdot (2 \cdot 3) = (2 \cdot 3) \cdot 9$

31. Each floor of the Clabber Building contains 96 windows. If there are 22 floors, how many windows does the building have?

32. If each automobile entering a "drive-in" theater carries a driver and 3 passengers, how many patrons attended the show on a night when 288 cars were admitted?

33. Each year the government issues new coins of 6 varieties. It is estimated that 320,000 of each variety are never circulated because they are held by collectors. Of each year's coin production, how many coins are not available for use for this reason?

34. If 9 dogs each chase 4 cats, and each cat chases 7 mice, how many mice, in all, are chased?

35. There are 5280 feet in a mile. Then a mountain "5 miles high" would have a height of how many feet?

Problems B

Find the following products.

1. 3·12   4. 22·4
2. 7·6   5. 23·17
3. 3·11   6. 176·398

Multiply in the order indicated by the parentheses.

7. 7·(8·9)
8. (4·20)·5
9. 6·(50·2)

Multiply from left to right.

10. 2·5·7
11. 4·25·27
12. 8·2·5·9

Find the following products by multiplying terms in any order desired.

13. 20·47·5
14. 12·30·14·5
15. 4·94·25

Find the following products.

16. 73
    64

17. 527
    601

18. 4108
    312

19. 2934
    557

20. 3706
    609

21. Express 50 as the product of two factors, the second of which is 5.

22. Express 72 as the product of two factors, the first of which is 6.

23. Express 27 as the product of three equal factors.

24. What number has the property that its product with any given number is that given number?

25. What number has the property that its product with any given number is always the same?

Give the complete name of the property each of the following statements illustrates.

26. 9 + (2 · 3) = (2 · 3) + 9
27. 6 · (3 + 2) = 6 · (2 + 3)
28. (4 + 5 + 9) · 2 = 2 · (4 + 5 + 9)
29. (12 + 3) · (2 + 5) = (2 + 5) · (12 + 3)
30. (12 + 3) · (2 + 5) = (3 + 12) · (5 + 2)

31. It is difficult to construct a dwelling at a cost of less than 12 dollars for each square foot of space provided. What is the least number of dollars, then, that a house with 2148 square feet of space would cost?

32. It is estimated that a modern rapid transit vehicle can seat 240 persons. If trains are made up of 12 cars, and 16 trains run into the city each hour, then how many passengers can be brought into the city each hour by this means?

33. Each season's ticket to the concert series entitles the purchaser to attend 24 concerts. If 342 people who bought season's tickets each missed 3 concerts, how many times were there tickets "wasted"?

34. It takes 120 formina each day to feed 1 goolob. To feed a spavier requires 48 goolobs each day. Each wohl eats 124 spaviers daily. How many formina are needed, each day, to sustain one wohl?

35. Every gallon of gasoline occupies 231 cubic inches of space. How many cubic inches of space are available in a gasoline tank whose capacity is 17 gallons?

SUMS AND PRODUCTS

1. For any whole numbers, a and b, the expression

    a · b

    represents their _____ .

PRODUCT

2. In the expression

    a · b

    a and b are called the _____ of the product.

FACTORS

3. And the product of any two whole numbers does not depend on the _____ of the factors.

ORDER

4. This property of multiplication, symbolized by writing

    a · b = b · a

    is called the _____ property of multiplication.

COMMUTATIVE

5. The commutative property of multiplication can be illustrated by writing

    12 · 7 = _____

7 · 12

6. Since multiplication is a binary operation, the product of three or more factors must by found by multiplying them _____ at a time.

TWO

7. For a product involving more than two factors, we may use parentheses to indicate which multiplication should be performed _____ .

FIRST

8. Thus

    4 · (5 · 2)

    indicates that the first product to be found is the one involving the factors _____ and _____ .

5;   2   (either order)

9. And hence

$4 \cdot (5 \cdot 2) = 4 \cdot \underline{\hphantom{xxxx}} = \underline{\hphantom{xxxx}}$

10;   40

10. But

$(4 \cdot 5) \cdot 2 = \underline{\hphantom{xxx}} \cdot \underline{\hphantom{xxx}} = \underline{\hphantom{xxx}}$

20;   2;   40

11. Since both $4 \cdot (5 \cdot 2)$ and $(4 \cdot 5) \cdot 2$ equal 40, we may write

$(4 \cdot 5) \cdot 2 = 4 \cdot (\underline{\hphantom{xxx}} \cdot \underline{\hphantom{xxx}})$

5;   2

12. In fact, if a, b, and c are any three whole numbers, we know that

$(a \cdot b) \cdot c = a \cdot (\underline{\hphantom{xxxxx}})$

b · c

13. And we call the fact that

$(a \cdot b) \cdot c = a \cdot (b \cdot c)$

the $\underline{\hphantom{xxxxxxxxxxxx}}$ property of $\underline{\hphantom{xxxxxxxxx}}$.

ASSOCIATIVE;   MULTIPLICATION

14. Another example of the associative property of multiplication is

$(17 \cdot 12) \cdot 34 = \underline{\hphantom{xxxxxxx}}$

17 · (12 · 34)

15. An expression like

$8 \cdot 2 \cdot 3$

means either

$(8 \cdot 2) \cdot 3$ or $8 \cdot (\underline{\hphantom{xxxxxxx}})$

2 · 3

16. And in either case we see that the product

$8 \cdot 2 \cdot 3 = \underline{\hphantom{xxxx}}.$

48

17. For a product of more than three factors we may multiply the factors $\underline{\hphantom{xxx}}$ at a time in any $\underline{\hphantom{xxxxxx}}$.

TWO;   ORDER

18. Thus

$4 \cdot 7 \cdot 9 \cdot 2 \cdot 6 = \underline{\hphantom{xxxxxx}}$

3024

19. For any two whole numbers a and b, the expression

$a + b$

represents their $\underline{\hphantom{xxxx}}$.

SUM

20. In the expression

$a + b$

we call a and b the $\underline{\hphantom{xxxxxx}}$ of the sum.

TERMS

21. And the sum of any two whole numbers does not depend on the _____ of the terms.

> ORDER

22. This property of addition, symbolized by writing

$$a + b = b + a$$

is called the _____ property of addition.

> COMMUTATIVE

23. Like multiplication, addition is a binary operation, and the sum of three or more terms must be found by adding them _____ at a time.

> TWO

24. Parentheses may be used to indicate which addition is performed first. Thus

$$(4 + 3) + 9 = _____ + _____ = _____$$

> 7;   9;   16

25. But

$$4 + (3 + 9) = _____ + _____ = _____$$

> 4;   12;   16

26. And since either sum is the same, we may write

$$(4 + 3) + 9 = 4 + (_____ + _____)$$

> 3;   9

27. In fact, if a, b and c are any three whole numbers we know that

$$(a + b) + c = a + (_____).$$

> b + c

28. The fact that

$$(a + b) + c = a + (b + c)$$

is called the _____ property of _____.

> ASSOCIATIVE;   ADDITION

29. An expression like

$$12 + 3 + 6$$

means either

$$(12 + 3) + 6 \quad \text{or}$$
$$12 + (_____ + _____),$$

for in either case the result is the same.

> 3;   6

30. And if a sum contains more than three terms, we may add them in any order, _____ at a time.

> TWO

31. Thus

$$7 + 12 + 6 + 3 + 4 = _____$$

> 32

32. However, when parentheses are used, we should remember that they indicate which operation is performed _____.

33. Hence, in the expression

$(2 + 3) \cdot 4$

The operation to be performed first is _____.

34. Then

$(2 + 3) \cdot 4 = $ _____ $\cdot 4$

35. Now only multiplication remains, and

$5 \cdot 4 = $ _____

36. Therefore

$(2 + 3) \cdot 4 = 5 \cdot 4 = 20$

Similarly,

$(6 + 8) \cdot 7 = $ _____ $\cdot 7 = $ _____

37. Also

$5 \cdot (9 + 13) = $ _____ $\cdot$ _____ $= $ _____

38. Remember that parentheses indicate "first." Find

$(4 + 9) \cdot 22 = $ _____

$(6 \cdot 7) + 8 = $ _____

39. Find

$4 + (9 \cdot 22) = $ _____

$(7 + 8) + 12 = $ _____

$5 \cdot (9 + 10) = $ _____

40. Be careful to distinguish between the following two problems.

$2 + (3 \cdot 5) = $ _____

$(2 + 3) \cdot 5 = $ _____

41. $2 + (3 \cdot 5) = 17$

$(2 + 3) \cdot 5 = 25$

Both problems involved the same numbers, and both contained one multiplication and one addition. But it was the _____ of the operations that made the difference.

42. Compare

$4 \cdot (3 + 5) = $ _____

and

$(4 \cdot 3) + 5 = $ _____

43. Again, when both multiplication and addition are involved the _____ of operations is important.

ORDER

44. And the _____ indicate which operation comes first.

PARENTHESES

45. If a problem involves both multiplication and addition, and no parentheses are used, it is understood that the multiplication comes first. Thus both

$2 \cdot 3 + 5$

and

$2 + 3 \cdot 5$

imply that _____ is the operation to perform first.

MULTIPLICATION

46. Then

$2 \cdot 3 + 5 = 6 + 5 = 11$

and

$2 + 3 \cdot 5 = 2 +$ _____ $=$ _____

15;   17

47. Remember, when no parentheses are used, the multiplication is performed first.

$14 \cdot 3 + 2 =$ _____

$22 + 7 \cdot 8 =$ _____

44;   78

48. But when parentheses are used, the operation within the parentheses if performed first.

$6 \cdot (5 + 11) =$ _____

$(7 + 4) \cdot 11 =$ _____

96;   121

49. Find

$3 + 7 \cdot 4 \ =$ _____

$9 \cdot 2 + 6 \ =$ _____

$(3 + 5) \cdot 7 =$ _____

$4 \cdot (1 + 7) =$ _____

31;   24;   56;   32

50. Notice

$2 + (7 \cdot 9) =$ _____

$2 + 7 \cdot 9 \ =$ _____

65;   65

51. $2 + (7 \cdot 9) = 2 + 7 \cdot 9$

The parentheses here do not change the _____ of operations. It is correct, although unnecessary, to use them.

ORDER

52. But

$8 + 2 \cdot 5 \ =$ _____

$(8 + 2) \cdot 5 =$ _____

18;   50

53. $8 + 2 \cdot 5 = 18$

$(8 + 2) \cdot 5 = 50$

Here the parentheses <u>do</u> change the order of operations, and are necessary to indicate which operation should be performed _____.

54. When there can be no doubt that multiplication is the operation to be performed, the multiplication symbol may be omitted. That is,

$(4 + 2) \cdot 8$

can be written

$(4 + 2)8$

Similarly,

$2 \cdot (8 + 9) = \underline{\hspace{1cm}} (8 + 9)$

55. Also

$3 \cdot (9 + 51) = \underline{\hspace{1cm}} (9 + 51)$

$5 \cdot (31 + 8) = 5(\underline{\hspace{1cm}} + \underline{\hspace{1cm}})$

56. Hence

$3(2 + 5) = 21$

$5(4 + 2) = \underline{\hspace{1cm}}$

$(8 + 1)2 = \underline{\hspace{1cm}}$

57. Sometimes confusion would result from omitting the multiplication symbol. The product of 3 and 4 should be indicated by writing

$3 \cdot 4$

Notice that writing 3 4 without the raised dot represents thirty four and not three times four. Could the dot be omitted in the expression $5 \cdot 12$? _____

58. In which of these may the dot be omitted?

a) $5 \cdot (4 + 2)$

b) $9 + 3 \cdot 2$

c) $(5 + 1) \cdot 7$

d) $6 \cdot 7$

e) $(6) \cdot (7)$ _____

59. Notice that

$(6) \cdot (7) = (6)(7)$

Similarly

$(5)(4) \quad = 5 \cdot 4 = \underline{\hspace{1cm}}$

$(9)(12) \quad = \underline{\hspace{1cm}}$

$5(4 + 2) = \underline{\hspace{1cm}}$

60. Find

$(7 + 12)19 = \underline{\hspace{1cm}}$

$3 + (4)(5) = \underline{\hspace{1cm}}$

$8 \cdot 9 + 6 \quad = \underline{\hspace{1cm}}$

$12(6 + 5) \quad = \underline{\hspace{1cm}}$

61. Remember that unless there are parentheses which indicate otherwise, in a problem involving both multiplication and addition the _____ is performed first.

> MULTIPLICATION

62. When there are two or more multiplications and addition in the same problem, we agree to perform all the _____ first, unless parentheses indicate otherwise.

> MULTIPLICATIONS

63. Thus, in the problem

$3 \cdot 4 + 3 \cdot 5$

two _____ should be performed before the _____.

> MULTIPLICATIONS; ADDITION

64. Then

$3 \cdot 4 + 3 \cdot 5 = 12 + \underline{\hspace{1cm}} = \underline{\hspace{1cm}}$

> 15;   27

65. Find

$7 \cdot 4 + 3 \cdot 3 \ = \underline{\hspace{0.8cm}} + \underline{\hspace{0.8cm}} = \underline{\hspace{0.8cm}}$

$(5 + 2)(3 + 1) = \underline{\hspace{0.8cm}} \cdot \underline{\hspace{0.8cm}} = \underline{\hspace{0.8cm}}$

> 28;   9;   37;   7;   4;   28

66. Remember, multiply first unless parentheses indicate otherwise.

$8 + 2 \cdot 5 + 1 = \underline{\hspace{1cm}}$

$3 \cdot 5 + 7 \cdot 9 \ = \underline{\hspace{1cm}}$

$(4 + 2)5 + 1 = \underline{\hspace{1cm}}$

$3 + 4(2 + 5) = \underline{\hspace{1cm}}$

> 19;   78;   31;   31

67. Notice:

$3 + 4(2 + 5) = 3 + 4 \cdot 7 = 3 + 28 = 31$

Here the parentheses indicate that the first operation is the _____ of 2 and 5. But in the resulting expression,

$3 + 4 \cdot 7$

the next operation is _____.

> ADDITION;   MULTIPLICATION

68. Find

$3 + 2(4 + 5) = \underline{\hspace{1cm}}$

$4(1 + 9) + 3 = \underline{\hspace{1cm}}$

$5(9 + 2) + 8(3 + 1) = \underline{\hspace{1cm}}$

> 21;   43;   87

69. When a problem involves both multiplication and addition, the _____ of operations is important.

> ORDER

70. When no parentheses are used, we agree to perform all the _____ first.

> MULTIPLICATIONS

71. But where _____ are used, the operations within them should be performed first.

> PARENTHESES

72. What is the last operation to be performed here?

$3 + 5 \cdot 2$ _____

> ADDITION

73. $3 + 5 \cdot 2$

Since the last operation to be performed here is addition, we call this expression a sum.

Similarly, for the expression

$(2)(3) + (4)(9),$

the last operation to be performed is _____ and we call this expression a _____.

> ADDITION; SUM

74. Which of the following are called sums?

a) $7 + 9$

b) $3 \cdot 5 + 2$

c) $(4 + 5)9$

d) $8 + 2 \cdot 3 + 6$ _____

> a, b, d

75. $(4 + 5)9$

The last operation to be performed here is _____, so we call this expression a P_____.

> MULTIPLICATION; PRODUCT

76. Which of the following are called products?

a) $(3 + 9) \cdot 2$

b) $7 \cdot 3 + 4 \cdot 5$

c) $2 + 9 \cdot 8$

d) $(4 + 5)(3 + 2)$ _____

> a and d

77. Then in an expression involving both multiplication and addition, the _____ operation performed determines whether it is called a sum or a product.

> LAST

78. Identify each as being a sum or a product.

$5 + 2 \cdot 7$ _____

$(4 + 1)8$ _____

$(9 + 1)(6 + 3)$ _____

$4(8 + 9) + 3$ _____

> SUM; PRODUCT; PRODUCT; SUM

79. For the sum

$5 + 7$

we call 5 and 7 the _____.

> TERMS

80. Similarly, for the sum

$3 \cdot 4 + 3 \cdot 5$

the terms are $3 \cdot 4$ and _____.

> 3 · 5

81. Consider the sums $4 \cdot 3 + 5$ and $2 \cdot 7 + 2 \cdot 9$.

In $4 \cdot 3 + 5$ the terms are $4 \cdot 3$ and _____.

In $2 \cdot 7 + 2 \cdot 9$ the terms are $2 \cdot 7$ and _____.

5; $2 \cdot 9$

82. For the product
$$8 \cdot 9$$
we call 8 and 9 the _____.

FACTORS

83. Hence the factors in the product
$$5(4 + 3)$$
are 5 and $(4 + 3)$.

Similarly the factors in
$$(2 + 3)(4 + 9) \quad \text{are} \quad (2 + 3) \quad \text{and}$$
_____.

$(4 + 9)$ or $4 + 9$

84. Consider the products $8(4 + 3)$ and $(2 + 7)3$.

In $8(4 + 3)$ the factors are 8 and _____.

In $(2 + 7)3$ the factors are $(2 + 7)$ and _____.

$(4 + 3)$;   3

85. The expression
$$4(3 + 5)$$
is called a _____, and the _____ are 4 and $(3 + 5)$

PRODUCT;   FACTORS

86. The expression
$$4 \cdot 3 + 4 \cdot 5$$
is called a _____, and the _____ are $4 \cdot 3$ and $4 \cdot 5$.

SUM;   TERMS

87. Notice that the sum
$$4 \cdot 3 + 4 \cdot 5$$
contains the two terms $4 \cdot 3$ and $4 \cdot 5$.

But each of these terms is a _____ of two factors.

PRODUCT

88. $4 \cdot 3 + 4 \cdot 5$

The first term of this sum is the product $4 \cdot 3$, while the second term is the product _____.

$4 \cdot 5$

89. $4 \cdot 3 + 4 \cdot 5$

The first term is a product of the factors 4 and 3, while the second term is a product of the factors _____ and _____.

4;   5   (either order)

90. $4 \cdot 3 + 4 \cdot 5$

Notice that 4 and 3 are factors of the first _____, while 4 and 5 are factors of the second.

TERM

91. $4 \cdot 3 + 4 \cdot 5$

Then both the first term and the second contain the same factor, _____.

> **4**

92. $4 \cdot 3 + 4 \cdot 5$

Since 4 is a factor of both terms, we say that both terms contain a COMMON FACTOR, 4.

Similarly, a common factor in

$2 \cdot 5 + 2 \cdot 3$

is _____.

> **2**

93. The expression

$7 \cdot 3 + 7 \cdot 4$

is called a _____, and 7 is called a common _____ of this sum.

> **SUM; FACTOR**

94. Identify the common factor.

$5 \cdot 4 + 5 \cdot 3$ The common factor is _____.

$8 \cdot 3 + 8 \cdot 1$ The common factor is _____.

$3 \cdot 7 + 5 \cdot 7$ The common factor is _____.

> **5;   8;   7**

95. The expression

$3(4 + 5)$

is called a _____, while the expression

$3 \cdot 4 + 3 \cdot 5$

is called a _____.

> **PRODUCT;   SUM**

96. Calculate

$3(4 + 5) = 3 \cdot 9 =$ _____

$3 \cdot 4 + 3 \cdot 5 = 12 + 15 =$ _____

> **27;   27**

97. Notice that the product

$3(4 + 5)$

and the sum

$3 \cdot 4 + 3 \cdot 5$

both equal 27, and we may write

$3(4 + 5) = 3 \cdot 4 +$ _____

> **3 · 5**

98. Calculate each of the following, performing operations in the order indicated.

$2 \cdot (4 + 3) =$ _____

$2 \cdot 4 + 2 \cdot 3 =$ _____

> **$2 \cdot (4 + 3) = 2 \cdot 7 = \underline{14}$;**
> **$2 \cdot 4 + 2 \cdot 3 = 8 + 6 = \underline{14}$**

99. Find each of the following.

$5(2 + 7) =$ _____

$5 \cdot 2 + 5 \cdot 7 =$ _____

> **$5(2 + 7) = 5 \cdot 9 = \underline{45}$;**
> **$5 \cdot 2 + 5 \cdot 7 = 10 + 35 = \underline{45}$**

100. $3(4 + 5) = 3 \cdot 4 + 3 \cdot 5$

Notice that on the left we have a product, while on the right we have a _____.

> **SUM**

101. $3(4 + 5) = 3 \cdot 4 + 3 \cdot 5$

The factors on the left are 3 and

_____ .

(4 + 5)

102. $3(4 + 5) = 3 \cdot 4 + 3 \cdot 5$

One of the factors on the left is 3.

The expression on the right is a sum, but it has a common factor of _____ .

3

103. $5(7 + 3) = 5 \cdot 7 + 5 \cdot 3$

The common factor on the right is _____, and this is also a factor on the left.

5

104. When we replace a product by a sum, as in

$4(2 + 7) = 4 \cdot 2 + 4 \cdot 7$

one of the factors on the left becomes a _____ _____ on the right.

COMMON FACTOR

105. We can express this in symbols by writing

$a(b + c) = ab + ac$

Notice that the common factor on the right is _____ .

a

106. We shall assume that for any whole numbers a, b, and c,

$a(b + c) = ab + ac$

This property is called the DISTRIBUTIVE PROPERTY.

107. An example of the distributive property is

$7(8 + 9) = 7 \cdot 8 +$ _____ .

7·9

108. The fact that

$3(6 + 2) = 3 \cdot 6 + 3 \cdot 2$

is another example of the _____ property.

DISTRIBUTIVE

109. The distributive property, symbolized by

$a(b + c) = ab + ac$

states that a product a(b+ c) may be replaced by a _____ ab + ac.

SUM

110. $a(b + c) = ab + ac$

A factor on the left becomes a _____ _____ of both terms on the right.

COMMON FACTOR

111. $3(7 + 2) = 3 \cdot 7 + 3 \cdot 2$

The expression on the right is a _____ with a common factor 3, while the expression on the left is a _____, one of whose factors is also 3.

SUM;   PRODUCT

112. The expression

$$5 \cdot 4 + 5 \cdot 9$$

is called a _____ but has a common factor of _____.

> SUM;   5

113. And

$$5 \cdot 4 + 5 \cdot 9 = 20 + 45 = \text{_____}.$$

> 65

114. The expression

$$5 \cdot (4 + 9)$$

is called a _____, and one of its _____ is 5.

> PRODUCT;   FACTORS

115. And

$$5 \cdot (4 + 9) = 5 \cdot 13 = \text{_____}.$$

> 65

116. $5 \cdot 4 + 5 \cdot 9 = 65$

   $5 \cdot (4 + 9) = 65$

Hence

   $5 \cdot 4 + 5 \cdot 9 = 5 \cdot (4 + 9)$

The _____ on the left is equal to the _____ on the right.

> SUM;   PRODUCT

117. Then

$$5 \cdot 4 + 5 \cdot 9 = 5 \cdot (4 + 9)$$

shows that a sum may be replaced by a product, and hence is also an example of the _____ property.

> DISTRIBUTIVE

118. The distributive property is illustrated by

$$3(7 + 2) = 3 \cdot 7 + \text{_____}$$
$$2 \cdot 5 + 2 \cdot 3 = 2(5 + \text{_____})$$

> 3·2;   3

119. Use the distributive property to complete each.

$$5 \cdot 3 + 5 \cdot 7 = 5(3 + \text{_____})$$
$$8 \cdot 7 + 8 \cdot 13 = 8(\text{_____} + \text{_____})$$

> 7;   7;   13

120. Change each product to a sum by the distributive property.

$$8(3 + 9) = \text{_____} + \text{_____}$$
$$19(31 + 27) = \text{_____} + \text{_____}$$

> 8·3;   8·9;   19·31;   19·27

121. Use the distributive property to change each sum to a product.

$$7 \cdot 3 + 7 \cdot 5 = 7(\text{_____} + \text{_____})$$
$$9 \cdot 7 + 9 \cdot 3 = \text{_____} (7 + 3)$$

> 3;   5;   9

122. Compute

$$8 \cdot 73 + 8 \cdot 27 = 584 + \underline{\hspace{1.5cm}} = \underline{\hspace{1.5cm}}$$

216;   800

123. $8 \cdot 73 + 8 \cdot 27 = 584 + 216 = 800$

But by the distributive property

$$8 \cdot 73 + 8 \cdot 27 = 8(\underline{\hspace{1.5cm}} + \underline{\hspace{1.5cm}})$$

73;   27

124.   An easier way to compute

$$8 \cdot 73 + 8 \cdot 27$$

is to use the distributive property first to write

$$8 \cdot 73 + 8 \cdot 27 = \underline{\hspace{1.5cm}} (\underline{\hspace{1.5cm}} + \underline{\hspace{1.5cm}})$$

8;   73;   27

125. $8 \cdot 73 + 8 \cdot 27 = 8(73 + 27) = 8 \cdot \underline{\hspace{1.5cm}}$
$$= \underline{\hspace{1.5cm}}$$

100;   800

126.   Use the distributive property to compute

$$7 \cdot 8 + 7 \cdot 12 = 7(\underline{\hspace{1.5cm}} + \underline{\hspace{1.5cm}})$$
$$= \underline{\hspace{1.5cm}}$$
$$27 \cdot 7 + 27 \cdot 3 = \underline{\hspace{1.5cm}}$$
$$56 \cdot 53 + 56 \cdot 47 = \underline{\hspace{1.5cm}}$$

8;   12;   140;   270;   5600

127.   Then we see that sometimes the
_____ property may change
a sum to a product which is easier to compute.

DISTRIBUTIVE

128.   Compute the following. Remember the order of operations.

$$(7 + 2)5 = \underline{\hspace{1.5cm}}$$
$$7 \cdot 5 + 2 \cdot 5 = \underline{\hspace{1.5cm}}$$

$(7 + 2)5 = 9 \cdot 5 = \underline{45}$;
$7 \cdot 5 + 2 \cdot 5 = 35 + 10 = \underline{45}$

129.   Find

$$(6 + 3)7 = \underline{\hspace{1.5cm}}$$
$$6 \cdot 7 + 3 \cdot 7 = \underline{\hspace{1.5cm}}$$

$(6 + 3)7 = 9 \cdot 7 = \underline{63}$;
$6 \cdot 7 + 3 \cdot 7 = 42 + 21 = \underline{63}$

130.   From these examples we see that

$$(7 + 2)5 = 7 \cdot 5 + 2 \cdot 5$$
$$(6 + 3)7 = 6 \cdot 7 + \underline{\hspace{2cm}}$$

3 · 7

131.   In fact it can be shown that for any whole numbers a, b, and c

$$(a + b)c = ac + \underline{\hspace{1.5cm}}$$

bc

132. Use the fact that

$$(a + b)c = ac + bc$$

to change each product to a sum.

$$(4 + 9)12 \ = \text{_____} + \text{_____}$$
$$(37 + 12)17 = \text{_____} + \text{_____}$$

$4 \cdot 12; \quad 9 \cdot 12; \quad 37 \cdot 17; \quad 12 \cdot 17$

133. We can also write

$$5 \cdot 7 + 2 \cdot 7 = (5 + 2)7$$
$$6 \cdot 5 + 9 \cdot 5 = (6 + 9) \text{_____}$$

5

134. The expression

$$6 \cdot 7 + 9 \cdot 7$$

is called a _____ but has a common factor of _____.

SUM; 7

135. And

$$6 \cdot 7 + 9 \cdot 7 = 42 + 63 = \text{_____}.$$

105

136. The expression

$$(6 + 9) \cdot 7$$

is called a _____ and one of its _____ is 7.

PRODUCT; FACTORS

137. And

$$(6 + 9) \cdot 7 = 15 \cdot 7 = \text{_____}.$$

105

138. $$6 \cdot 7 + 9 \cdot 7 = 105$$
$$(6 + 9) \cdot 7 \ = 105$$

Hence

$$6 \cdot 7 + 9 \cdot 7 = (6 + 9) \cdot 7$$

The _____ on the left and the _____ on the right are equal.

SUM;   PRODUCT

139. Change each sum to a product.

$$9 \cdot 7 + 3 \cdot 7 \ = \text{_____}$$
$$136 \cdot 12 + 15 \cdot 12 = \text{_____}$$
$$7 \cdot 9 + 7 \cdot 2 \ = \text{_____}$$

$(9 + 3) \cdot 7; \quad (136 + 15) \cdot 12; \quad 7 \cdot (9 + 2)$

140. Compute. Change to a product first, if that is easier.

$$7 \cdot 19 + 3 \cdot 19 \ = \text{_____}$$
$$4 \cdot 17 + 4 \cdot 8 \ = \text{_____}$$
$$19 \cdot 19 + 19 \cdot 31 = \text{_____}$$

190;   100;   950

141. Let us review. When there are no parentheses in a problem involving both additions and multiplications all the _____ are performed first.

MULTIPLICATIONS

142. The _____ operation performed determines whether the expression is called a sum or a product.

> LAST

143. The fact that

a(b + c) = ab + ac

is called the _____ property.

> DISTRIBUTIVE

144. The distributive property says that under certain conditions a _____ and a _____ are equal.

> PRODUCT;   SUM   (either order)

145. But the _____ must contain a common factor which is also one of the factors of the _____.

> SUM;   PRODUCT

146. It is also true that, if x, y, and z represent whole numbers,

(x + y)z = _____ + _____

> xz;   yz

147. Sometimes the _____ property may be used to change a sum to a _____ which is easier to compute.

> DISTRIBUTIVE;   PRODUCT

Chapter 5

Problems A (Answers on page 507) | **Problems B**

Express each of the following numbers in simplest form.

1. $2 + 7 \cdot 5$
2. $2 \cdot 4 + 9$
3. $3 \cdot 6 + 2 \cdot 5$
4. $2(5 + 9)$
5. $(3)(2) + 7$
6. $6 + (3 \cdot 2)$
7. $(3 + 5)9$
8. $6 + 3(4 + 1)$
9. $(3 + 2) \cdot (4 + 5)$
10. $3 + 2 \cdot 4 + 8$

Identify each of the following as either a "sum" or a "product." Use the properties of whole numbers to express each sum as a product and each product as a sum. Do no computations.

Example: $3(7 + 5)$. Answer: Product (since multiplication is the last operation performed); $3 \cdot 7 + 3 \cdot 5$

Example: $2 \cdot 9 + 2 \cdot 5$. Answer: Sum; $2(9 + 5)$ or $2 \cdot (9 + 5)$

11. $7(3 + 5)$
12. $(4 + 5) \cdot 11$
13. $2 \cdot 5 + 2 \cdot 7$
14. $9 \cdot 4 + 8 \cdot 4$
15. $(12)(6) + (12)(4)$
16. $12 \cdot (13 + 20)$
17. $(41 + 9)27$
18. $(64)(18) + (36)(18)$
19. $2 \cdot 3 + 2 \cdot 1$
20. $2 \cdot 3 + 2$

Name the general property of whole numbers which each of the following illustrates.

Example: $3 \cdot 2 + 3 \cdot 5 = 3(2 + 5)$. Answer: Distributive property.

Example: $3(4 + 9) = (4 + 9)3$. Answer: Commutative property of multiplication.

21. $5(4 + 2) = 5 \cdot 4 + 5 \cdot 2$
22. $(3 + 9)8 = (9 + 3)8$
23. $4 \cdot 2 + 5 \cdot 2 = 2 \cdot 4 + 2 \cdot 5$
24. $(3 \cdot 5)4 = 3(5 \cdot 4)$
25. $4 \cdot 27 = 4 \cdot 25 + 4 \cdot 2$
26. $7 \cdot 13 + 7 \cdot 57 = 7 \cdot 70$
27. $(4 + 17) + 30 = 4 + (17 + 30)$
28. $7 + 8 \cdot 9 = 7 + 9 \cdot 8$
29. $4 \cdot (3 + 5) = (3 + 5) \cdot 4$
30. $(5 \cdot 7) \cdot 9 = (7 \cdot 5) \cdot 9$

Problems B

Express each of the following numbers in simplest form.

1. $7 \cdot 8 + 9$
2. $3 + 12 \cdot 3$
3. $4 \cdot 2 + 5 \cdot 7$
4. $(2 + 11) \cdot 3$
5. $4 + (5)(9)$
6. $(1 + 7)(5 + 4)$
7. $1 + (6 + 3)(4)$
8. $(2 + 5)(7 + 7)$
9. $(5 + 16) + 3 \cdot 2$
10. $4 \cdot 3 + 5 \cdot 6 + 8 \cdot 8$

Identify each of the following as either a "sum" or a "product." Use the properties of whole numbers to express each sum as a product and each product as a sum. Do no computations.

11. $9(1 + 9)$
12. $(3 + 11)7$
13. $(5)(4) + (5)(12)$
14. $3 \cdot 17 + 8 \cdot 17$
15. $6 \cdot (3 + 4 + 5)$
16. $2 \cdot 7 + 2 \cdot 8 + 2 \cdot 9$
17. $(13 + 7 + 5)(12)$
18. $7 \cdot 15 + 7 \cdot 1$
19. $8 \cdot 14 + 8$
20. $13 + 13$

The distributive and other properties of whole numbers can sometimes be used as a means of simplifying a computation. Thus

$$5 \cdot 17 + 5 \cdot 3 = 5 \cdot (17 + 3) = 5 \cdot 20 = 100$$

may be somewhat easier to compute than

$$5 \cdot 17 + 5 \cdot 3 = 85 + 15 = 100$$

Again, it may be easier to compute

$$17 \cdot (103) = 17 \cdot (100 + 3) = 17 \cdot 100 + 17 \cdot 3$$
$$= 1700 + 51 = 1751$$

than to do so by direct multiplication, particularly if certain steps are performed mentally. Use any method to compute each of the following.

21. $7 \cdot 12 + 7 \cdot 88$
22. $47 \cdot 93 + 47 \cdot 7$
23. $73 \cdot 814 + 73 \cdot 186$
24. $6 \cdot (100 + 5)$
25. $15(105)$
26. $21 \cdot 5 + 5 \cdot 5$
27. $(100 + 2) \cdot 45$
28. $17 \cdot 7 + 53 \cdot 7$
29. $(612)(5)$
30. $4 \cdot 19 + 4 \cdot 37 + 4 \cdot 44$

ORDER

1. We have called a collection of any sort of objects a _____.

> **SET**

2. Those objects which comprise the set are called _____ of the set.

> **MEMBERS**

3. To describe a set we either state some test which can be used to decide whether any object does or does not belong to the set, or we list the members of the set. When they are listed, the members may be listed in any _____.

> **ORDER**

4. If A = {2, 5, *, %}, then set B = {5, *}, all of whose members are also in A, is called a _____ of set A.

> **SUBSET**

5. A = {2, 5, *, %}
   Which of the following are subsets of A?
   C = {2, 5, %}
   D = {5, *}
   E = {2, *, 5, %}
   φ   _____

> **ALL ARE**

6. If two sets have exactly the same members, then we call the sets _____.

> **EQUAL**

7. And if the members of one set can be paired exactly with the members of another, we say the two sets have the same _____.

> **SIZE**

8. Let set $P = \{1, a, \#\}$

Which of the following sets have the same size as P?

$Q = \{*, \#, b\}$

$R = \{x, y, z\}$

$S = \{2, 4, 6\}$

ϕ _____

> Q;　R;　S　(ϕ has <u>no</u> members)

9. Many other sets have the same size as set $P = \{1, a, \#\}$. The property that all such sets have in common is called the _____ _____ three.

> NATURAL NUMBER

10. Similarly, the property shared by the set $M = \{a, b, c, d, e\}$ and all other sets of the same size is called the _____ _____.

> NATURAL NUMBER FIVE

11. The other natural numbers are defined in a similar way. Each is that property shared by sets of the _____ _____.

> SAME SIZE

12. The number 0 has been defined as the size of the _____ _____.

> EMPTY SET

13. The sum of two numbers is the size of the _____ of two disjoint sets whose sizes are the terms of the sum.

> UNION

14. If a and b are any two whole numbers, we represent their sum by writing

a _____ b

> +

15. $a + b$

represents the sum of a and b.

The numbers a and b are called the _____ of the sum.

> TERMS

16. The order in which the terms appear does not affect the sum. This can be symbolized by writing

$a + b =$ _____

> b + a

17. This property of whole numbers, symbolized by writing

$a + b = b + a$

is known as the _____ property of _____.

> COMMUTATIVE;　ADDITION

18. Since, for any whole number a,

$a + 0 = 0 + a = a$

we call the number 0 the additive _____.

> IDENTITY

19. Find

7 + 12 = _____

16 + 5 = _____

31 + 0 = _____

22 + 11 = _____

19;   21;   31;   33

20.   16 + 5 = 21

We call 21 the _____ of 16 and 5.

SUM

21.   16 + 5 = 21

We call 16 and 5 the _____ of the sum.

TERMS

22. It may be possible to find one of the terms, if the sum and the other term are known.

Find the missing term.

4 + _____ = 7

13 + _____ = 18

3;   5

23. Find the missing term.

11 + _____ = 20

4 + _____ = 16

20 + _____ = 35

7 + _____ = 40

9;   12;   15;   33

24. Find the missing term.

20 + _____ = 31

7 + _____ = 58

25 + _____ = 100

16 + _____ = 20

11;   51;   75;   4

25. In the statement

14 + [ ]* = 2

one of the terms is missing. Can you find the missing term? (Answer YES or NO.) _____.

NO   (see next frame)

26. No natural number can be added to 14 to give a sum of 2.

Find the missing term, where possible.

5 + _____ = 33

14 + _____ = 12

6 + _____ = 22

55 + _____ = 10

28;   IMPOSSIBLE;   16;   IMPOSSIBLE

27. Consider the problem

16 + [ ] = 20

Since there is a natural number, 4, which, when added to 16, yields a sum of 20, we shall say that 16 IS LESS THAN 20.

_____

*The position of the missing term is indicated by the brackets, [ ]. When used to indicate an omitted symbol, brackets do not call for a response.

28. Consider the problem

$5 + [\ \ ] = 33$

Since there is a natural number, 28, which, when added to 5, yields a sum of 33, we say that 5 is _____ _____ 33.

LESS THAN

29. Find the missing term.

$6 + \underline{\hspace{1cm}} = 19$

13

30. $6 + 13 = 19$

Since it is possible to find a natural number which, when added to 6, yields a sum of 19, we say that _____ is less than _____.

6; 19

31. We shall use the symbol $<$ in place of "is less than." Then we can write

$5 < 33$

and

$6 \underline{\hspace{1cm}} 19$.

$<$

32. Since $7 + 4 = 11$ we can write

$7 \underline{\hspace{1cm}} 11$

$<$

33. And $3 < 22$, since we can find a natural number which, when added to _____, gives a sum of _____. It is the natural number _____.

3; 22; 19

34. Then

$16 < 20$	since	$16 + 4 = 20$
$25 < 40$	since	$25 + \underline{\hspace{0.8cm}} = 40$
$30 < 37$	since	$30 + \underline{\hspace{0.8cm}} = 37$
$12 < 18$	since	$12 + \underline{\hspace{0.8cm}} = \underline{\hspace{0.8cm}}$

15; 7; 6; 18

35. Is

$14 < 2?$ _____

NO   (see next frame)

36. Since there is no natural number which we can add to 14 to give a sum of 2, we cannot say that 14 is less than 2.

Is

$6 < 55?$ _____

YES $(6 + 49 = 55)$

37. Which of the following are true?

a) $6 < 19$

b) $22 < 7$

c) $3 < 6$

d) $4 < 84$ _____

a, c, d ARE TRUE

38. Which of the following are true?

    a) $22 < 17$

    b) $6 < 49$

    c) $2 < 13$

    d) $7 < 7$ _____

b AND c ARE TRUE

39. Note that $7 < 7$ is <u>not</u> true. There is no <u>natural</u> <u>number</u> which can be added to 7 to give a sum of 7. Of course,

    $7 + _____ = 7$

but _____ is not a natural number.

0;   0

40. Is

    $0 < 12?$ _____

YES   (see next frame)

41. Since there is a natural number, **12**, which, when added to 0, gives a sum of 12, we write $0 < 12$.

Which of the following are true?

    a) $3 < 19$

    b) $0 < 44$

    c) $5 < 6$

    d) $2 < 22$ _____

ALL ARE TRUE

42. Let a and b represent any whole numbers. If we can find a natural number, d, which when added to a yields a sum of b, we say that a is _____ _____ b.

LESS THAN

43. That is, if there is a natural number d such that

    $a + d = b$

we write

    $a < _____$

b

44. Since $7 + 44 = 51$, we can write

    $7 _____ 51$

<

45. But $7 + 44 = 44 + 7$ by the _____ property of _____.

COMMUTATIVE;   ADDITION

46. $7 + 44 = 51$ and $7 + 44 = 44 + 7$

Hence

    $44 + 7 = 51$

and so we can also write

    $44 < _____$

51

47. $13 + 21 = 34$

and so we can write

    $13 _____ 34$

<

48. $13 + 21 = 34$

But

$13 + 21 = 21 + 13$

Hence

$21 + 13 = 34$

and so we can write

$21 < \underline{\hspace{2em}}$

34

49. The statement $a < b$ means that there is some natural number d such that

$a + d = \underline{\hspace{2em}}$

b

50. Since $6 + 9 = 15$, we say that 6 is less than 15 and write $6 < 15$. We shall also say that 15 IS GREATER THAN 6 and symbolize this by writing $15 > 6$.

Since $4 < 11$, we shall say 11 is greater than 4 and write

$11 \underline{\hspace{2em}} 4$

$>$

51. Which of the following are true?

a) $22 > 17$

b) $6 > 4$

c) $12 > 15$

d) $61 > 19$ $\underline{\hspace{3em}}$

a, b, d ARE TRUE

52. Let a and b represent any whole numbers. When we say a is greater than b we mean, simply, that b is $\underline{\hspace{3em}}$ than a.

LESS

53. In symbols, to say that $a > b$ means that

$\underline{\hspace{3em}}$

$b < a$

54. Since $2 + 3 = 5$, we can write

$2 \underline{\hspace{2em}} 5$.

$<$

55. $2 < 5$

Consider the set

$L = \{a, b, c, d, e\}$

The size of L is $\underline{\hspace{2em}}$.

5

56. $2 < 5$

$L = \{a, b, c, d, e\}$

The size of L is 5.

Let

$S = \{a, e\}$

Then S is a $\underline{\hspace{3em}}$ of set L, and the size of S is $\underline{\hspace{2em}}$.

SUBSET; 2

57. $2 < 5$

L = {a, b, c, d, e} and has size 5.

S = {a, e} is a subset of set L and has size 2.

$2 < 5$ and a set of size 5 has a subset of size 2.

58. Since $3 + 4 = 7$, we can write 3 _____ 7.

$<$

59. $3 < 7$

Consider the set

H = {a, b, c, d, e, f, g}

The size of H is _____.

7

60. $3 < 7$

H = {a, b, c, d, e, f, g} and has size 7.

Let

T = {b, d, f}

Then T is a _____ of set H, and the size of T is _____.

SUBSET; 3

61. $3 < 7$

H = {a, b, c, d, e, f, g} and has size 7.

T = {b, d, f} is a subset of H and has size 3.

$3 < 7$ and a set of size _____ has a _____ of size _____.

7; **SUBSET;** 3

62. From these examples it appears that if a and b represent any whole numbers, and if $a < b$, then some set of size _____ has a subset of size _____.

b; a

63. If $a < b$, then some set of size b has a subset of size a.

Next consider set

A = {#, *, !}

The size of A is _____.

3

64. A = {#, *, !}

Which of the following are subsets of A?

φ

F = {#}

G = {#, *} _____

ALL ARE

65. What is the size of each set?

φ   _____

F = {#}   _____

G = {#, *}   _____

0; 1; 2

66. Set A = {#, *, !} has size 3.

Its subsets φ, F, and G have sizes 0, 1, and 2, and

0 < 3

1 _____ 3

2 _____ 3

67.   A = {#, *, !}

Consider the set B = {#, *, !}. Since every member of set B is also a member of set A, B is a _____ of A.

68.   A = {#, *, !}

B = {#, *, !} is a subset of A

Since the sets A and B have exactly the same members we can write

A _____ B

69.   A = {#, *, !}   and   B = {#, *, !}

B is a subset of A and A = B.

Hence, set A is a _____ of itself.

70. The size of A is 3

Is 3 < 3?   _____

71. 3 is not less than 3 since there is no natural number which can be added to 3 to give a sum of 3. But, other than set A itself, all subsets of A we have considered have a size which is _____ _____ the size of A.

72. Consider the set

Q = {$, !, *, ?, #, %}

The size of Q is _____.

73.   Q {$, !, *, ?, #, %}

Which of the following are subsets of Q?

φ

A = {*}

B = {$, !}

C = {*, ?, %}   _____

74. What is the size of each set?

φ   _____

A = {*}   _____

B = {$, !}   _____

C = {*, ?, %}   _____

75. Set Q = {$, !, *, ?, #, %} has size 6.
It has subsets φ, A, B, and C of sizes 0, 1, 2, and 3.

And

    0 < 6

    1 _____ 6

    2 _____ 6

    3 _____ 6

76.   D = {$, !. *, #}

is also a _____ of

Q = {$, !, *, ?, #, %}

The size of D is 4 and the size of Q is 6.

Is 4 < 6? _____

77.   E = { !, *, ?, #, %}

is another subset of set

Q = {$, !, *, ?, #, %}.

The size of E is _____ and the size of Q is _____.

Is 5 < 6? _____

78. We have not considered every subset of Q, but the size of each one we did consider was _____ _____ the size of Q.

79. Is Q = {$, !, *, ?, #, %} a subset of Q? _____

80. The size of Q is 6.

Is 6 < 6? _____

81. 6 is not less than 6.

But for all subsets of Q, other than Q itself, their _____ is _____ than the size of Q.

82. Let X be any set. With the exception of set X itself, the size of every subset of X is less than the _____ of X.

83. In fact, we could define the relation < in terms of sets. Let a and b be any whole numbers. Then a < b if there is some set of size b which has a subset, different from itself, whose size is _____.

84. However, we have defined the relation < in terms of the operation of addition:

a < b   if   there is a natural number d such that _____

85. Consider the numbers 7 and 15.

    Is $7 < 15$?   _____

    Is $7 = 15$?   _____

    Is $7 > 15$?   _____

    YES;   NO;   NO

86. Consider the numbers 9 and 4.

    Is $9 < 4$?   _____

    Is $9 = 4$?   _____

    Is $9 > 4$?   _____

    NO;   NO;   YES

87. Consider the numbers 0 and 8.

    Is $0 < 8$?   _____

    Is $0 = 8$?   _____

    Is $0 > 8$?   _____

    YES;   NO;   NO

88. Is $11 < 11$?   _____

    Is $11 = 11$?   _____

    Is $11 > 11$?   _____

    NO;   YES;   NO

89. In fact, no matter which two whole numbers a and b we consider, we can ask three questions:

    Is $a < b$?

    Is $a = b$?

    Is $a > b$?

    and only _____ of the answers will be YES.

    ONE

90. Now consider the three numbers 3, 7, and 20.

    Is $3 < 7$?   _____

    Is $7 < 20$?   _____

    Is $3 < 20$?   _____

    YES;   YES;   YES

91. Next consider the numbers 5, 6, and 13.

    Is $5 < 6$?   _____

    Is $6 < 13$?   _____

    Is $5 < 13$?   _____

    YES;   YES;   YES

92. $50 < 60$ and $60 < 74$

    and

    50 _____ 74

    $<$

93. In fact, if a, b, and c are any whole numbers, and if $a < b$ and also $b < c$, we can conclude that

    a _____ c

    $<$

94. If $a < b$ and $b < c$, then $a < c$.

    Let us show that this is so.

    If $a < b$, there is a natural number d such that _____.

    $a + d = b$

95. If $b < c$, there is a natural number e such that

$b + e =$ _____

c

96. If $a < b$ and $b < c$, we have

$a + d = b$ and $b + e = c$

Consider the sum $a + (d + e)$.

By the associative property of addition we can write

$a + (d + e) = (a +$ _____ $) +$ _____

d;   e

97. $a < b$

$a + d = b$

and

$a + (d + e) = (a + d) + e$

Hence

$a + (d + e) =$ _____ $+ e$.

b

98. $b < c$

$b + e = c$

and

$a + (d + e) = b + e$

Hence

$a + (d + e) =$ _____ .

c

99. $a + (d + e) = c$

Since d and e are natural numbers, their sum, $d + e$, is also a _____ number.

NATURAL

100. $a + (d + e) = c$

But then we have a natural number, $d + e$, which, when added to a, gives a sum of c.

Hence

a _____ c.

<

101. We have shown, therefore, that if $a < b$ and $b < c$, then _____

$a < c$

102. For any natural number a

$0 + a =$ _____

a

103. $0 + a = a$

Hence there is a natural number which can be added to 0 to give a sum of a.

We can conclude, therefore, that

0 _____ a

for any natural number a.

<

104. Let us establish an ORDER for the whole numbers. We do so by arranging them so that any number is less than every number following it. Hence, in our ordering of the whole numbers, the first number must be _____ .

0

105. Let a be any natural number other than 1. Let A be any set whose size is a. Since A is not the empty set, it has at least one member. The set consisting of this member alone is a _____ of set A.

SUBSET

106. Let U be this subset of A which has only one number. The size of U is _____ .

1

107. Set A has size a. U is a subset of size 1. Since a is not 1, U is not the set A. Hence A, a set of size a, has a subset other than itself of size 1. Therefore

1 _____ a

<

108. Then in our ordering of the whole numbers, the second number, after zero, is the natural number _____ .

1

109. We shall not attempt to show that the number following 1 is the natural number _____ .

2

110. And the next four numbers after two are, in order,

3, _____, _____, _____

4,   5,   6

111. In fact, you already know the ordering of the natural numbers. It is the very same order in which you count. The first ten whole numbers in our ordering, then, are

0, 1, 2, 3, 4, 5, 6, _____,

_____, _____

7,   8,   9

112. The next five numbers, in order, are

10, _____, _____, _____,

_____

11,   12,   13,   14

113. The list of natural numbers goes on, without end. But note that any number in the list is _____ _____ every number which appears after it.

LESS THAN

114. Let us conclude with this observation. In the ordering we have established, the addition of 1 to any number gives a sum which is the N_____ number in the list.

NEXT

115. That is, the number which follows, in order, after 215 is

$$215 + 1 = \underline{\hspace{2cm}}.$$

216

116. And the number which succeeds 329 is

$$329 + \underline{\hspace{2cm}} = \underline{\hspace{2cm}}.$$

1;   330

117. It is this property of the number 1 and the operation of addition which insures that the list of natural numbers never ends. If 1 is added to any natural number, the result is the _____ natural number.

NEXT

118. There could never be any "last" natural number. If there were, adding _____ to it would give the "next" natural number <u>after</u> the last one. The "last" one would not be the last.

1

119. In this chapter we have defined a relation between numbers. We call the relation "is less than." The statement

6 is less than 14

is represented by the symbols _____.

$6 < 14$

120. And $6 < 14$ since there is a natural number whose sum with _____ is _____ . It is the natural number _____ .

6;   14;   8

121. $6 < 14$

and we can find a _____ of size 14 which has a _____ of size 6.

SET;   SUBSET

122. If a and b are any two whole numbers, then one, and only one, of the following is true:

$a < b$;   a _____ b;   a _____ b

=;   >   (either order)

123. If a and b represent any whole numbers, then $a < b$ if there is a natural number d such that _____

$a + d = b$

124. And $a < b$ if there is a set, B, of size b which has a subset (other than B itself) of size _____ .

a

125. The statement "x is greater than y" means that y is _____ _____ x.

LESS THAN

126. In symbols,

   $x > y$ means _____ .

   y < x

127. We agree to order the whole numbers. Any number in our ordering is _____ _____ every number which follows it.

   LESS THAN

128. The first ten whole numbers, in order, are:

   _____, _____, _____, _____,
   _____, _____, _____, _____,
   _____, _____

   0, 1, 2, 3, 4, 5, 6, 7, 8, 9

Chapter 6

Problems A (Answers on page 507)

Each of the following true statements of addition yields up to four statements of inequality. Give them.

Example: $4 + 9 = 13$. Answer: $4 < 13$
$13 > 4$
$9 < 13$
$13 > 9$

Example: $7 + 0 = 7$. Answer: $0 < 7$
$7 > 0$

1. $5 + 6 = 11$
2. $17 + 3 = 20$
3. $0 + 8 = 8$
4. $4 + 4 = 8$
5. $6 + 19 = 25$
6. $10 + 20 = 30$
7. $6 + 11 = 17$
8. $4 + 0 = 4$
9. $12 + 7 = 19$
10. $13 + 50 = 63$

In each of the following, insert one of the symbols

$<$ $>$ $=$

so as to form a true statement.

11. 3 _____ 9
12. 17 _____ 12
13. $(2 + 3)$ _____ 5
14. $3 \cdot 9$ _____ $4 \cdot 7$
15. $6 \cdot 7$ _____ $3 \cdot 14$
16. $2 + 3 \cdot 4$ _____ $(2 + 3) \cdot 4$
17. $(5 + 6) \cdot 8$ _____ $5 \cdot 8 + 6 \cdot 8$
18. $(3 + 5) (2 + 4)$ _____ $3 + 5 \cdot 2 + 4$
19. $4 + 7 \cdot 0 + 6 \cdot 1$ _____ $4 + 7 + 6$
20. $7 \cdot 9 + 7 \cdot 11$ _____ $7 \cdot 20$

Arrange the following lists of whole numbers in order.

21. $7, 19, 1, 6$
22. $4, 5, 0, 12, 8, 101$
23. $0, 2, 4, 6, 1, 3, 5, 7, 9$
24. $13, 15, 18, 23, 25, 28, 16, 26, 36$
25. $10, 9, 8, 7, 6, 1, 2, 0, 90, 100$

Insert $<$, $>$, or $=$ to form a true statement.

26. If $a < 2$ and $2 < b$, then a _____ b.
27. If $x > 3$ and $y < 3$, then x _____ y.
28. If $r = 4$ and $s < 4$, then r _____ s.
29. If $7 < x$, then $7 + 5$ _____ $x + 5$.
30. If $8 < x$, then $8 \cdot 4$ _____ $x \cdot 4$.

Problems B

Each of the following true statements of addition yields up to four statements of inequality. Give them.

1. $14 + 4 = 18$
2. $9 + 11 = 20$
3. $0 + 12 = 12$
4. $2 + 2 = 4$
5. $87 + 13 = 100$
6. $24 + 1 = 25$
7. $18 + 18 = 36$
8. $47 + 0 = 47$
9. $17 + 18 = 35$
10. $1 + 0 = 1$

In each of the following, insert one of the symbols

$<$ $>$ $=$

so as to form a true statement.

11. 45 _____ 54
12. 88 _____ 44
13. $(7 + 9)$ _____ 15
14. $12 \cdot 7$ _____ 72
15. $6 \cdot 9$ _____ $8 \cdot 7$
16. $12 + 8 \cdot 2$ _____ $2 \cdot 12 + 8$
17. $4 + 3 \cdot 9 + 7$ _____ $(4 + 3) (9 + 7)$
18. $15 \cdot 7 + 4 \cdot 0$ _____ $15 \cdot 7 + 4$
19. $6 \cdot 8 + 0 \cdot 7$ _____ $4 \cdot 12 + 0 \cdot 12$
20. $(5 + 7) (8 + 10)$ _____ $5 \cdot 8 + 7 \cdot 10$

Arrange the following lists of whole numbers in order.

21. $10, 20, 15, 30, 40, 60, 45, 90$

22. 17, 57, 87, 7, 97, 67, 77, 37, 47, 27

23. 1, 0, 3, 2, 7, 6, 19, 18, 10

24. 45, 40, 54, 63, 80, 72, 9, 18, 0

25. $7 \cdot 8$, $5 \cdot 8$, $6 \cdot 8$, $0 \cdot 8$, $8 \cdot 8$, $9 \cdot 8$, $4 \cdot 8$

26. The set $\{*, \#, \Delta, \natural \}$ has the subset $\{\#, \natural\}$. What two statements of inequality follow from this?

27. The set $\{1, 2, 3, 4, 5, 10\}$ has the subset $\{3, 4, 5\}$. What two statements of inequality follow from this?

28. Show that if a and b are whole numbers with

$$a < b$$

and c is any whole number, then

$$a + c < b + c$$

(Hint: You must show that there is a natural number whose sum with $a + c$ is $b + c$.)

29. Show that if a and b are whole numbers with

$$a < b$$

then

$$a \cdot 0 = b \cdot 0$$

30. Show that if a and b are whole numbers with

$$a < b$$

and c is any natural number, then

$$ac < bc$$

CHAPTER 7

INVERSE OPERATIONS

1. If the members of two sets can be paired, exactly, with one another, the sets are said to have the _____ _____.

> SAME SIZE

2. If one considers all sets of the same size, the property they have in common is called a _____ _____.

> NATURAL NUMBER

3. The number 0 is defined as the size of the _____ set.

> EMPTY

4. To add two numbers we find the size of the union of two _____ sets whose sizes are the numbers to be added.

> DISJOINT

5. If a and b represent two whole numbers, we represent the result of adding these numbers by writing

a _____ b

and we call this result their _____.

> +; SUM

6. In the sum a + b, we call a and b the _____, and we recognize that the sum does not depend on their _____.

> TERMS; ORDER

7. We call two number symbols equal only if they name the _____ number.

> SAME

8. Thus, 7 + 16 = 23, since both 7 + 16 and 23 name the _____ number.

> SAME

9. We say that a whole number a is less than a whole number b if we can find a _____ _____ which, when added to a, yields a sum of b.

10. That is, a $<$ b if there is a natural number d such that _____ .

11. Any addition problem includes three numbers: two terms and their sum. Given the two terms, their sum can be determined. Find

$6 + 23 =$ _____

$14 + 78 =$ _____

$15 + 6 =$ _____

$33 + 12 =$ _____

12. Or, it may be possible to find one of the terms when the other term and the sum are known. Find

_____ $+ 7 = 20$

$5 +$ _____ $= 16$

$6 +$ _____ $= 20$

_____ $+ 26 = 31$

13. Find the missing number:

$44 + 57$ $=$ _____

_____ $+ 32 = 35$

$9 +$ _____ $= 51$

_____ $+ 16 = 80$

14. It appears that when two whole numbers in an addition problem are known, the third can be determined. But consider

$16 + [\ ] = 5$

Can the third number be determined here? _____

15. No whole number, when added to 16, yields a sum of t. Hence the problem

$16 + [\ ] = 5$

has no solution. Which of the following problems has a solution?

a) $14 + [\ ] = 9$

b) $60 + [\ ] = 27$

c) $50 + [\ ] = 80$ _____

16. Find, where possible:

$24 + 51$ $=$ _____

$16 +$ _____ $= 24$

$3 + 17$ $=$ _____

$21 +$ _____ $= 9$

17. Find, where possible:

$14 + 0 = \underline{\hspace{3em}}$

$23 + \underline{\hspace{3em}} = 24$

$44 + 54 = \underline{\hspace{3em}}$

$17 + 17 = \underline{\hspace{3em}}$

14;   1;   98;   34

18. Find, where possible:

$16 + 1 = \underline{\hspace{3em}}$

$23 + \underline{\hspace{3em}} = 33$

$14 + \underline{\hspace{3em}} = 14$

$22 + 23 = \underline{\hspace{3em}}$

17;   10;   0;   45

19. Find, where possible:

$27 + 36 = \underline{\hspace{3em}}$

$22 + \underline{\hspace{3em}} = 4$

$5 + \underline{\hspace{3em}} = 66$

$33 + \underline{\hspace{3em}} = 30$

63;   IMPOSSIBLE;   61;
IMPOSSIBLE

20. As these examples illustrate, when two terms are known, their sum can always be determined. And if the terms are whole numbers, their sum is also a \underline{\hspace{6em}} number.

WHOLE

21. That is, if a and b represent whole numbers, then their sum, a + b, is also a whole number. We say that the whole numbers are CLOSED WITH RESPECT TO ADDITION.

22. 7 and 12 are natural numbers. Their sum is \underline{\hspace{3em}}. That the sum of 7 and 12 is also a natural number illustrates the fact that the natural numbers, too, are \underline{\hspace{4em}} with respect to addition.

19;   CLOSED

23. The natural numbers are closed with respect to addition since the sum of two natural numbers is a \underline{\hspace{4em}} \underline{\hspace{4em}}.

NATURAL NUMBER

24. But, as we have seen, when only one term and the sum are known, it may not be possible to determine the other term. Find, if possible:

$35 + \underline{\hspace{3em}} = 26$

$16 + \underline{\hspace{3em}} = 22$

IMPOSSIBLE;   6

25. Let us attempt to formulate a requirement on the known term and the sum to insure that the other term can be determined. Find

$29 + \underline{\hspace{3em}} = 29$

0

26. Find

$66 + \underline{\hspace{3em}} = 66$

$77 + \underline{\hspace{3em}} = 77$

$103 + \underline{\hspace{3em}} = 103$

$2 + \underline{\hspace{3em}} = 2$

0;   0;   0;   0

27. Since 0 is the additive identity, we know that, for any whole number a,

$$a + 0 = \underline{\hphantom{aaa}}$$

a

28. Hence, if the sum and the known term are equal, it is always possible to find the other term. It will be the number _____ in every case.

0

29. If the sum and the known term are not equal, there is another condition which will insure the existence of the other term.

Consider the statement

$$7 < 15$$

This means that there is a natural number which, when added to _____, yields a sum of _____.

7;   15

30. $7 < 15$ because there is a natural number, _____, such that

$$7 + \underline{\hphantom{aaa}} = 15$$

8;   8

31. But then the problem

$$7 + [\ \ ] = 15$$

clearly has a solution. The missing term is 8.

Now

$$55 < 60$$

Since

$$55 + \underline{\hphantom{aaa}} = 60.$$

5

32. Hence, the problem

$$55 + [\ \ ] = 60$$

has a solution. It is the number _____.

5

33. Let a and b represent any whole numbers. Then $a < b$ means there is a natural number d whose sum with a is b. That is,

$$a + \underline{\hphantom{aaa}} = b$$

d

34. Consider the problem, then, of finding the second term when the sum, b, and the first term, a, are known.

$$a + [\ \ ] = b$$

The second term can <u>always</u> be found (and it will be a natural number) whenever

$$a \underline{\hphantom{aaa}} b$$

<

35. Therefore, the problem

$$a + [\ \ ] = b$$

will <u>always</u> have a solution whenever $a = b$ or _____ < _____.

a;   b

36. When it <u>is</u> possible to find the second term, if the sum and the first term are known, we shall refer to the process of determining the second term as the operation of SUBTRACTION.

37. To SUBTRACT 6 from 16 means to find the missing term in the problem

$$6 + [\ \ ] = 16$$

The missing term is _____ .

> 10

38. Subtract 4 from 27. That is, find the missing term in the problem

$$4 + \_\_\_\_\_ = 27$$

> 23

39. Subtract 12 from 16. _____

Subtract 5 from 31. _____

> 4 (since 12 + 4 = 16); 26 (since 5 + 26 = 31)

40. Find the missing term:

$$45 + \_\_\_\_\_ = 53$$

That is, subtract _____ from _____ .

> 8; 45; 53

41. Subtract 12 from 15. _____

Subtract 6 from 21. _____

Subtract 30 from 48. _____

Subtract 23 from 52. _____

> 3; 15; 18; 29

42. We shall use the MINUS SIGN as a symbol for subtraction. The problem

"Subtract 44 from 50"

will be written

"50 – 44"

and

$$50 - 44 = \_\_\_\_\_ .$$

> 6

43. Then 15 – 3 means to subtract _____ from 15.

> 3

44. And 36 – 13 means to subtract _____ from _____ .

> 13; 36

45. 14 – 5 = _____

23 – 8 = _____

48 – 30 = _____

75 – 50 = _____

> 9; 15; 18; 25

46. If a and b represent whole numbers, then a – b means to subtract _____ from _____ .

> b; a

47. That is, a − b means the missing term in the problem

$$b + [\ ] = \underline{\qquad}$$

a

48. $47 - 13 = \underline{\qquad}$

34

49. $47 - 13 = 34$

Let us call the result, 34, the DIFFERENCE of 47 and 13. Then, since 14 − 5 = 9, we call 9 the _____ of 14 and 5.

DIFFERENCE

50. $26 - 14 = 12$

and so _____ is the difference of _____ and _____ .

12; 26; 14

51. Find the difference of 23 and 7. _____

Find the difference of 51 and 6. _____

16; 45

52. By the difference of a and b we mean the result of subtracting _____ from _____ .

b; a

53. And we write the difference of a and b as

$$\underline{\qquad} - \underline{\qquad}$$

a; b

54. By a − b we mean the number which must be _____ to b to yield a _____ of a.

ADDED; SUM

55. So if

$$a - b = d$$

then

$$\underline{\qquad} + d = \underline{\qquad}$$

b; a

56. $a - b = d$

We call d the difference of a and b. We shall call the number a the MINUEND and the number b the SUBTRAHEND in the subtraction problem.

57. In the problem

$$33 - 6 = 27$$

we call 33 the M_____ and 6 the S_____ .

MINUEND; SUBTRAHEND

58. In the problem

$$88 - 16 = 72$$

we call 88 the _____ ;

we call 16 the _____ ; and

we call 72 the _____ .

MINUEND; SUBTRAHEND; DIFFERENCE

59. Find

$12 +$ _____ $= 31$

$31 - 12 =$ _____

19;   19

60. Find

$16 +$ _____ $= 25$

$25 - 16 =$ _____

Find

$33 - 20 =$ _____

$20 +$ _____ $= 33$

9;   9;   13;   13

61. Find

$71 - 44 =$ _____

$44 +$ _____ $= 71$

Find

$39 +$ _____ $= 50$

$50 - 39 =$ _____

27;   27;   11;   11

62. The examples in the last few frames show a connection between the operations of subtraction and addition. Each subtraction problem is associated with a problem involving addition.

Note also:

$47 - 5 =$ _____

$42 + 5 =$ _____

42;   47

63. And:

$33 - 7 =$ _____

$26 + 7 =$ _____

26;   33

64. $33 - 7 = 26$

$26 + 7 = 33$

Note that the sum in the addition problem is equal to the _____ in the subtraction problem.

MINUEND

65. $48 + 14 =$ _____

$62 - 14 =$ _____

62;   48

66. $63 + 15 =$ _____

$78 - 15 =$ _____

78;   63

67. $63 + 15 = 78$

$78 - 15 = 63$

And note that the difference in the subtraction problem is equal to one of the _____ in the addition problem.

TERMS

68. As these examples illustrate, the operations of addition and subtraction are opposite. We shall say that subtraction is the INVERSE of addition.

69. Recall, again, the meaning of subtraction.

To subtract 7 from 18 is to find the second term in the problem

$$7 + [\quad] = 18$$

and

$$18 - 7 = \underline{\qquad}.$$

11

70. $18 - 7 = 11$ since $7 + 11 = 18$

The operation of subtraction is defined by addition.

To subtract b from a is to find a number which, when _____ to b yields a sum of _____ .

ADDED;   a

71. That is,

$$a - b = d$$

If

$$b + \underline{\qquad} = a$$

d

72. $a - b = d$ if $b + d = a$

But, as we have seen, the number d can only be found if a = b or if _____ < _____ .

b;   a

73. Hence, it will only be possible to find the difference of two numbers if the subtrahend is _____ to the minuend or if the subtrahend is _____ than the minuend.

EQUAL;   LESS

74. Thus

$$47 - 13 = \underline{\qquad}$$

whereas the expression 13 − 47 has no meaning.

34

75. Find, where possible:

$$59 - 22 = \underline{\qquad}$$
$$33 - 5 = \underline{\qquad}$$
$$39 - 28 = \underline{\qquad}$$
$$16 - 16 = \underline{\qquad}$$

37;   28;   11;   0

76. Find, where possible:

$$83 - 50 = \underline{\qquad}$$
$$27 - 20 = \underline{\qquad}$$
$$32 - 31 = \underline{\qquad}$$
$$66 - 80 = \underline{\qquad}$$

33;   7;   1;   IMPOSSIBLE

77. The difference of a and b is defined only if a = b or if b < a. Hence, given any two whole numbers, it may not be possible to subtract the first from the second. The whole numbers are not _____ with respect to subtraction.

CLOSED

78. If a and b represent two numbers, we can represent the result of multiplying them by writing a · b or ab, and we call this result their _____ .

PRODUCT

79. In the expression ab, we call a and b _____ of the product, and we recognize that the product does not depend on their order.

80. Any multiplication problem includes three numbers; two factors and their product. Given the two factors, their product can be determined.

Find

$5 \cdot 6$ = _____

$7 \cdot 4$ = _____

$15 \cdot 8$ = _____

$6 \cdot 21$ = _____

30; 28; 120; 126

81. Or, it may be possible to find one of the factors when the product and the other factor are known.

Find

$4 \cdot$ _____ $= 28$

_____ $\cdot 5 = 45$

$13 \cdot$ _____ $= 39$

_____ $\cdot 9 = 54$

7; 9; 3; 6

82. Find the missing number:

$4 \cdot$ _____ $= 20$

$6 \cdot 11$ = _____

_____ $\cdot 8 = 72$

_____ $\cdot 7 = 56$

5; 66; 9; 8

83. It appears that when two whole numbers in a multiplication problem are known, the third can be determined.

But consider

$[\ ] \cdot 7 = 25$

Can the third number be determined here?

_____

NO

84. No whole number, when multiplied by 7, yields a product of 25. Hence the problem $[\ ] \cdot 7 = 25$ has no solution. Which of the following problems has a solution?

a) $[\ ] \cdot 5 \ = 35$

b) $[\ ] \cdot 7 \ = 80$

c) $[\ ] \cdot 4 \ = 55$

d) $[\ ] \cdot 12 = 84$ _____

a AND d

85. Find, where possible:

$3 \cdot 14$ = _____

_____ $\cdot 6 = 90$

$7 \cdot 12$ = _____

_____ $\cdot 14 = 70$

42; 15; 84; 5

86. Find, where possible:

$12 \cdot 9$ = _____

_____ $\cdot 6 = 36$

_____ $\cdot 20 = 320$

$50 \cdot 8$ = _____

108; 6; 16; 400

87. Find, where possible:

$$17 \cdot 0 \quad = \underline{\hspace{2cm}}$$

$$\underline{\hspace{2cm}} \cdot 8 \; = 77$$

$$1 \cdot 44 \quad = \underline{\hspace{2cm}}$$

$$\underline{\hspace{2cm}} \cdot 16 = \; 3$$

0;   IMPOSSIBLE;   44;   IMPOSSIBLE

88. As these examples show, when two factors are known, their product can always be determined. And if the factors are whole numbers, their product is also a _____ number.

WHOLE

89. That is, if a and b represent whole numbers, their product, ab, is also a whole number. We say that the whole numbers are _____ with respect to multiplication.

CLOSED

90. 7 and 16 are natural numbers. Their product, _____, is also a natural number. This illustrates the fact that the natural numbers are closed with respect to _____.

112;   MULTIPLICATION

91. But, as we have seen, when only one factor and the product are known, it may not be possible to determine the other factor.

Find, if possible:

$$\underline{\hspace{2cm}} \cdot 7 = 25$$

$$\underline{\hspace{2cm}} \cdot 6 = 78$$

IMPOSSIBLE;   13

92. Whenever it is possible to find the first factor if the product and the second factor are known, we shall refer to the process of determining the first factor as the operation of DIVISION.

93. TO DIVIDE 16 by 8 means to find the missing factor in the problem

$$[\;] \cdot 8 = 16$$

The missing factor is _____.

2

94. Divide 96 by 8.

That is, find the missing factor in the problem

$$\underline{\hspace{2cm}} \cdot 8 = 96$$

12

95. Divide 42 by 6. _____
Divide 88 by 22. _____

7 (since $7 \cdot 6 = 42$);   4 (since $4 \cdot 22 = 88$)

96. Find the missing factor.

$$\underline{\hspace{2cm}} \cdot 12 = 132$$

That is, divide _____ by _____.

11;   132;   12

97. Divide 78 by 2. _____
Divide 54 by 3. _____
Divide 135 by 5. _____
Divide 66 by 6. _____

39;   18;   27;   11

98. We shall use the BAR as a symbol for division. The problem

"Divide 96 by 6"

will be written "96/6" (or $\frac{96}{6}$) and

96/6 = _____

16

99. Then 88/4 means 88 _____ by 4.

DIVIDED

100. And 136/8 means _____ divided by _____.

136;   8

101. Find

108/9 = _____

54/6 = _____

65/13 = _____

27/27 = _____

12;   9;   5;   1

102. If a and b represent natural numbers,

a/b means to divide _____ by _____.

a;   b

103. That is, a/b means to find the missing factor in the problem

[   ] · b = _____

a

104.   72/4 = _____

18

105.   72/4 = 18

Let us call the result of the division, 18, the QUOTIENT of 72 AND 4. Then, since

216/36 = 6

we call 6 the _____ of 216 and 36.

QUOTIENT

106.   343/7 = 49

and so _____ is the quotient of _____ and _____.

49;   343;   7

107. Find the quotient of 84 and 4.   _____

Find the quotient of 125 and 5.   _____

21;   25

108. By the quotient of a and b we mean the result of the division problem _____.

a/b

109. That is, the quotient of a and b, a/b, is the missing factor in the problem

[   ] · b = a

Hence, the quotient of a and b is the number which must be _____ by b to yield a _____ of a.

MULTIPLIED;   PRODUCT

110. Then, if a/b = q, we must have

$$q \cdot \underline{\hspace{2cm}} = \underline{\hspace{2cm}}$$

> b;   a

111. If a/b = q, we call q the quotient of a and b. We shall call the number a the DIVIDEND and the number b the DIVISOR in the division problem.

112. Then, in the problem

$$64/16 = 4$$

we call 64 the dividend and 16 the
_____.

> DIVISOR

113. And in the problem

$$120/24 = 5$$

we call 120 the _____,
we call 24 the _____,
we call 5 the _____.

> DIVIDEND;   DIVISOR;   QUOTIENT

114. Find

$$\underline{\hspace{2cm}} \cdot 7 = 42$$
$$42/7 = \underline{\hspace{2cm}}$$

> 6;   6

115. Find

$$\underline{\hspace{2cm}} \cdot 11 = 132$$
$$132/11 = \underline{\hspace{2cm}}$$

Find

$$\underline{\hspace{2cm}} \cdot 4 = 52$$
$$52/4 = \underline{\hspace{2cm}}$$

> 12;   12;   13;   13

116. Find

$$114/6 = \underline{\hspace{2cm}}$$
$$\underline{\hspace{2cm}} \cdot 6 = 114$$

Find

$$\underline{\hspace{2cm}} \cdot 5 = 75$$
$$75/5 = \underline{\hspace{2cm}}$$

> 19;   19;   15;   15

117. The examples in the last few frames show a connection between the operations of division and multiplication. Each division problem is associated with a problem in multiplication.

Note also

$$28/4 = \underline{\hspace{2cm}}$$
$$7 \cdot 4 = \underline{\hspace{2cm}}$$

> 7;   28

118. Find

$$112/4 = \underline{\hspace{2cm}}$$
$$28 \cdot 4 = \underline{\hspace{2cm}}$$

> 28;   112

119. $112/4 = 28$ and $28 \cdot 4 = 112$

Note that the product in the multiplication problem is equal to the _____ in the division problem.

> **DIVIDEND**

120. $7 \cdot 12 =$ _____

$84/7 =$ _____

> **84;   12**

121. $16 \cdot 6 =$ _____

$96/16 =$ _____

> **96;   6**

122. $16 \cdot 6 = 96$ and $96/16 = 6$

Note that the quotient in the division problem is equal to one of the _____ in the multiplication problem.

> **FACTORS**

123. As these examples illustrate, the operations of multiplication and division are opposite. We call division the I_____ of multiplication.

> **INVERSE**

124. If a and b represent natural numbers, then a/b represents the _____ of a and b.

> **QUOTIENT**

125. And by the quotient of a and b we mean the missing factor in the problem

$[\ \ ] \cdot b = a$

That is, $a/b = q$ if _____ $\cdot b = a$.

> **q**

126. We have seen that it may not always be possible to find the missing factor, q.

Find, where possible:

_____ $\cdot \ 7 = \ 88$

_____ $\cdot \ 6 = \ 54$

_____ $\cdot 51 = 120$

_____ $\cdot 13 = \ 39$

> **IMPOSSIBLE;   9;   IMPOSSIBLE;   3**

127. Since $9 \cdot 6 = 54$, we have $54/6 = 9$.

But since $[\ \ ] \cdot 7 = 88$ has no solution, the "division" $88/7$ has no meaning.

Find, where possible:

$56/6 \ =$ _____

$29/13 =$ _____

$72/7 \ =$ _____

> **ALL ARE IMPOSSIBLE**

128. We can see, then, that the whole numbers are _____ closed with respect to the operation of division.

> **NOT**

129. 59/6 is not defined, since the problem
[   ] · 6 = $\overline{56}$ has no solution. But 56/7 = [   ]
is possible, since

_____ · 7 = 56

8

130. 56/7 is defined because the divisor, 7, is a
F _____ of 56.

FACTOR

131. But 56/6 is not defined since the divisor, 6,
is _____ a factor of 56.

NOT

132. The natural numbers are not closed with respect to division. Only when the
_____ is a factor of the dividend is
the division possible.

DIVISOR

133. In this chapter we have introduced the operations of subtraction and division. Subtraction is possible only when the _____
is equal to, or less than, the _____.

SUBTRAHEND;   MINUEND

134. Hence, the whole numbers are not closed
with respect to subtraction.

Division is possible only when the
_____ is a factor of the
_____.

DIVISOR;   DIVIDEND

135. With respect to division, too, the whole numbers do not form a closed system.

But the whole numbers are closed with respect to the operations of _____ and
_____.

ADDITION;   MULTIPLICATION
(either order)

Chapter 7

Problems A (Answers on page 508)

Each of the following requires the insertion of a number to form a true statement. Tell which <u>operation</u> must be performed to determine the missing number, but do <u>not</u> compute it.

Example: 47 + [ ] = 95. Answer: Subtraction

Example: 4 · 18 = [ ]. Answer: Multiplication

1. 14 + 87 = [ ]

2. 27 + [ ] = 65

3. 14 · 112 = [ ]

4. [ ] + 112 = 315

5. [ ] · 2 = 36

6. 44 · [ ] = 264

7. 15 + 18 = [ ]

8. 45 · 7 = [ ]

9. 8 · [ ] = 128

10. 74 + [ ] = 74

Compute the missing number in each of the following.

11. 12 + 9 = ?

12. 14 + ? = 35

13. 9 · 13 = ?

14. ? · 12 = 72

15. 83 + ? = 117

16. 14 · ? = 182

17. ? + 32 = 77

18. ? · 21 = 252

19. ? + 87 = 301

20. 49 · ? = 784

Perform the following operations with whole numbers, where possible. When impossible, indicate this.

21. 57 + 29

22. 44 · 7

23. 71 − 44

24. 88/4

25. 16 − 40

26. 174/6

27. 321 − 185

28. 462/73

29. 2177 − 849

30. 666/18

The members of the set

$$E = \{0, 2, 4, 6, 8, 10, \ldots\}$$

are called even numbers. The members of the set

$$D = \{1, 3, 5, 7, 9, 11, \ldots\}$$

are called odd numbers.

Example: Is the set E closed with respect to the operation of addition? Answer: Yes, for the sum of any two even numbers is also an even number.

31. Is the set E closed with respect to the operation of multiplication?

32. Is the set D closed with respect to the operation of addition?

33. Is the set D closed with respect to the operation of multiplication?

34. A rectangular building is being converted to a cinema theater. 65 rows of seats are installed, each containing 24 seats. What is the seating capacity of the theater?

35. The treasurer of a county political organization "paid out" 252 dollars more than the treasury contained. If there were 18 members in the club, how much did each have to contribute to "clear" this deficit?

36. Each automobile licensed for the first time in one state must pay a 23-dollar registration fee. In a year in which 39,216 cars were registered, how much was collected in fees?

37. A shipment of cement contains 1222 bags. If the bags are unloaded and stored in piles containing 26 bags each, how many such piles will be formed?

38. This year's production of 18,429 presses is an increase of 1813 over last year. How many presses were produced last year?

39. Student enrollment in one college dropped 488 from enrollment last year. If 8209 students attended last year, what is this year's enrollment?

40. The number of color TV sets sold this year is estimated as 7 times the number sold 5 years ago. If 99,533 color TV sets are sold this year, then how many sets were sold 5 years ago?

Problems B

In each of the following, tell which <u>operation</u> must be performed to determine the missing number, but do not <u>compute</u> it.

1. $47 + [\ ] = 321$
2. $[\ ] \cdot 16 = 176$
3. $81 \cdot 107 = [\ ]$
4. $175 + 361 = [\ ]$
5. $16 \cdot [\ ] = 496$
6. $[\ ] + 188 = 494$
7. $27 \cdot 107 = [\ ]$
8. $[\ ] \cdot 55 = 385$
9. $42 \cdot [\ ] = 42$
10. $413 + [\ ] = 1026$

Compute the missing number in each of the following.

11. $127 + 48 = ?$
12. $? + 13 = 51$
13. $? \cdot 53 = 5141$
14. $14 \cdot 9 = ?$
15. $81 + ? = 128$
16. $27 \cdot ? = 243$
17. $103 \cdot ? = 2781$
18. $177 + ? = 304$
19. $? + 203 = 1061$
20. $? \cdot 23 = 414$

Perform the following operations with whole numbers, where possible. When impossible, indicate this.

21. $147 \cdot 18$
22. $1206/7$
23. $571 - 186$
24. $812 - 4110$
25. $429/13$
26. $1665/37$
27. $3010 - 2947$
28. $7125/25$
29. $111/11$
30. $3672/306$

The members of the set

$$E = \{0, 2, 4, 6, 8, 10, \ldots\}$$

are called even numbers. The members of the set

$$D = \{1, 3, 5, 7, 9, 11, \ldots\}$$

are called odd numbers.

Consider a new operation for whole numbers, "average." The average of two whole numbers is obtained by first finding their sum and then dividing this result by 2.

Example: Find the "average" of 2 and 12.
Answer: $2 + 12 = 14$ and $14/2 = 7$. The "average" is 7.

Example: Find the "average" of 5 and 15.
Answer: $5 + 15 = 20$ and $20/2 = 10$. The "average" is 10.

31. Is the set E closed with respect to the operation "average"?

32. Is the set D closed with respect to the operation "average"?

33. Is the set of whole numbers closed with respect to the operation of "average"?

34. In a printing plant a large piece of paper is cut and folded so as to produce 32 pages of a book. How many such sheets of paper are needed for a 1504-page dictionary?

35. Each scout attending summer camp consumes 7 candy bars a day. If the camp store stocks a box of 105 candy bars for each of the camp's 87 scouts, how many days can the boys attend before the supply runs out?

36. A factory turns out switching units and numbers them consecutively. The first unit turned out in March is numbered 42,109 and

the last unit produced that month is numbered 47,366. How many switching units were produced in March?

37. One city's municipal code requires that an auditorium have 320 cubic feet of space for each member of the audience. If the "Civic Theater" has a volume of 728,000 cubic feet, what is the largest audience it can legally hold?

38. A room can be tiled using 240 large tiles which cost 13 cents each or 540 small tiles which cost 6 cents each. How many cents are saved by using the large tiles?

39. Each member of a service club contributes 3 dollars to a "party reserve." In all 147 dollars was collected, although 2 club members did not make a contribution. What is the total number of members in the club?

40. Each square foot of 11-gauge steel plate weighs 5 pounds. How many square feet of steel are there in a tank made of 11-gauge plate which weighs 3905 pounds?

FACTORS, MULTIPLES, AND DIVISIBILITY

1. In the last chapter we introduced two inverse operations: _____ and
   _____ .

   > SUBTRACTION; DIVISION (either order)

2. To subtract a from b is to find a number which, when _____ to a, yields a _____ of b.

   > ADDED; SUM

3. That is, b − a = d if _____ + d = _____ .

   > a; b

4. b − a = d if a + d = b
   We call d the _____ of b and a.

   > DIFFERENCE

5. We have established the commutative property of addition. It asserts that a sum does not depend on the _____ of the terms.

   > ORDER

6. For all whole numbers a and d, the commutative property of addition allows us to write

   a + d = _____

   > d + a

7. a + d = d + a
   But then the statement
   b − a = d if a + d = b
   can be replaced by
   b − a = d if _____ = b

   > d + a

8. $b - a = d$ if either $a + d = b$ or $d + a = b$

Therefore our definition of subtraction can be modified.

To subtract a from b is to find a number which, when added to a or when a is added to it, yields a sum of _____ .

> b

9. $b - a = d$ if either _____ or _____

> $a + d = b$; $d + a = b$ (either order)

10. If a and b are any whole numbers, we define the difference, $b - a$, only if a _____ b or if a _____ b.

> $=$; $<$ (either order)

11. That is, we only consider the operation of subtraction if the _____ is less than, or equal to, the minuend.

> SUBTRAHEND

12. Hence we see that the whole numbers are _____ _____ with respect to subtraction.

> NOT CLOSED

13. To divide a by b is to find a number which, when _____ by b yields a _____ of a.

> MULTIPLIED;   PRODUCT

14. That is, $a/b = q$ if $q \cdot$ _____ $=$ _____

> b;   a

15. $a/b = q$ if $qb = a$

We call q the _____ of a and b.

> QUOTIENT

16. $a/b = q$

We call the number a the dividend and the number b the _____ in the division problem.

> DIVISOR

17. We have established the commutative property of multiplication. It asserts that a product does not depend on the _____ of the factors.

> ORDER

18. For all whole numbers q and b, the commutative property of multiplication allows us to write

$qb =$ _____

> bq

19. $qb = bq$

But then the statement

$a/b = q$ if $qb = a$

can be replaced by

$a/b = q$ if   _____ $= a$

> bq

20. $a/b = q$ if either $qb = a$ or $bq = a$

Therefore our definition of division can be modified.

To divide a by b is to find a number which, when multiplied by b or when b is multiplied by it, yields a product of _____ .

a

21. $a/b = q$ if either _____ or _____

$qb = a$; $bq = a$ (either order)

22. We have seen that for some numbers, a and b, the quotient cannot be found. That is, the whole numbers are _____ _____ with respect to division.

NOT CLOSED

23. In fact, only when the divisor is a _____ of the dividend is the operation of division possible.

FACTOR

24. In later chapters we shall enlarge our system of numbers. Then some problems we cannot perform now will become possible. But for now we consider only the whole numbers.

Let us investigate the role of the number 0 in the operation of division.

25. Find

$0 \cdot 7$ = _____

$0 \cdot 53$ = _____

$0 \cdot 84$ = _____

$0 \cdot 113$ = _____

0;   0;   0;   0

26. In fact, if a is any natural number,

$0 \cdot a =$ _____

0

27. $0 \cdot 7 = 0$

Now consider the problem 0/7. That is, find a number which, when multiplied by 7, gives a product of 0. But since $0 \cdot 7 = 0$,

$0/7 =$ _____

0

28. And $0/53 =$ _____ because $0 \cdot 53 = 0$.

0

29. Similarly

$0/84 = 0$ and $0/113 = 0$.

In fact, if a is any natural number, by 0/a we mean a number which, when _____ by a, yields a product of _____ .

MULTIPLIED;   0

30. But for all natural numbers a,

$0 \cdot a = 0$

Hence for all natural numbers a,

$0/a = \underline{\hphantom{0000}}$

> 0

31. Now consider the problem 7/0

This means to find a number which, when multiplied by 0, gives a product of 7.

And

$7/0 = \underline{\hphantom{0000}}$

> THERE IS NO POSSIBLE ANSWER
> (see next frame)

32. Since any whole number, when multiplied by 0, gives a product of 0, no number, when multiplied by 0, can give a product of 7. Hence 7/0 is an impossible problem.

Find, where possible:

$0/5 = \underline{\hphantom{0000}}$

$53/0 = \underline{\hphantom{0000}}$

> 0;   IMPOSSIBLE

33. Find

$84/0 = \underline{\hphantom{0000}}$

$113/0 = \underline{\hphantom{0000}}$

$50/0 = \underline{\hphantom{0000}}$

$0/1 = \underline{\hphantom{0000}}$

> IMPOSSIBLE;   IMPOSSIBLE;   IM-
> POSSIBLE;   0

34. For any natural number a,

$0/a = 0$

since

$0 \cdot a = 0.$

But, for any natural number a,

$a/0$

can have no meaning.

35. We shall say that division by zero is undefined.

Find

$38/2 = \underline{\hphantom{0000}}$

$0/16 = \underline{\hphantom{0000}}$

$17/1 = \underline{\hphantom{0000}}$

$17/0 = \underline{\hphantom{0000}}$

> 19;   0;   17;   UNDEFINED

36. $6 \cdot 9 = 54$

54 is called the _____ of 6 and 9.
6 and 9 are called _____ of 54.

> PRODUCT;   FACTORS

37. $6 \cdot 9 = 54$

We shall also call 54 a MULTIPLE of 6 and a _____ of 9.

> MULTIPLE

38. $12 \cdot 10 = 120$

120 is the _____ of 12 and 10.
12 and 10 are _____ of 120.

> PRODUCT;   FACTORS

39. $12 \cdot 10 = 120$

But we also call 120 a _____ of 12 and a _____ of 10.

MULTIPLE;   MULTIPLE

40. $7 \cdot 13 = 91$

7 and 13 are _____ of 91. 91 is a _____ of 7 and also a _____ of 13.

FACTORS;   MULTIPLE;   MULTIPLE

41. $16 \cdot 9 = 144$

144 is the product of 16 and 9.

144 is a _____ of 16 and a _____ of 9.

16 and 9 are _____ of 144.

MULTIPLE;   MULTIPLE;   FACTORS

42. $14 \cdot 6 = 84$

84 is the _____ of 14 and 6.

84 is a _____ of 14 and a _____ of 6.

14 is a factor of 84 and 6 is also a _____ of 84.

PRODUCT;   MULTIPLE;
MULTIPLE;   FACTOR

43. If a, b, and c represent natural numbers, and if

$ab = c$

we call c the _____ of a and b and we call a and b _____ of c.

PRODUCT;   FACTORS

44. If a, b, and c represent natural numbers, and if

$ab = c$

we call c a _____ of a.

c is also a _____ of b.

MULTIPLE;   MULTIPLE

45. $ab = c$

a and b are factors of _____ and _____ is a multiple of a and of b.

c;   c

46. In general, every natural number is a multiple of any of its _____ .

FACTORS

47. We next introduce the concept of divisibility.

14 IS DIVISIBLE BY 7 since the quotient of 14 and 7 is the natural number _____ .

2

48. 32 is _____ by 4 since the quotient of 32 and 4 is the natural number _____ .

DIVISIBLE;   8

49. 56 is divisible by 8 since the _____ of 56 and 8 is the natural number _____ .

QUOTIENT;   7

50. But 42 is not divisible by 5 since their quotient is not a _____ number.

> **NATURAL**

51. If a and b are natural numbers, a is divisible by b if the quotient of a and b is a _____ _____.

> **NATURAL NUMBER**

52. That is, a is divisible by b if there is a natural number which, when multiplied by _____, yields a product of _____.

> **b;   a**

53. If a is divisible by b, we shall call b an EXACT DIVISOR of a.

Then, since 24 is divisible by 3, 3 is an _____ _____ of 24.

> **EXACT DIVISOR**

54. And since 48 is divisible by 6, 6 is an _____ _____ of 48.

> **EXACT DIVISOR**

55. 74 is _____ by 37 and so 37 is an exact _____ of 74.

> **DIVISIBLE;   DIVISOR**

56. If b is an exact divisor of a, then a is _____ by b.

> **DIVISIBLE**

57. Since the quotient of 24 and 6 is the natural number 4, 24 is _____ by 6 and 6 is an _____ _____ of 24.

> **DIVISIBLE;   EXACT DIVISOR**

58. 6 is an exact divisor of 24.

But since $6 \cdot 4 = 24$, 6 is also a _____ of 24.

> **FACTOR**

59. 24 is divisible by 6 and 6 is both a _____ of 24 and an _____ _____ of 24.

> **FACTOR;   EXACT DIVISOR**

60. Since the quotient of 75 and 25 is the natural number 3, 75 is _____ by 25 and 25 is an _____ _____ of 75.

> **DIVISIBLE;   EXACT DIVISOR**

61. $75/25 = 3$ because $3 \cdot 25 = 75$

25 is also a _____ of 75.

> **FACTOR**

62. 75 is divisible by 25 and 25 is both a
_____ of 75 and an _____
_____ of 75.

FACTOR;   EXACT DIVISOR

63. If a is divisible by b, then b is an exact
_____ of a, and b is also a
_____ of a.

DIVISOR;   FACTOR

64. $9 \cdot 6 = 54$ and $54/6 = 9$

6 is a _____ of 54 and 6 is also an
_____ _____ of 54.

FACTOR;   EXACT DIVISOR

65. $9 \cdot 6 = 54$ $54/6 = 9$

6 is a factor of 54 and 6 is also an exact
divisor of 54. 54 is a _____ of 6.

MULTIPLE

66. $256/32 = 8$ $8 \cdot 32 = 256$

32 is an _____ _____ of 256
and 32 is also a _____ of 256.

EXACT DIVISOR;   FACTOR

67. $256/32 = 8$ $8 \cdot 32 = 256$

32 is an exact divisor of 256 and 32 is also a
factor of 256. 256 is a _____ of 32.

MULTIPLE

68. If b is a factor of a, b is also an
_____ _____ of a.

EXACT DIVISOR

69. But if b is a factor of a, then a is a
_____ of b.

MULTIPLE

70. 88 is a _____ of 11 and 88 is also
_____ by 11.

MULTIPLE;   DIVISIBLE

71. 11 is a _____ of 88 and 11 is also an
exact _____ of 88.

FACTOR;   DIVISOR

72. 36 is _____ by 9 and 36 is also a
_____ of 9.

DIVISIBLE;   MULTIPLE

73. 9 is an exact _____ of 36 and 9 is also
a _____ of 36.

DIVISOR;   FACTOR

74. If b is an exact divisor of a, then a is
_____ by b.

DIVISIBLE

75. And if a is divisible by b, then a is a

_____ of b.

76. To repeat:

Every exact _____ of a number is also a _____ of that number.

Every multiple of a number is _____ by that number.

77. $132/22 = 6$ since $6 \cdot 22 = 132$

In the division problem:

132 is called the dividend
22 is called the _____
6 is called the _____

78. $132/22 = 6$ $6 \cdot 22 = 132$

The quotient, 6, is a F_____ of the dividend, 132.

79. $132/22 = 6$ $6 \cdot 22 = 132$

But if 6 is a factor of 132, then 6 is an _____ _____ of 132.

80. $132/22 = 6$ $6 \cdot 22 = 132$

If 6 is an exact divisor of 132, then 132 is divisible by 6. And $132/6 =$ _____.

81. $132/6 = 22$ since $22 \cdot 6 = 132$

Note that the quotient here, 22, was our original divisor in the problem

$132/22 = 6$

When 132 is divided by an exact divisor, the quotient is also an exact _____.

82. $180/15 = 12$ since $12 \cdot 15 = 180$

In the division problem

15 is the _____.

12 is the _____.

Both 15 and 12 are _____ of the dividend, 180.

83. $180/15 = 12$ $12 \cdot 15 = 180$

But if 12 is a factor of 180, then 12 is also an exact _____ of 180.

Hence 180 is divisible by 12 and

$180/12 =$ _____

84. $180/12 = 15$ because $15 \cdot 12 = 180$

Note that the quotient here, 15, is our original divisor in $180/15 = 12$.

When 180 is divided by one exact divisor, the _____ is also an exact divisor.

QUOTIENT

85. Suppose b is any exact divisor of a.

Then $a/b = q$ and hence a = _____ .

q·b

86. $a/b = q$ and $a = qb$

Observe that both _____ and _____ are factors of a, since $a = qb$.

q;   b   (either order)

87. $a/b = q$ and $a = qb$

Since q is a factor of a, it follows that q is an exact divisor of a. In fact,

$a/q =$ _____ , since $a = bq$

b

88. $a/b = q$ $a/q = b$

Note that if a is divisible by b, and the quotient is q, then a is also divisible by q, and the quotient is _____ .

b

89. If a first natural number is divisible by a second, then the first number is also _____ by the quotient. The quotient and divisor may be interchanged since each are _____ , and hence exact _____ , of the first number.

DIVISIBLE;   FACTORS;   DIVISORS

90. We have said that 42 is not divisible by 5 since there is no natural number such that

$42 = [\ \ ] \cdot 5$

However, we can write

$42 = (6) \cdot 5 + 12.$

We can also write

$42 = (7) \cdot 5 +$ _____

and

$42 = (8) \cdot 5 +$ _____

7;   2

91. Similarly, 63 is not divisible by 4 since we cannot find the missing factor in

$63 = [\ \ ] \cdot 4$

However, we can write:

$63 = (5) \cdot 4\ +$ _____

$63 = (12) \cdot 4 +$ _____

$63 = (15) \cdot 4 +$ _____

43;   15;   3

92. Although 55 is not divislble by 6, we can write:

$55 = (3) \cdot 6 +$ _____

$55 = (5) \cdot 6 +$ _____

$55 = (7) \cdot 6 +$ _____

$55 = (8) \cdot 6 +$ _____

37;   25;   13;   7

93. 55/6 is not defined since there is no solution to the problem

$$55 = [\quad] \cdot 6$$

But it is possible to find solutions to a slightly different problem:

$$55 = [\quad]6 + [\quad].$$

Find

$$55 = (9) \cdot 6 + \underline{\hphantom{xxxx}}$$

> 1

94. Find

$$48 = (3) \cdot 6 + \underline{\hphantom{xxxx}}$$
$$48 = (6) \cdot 6 + \underline{\hphantom{xxxx}}$$
$$48 = (7) \cdot 6 + \underline{\hphantom{xxxx}}$$
$$48 = (8) \cdot 6 + \underline{\hphantom{xxxx}}$$

> 30;   12;   6;   0

95. 48/6 is defined since there is a solution to the problem

$$48 = [\quad] \cdot 6$$

Nevertheless, we can still find solutions to the different problem

$$48 = [\quad] \cdot 6 + [\quad]$$

96. Find

$$27 = (0) \cdot 6 + \underline{\hphantom{xxxx}}$$
$$27 = (1) \cdot 6 + \underline{\hphantom{xxxx}}$$
$$27 = (2) \cdot 6 + \underline{\hphantom{xxxx}}$$
$$27 = (3) \cdot 6 + \underline{\hphantom{xxxx}}$$

> 27;   21;   15;   9

97. 27/6 is not defined since we cannot find a solution to

$$27 = [\quad] \cdot 6$$

But we have found solutions to the problem

$$27 = [\quad] \cdot 6 + [\quad]$$

Note that the terms which have been added to the products are: 27, 21, 15, and 9.

Find

$$27 = (4) \cdot 6 + \underline{\hphantom{xxxx}}$$

> 3

98. $27 = (4) \cdot 6 + 3$

Here the term which is added, 3, is as small as possible. For if we consider the problem

$$27 = (5) \cdot 6 + [\quad]$$

we find it has no solution.

99. Find

$$41 = (0) \cdot 9 + \underline{\hphantom{xxxx}}$$
$$41 = (2) \cdot 9 + \underline{\hphantom{xxxx}}$$
$$41 = (3) \cdot 9 + \underline{\hphantom{xxxx}}$$
$$41 = (4) \cdot 9 + \underline{\hphantom{xxxx}}$$

> 41;   23;   14;   5

100. The terms added to the product were 41, 23, 14, and 5. Let us call the smallest term, 5, the REMAINDER WHEN 41 IS DIVIDED BY 9.

Note that 41 is not divisible by 9 since 41 = [ ] · 9 has no solution. But

$$41 = [\quad] \cdot 9 + [\quad]$$

has solutions, and 5 is the _____ term which can be added to the product.

> SMALLEST

101. 19 is not divisible by 6 since $19 = [\ \ ] \cdot 6$ has no solution.

But

$19 = (2) \cdot 3 +$ _____

$19 = (3) \cdot 3 +$ _____

$19 = (5) \cdot 3 +$ _____

$19 = (6) \cdot 3 +$ _____

13;   10;   4;   1

102. Since $19 = (6) \cdot 3 + 1$

we call 1 the _____ when 19 is divided by 3.

REMAINDER

103. 30 is not divisible by 4 since $30 = [\ \ ] \cdot 4$ has no solution.

But we can write

$30 = (7) \cdot 4 +$ _____

and _____ is the remainder when _____ is divided by 4.

2;   2;   30

104. $30 = (7) \cdot 4 + 2$

2 is the remainder when 30 is divided by 4. We shall call 7 the PARTIAL QUOTIENT in the problem, 30 the dividend, and 4 the divisor, even though 30 is not _____ by 4.

DIVISIBLE

105. 55/3 is not defined since

$55 = [\ \ ] \cdot 3$

has no solution.

But we can write

$55 = (18) \cdot 3 + 1$

and so we call 1 the _____ and 18 the partial _____ when 55 is divided by 3.

REMAINDER;   QUOTIENT

106. 91/8 is not defined since $91 = [\ \ ] \cdot 8$ has no solution.

But $91 = (11) \cdot 8 + 3$

Hence, when 91 is divided by 8, the remainder is _____ and the _____ is 11.

3;   PARTIAL QUOTIENT

107. Note that $91 = (10) \cdot 8 + 11$

But 11 is not the remainder and 10 is not the partial quotient when 91 is divided by 8, since a smaller term than 11 has been determined; namely, 3.

Find the partial quotient and remainder when 16 is divided by 7. That is,

$16 = ($_____$) \cdot 7 +$ _____

2;   2

108. Partial quotients and remainders can be found, of course, by "long division." Find the partial quotient and remainder in each division:

$21 = ($_____$) \cdot 5 +$ _____

$59 = ($_____$) \cdot 9 +$ _____

4;   1;   6;   5

109. Find the partial quotients and remainders:

$$102 = (\underline{\hspace{2cm}}) \cdot 15 + \underline{\hspace{2cm}}$$
$$87 = (\underline{\hspace{2cm}}) \cdot 20 + \underline{\hspace{2cm}}$$

> 6;   12;   4;   7

110. 36 is divisible by 9. In fact $36/9 = \underline{\hspace{2cm}}$ since

$$36 = (\underline{\hspace{2cm}}) \cdot 9$$

> 4;   4

111. $36 = (4) \cdot 9$

But we can also write $36 = (4) \cdot 9 + 0$.

We might wish to call 4 the partial quotient and 0 the remainder. Often, we shall not do so. Instead we shall call 4 the $\underline{\hspace{2cm}}$ of 36 and 9 and say there is "no remainder."

> QUOTIENT

112. Find the quotient, where possible. When the dividend is not divisible by the divisor, find the partial quotient and the remainder.

$$18 = (\underline{\hspace{2cm}}) \cdot 9 + \underline{\hspace{2cm}}$$
$$16 = (\underline{\hspace{2cm}}) \cdot 3 + \underline{\hspace{2cm}}$$

> 2;   0;   5;   1

113. $18 = 2 \cdot 9 + 0$

Hence 18 is $\underline{\hspace{2cm}}$ by 9, and 2 is the $\underline{\hspace{2cm}}$.

> DIVISIBLE;   QUOTIENT

114. $16 = 5 \cdot 3 + 1$

Hence 16 is not divisible by 3, but when 16 is divided by 3, the $\underline{\hspace{2cm}}$ $\underline{\hspace{2cm}}$ is 5, and 1 is the $\underline{\hspace{2cm}}$.

> PARTIAL QUOTIENT;   REMAINDER

115. Let us summarize.

If a and b are natural numbers, a is divisible by b if their quotient, q, is also a $\underline{\hspace{2cm}}$ $\underline{\hspace{2cm}}$.

> NATURAL NUMBER

116. But a will be divisible by b only if a is a $\underline{\hspace{2cm}}$ of b and b is a $\underline{\hspace{2cm}}$ of a.

> MULTIPLE;   FACTOR

117. If a is divisible by b, their quotient, q, is also a $\underline{\hspace{2cm}}$ of a.

In fact, a is also divisible by q and the quotient of a and q is $\underline{\hspace{2cm}}$.

> FACTOR;   b

118. If a is divisible by b, we call b an $\underline{\hspace{2cm}}$ $\underline{\hspace{2cm}}$ of a.

If a is not divisible by b we can find a partial $\underline{\hspace{2cm}}$ and a nonzero $\underline{\hspace{2cm}}$ when a is divided by b.

> EXACT DIVISOR;   QUOTIENT; REMAINDER

119. Both quotients and partial quotients and remainders can be found by the process of
"_____ _____."

LONG DIVISION

Chapter 8

Problems A (Answers on page 508)

In each of the following, insert either the word "factor" or the word "multiple" so as, if possible, to form a true statement. When this cannot be done, write "neither" after the statement.

1. 16 is a _____ of 4.

2. 12 is a _____ of 48.

3. 15 is a _____ of 10.

4. 27 is a _____ of 9.

5. 400 is a _____ of 800.

6. 121 is a _____ of 11.

7. 9 is a _____ of 145.

8. 17 is a _____ of 51.

9. 20 is a _____ of 10.

10. $4 \cdot 4$ is a _____ of 4.

11. $14 - 5$ is a _____ of 3.

12. 15/3 is a _____ of 100.

13. $3 \cdot 5$ is a _____ of 5.

14. 12 is a _____ of $12 \cdot 3$.

15. $1 \cdot 9$ is a _____ of 19.

16. $837 \cdot 317$ is a _____ of 317.

17. 1297 is a _____ $17 \cdot 1297$.

18. 43 is a _____ of 43.

19. $a \cdot b$ is a _____ of a.

20. b is a _____ of b.

In each of the following, insert either the phrase "an exact divisor of" or the phrase "divisible by" so as, if possible, to form a true statement. When this cannot be done, write "neither" after the statement.

21. 12 is _____ 4.

22. 14 is _____ 70.

23. 3 is _____ 21.

24. $9 \cdot 8$ is _____ 9.

25. 17 is _____ $17 \cdot 93$.

26. 20 is _____ 30.

27. $4 + 5$ is _____ 27.

28. 12/4 is _____ 12.

29. 47 is _____ 47.

30. a is _____ ab.

In each of the following, use long division to find the partial quotient and remainder called for.

31. $75 = $ _____ $\cdot \; 9 + $ _____

32. $385 = $ _____ $\cdot \; 76 + $ _____

33. $639 = $ _____ $\cdot \, 417 + $ _____

34. $86 = $ _____ $\cdot \; 95 + $ _____

35. $4715 = $ _____ $\cdot \; 23 + $ _____

36. A felt marking pen can write a line 1245 feet long. How many boxes can be addressed by one pen if each box requires 17 feet of marking, and how many additional feet of line remain in the pen?

37. A 2824-mile automobile trip is planned. If no more than 550 miles are driven in any one day, what is the fewest number of complete days the trip will require?

38. A stock of 17 tons (34,000 pounds) of special alloy is reported on hand. Each engine produced requires 202 pounds of this alloy. How many engines can be made before the supply of alloy is exhausted, and how much of the metal will then still be on hand?

39. It costs 42 dollars to "uniform" each member of a "little league" team. If the team has 10 members and 524 dollars has been raised for expenses, how much money will be available after uniforms have been purchased?

40. One kind of wire used in building construction comes on 324-foot reels. How many reels will be required for a job that calls for 78,286 feet of wire, and how many feet of wire will be "left over"?

Problems B

In each of the following, insert either the word "factor" or the word "multiple" so as, if possible, to form a true statement. When this cannot be done, write "neither" after the statement.

1. 46 is a _____ of 23.

2. 108 is a _____ of 9.

3. 6 is a _____ of 78.

4. 13 is a _____ of 39.

5. 5 is a _____ of 6.

6. 30/5 is a _____ of 3.

7. 6 + 9 is a _____ of 60.

8. 64/4 is a _____ of 12.

9. 6 · 9 is a _____ of 6.

10. 6 · 9 is a _____ of 9.

11. 3 is a _____ of 3 · 4.

12. 17 is a _____ of 17.

13. a · b is a _____ of b.

14. 7 + 3 is a _____ of 73.

15. 12 − 8 is a _____ of 12.

16. 419 · 7 is a _____ of 419.

17. 27 is a _____ of 45 · 27.

18. 17 − 2 is a _____ of 40.

19. 2 is a _____ of 20 · 3.

20. 7 + 3 is a _____ of 7.

In each of the following, insert either the phrase "an exact divisor of" or the phrase "divisible by" so as, if possible, to form a true statement. When this cannot be done, write "neither" after the statement.

21. 84 is _____ 7.

22. 6 is _____ 66.

23. 13 is _____ 6 · 7.

24. 15 is _____ 15.

25. ab is _____ a.

26. 7 + 7 is _____ 7.

27. 5 is _____ 5 · 5.

28. 4 · 5 is _____ 5 · 5.

29. 12 − 1 is _____ 121.

30. 29 is _____ 1.

In each of the following, assume that x and y are natural numbers.

31. If x is a factor of y, could x be greater than y? Could x equal y? Explain.

32. If x is a multiple of y, could x be less than y? Could x equal y? Explain.

33. If x is divisible by y, could x be less than y? Could x equal y? Explain.

34. If x is an exact divisor of y, could x be greater than y? Could x equal y? Explain.

35. Could the remainder in a division problem ever be greater than the divisor? Could the partial quotient ever be greater than the divisor? Explain.

In each of the following, use long division to find the partial quotient and remainder called for.

36. 751 = _____ · 18 + _____

37. 529 = _____ · 43 + _____

38. 600 = _____ · 28 + _____

39. 5271 = _____ · 400 + _____

40. 881 = _____ · 94 + _____

PRIMES, COMPOSITES, AND FACTORIZATION

1. When two numbers are multiplied, the answer is called their _____ .

> **PRODUCT**

2. If a and b represent two natural numbers, their product is represented by

   _____ .

> **ab or a·b**

3. And if ab = c, we call a and b _____ of the product, c.

> **FACTORS**

4. ab = c

   a and b are factors of c. We call c a _____ of both a and b.

> **MULTIPLE**

5. ab = c

   a and b are factors of c.

   a and b are also _____

   _____ of c.

> **EXACT DIVISORS**

6. In fact, every exact divisor of a natural number is also a _____ of that number.

> **FACTOR**

7. Hence, if we wish to find all the <u>exact divisors</u> of any natural number, we can consider all the <u>factors</u> of that number.

   Find the following products:

   $4 \cdot 3 =$ _____

   $6 \cdot 2 =$ _____

   $12 \cdot 1 =$ _____

   $2 \cdot 6 =$ _____

> **12;   12;   12;   12**

8. Since   4 · 3 = 12

   4 and 3 are _____ of 12.

9.   6 · 2 = 12

   12 · 1 = 12

   Hence, 6 and 2, and also 12 and 1, are factors of _____.

10. We have found six factors of 12. In order, they are:

   1, 2, 3, 4, 6, and 12.

   Find:

   2 · 3 · 2 = _____

   3 · 4 = _____

   2 · 6 · 1 = _____

   1 · 2 · 2 · 3 = _____

11. While many products equal 12, the number 12 has only the six factors we have already found, namely

   _____, _____, _____, _____, _____, and _____.

12. Find the following products:

   10 · 2 = _____

   5 · 4 = _____

   2 · 5 · 2 = _____

   1 · 20 = _____

13. Since

   10 · 2 = 20

   10 and 2 are _____ of 20.

14. As well as 10 and 2, 20 has four other factors: _____, _____, _____, and _____.

15. Find:

   1 · 2 · 2 · 5 = _____

   1 · 1 · 2 · 10 = _____

   4 · 5 = _____

   2 · 2 · 1 · 5 = _____

16. Although many products equal 20, the number 20 has only the six factors we have already found, namely

   _____, _____, _____, _____, _____, and _____.

17. Consider the number 21.

$$21 = \underline{\hspace{2cm}} \cdot 7$$
$$21 = 1 \cdot \underline{\hspace{2cm}}$$

> 3;   21

18. Hence 3 and 7 are factors of 21. 21 and 1 are also _____ of 21.

> FACTORS

19. The number 21 has only the four factors we have found, namely

_____, _____, _____, and _____.

> 1, 3, 7, 21   (any order)

20. Consider the number 17.

$$\underline{\hspace{1.5cm}} \cdot \underline{\hspace{1.5cm}} = 17$$

> 1;   17   (either order)

21. $1 \cdot 17 = 17$

The number 17, however, has only two factors. They are _____ and _____.

> 1;   17   (either order)

22. Which of the following are factors of 30?

1, 2, 3, 5, 6, 10, 15, 30 _____.

> ALL ARE

23. There are exactly eight factors of the number 30.

How many factors has the number 5? _____

> TWO   (only 1 and 5 are factors of 5)

24. Let us attempt to answer the following general question.

Given any whole number, how many factors does it have, and what are they?

We begin with the number 0.

25. $0 \cdot 0 = 0$

And if a is any natural number,

$$0 \cdot a = a \cdot 0 = \underline{\hspace{2cm}}$$

> 0

26. Hence any natural number and 0 are _____ of 0.

> FACTORS

27. Any natural number is a factor of 0. Therefore, 0 is a _____ of any natural number.

> MULTIPLE

28. Any natural number is a factor of 0, provided the other factor is 0. For this reason, we shall not hereafter consider the factors of 0.

Moreover, since 0 is a multiple of any natural number, we shall, again, omit 0 from all further considerations of multiples of natural numbers.

What are the factors of 1? _____

> ONLY 1

29. Since $1 \cdot 1 = 1$, 1 is certainly a factor of 1. And there are no other factors of 1. The number 1 has only a single factor.

What are the factors of 2? _____ , _____

    1, 2   (either order)

30. The only ways to express 2 as a product are $1 \cdot 2 = 2$ and $2 \cdot 1 = 2$. Hence the only factors of 2 are 1 and 2.

What are the factors of 3? _____ , _____

    1, 3   (either order)

31. $1 \cdot 4 = 4$ and also $2 \cdot 2 = 4$

Hence the factors of 4 are _____ , _____ , and _____ .

    1, 2, 4   (any order)

32. The only factors of 5 are 1 and _____ , while the number 6 has four factors: 1, 2, 3, and _____ .

    5, 6

33. The only factors of 7 are _____ and _____ .

    1, 7   (either order)

34. But 8 has four factors. They are _____ , _____ , _____ , and _____ .

    1, 2, 4, 8   (any order)

35. We have previously seen that

10 has four factors:	1, 2, 5, and 10
12 has six factors:	1, 2, 3, 4, 6, and 12
17 has two factors:	1 and 17
20 has six factors:	1, 2, 4, 5, 10, and 20
21 has four factors:	1, 3, 7, and 21
30 has eight factors:	1, 2, 3, 5, 6, 10, 15, and 30.

36. But the general question of how many and which factors any natural number has has not been answered.

Recall that the multiplicative identity is the natural number _____ .

    1

37. That is, for any natural number a,

$1 \cdot a = a \cdot 1 = $ _____

    a

38. Since $a = 1 \cdot a$ for every natural number a, then every natural number a has as factors _____ and _____ .

    1;   a   (either order)

39. $57 = 1 \cdot 57$

Hence two factors of 57 are 1 and 57.

    $67 = 1 \cdot 67$

Therefore two factors of 67 are _____ and _____ .

    1;   67   (either order)

40. Are 1 and 90 factors of 90? _____

Are 1 and 103 factors of 103? _____

YES;   YES

41. Indeed, any natural number greater than 1 has at least two factors. They are the number _____ and the natural number itself.

1

42. But some natural numbers greater than 1 have only two factors. We have already noted that the numbers 2, 3, 5, 7, and 17 have only themselves and the number _____ as factors.

1

43. A natural number greater than 1 whose only factors are the number itself and 1, is called a PRIME number.

2, 3, 5, 7, and 17 are all _____ numbers.

PRIME

44. Since the only factors of 11 are 1 and 11, 11 is another _____ number.

PRIME

45. Is 1 a prime number? _____

NO

46. 1 is not a prime number. A prime number is a natural number greater than 1 whose only factors are the number itself and 1.

1 is not greater than 1, and so is not a prime number.

Is 6 a prime number? _____

NO

47. 6 is not a prime number. A prime number is a natural number greater than 1 whose only factors are the number itself and 1.

6 has four factors—1, 2, 3, and 6—and so cannot be a _____ .

PRIME

48. A natural number greater than 1 which is not a prime number will be called a COMPOSITE number.

Since 6 is not a prime number, 6 is a _____ number.

COMPOSITE

49. 4, 6, 8, 12, 20, and 21 are all _____ numbers.

COMPOSITE

50. 9 has 1, 3, and 9 as factors. Hence 9 is a _____ number.

19 has only 1 and 19 as factors. Hence 19 is a _____ number.

COMPOSITE;   PRIME

51. Is 1 a composite number? _____

52. 1 is not a composite number. A composite number is a natural number greater than 1 which is not a prime number. 1 is not greater than 1.

Note that 1 is neither a _____ nor a _____ number.

53. Since 0 is not a natural number it is neither a prime nor a composite number.

But with the exception of 1, every natural number must be either a prime or a composite.

We shall present a means of determining which natural numbers are primes, and which are composites.

54. We begin by listing the natural numbers greater than 1.

2, 3, 4, 5, 6, 7, 8, 9, 10, 11, 12, 13, 14, 15, 16, 17, 18, 19, 20, 21, 22, 23, 24, 25, 26, 27, 28, 29, 30, 31, 32, 33, 34, 35, 36, 37, 38, 39, 40, 41, 42, 43, 44, 45, 46, 47, 48, 49, 50, . . .

We next devise a scheme for crossing out all of the composite numbers in our list. Numbers which are not crossed out will therefore be _____ numbers.

55. Since $2 \cdot 2 = 4$,   4 is a multiple of 2.

Since $2 \cdot 3 = 6$,   6 is a multiple of 2.

Since $2 \cdot 4 = 8$, _____ is also a _____ of 2.

56. Since $2 \cdot 5 = 10$,   10 is a multiple of 2.

Since $2 \cdot 6 =$ _____, _____ is a multiple of _____.

Since $2 \cdot 7 = 14$,   14 is a _____ of 2.

57. Is 16 a multiple of 2? _____

Is 2 a multiple of 2? _____

58. Hence, 2, 4, 6, 8, 10, 12, 14, and 16 are all _____ of 2.

59. Are there other multiples of 2? _____

60. In fact, there is no end to multiples of 2. The next four multiples of 2, after 16, are

$2 \cdot 9 = 18$

$2 \cdot 10 =$ _____

$2 \cdot 11 =$ _____

$2 \cdot 12 =$ _____

61. The first twelve multiples of 2 are:

2, 4, 6, 8, 10, 12, 14, 16, 18, 20, 22, 24

and each multiple of 2 has 2 as a _____.

62. 2, 4, 6, 8, 10, 12, 14, 16, 18, 20, 22, 24, ... are multiples of 2.

Now 2 is a prime number, but every other multiple of 2 has 2 as a factor and hence is a _____ number.

COMPOSITE

63. Let us cross out of our list of natural numbers greater than 1 all such composite numbers. That is, we delete all multiples of 2 which appear after 2.

2, 3, 4̸, 5, 6̸, 7, 8̸, 9, 1̸0̸, 11, 1̸2̸, 13, 1̸4̸, 15, 1̸6̸, 17, 1̸8̸, 19, 2̸0̸, 21, 2̸2̸, 23, 2̸4̸, 25, 2̸6̸, 27, 2̸8̸, 29, 3̸0̸, 31, 3̸2̸, 33, 3̸4̸, 35, 3̸6̸, 37, 3̸8̸, 39, 4̸0̸, 41, 4̸2̸, 43, 4̸4̸, 45, 4̸6̸, 47, 4̸8̸, 49, 5̸0̸, ...

Note that we have crossed out every second number after 2 and that all such numbers were _____ numbers.

COMPOSITE

64. Similarly,

$3 \cdot 1 = 3$

$3 \cdot 2 = 6$

$3 \cdot 3 = 9$

$3 \cdot 4 = 12$

Hence 3, 6, 9, and 12 are all _____ of 3.

MULTIPLES

65. But 3, 6, 9, and 12 are not the only multiples of 3. List the first ten multiples of 3.

3, 6, 9, 12, _____, _____, _____, _____, _____, _____.

15, 18, 21, 24, 27, 30

66. 3, 6, 9, 12, 15, 18, 21, 24, 27, 30, ... are multiples of 3.

Now 3 is a prime number, but every other multiple of 3 has 3 as a _____ and hence is a _____ number.

FACTOR;   COMPOSITE

67. We have already deleted the multiples of 2, after 2, from the list of natural numbers greater than 1.

2, 3, 4̸, 5, 6̸, 7, 8̸, 9, 1̸0̸, 11, 1̸2̸, 13, 1̸4̸, 15, 1̸6̸, 17, 1̸8̸, 19, 2̸0̸, 21, 2̸2̸, 23, 2̸4̸, 25, 2̸6̸, 27, 2̸8̸, 29, 3̸0̸, 31, 3̸2̸, 33, 3̸4̸, 35, 3̸6̸, 37, 3̸8̸, 39, 4̸0̸, 41, 4̸2̸, 43, 4̸4̸, 45, 4̸6̸, 47, 4̸8̸, 49, 5̸0̸, ...

Cross out of the list of numbers, below, all multiples of 3 after 3. All such numbers have 3 as a factor and so are composite numbers.

2, 3, 4̸, 5, 6̸, 7, 8̸, 9, 1̸0̸, 11, 1̸2̸, 13, 1̸4̸, 15, 1̸6̸, 17, 1̸8̸, 19, 2̸0̸, 21, 2̸2̸, 23, 2̸4̸, 25, 2̸6̸, 27, 2̸8̸, 29, 3̸0̸, 31, 3̸2̸, 33, 3̸4̸, 35, 3̸6̸, 37, 3̸8̸, 39, 4̸0̸, 41, 4̸2̸, 43, 4̸4̸, 45, 4̸6̸, 47, 4̸8̸, 49, 5̸0̸, ...

2, 3, 4̸, 5, 6̸, 7, 8̸, 9̸, 1̸0̸, 11, 1̸2̸, 13, 1̸4̸, 1̸5̸, 1̸6̸, 17, 1̸8̸, 19, 2̸0̸, 2̸1̸, 2̸2̸, 23, 2̸4̸, 25, 2̸6̸, 2̸7̸, 2̸8̸, 29, 3̸0̸, 31, 3̸2̸, 3̸3̸, 3̸4̸, 35, 3̸6̸, 37, 3̸8̸, 3̸9̸, 4̸0̸, 41, 4̸2̸, 43, 4̸4̸, 4̸5̸, 4̸6̸, 47, 4̸8̸, 49, 5̸0̸, ...

68. 2, 3, 4̸, 5, 6̸, 7, 8̸, 9̸, 1̸0̸, 11, 1̸2̸, 13, 1̸4̸, 1̸5̸, 1̸6̸, 17, 1̸8̸, 19, 2̸0̸, 2̸1̸, 2̸2̸, 23, 2̸4̸, 25, 2̸6̸, 2̸7̸, 2̸8̸, 29, 3̸0̸, 31, 3̸2̸, 3̸3̸, 3̸4̸, 35, 3̸6̸, 37, 3̸8̸, 3̸9̸, 4̸0̸, 41, 4̸2̸, 43, 4̸4̸, 4̸5̸, 4̸6̸, 47, 4̸8̸, 49, 5̸0̸, ...

Note that you have crossed out every third number after 3.

Note also, that 6, 12, 18, ... were already crossed out, but all numbers that were deleted were _____ numbers.

COMPOSITE

69. The first ten multiples of 4 are:

4, 8, 12, 16, _____, _____, _____,

_____, _____, _____.

20, 24, 28, 32, 36, 40

70. 4, 8, 12, 16, 20, 24, 28, 32, ...are multiples of 4 and hence have 4 as a factor. None of the multiples of 4 is a prime; hence, all should be crossed out of our list. Do so.

2, 3, 4̸, 5, 6̸, 7, 8̸, 9̸, 1̸0̸, 11, 1̸2̸, 13, 1̸4̸, 1̸5̸, 1̸6̸, 17, 1̸8̸, 19, 2̸0̸, 2̸1̸, 2̸2̸, 23, 2̸4̸, 25, 2̸6̸, 2̸7̸, 28, 29, 3̸0̸, 31, 3̸2̸, 3̸3̸, 3̸4̸, 35, 3̸6̸, 37, 3̸8̸, 3̸9̸, 4̸0̸, 41, 4̸2̸, 43, 4̸4̸, 4̸5̸, 4̸6̸, 47, 48, 49, 5̸0̸, ...

ALL MULTIPLES OF 4 HAVE ALREADY BEEN DELETED!

71. Every fourth number after 4 is a multiple of 4, but it is unnecessary to cross them out since all have already been deleted.

5, 10, 15, 20, 25, 30, ...are all _____ of 5 and so have _____ as a factor.

MULTIPLES;   5

72. 5 is a _____ number, but every other multiple of 5 has 5 as a factor and so is a _____ number.

PRIME;   COMPOSITE

73. Hence, cross out of the list below all multiples of 5, after 5.

2, 3, 4̸, 5, 6̸, 7, 8̸, 9̸, 1̸0̸, 11, 1̸2̸, 13, 1̸4̸, 1̸5̸, 1̸6̸, 17, 1̸8̸, 19, 2̸0̸, 2̸1̸, 2̸2̸, 23, 24, 25, 2̸6̸, 2̸7̸, 2̸8̸, 29, 3̸0̸, 31, 3̸2̸, 3̸3̸, 34, 35, 3̸6̸, 37, 3̸8̸, 3̸9̸, 40, 41, 4̸2̸, 43, 4̸4̸, 4̸5̸, 46, 47, 4̸8̸, 49, 5̸0̸, ...

2, 3, 4̸, 5, 6̸, 7, 8̸, 9̸, 1̸0̸, 11, 1̸2̸, 13, 1̸4̸, 1̸5̸, 1̸6̸, 17, 1̸8̸, 19, 2̸0̸, 21, 2̸2̸, 23, 24, 2̸5̸, 2̸6̸, 2̸7̸, 2̸8̸, 29, 3̸0̸, 31, 3̸2̸, 3̸3̸, 3̸4̸, 3̸5̸, 36, 37, 3̸8̸, 3̸9̸, 40, 41, 4̸2̸, 43, 4̸4̸, 4̸5̸, 46, 47, 4̸8̸, 49, 5̸0̸, ...

74. 2, 3, 4̸, 5, 6̸, 7, 8̸, 9̸, 1̸0̸, 11, 1̸2̸, 13, 1̸4̸, 1̸5̸, 1̸6̸, 17, 1̸8̸, 19, 2̸0̸, 21, 2̸2̸, 23, 2̸4̸, 2̸5̸, 2̸6̸, 2̸7̸, 2̸8̸, 29, 3̸0̸, 31, 3̸2̸, 3̸3̸, 3̸4̸, 3̸5̸, 36, 37, 3̸8̸, 3̸9̸, 4̸0̸, 41, 4̸2̸, 43, 4̸4̸, 4̸5̸, 4̸6̸, 47, 4̸8̸, 49, 5̸0̸, ...

Again, note that you have crossed out every _____ number after 5, that many of the multiples of 5 had already been deleted, and that all numbers that were crossed out were _____ numbers.

FIFTH;   COMPOSITE

75. 6, 12, 18, 24, 30, ...are multiples of 6. Beginning with 6, they appear in our list as every sixth number. And all multiples of 6 are composites.

7, 14, 21, 28, 35, ...are multiples of 7. Beginning with 7, they appear in our list as every _____ number. 7 is a _____ number, but all other multiples of 7 are composites.

SEVENTH;   PRIME

76. Cross out all multiples of 6 and all multiples of 7 after 7.

2, 3, 4̶, 5, 6̶, 7, 8̶, 9̶, 10̶, 11, 12̶, 13, 14̶, 15̶,
16̶, 17, 18̶, 19, 20̶, 21̶, 22̶, 23, 24̶, 25̶, 26̶,
27̶, 28̶, 29, 30̶, 31, 32̶, 33̶, 34̶, 35̶, 36̶, 37,
38̶, 39̶, 40̶, 41, 42̶, 43, 44̶, 45̶, 46̶, 47, 48̶,
49, 50̶, . . .

> 2, 3, 4̶, 5, 6̶, 7, 8̶, 9̶, 10̶, 11, 12̶, 13, 14̶, 15̶,
> 16̶, 17, 18̶, 19, 20̶, 21̶, 22̶, 23, 24̶, 25̶, 26̶,
> 27̶, 28̶, 29, 30̶, 31, 32̶, 33̶, 34̶, 35̶, 36̶, 37,
> 38̶, 39̶, 40̶, 41, 42̶, 43, 44̶, 45, 46̶, 47, 48̶,
> 49̶, 50̶, . . .

77. 2, 3, 4̶, 5, 6̶, 7, 8̶, 9̶, 10̶, 11, 12̶, 13, 14̶, 15̶,
16̶, 17, 18̶, 19, 20̶, 21̶, 22̶, 23, 24̶, 25̶, 26̶,
27̶, 28̶, 29, 30̶, 31, 32̶, 33̶, 34̶, 35̶, 36̶, 37,
38̶, 39̶, 40̶, 41, 42̶, 43, 44̶, 45, 46̶, 47, 48̶,
49̶, 50̶, . . .

Note that every sixth number after 6 had already been crossed out, and 6 is a _____ number.

But not every seventh number after 7 had already been crossed out, and 7 is a _____ number.

> COMPOSITE;   PRIME

78. Similarly, beginning with 8 we could cross out every _____ number after 8 and, beginning with 9, every ninth number after _____. All numbers deleted are multiples of 8 or 9 and hence have 8 or 9 as factors. Hence, they are _____ numbers.

> EIGHTH;   9;   COMPOSITE

79. The process which we are describing can be carried on without end. We shall not continue it here, but shall observe that:

   1) Many numbers in the list will be crossed out.
   2) Not every number in the list will be crossed out.
   3) The first 10 numbers which are not now crossed out will never be crossed out, even if the process is continued.

80. 2, 3, 4̶, 5, 6̶, 7, 8̶, 9̶, 10̶, 11, 12̶, 13, 14̶, 15̶,
16̶, 17, 18̶, 19, 20̶, 21̶, 22̶, 23, 24̶, 25̶, 26̶,
27̶, 28̶, 29, 30̶, 31, 32̶, 33̶, 34̶, 35̶, 36̶, 37,
38̶, 39̶, 40̶, 41, 42̶, 43, 44̶, 45̶, 46̶, 47, 48̶,
49̶, 50̶, . . .

The first 10 numbers remaining in the list are:

_____, _____, _____, _____,
_____, _____, _____, _____,
_____, _____

and each of these numbers is a _____.

> 2, 3, 5, 7, 11, 13, 17, 19, 23, 29;   PRIME

81. At any stage in the process we have been describing, we should observe that not all numbers remaining are prime numbers. The number 121 would still be in our list (if it extended that far), and $121 = 11 \cdot 11$ and so is not a prime.

But every number that has been crossed out is a _____.

> COMPOSITE

82. If the process could be continued, only prime numbers would remain. The device we have been describing is called the SIEVE OF ERATOSTHENES. By means of the Sieve, as far as we have constructed it, we can list the first fifteen prime numbers:

2, 3, 5, 7, 11, 13, 17, 19, 23, 29, 31, 37, 41, 43, 47

83. It will be helpful if you will memorize the first ten prime numbers. They are, in order,

_____, _____, _____, _____,
_____, _____, _____, _____,
_____, _____.

> 2, 3, 5, 7, 11, 13, 17, 19, 23, 29

84. Let us continue our attempt to answer the general question of how many, and which, factors any natural number has.

Consider the number 24. We can write

$$24 = 1 \cdot 24$$

Now 24 has been crossed out of our list, and so it is a _____ number.

COMPOSITE

85. Since 24 is not a prime, it has a factor other than 1 and 24. In fact, 24 was crossed out when we were deleting the multiples of 2. Hence 24 has _____ as a factor.

2

86. $24 = 1 \cdot 24$

But since 2 is a factor of 24, we can write

$$24 = 2 \cdot \underline{\hspace{1cm}}$$

12

87. Hence

$$24 = 1 \cdot 24$$
$$= 1 \cdot 2 \cdot 12$$

But 12 is not a prime. It, too, was crossed out as a multiple of 2.

And

$$12 = 2 \cdot \underline{\hspace{1cm}}$$

6

88. Therefore

$$24 = 1 \cdot 2 \cdot 12$$
$$= 1 \cdot 2 \cdot 2 \cdot 6$$

6, too, is a composite. It is a multiple of 2 and so we can write

$$6 = 2 \cdot \underline{\hspace{1cm}}$$

3

89. Thus

$$24 = 1 \cdot 2 \cdot 2 \cdot 6$$
$$= 1 \cdot 2 \cdot 2 \cdot \underline{\hspace{1cm}} \cdot \underline{\hspace{1cm}}$$

2 · 3

90. $24 = 1 \cdot 2 \cdot 2 \cdot 2 \cdot 3$

Note that with the exception of the factor 1, all factors listed are _____ numbers. Note also that we have arranged the factors in order of increasing size.

PRIME

91. $24 = 1 \cdot 2 \cdot 2 \cdot 2 \cdot 3$

We have expressed 24 as a product of the factor 1 and of prime numbers. It is not possible to find any other prime factors of 24.

We call $1 \cdot 2 \cdot 2 \cdot 2 \cdot 3$ the COMPLETE FACTORIZATION of 24.

92. Let us find the complete factorization of 54.

We begin by writing

$$54 = 1 \cdot 54$$

54 is a composite. In fact, 54 is a multiple of 2 and so we write

$$54 = \underline{\hspace{1cm}} \cdot \underline{\hspace{1cm}}$$

2;   27   (either order)

93. Hence

$$54 = 1 \cdot 54$$

$$= 1 \cdot 2 \cdot 27$$

But 27 is also a composite. It is a multiple of 3 and hence

$$27 = \underline{\hspace{2cm}} \cdot \underline{\hspace{2cm}}$$

> 3;   9   (either order)

94. Therefore

$$54 = 1 \cdot 2 \cdot 27$$

$$= 1 \cdot 2 \cdot 3 \cdot 9$$

9 is also a composite. Since it is a multiple of 3, we can write $9 = 3 \cdot 3$ and so

$$54 = 1 \cdot 2 \cdot 3 \cdot \underline{\hspace{1.5cm}} \cdot \underline{\hspace{1cm}}$$

> 3;   3

95. Thus $1 \cdot 2 \cdot 3 \cdot 3 \cdot 3$ is the complete
    $\underline{\hspace{4cm}}$ of 54.

> FACTORIZATION

96. Note that

$$60 = 1 \cdot 60$$

$$= 1 \cdot 2 \cdot 30$$

$$= 1 \cdot 2 \cdot 2 \cdot 15$$

$$= 1 \cdot 2 \cdot 2 \cdot \underline{\hspace{1.5cm}} \cdot \underline{\hspace{1cm}}.$$

> 3 · 5

97. Hence the complete factorization of 60 is

$$1 \cdot 2 \cdot 2 \cdot 3 \cdot 5$$

and

$$55 = 1 \cdot 55$$

$$= 1 \cdot 5 \cdot 11$$

But 5 and 11 are prime numbers and so $1 \cdot 5 \cdot 11$ is the $\underline{\hspace{2cm}}$ $\underline{\hspace{2cm}}$ of 55.

> COMPLETE FACTORIZATION

98. Since 29 is a prime number, its complete factorization is $\underline{\hspace{2cm}}$.

> 1 · 29

99. Every natural number has just one complete factorization, if the factors are arranged so that they do not decrease in size. The first factor is $\underline{\hspace{1.5cm}}$, and all remaining factors are $\underline{\hspace{2cm}}$ numbers.

> 1;   PRIME

100. Is $7 \cdot 11$ the complete factorization of 77?
    $\underline{\hspace{1.5cm}}$

Is $1 \cdot 2 \cdot 9$ the complete factorization of 18?
    $\underline{\hspace{1.5cm}}$

> NO   (the complete factorization is 77
> $= 1 \cdot 7 \cdot 11$)
> NO   (9 is not a prime; $18 = 1 \cdot 2 \cdot 3 \cdot 3$)

101. Let us illustrate a general method of determining the complete factorization of any natural number.

Consider the number 210. Since we did not construct the Sieve of Eratosthenes as far as 210, we may not know whether 210 is a prime or a composite.

But certainly we can begin by writing

$$210 = 1 \cdot \underline{\hspace{2cm}}$$

210

102. The smallest prime if 2. If 2 is a factor of 210, then 2 will also be an exact _____ of 210.

DIVISOR

103. Hence let us divide 210 by 2.

$$210/2 = \underline{\hspace{2cm}}$$

105

104. Since $210/2 = 105$, we can write $210 = 2 \cdot 105$.

Then 210 has 2 as a _____ and so is not a _____ .

FACTOR; PRIME

105. Hence

$$210 = 1 \cdot 210$$
$$= 1 \cdot 2 \cdot 105$$

Since we did not construct the Sieve that far, we do not know if 105 is a prime or a composite. Let us test 105 in the same manner. If 2 is a factor of 105, then 2 is also an _____ _____ of 105.

EXACT DIVISOR

106. But $105/2$ is impossible since 105 is not divisible by 2. Hence 2 is not a _____ of 105.

FACTOR

107. The next prime is 3. Is 3 a factor of 105? If so, then 3 is an exact divisor of 105.

$$105/3 = \underline{\hspace{2cm}}$$

35

108. Since $105/3 = 35$, we can write $105 = 3 \cdot 35$.
But

$$210 = 1 \cdot 2 \cdot 105$$

Hence

$$210 = 1 \cdot 2 \cdot \underline{\hspace{1.5cm}} \cdot \underline{\hspace{1.5cm}}$$

$\underline{3 \cdot 35}$

109. $210 = 1 \cdot 2 \cdot 3 \cdot 35$

From the Sieve, we can see that 35 is not a prime number. But the prime number 2 cannot be a factor of 35, since we have already seen that 2 is not a factor of its multiple, 105.

Is 3 a factor of 35? _____

NO   (35/3 is impossible)

110. Since we are only seeking prime factors, we go to the next prime, 5. Is 5 a factor of 35? _____

YES

111. In fact

$$35 = 5 \cdot 7$$

And since $210 = 1 \cdot 2 \cdot 3 \cdot 35$, the complete factorization of 210 is

_____ · _____ · _____ · _____ ·
_____

1;   2;   3;   5;   7

112. $210 = 1 \cdot 2 \cdot 3 \cdot 5 \cdot 7$

Note that we have found the complete factorization of 210 by considering the prime numbers 2, 3, and 5, in turn, as divisors.

Let us find the complete factorization of 882. Of course

$$882 = 1 \cdot 882$$

But 882 is divisible by 2

$$882/2 = \underline{\qquad}$$

441

113. $882 = 1 \cdot 882$

$882/2 = 441$ and so $882 = 2 \cdot 441$.

Therefore:

$$882 = 1 \cdot 2 \cdot 441$$

441 is <u>not</u> divisible by 2 and so cannot have 2 as a factor. But 441 <u>is</u> divisible by 3.

$$441/3 = \underline{\qquad}$$

147

114. $882 = 1 \cdot 2 \cdot 441$

$441/3 = 147$ and so $441 = 3 \cdot 147$.

Therefore:

$$882 = 1 \cdot 2 \cdot 3 \cdot 147.$$

We do not need to consider 2 as a divisor of 147 since 2 was not a factor of its multiple, 441.

But 147 is, again, divisible by 3.

$$147/3 = \underline{\qquad}$$

49

115. $882 = 1 \cdot 2 \cdot 3 \cdot 147$

$147/3 = 49$ and so $147 = 3 \cdot 49$.

Therefore:

$$882 = 1 \cdot 2 \cdot 3 \cdot 3 \cdot 49.$$

Again, 49 cannot have 2 as a factor. And since 49 is not divisible by 3 or 5, it cannot have 3 or 5 as factors. But 49 is divisible by the next prime, 7.

Hence

$$49 = \underline{\qquad} \cdot \underline{\qquad}$$

7 · 7

116. $882 = 1 \cdot 2 \cdot 3 \cdot 3 \cdot 49$

But

$$49 = 7 \cdot 7$$

and so the complete factorization of 882 is

$$1 \cdot 2 \cdot 3 \cdot 3 \cdot 7 \cdot 7$$

To find the complete factorization of 60, note that

$$60/2 = \underline{\qquad}$$
$$30/2 = \underline{\qquad}$$
$$15/3 = \underline{\qquad}$$

30;   15;   5

117.　$60/2 = 30.$　Hence　$60 = 2 \cdot 30$

　　　$30/2 = 15.$　Hence　$30 = 2 \cdot$ _____

　　　$15/3 = 5.$　Hence　$15 =$ _____

> 15;　　$3 \cdot 5$

118.　$60 = 2 \cdot 30$　　$30 = 2 \cdot 15$　　$15 = 3 \cdot 5$

Hence

$$60 = 1 \cdot 60$$
$$= 1 \cdot 2 \cdot 30$$
$$= 1 \cdot 2 \cdot 2 \cdot 15$$
$$= 1 \cdot 2 \cdot 2 \cdot 3 \cdot 5$$

Therefore

$1 \cdot 2 \cdot 2 \cdot 3 \cdot 5$ is the _____

_____ of 60.

COMPLETE FACTORIZATION

119.　Every natural number has one complete factorization.

The first factor is the number _____.

For a prime number, the only other factor is the _____ number, itself.

> 1;　　PRIME

120.　Every natural number has one complete factorization.

The first factor is the number 1.

For a composite number, the other factors are _____ numbers and are found by dividing by the primes as often as possible.

> PRIME

121.　Find the complete factorizations of:

$12 = 1 \cdot$ _____ $\cdot$ _____ $\cdot$ _____

$30 =$ _____ $\cdot$ _____ $\cdot$ _____ $\cdot$ _____

> $12 = 1 \cdot 12 = 1 \cdot 2 \cdot 6 = 1 \cdot 2 \cdot 2 \cdot 3;$
> $30 = 1 \cdot 30 = 1 \cdot 2 \cdot 15 = 1 \cdot 2 \cdot 3 \cdot 5$

122.　$12 = 1 \cdot 2 \cdot 2 \cdot 3$　　and　　$30 = 1 \cdot 2 \cdot 3 \cdot 5$

Recall that we previously found all the factors of these numbers. They were:

12: 1, 2, 3, 4, 6, 12

30: 1, 2, 3, 5, 6, 10, 15, 30

It is possible to obtain the list of all factors of 12 from its complete factorization.

123.　$1 \cdot 2 \cdot 2 \cdot 3$

is the complete factorization of 12.

Note that each of the factors which appear in the complete factorization of 12,

1, 2, and 3

are _____ of 12.

FACTORS

124.　$1 \cdot 2 \cdot 2 \cdot 3$

is the complete factorization of 12.

Note that the prime factors which occur in the complete factorization of 12 are

2, 2, and 3

and can be grouped to form three different products:

$2 \cdot 2 =$ _____　　　$2 \cdot 3 =$ _____

$2 \cdot 2 \cdot 3 =$ _____

> 4;　　6;　　12

125. $12 = 1 \cdot 2 \cdot 2 \cdot 3$

Finally note that the numbers 1, 2, 3, 4, 6, and 12 are precisely all the factors of 12.

$1 \cdot 2 \cdot 2 \cdot 3 \cdot 5$

is the complete factorization of 60.

Note that each of the factors

1, 2, 3, and 5,

are _____ of 60.

126. $1 \cdot 2 \cdot 2 \cdot 3 \cdot 5$

is the complete factorization of 60.

Note that the prime factors,

2, 2, 3, and 5

can be grouped to form eight products:

$2 \cdot 2 =$ _____, $2 \cdot 3 =$ _____,
$2 \cdot 5 =$ _____, $3 \cdot 5 =$ _____

$2 \cdot 2 \cdot 3 =$ _____, $2 \cdot 2 \cdot 5 =$ _____,
$2 \cdot 3 \cdot 5 =$ _____,   and
$2 \cdot 2 \cdot 3 \cdot 5 =$ _____.

127. $60 = 1 \cdot 2 \cdot 2 \cdot 3 \cdot 5$

Finally, note that the numbers 1, 2, 3, 5, 4, 6, 10, 15, 12, 20, 30, and 60 are precisely all the factors of 60.

$1 \cdot 2 \cdot 2 \cdot 7$

is the complete factorization of 28. From this, we see that three factors of 28 are _____, _____, and _____.

128. $28 = 1 \cdot 2 \cdot 2 \cdot 7$

Three more factors of 28 are

$2 \cdot 2 =$ _____ $2 \cdot 7 =$ _____
$2 \cdot 2 \cdot 7 =$ _____

129. $28 = 1 \cdot 2 \cdot 2 \cdot 7$

and 1, 2, 7, 4, 14, and 28 are all the factors of 28.

The complete factorization of 36 is

$1 \cdot 2 \cdot 2 \cdot 3 \cdot 3$

Hence 36 has the factors

_____, _____, _____, _____,
_____, _____, _____, _____, and
_____.

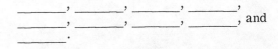

130. To review: Every exact divisor of a number is also a _____ of that number.

131. Hence, to find all of the exact divisors of a number, we need only find all of the factors of the number.

A _____ number has only two factors. They are the number itself and _____.

132. A natural number greater than 1 which is not a prime is a _____ number.

133. We can use the Sieve of Eratosthenes to determine which numbers are prime. And then we can use the _____ numbers as divisors to find the _____ factorization of any natural number.

PRIME;   COMPLETE

134. In the complete factorization of a natural number we have _____ as the first factor. All other factors are _____ numbers, arranged in order.

1;   PRIME

135. From the complete factorization of a number we can construct the list of all its factors. We note that every number which occurs in the complete factorization of a number is a _____ of that number.

FACTOR

136. And all possible products of those prime factors in the complete factorization of a number are also _____ of that number.

FACTORS

Chapter 9

Problems A   (Answers on page 508)

For each of the following tell what natural number it is the complete factorization of, or tell why it is not the complete factorization of any natural number.

Example: $1 \cdot 2 \cdot 3 \cdot 5$. Answer: Complete factorization of 30.

Example: $1 \cdot 2 \cdot 3 \cdot 6$. Answer: Not a complete factorization, since 6 is a composite.

1. $1 \cdot 3 \cdot 3 \cdot 5$
2. $1 \cdot 2 \cdot 2 \cdot 2 \cdot 3$
3. $1 \cdot 4 \cdot 5$
4. $2 \cdot 2 \cdot 3 \cdot 3$
5. $1 \cdot 2 \cdot 7 \cdot 9$
6. $1 \cdot 3 \cdot 7 \cdot 11$
7. $5 \cdot 7 \cdot 11$
8. $1 \cdot 5 \cdot 5 \cdot 5$
9. $1 \cdot 3 \cdot 13$
10. $1 \cdot 11 \cdot 17 \cdot 18$

Find the complete factorization of each of the following:

Example: 1980.

Answer: $1980 = 1 \cdot 1980$

$[1980/2 = 990]$ $= 1 \cdot 2 \cdot 990$
$[990/2 = 495]$ $= 1 \cdot 2 \cdot 2 \cdot 495$
$[495/3 = 165]$ $= 1 \cdot 2 \cdot 2 \cdot 3 \cdot 165$
$[165/3 = 55]$ $= 1 \cdot 2 \cdot 2 \cdot 3 \cdot 3 \cdot 55$
$[55/5 = 11]$ $= 1 \cdot 2 \cdot 2 \cdot 3 \cdot 3 \cdot 5 \cdot 11$

11. 16
12. 36
13. 40
14. 44
15. 50
16. 54
17. 69
18. 100
19. 260
20. 23,100

For each of the following, form all possible products using the given numbers as factors.

Example: 2, 3, 3, 5.

Answer:
$2 \cdot 3 = 6$	$2 \cdot 3 \cdot 3 = 18$
$2 \cdot 5 = 10$	$2 \cdot 3 \cdot 5 = 30$
$3 \cdot 3 = 9$	$3 \cdot 3 \cdot 5 = 45$
$3 \cdot 5 = 15$	$2 \cdot 3 \cdot 3 \cdot 5 = 90$

21. 2, 3, 7
22. 1, 2, 3
23. 3, 3, 5
24. 2, 3, 5, 7
25. 2, 2, 2, 2, 2

Use the complete factorization of each of the following numbers to list, in order, all of its factors.

Example: $28 = 1 \cdot 2 \cdot 2 \cdot 7$. Answer: 1, 2, and 7 are factors. So are all possible products of the prime factors 2, 2, 7.

$2 \cdot 2 = 4$
$2 \cdot 7 = 14$
$2 \cdot 2 \cdot 7 = 28$
$\underline{1, 2, 4, 7, 14, 28}$

26. $15 = 1 \cdot 3 \cdot 5$
27. $42 = 1 \cdot 2 \cdot 3 \cdot 7$
28. $98 = 1 \cdot 2 \cdot 7 \cdot 7$
29. 64
30. 300

Problems B

For each of the following, tell what natural number it is the complete factorization of, or tell why it is not the complete factorization of any natural number.

1. $1 \cdot 2 \cdot 3 \cdot 11$
2. $1 \cdot 3 \cdot 5 \cdot 7 \cdot 9$
3. $2 \cdot 3 \cdot 5 \cdot 13$
4. $1 \cdot 7 \cdot 11 \cdot 29$
5. $1 \cdot 2 \cdot 4 \cdot 8 \cdot 16$
6. $5 \cdot 7 \cdot 17$
7. $1 \cdot 2$
8. $1 \cdot 7 \cdot 7 \cdot 7$
9. $1 \cdot 11 \cdot 11$
10. $1 \cdot 5 \cdot 13 \cdot 23$

Find the complete factorization of each of the following.

11. 18
12. 32

13. 48

14. 72

15. 250

16. 360

17. 1000

18. 728

19. 1320

20. 10,000

For each of the following, form all possible products using the given numbers as factors.

21. 3, 5, 7

22. 2, 5, 11

23. 3, 7, 7

24. 2, 5, 7, 11

25. 2, 3, 3, 3, 3

Use the complete factorization of each of the following numbers to list, in order, all of its factors.

26. $14 = 1 \cdot 2 \cdot 7$

27. $56 = 1 \cdot 2 \cdot 2 \cdot 2 \cdot 7$

28. $315 = 1 \cdot 3 \cdot 3 \cdot 5 \cdot 7$

29. 144

30. 365

CHAPTER 10

LCM AND GCD

1. Let a, b, and c represent natural numbers. If ab = c, we call c the _____ of a and b, and we call a and b _____ of c. We also call c a _____ of a and a _____ of b.

> PRODUCT;   FACTORS;   MULTIPLE; MULTIPLE

2. If d is any natural number greater than 1, then d has, as two factors, the numbers _____ and _____ .

> 1, d   (either order)

3. If d is a natural number greater than 1, and if the only factors of d are 1 and d, then d is called a _____ number.

> PRIME

4. Any natural number greater than 1 which is not a prime number is called a _____ .

> COMPOSITE

5. The Sieve of Eratosthenes can be used to determine the prime numbers. By means of the Sieve,

2, 3, 4, 5, 6, 7, 8, 9, 10, 11, 12, 13, 14, 15, 16, 17, 18, 19, 20, 21, 22, 23, 24, 25, 26, 27, 28, 29, 30, 31, 32, 33, 34, 35, 36, 37, 38, 39, 40, 41, 42, 43, 44, 45, 46, 47, 48, 49, 50, . . .

the first ten prime numbers are, in order,

_____, _____, _____, _____, _____, _____, _____, _____, _____, _____ .

> 2, 3, 5, 7, 11, 13, 17, 19, 23, 29

6. Every natural number has a complete factorization. The complete factorization represents the number as a product whose first factor is _____ and whose remaining factors are all _____ numbers, arranged in order.

> 1;   PRIME

7. The complete factorizations of the first ten natural numbers are:

$$1 = 1$$
$$2 = 1 \cdot 2$$
$$3 = 1 \cdot 3$$
$$4 = 1 \cdot 2 \cdot 2$$
$$5 = 1 \cdot 5$$
$$6 = 1 \cdot 2 \cdot 3$$
$$7 = 1 \cdot 7$$
$$8 = \underline{\quad} \cdot \underline{\quad} \cdot \underline{\quad} \cdot \underline{\quad}$$
$$9 = \underline{\quad} \cdot \underline{\quad} \cdot \underline{\quad}$$
$$10 = \underline{\quad} \cdot \underline{\quad} \cdot \underline{\quad}$$

$$8 = \underline{1} \cdot \underline{2} \cdot \underline{2} \cdot \underline{2}; \quad 9 = \underline{1} \cdot \underline{3} \cdot \underline{3}; \quad 10 = \underline{1} \cdot \underline{2} \cdot \underline{5}$$

8. And the complete factorizations of the next ten numbers are

$$11 = 1 \cdot 11 \qquad 16 = \underline{\quad}$$
$$12 = 1 \cdot 2 \cdot 2 \cdot 3 \qquad 17 = 1 \cdot 17$$
$$13 = 1 \cdot 13 \qquad 18 = \underline{\quad}$$
$$14 = 1 \cdot 2 \cdot 7 \qquad 19 = 1 \cdot 19$$
$$15 = \underline{\quad} \qquad 20 = \underline{\quad}$$

$$15 = \underline{1} \cdot \underline{3} \cdot \underline{5}; \quad 16 = \underline{1} \cdot \underline{2} \cdot \underline{2} \cdot \underline{2} \cdot \underline{2};$$
$$18 = \underline{1} \cdot \underline{2} \cdot \underline{3} \cdot \underline{3}; \quad 20 = \underline{1} \cdot \underline{2} \cdot \underline{2} \cdot \underline{5}$$

9.
$$6 \cdot 1 = 6$$
$$6 \cdot 2 = 12$$
$$6 \cdot 3 = 18$$
$$6 \cdot 4 = 24$$

Hence 6, 12, 18, and 24 are $\underline{\qquad\qquad}$ of 6.

MULTIPLES

10. 6, 12, 18, and 24 are multiples of 6. The next four multiples of 6 are, in order, $\underline{\qquad}$, $\underline{\qquad}$, $\underline{\qquad}$, and $\underline{\qquad}$.

30, 36, 42, 48

11. There is no last multiple of 6. In order, the first twelve multiples of 6 are:

6, 12, 18, 24, 30, 36, 42, 48, $\underline{\qquad}$, $\underline{\qquad}$, $\underline{\qquad}$, $\underline{\qquad}$.

54, 60, 66, 72

12.
$$8 \cdot 1 = 8$$
$$8 \cdot 2 = 16$$
$$8 \cdot 3 = 24$$
$$8 \cdot 4 = 32$$

Hence 8, 16, 24, and 32 are $\underline{\qquad\qquad}$ of 8.

MULTIPLES

13. 8, 16, 24, and 32 are multiples of 8. The next four multiples of 8 are, in order, $\underline{\qquad}$, $\underline{\qquad}$, $\underline{\qquad}$, and $\underline{\qquad}$.

40, 48, 56, 64

14. There is no limit to the number of multiples of 8.

The first ten multiples of 8 are, in order,

8, 16, 24, 32, 40, 48, 56, 64, $\underline{\qquad}$, $\underline{\qquad}$.

72, 80

15. Let us list multiples of 6 and multiples of 8.

    6: 6, 12, 18, 24, 30, 36, 42, 48, 54, 60, 66, 72, . . .

    8: 8, 16, 24, 32, 40, 48, 56, 64, 72, 80, . . .

    The numbers 24, 48, and 72 appear in _____ lists. Hence, these numbers are multiples of _____ of 6 and 8. We shall call 24, 48, and 72 COMMON MULTIPLES OF 6 AND 8.

    BOTH;   BOTH

16. Since 24, 48, and 72 are multiples of 6 and also are multiples of 8, we call these numbers _____ _____ of 6 and 8.

    COMMON MULTIPLES

17. But 24, 48, and 72 are not the only common multiples of 6 and 8. If we extend the lists of multiples of 6 and 8, other common multiples can be found. The next common multiple would be the number _____ .

    96

18. 24, 48, 72, and 96 are among the common multiples of 6 and 8.

    Of all such common multiples, 24 is the smallest. We shall call 24 the LEAST COMMON MULTIPLE OF 6 AND 8.

    Note that 24 is a common multiple of 6 and 8, and 24 is the L_____ possible such _____ multiple.

    LEAST;   COMMON

19. We use the letters LCM to represent "least common multiple." Hence 24 is the _____ of 6 and 8.

    LCM   (or LEAST COMMON MULTIPLE)

20. $10 \cdot 1 = 10$

    $10 \cdot 2 = 20$

    $10 \cdot 3 = 30$

    $10 \cdot 4 = 40$

    $10 \cdot 5 = 50$

    $10 \cdot 6 = 60$

    10, 20, 30, 40, 50, 60 are multiples of 10. The next eight multiples of 10 are, in order:

    _____, _____, _____, _____,
    _____, _____, _____, _____.

    70, 80, 90, 100, 110, 120, 130, 140

21. $12 \cdot 1 = 12$

    $12 \cdot 2 = 24$

    $12 \cdot 3 = 36$

    $12 \cdot 4 = 48$

    $12 \cdot 5 = 60$

    $12 \cdot 6 = 72$

    12, 24, 36, 48, 60, 72 are all multiples of 12. The next six multiples of 12 are, in order:

    _____, _____, _____, _____,
    _____, _____.

    84, 96, 108, 120, 132, 144

22. 10, 20, 30, 40, 50, 60, 70, 80, 90, 100, 110, 120, 130, 140, ...are multiples of 10.

12, 24, 36, 48, 60, 72, 84, 96, 108, 120, 132, 144, ...are multiples of 12.

Of the numbers listed, the common multiples of 10 and 12 are _____ and _____.

> 60; 120 (either order)

23. 60 and 120 are common multiples of 10 and 12.

While not appearing in our lists, the numbers 180, 240, and 300 are also _____ _____ of 10 and 12.

However, the least common multiple of 10 and 12 is _____.

> COMMON MULTIPLES; 60

24. The LCM of 10 and 12 is 60.

Let us find the LCM of 5 and 9.

The first ten multiples of 5 are

5, 10, 15, 20, 25, _____, _____, _____, _____, _____.

> 30, 35, 40, 45, 50

25. We are seeking the LCM of 5 and 9.

The first ten multiples of 5 are

5, 10, 15, 20, 25, 30, 35, 40, 45, 50

The first six multiples of 9 are

9, 18, _____, _____, _____, _____.

> 27, 36, 45, 54

26. We are seeking the LCM of 5 and 9.

5, 10, 15, 20, 25, 30, 35, 40, 45, 50, ...are multiples of 5.

9, 18, 27, 36, 45, 54, ...are multiples of 9.

Any number which appears in both lists is a _____ _____ of 5 and 9.
Since we seek the least common multiple, we shall choose the F_____ number which appears in both lists.

> COMMON MULTIPLE; FIRST

27. 5, 10, 15, 20, 25, 30, 35, 40, 45, 50, ...are multiples of 5.

9, 18, 27, 36, 45, 54, ...are multiples of 9.

The LCM of 5 and 9 is _____.

Note that other common multiples of 5 and 9 exist, but, since we only seek the smallest of the common multiples, it is not necessary to extend the lists or investigate further.

> 45

28. 5, 10, 15, 20, 25, 30, ...are multiples of 5.

15, 30, 45, 60, 75, 90, ...are multiples of 15.

The LCM of 5 and 15 is _____.

> 15

29. 12, 24, 36, 48, 60, 72, ...are multiples of 12.

15, 30, 45, 60, 75, 90, ...are multiples of 15.

The LCM of 12 and 15 is _____.

> 60

30. 13, 26, 39, 52, 65, 78, 91, 104, 117, 130, 143, 156, ... are multiples of 13.

11, 22, 33, 44, 55, 66, 77, 88, 99, 110, 121, 132, 143, 154, ... are multiples of 11.

And 143 is the _____ of 13 and 11.

LCM

31. To find common multiples of two numbers, then, we list multiples of each and choose numbers which appear in _____ lists.

BOTH

32. And to find the LCM of two numbers, we merely select the _____ of their common multiples.

SMALLEST

33. That is, the LCM of two numbers can be found by listing, in order, multiples of each and choosing the _____ number that appears in both lists.

FIRST   or   SMALLEST

34. We can also find the LCM of three, or more, numbers in this way.

4, 8, 12, 16, 20, 24, 28, 32, 36, 40, 44, 48, 52, ... are multiples of 4.

6, 12, 18, 24, 30, 36, 42, 48, 54, 60, 66, ... are multiples of 6.

8, 16, 24, 32, 40, 48, 56, 64, ... are multiples of 8.

Since the numbers 24 and 48 appear in all three lists, 24 and 48 are _____ _____ of 4, 6, and 8.

COMMON MULTIPLES

35. 24 and 48 are common multiples of 4, 6, and 8.

The LCM of 4, 6, and 8 is _____.

24

36. For some pairs of numbers, the LCM can be determined quite easily.

Consider the numbers 6 and 42.

$42 = 6 \cdot 7$

and so 42 is a _____ of 6.

MULTIPLE

37. 42 is a multiple of 6.

But

$42 = 42 \cdot 1$

and so 42 is also a multiple of 42.

Hence 42 is a _____ _____ of 6 and 42.

COMMON MULTIPLE

38. 42 is a common multiple of 6 and 42.

But no smaller common multiple could be found, since 42 is the first multiple of 42. Therefore, the LCM of 6 and 42 is _____.

42

39. Consider the numbers 8 and 32.

$$32 = 8 \cdot 4$$

and so 32 is a multiple of 8.

Also,

$$32 = 32 \cdot 1$$

and so 32 is a multiple of 32.

Hence, 32 is a _____ _____ of 8 and 32.

COMMON MULTIPLE

40. But there can be no multiple of 32 smaller than 32, and so 32 is the _____ of 8 and 32.

LCM

41. In fact, whenever one of two numbers is a multiple of the other, their LCM can be easily found. It is merely the _____ of the two numbers.

LARGER

42. Find the LCM of:

4 and 24 _____

15 and 150 _____

1 and 6 _____

5 and 20 _____

24;   150;   6;   20

43. For other natural numbers, finding their LCM by the method we have been describing can be difficult.

To find the LCM of 21 and 120 would require writing down no less than 40 multiples of 21!

44. However, we can find a common multiple of 21 and 120 by merely finding their product. While not necessarily their least common multiple, their product will certainly be a multiple of each.

$$21 \cdot 120 = _____.$$

2520

45. Similarly, a common multiple of 16 and 50 is their _____.

PRODUCT

46. $16 \cdot 50$ is a common multiple of 16 and 50, although it is not their LCM.

In simplest form

$$16 \cdot 50 = _____$$

but there may be occasions when it is preferable to express the result as $16 \cdot 50$.

800

47. Find a common multiple of 25 and 36.

_____

Find a common multiple of 3, 5, and 18.

_____

$25 \cdot 36$; $3 \cdot 5 \cdot 18$

48. If a and b represent natural numbers, then their product, ab, is certainly a

_____ _____ of a and b,

although it may not be their LCM.

COMMON MULTIPLE

49. Let us return to the problem of finding the LCM of two natural numbers. The LCM of 8 and 20 is the _____ number which is a _____ of both 8 and 20.

50. Any number which is a multiple of 8 must have 8 as a factor. And any number which is a multiple of 20 must have 20 as a factor.

Hence, any number which is a multiple of both 8 and 20 must have _____ 8 and 20 as _____.

51. The complete factorizations of 8 and 20 are:

$$8 = 1 \cdot 2 \cdot 2 \cdot 2$$
$$20 = 1 \cdot 2 \cdot 2 \cdot 5$$

We shall find the complete factorization of their LCM.

Certainly $20 = 1 \cdot 2 \cdot 2 \cdot 5$ is a multiple of 20, but it is not a multiple of 8, since it does not have _____ as a factor.

52. $20 = 1 \cdot 2 \cdot 2 \cdot 5$

is not a common multiple of 8 and 20 since it is not a multiple of 8. However, if we form the product

$$20 \cdot 2 = 1 \cdot 2 \cdot 2 \cdot 5 \cdot 2$$

we have a number which is still a _____ of 20.

53. $20 \cdot 2 = 1 \cdot 2 \cdot 2 \cdot 5 \cdot 2$

is a multiple of 20. But

$$1 \cdot 2 \cdot 2 \cdot 5 \cdot 2 = 1 \cdot 2 \cdot 2 \cdot 2 \cdot 5 = 8 \cdot 5$$

and so is also a _____ of 8.

54. $1 \cdot 2 \cdot 2 \cdot 2 \cdot 5$

is a multiple of 8 and also a multiple of 20, and hence is a _____ _____ of 8 and 20.

55. $1 \cdot 2 \cdot 2 \cdot 2 \cdot 5$

is a common multiple of 8 and 20. And no smaller multiple of 20 is also a multiple of 8. Hence

$$1 \cdot 2 \cdot 2 \cdot 2 \cdot 5$$

is the _____ of 8 and 20.

56. $8 = 1 \cdot 2 \cdot 2 \cdot 2$ $20 = 1 \cdot 2 \cdot 2 \cdot 5$

The LCM of 8 and 20 has the complete factorization

$$1 \cdot 2 \cdot 2 \cdot 2 \cdot 5$$

Observe that the complete factorization of the LCM contains the factor 1 and every prime factor which appears in the complete factorization of either 8 or 20, or in both.

57. $8 = 1 \cdot 2 \cdot 2 \cdot 2$

$20 = 1 \cdot 2 \cdot 2 \cdot 5$

The LCM of 8 and 20 has the complete factorization

$1 \cdot 2 \cdot 2 \cdot 2 \cdot 5$

Also note that the prime factor 2 appears three times in 8, two times in 20, and _____ times in the LCM.

58. $8 = 1 \cdot 2 \cdot 2 \cdot 2$

$20 = 1 \cdot 2 \cdot 2 \cdot 5$

And the LCM of 8 and 20 is, in simplest form,

$1 \cdot 2 \cdot 2 \cdot 2 \cdot 5 =$ _____

59. Let us find the LCM of 12 and 18. Since the LCM will be a multiple of 12 and also a multiple of 18, it must contain both 12 and 18 as _____ .

60. The complete factorizations of 12 and 18 are

$12 = 1 \cdot 2 \cdot 2 \cdot 3$

$18 = 1 \cdot 2 \cdot 3 \cdot 3$

Again $18 = 1 \cdot 2 \cdot 3 \cdot 3$ is a multiple of 18, but it is not a multiple of 12, since it does not have 12 as a factor.

However, $18 \cdot 2 = 1 \cdot 2 \cdot 3 \cdot 3 \cdot 2$ is certainly a multiple of 18.

And $1 \cdot 2 \cdot 3 \cdot 3 \cdot 2 = 1 \cdot 2 \cdot 2 \cdot 3 \cdot 3 = 12 \cdot 3$ is also a _____ of 12.

61. $12 = 1 \cdot 2 \cdot 2 \cdot 3$

$18 = 1 \cdot 2 \cdot 3 \cdot 3$

$18 \cdot 2 = 1 \cdot 2 \cdot 2 \cdot 3 \cdot 3$ is a multiple of 12 and 18, and so is a common multiple. But no smaller multiple of 18 is also a multiple of 12. Hence

$1 \cdot 2 \cdot 2 \cdot 3 \cdot 3$

is the _____ of 12 and 18.

62. $12 = 1 \cdot 2 \cdot 2 \cdot 3$

$18 = 1 \cdot 2 \cdot 3 \cdot 3$

The LCM of 12 and 18 has the complete factorization

$1 \cdot 2 \cdot 2 \cdot 3 \cdot 3$

Again, note that the LCM contains 1 and every prime factor found in either 12, or 18, or both, and that a repeated prime factor appears in the LCM the maximum number of times it occurs in either 12 or 18. Finally, in simplest form,

$1 \cdot 2 \cdot 2 \cdot 3 \cdot 3 =$ _____

63. These examples suggest a way to find the LCM of two numbers.

Obtain the complete factorizations of the numbers and form a number which includes 1 and every prime factor found in _____ or _____ of the two numbers.

64. And if a prime factor is repeated in one or both of the original numbers, in the LCM it must appear the G_____ number of times.

65. Consider the numbers 14 and 30.

Their complete factorizations are

$14 = 1 \cdot 2 \cdot 7$

$30 = 1 \cdot 2 \cdot 3 \cdot 5$

Then their LCM has the complete factorization

_____ · _____ · _____ · _____ ·

_____

$1 \cdot 2 \cdot 3 \cdot 5 \cdot 7$

66. $14 = 1 \cdot 2 \cdot 7$

$30 = 1 \cdot 2 \cdot 3 \cdot 5$

The LCM of 14 and 30 is, in simplest form,

$1 \cdot 2 \cdot 3 \cdot 5 \cdot 7 =$ _____

210

67. The complete factorizations of 16 and 24 are

$16 = 1 \cdot 2 \cdot 2 \cdot 2 \cdot 2$

$24 = 1 \cdot 2 \cdot 2 \cdot 2 \cdot 3$

Their LCM has the complete factorization

_____ · _____ · _____ · _____ ·

_____

$1 \cdot 2 \cdot 2 \cdot 2 \cdot 2 \cdot 3$

68. $16 = 1 \cdot 2 \cdot 2 \cdot 2 \cdot 2$

$24 = 1 \cdot 2 \cdot 2 \cdot 2 \cdot 3$

The LCM of 16 and 24 is, in simplest form,

$1 \cdot 2 \cdot 2 \cdot 2 \cdot 2 \cdot 3 =$ _____

48

69. Find the complete factorization of the LCM of

$10 = 1 \cdot 2 \cdot 5$

and

$27 = 1 \cdot 3 \cdot 3 \cdot 3$ _____

$1 \cdot 2 \cdot 3 \cdot 3 \cdot 3 \cdot 5$

70. Find the complete factorization of the LCM of the numbers

$1 \cdot 2 \cdot 3 \cdot 3 \cdot 5$

$1 \cdot 3 \cdot 5 \cdot 5$ _____

$1 \cdot 2 \cdot 3 \cdot 3 \cdot 5 \cdot 5$

71. We can also find the LCM of three (or more) numbers in this way.

$7 = 1 \cdot 7$

$20 = 1 \cdot 2 \cdot 2 \cdot 5$

$28 = 1 \cdot 2 \cdot 2 \cdot 7$

The LCM of 7, 20, and 28 has the complete factorization:

_____ · _____ · _____ · _____ ·

$1 \cdot 2 \cdot 2 \cdot 5 \cdot 7$

72. Find the complete factorization of the LCM of

$54 = 1 \cdot 2 \cdot 3 \cdot 3 \cdot 3$

and

$75 = 1 \cdot 3 \cdot 5 \cdot 5$ _____

$1 \cdot 2 \cdot 3 \cdot 3 \cdot 3 \cdot 5 \cdot 5$

73. Find the complete factorization of the LCM of

$$30 = 1 \cdot 2 \cdot 3 \cdot 5$$

and

$$48 = 1 \cdot 2 \cdot 2 \cdot 2 \cdot 2 \cdot 3 \underline{\hspace{3cm}}$$

> $1 \cdot 2 \cdot 2 \cdot 2 \cdot 2 \cdot 3 \cdot 5$

74. Find the complete factorization of the LCM of

$$8 = 1 \cdot 2 \cdot 2 \cdot 2$$
$$20 = 1 \cdot 2 \cdot 2 \cdot 5$$

and

$$36 = 1 \cdot 2 \cdot 2 \cdot 3 \cdot 3 \underline{\hspace{3cm}}$$

> $1 \cdot 2 \cdot 2 \cdot 2 \cdot 3 \cdot 3 \cdot 5$

75. In the last chapter we considered the problem of finding all the factors of a number. Since every factor of a number is also an _____ of that number, we used the complete factorization as a means of obtaining all the exact divisors of a number.

> EXACT DIVISOR

76. Thus

$$8 = 1 \cdot 2 \cdot 2 \cdot 2$$

and so, in order, the exact divisors of 8 are

_____, _____, _____, _____

> 1, 2, 4, 8

77. And

$$12 = 1 \cdot 2 \cdot 2 \cdot 3$$

Hence, in order, the exact divisors of 12 are

_____, _____, _____, _____,

_____, _____

> 1, 2, 3, 4, 6, 12

78. The exact divisors of 8 are 1, 2, 4, 8.

The exact divisors of 12 are 1, 2, 3, 4, 6, 12.

The numbers 1, 2, and 4 appear in _____ lists. Hence these numbers are exact divisors of _____ 8 and 12. We shall call 1, 2, and 4 COMMON DIVISORS OF 8 AND 12.

> BOTH;   BOTH

79. Since 1, 2, and 4 are exact divisors of 8 and are also exact divisors of 12, we call these numbers _____ _____ of 8 and 12.

> COMMON DIVISORS

80. And 1, 2, and 4 are the only common divisors of 8 and 12, since we have considered all the exact divisors of each.

Of these numbers, 4 is the largest. We shall call 4 the GREATEST COMMON DIVISOR OF 8 AND 12.

Note that 4 is a common divisor of 8 and 12, and that 4 is the G_____ of their _____ divisors.

> GREATEST;   COMMON

81. We use the letters GCD to represent "greatest common divisor." Hence 4 is the _____ of 8 and 12.

> **GCD** (or GREATEST COMMON DIVISOR)

82. $18 = 1 \cdot 2 \cdot 3 \cdot 3$

Hence, in order, the exact divisors of 18 are

_____, _____, _____, _____, _____, _____

> 1, 2, 3, 6, 9, 18

83. $30 = 1 \cdot 2 \cdot 3 \cdot 5$

Therefore, in order, the exact divisors of 30 are

_____, _____, _____, _____, _____, _____, _____, _____

> 1, 2, 3, 5, 6, 10, 15, 30

84. The exact divisors of 18 are

1, 2, 3, 6, 9, 18

The exact divisors of 30 are

1, 2, 3, 5, 6, 10, 15, 30

The common divisors of 18 and 30 are

_____, _____, _____, and _____.

> 1, 2, 3, 6   (any order)

85. And the greatest common divisor of 18 and 30 is _____.

> 6

86. The GCD of 18 and 30 is 6.

Let us find the GCD of 7 and 15.

The complete factorizations of 7 and 15 are

$7 = 1 \cdot 7$

$15 = 1 \cdot 3 \cdot 5$

Hence the exact divisors of 7 and 15 are, in order,

7: _____, _____

15: _____, _____, _____, _____

> 7: 1, 7;   15: 1, 3, 5, 15

87. We are seeking the GCD of 7 and 15.

The exact divisors of 7 are 1, 7.

The exact divisors of 15 are 1, 3, 5, 15.

Any number which appears in both lists is a _____ _____ of 7 and 15.

Since we seek the greatest common divisor, we choose the L_____ number which appears in both lists.

> COMMON DIVISOR;   LARGEST

88. The exact divisors of 7 are 1, 7.

The exact divisors of 15 are 1, 3, 5, 15.

The GCD of 7 and 15 is _____.

> 1

89. The exact divisors of 45 are 1, 3, 5, 9, 15, 45.

The exact divisors of 60 are 1, 2, 3, 4, 5, 6, 10, 12, 15, 20, 30, 60.

The GCD of 45 and 60 is _____.

> 15

90. The exact divisors of 9 are 1, 3, 9.

The exact divisors of 36 are 1, 2, 3, 4, 6, 9, 12, 18, 36.

The GCD of 9 and 36 is _____ .

> 9

91. The exact divisors of 11 are 1, 11.

The exact divisors of 16 are 1, 2, 4, 8, 16.

And 1 is the _____ of 11 and 16.

> GCD

92. To find common divisors of two numbers, then, we list the _____ _____ of each and choose numbers which appear in both lists.

> EXACT DIVISORS

93. And to find the GCD of two numbers, we merely select the _____ of their common divisors.

> LARGEST or GREATEST

94. That is, the GCD of two numbers can be found by listing, in order, the exact divisors of each and choosing the L_____ number which appears in both lists.

> LAST or LARGEST

95. We can also find the GCD of three (or more) numbers in this way.

The exact divisors of 12 are 1, 2, 3, 4, 6, 12.

The exact divisors of 18 are 1, 2, 3, 6, 9, 18.

The exact divisors of 60 are 1, 2, 3, 4, 5, 6, 10, 12, 15, 20, 30, 60.

Since the numbers 1, 2, 3, and 6 appear in all three lists, these numbers are _____ _____ of 12, 18, and 60.

> COMMON DIVISORS

96. 1, 2, 3, and **6** are common divisors of 12, 18, and 60.

The GCD of 12, 18, and 60 is _____ .

> 6

97. For some pairs of numbers, the GCD can be found quite easily. Consider again the numbers 6 and 42.

42 = 6 · 7

Hence 42 is a multiple of 6. But then 6 is an _____ _____ of 42.

> EXACT DIVISOR

98. 6 is an exact divisor of 42.

But 6 = 6 · 1, and so 6 is certainly an exact divisor of 6. Hence 6 is a _____ _____ of 6 and 42.

> COMMON DIVISOR

99. 6 is a common divisor of 6 and 42.

No larger common divisor could be found, since no number larger than 6 is an exact divisor of 6.

Hence, the GCD of 6 and 42 is _____.

> 6

100. Consider the numbers 8 and 32.

$8 = 8 \cdot 1$ and so 8 is an exact divisor of 8.

$32 = 8 \cdot 4$ and so 8 is an exact divisor of 32.

Then 8 is a _____ _____ of 8 and 32.

> COMMON DIVISOR

101. But no exact divisor of 8 can be larger than 8, and so 8 is the _____ of 8 and 32.

> GCD

102. Indeed, whenever one of two numbers is a multiple of the other, their GCD can easily be found. It is merely the _____ of the two numbers.

> SMALLER

103. Find the GCD of

5 and 30 _____

14 and 140 _____

1 and 8 _____

12 and 84 _____

> 5;   14;   1;   12

104. The process we have described for finding the GCD of several numbers can be very tedious. Listing all the divisors of the numbers 210 and 330 would require writing 32 numbers. Let us seek another method of finding the GCD of two numbers.

105. The GCD of 12 and 14 is the L_____ number which is an exact _____ of both 12 and 14.

> LARGEST;   DIVISOR

106. Any number which is an exact divisor of 12 must also be a factor of 12. And any number which is an exact divisor of 14 must also be a factor of 14.

Hence, any number which is an exact divisor of both 12 and 14 must be a _____ of both numbers.

> FACTOR

107. The complete factorizations of 12 and 14 are:

$12 = 1 \cdot 2 \cdot 2 \cdot 3$

$14 = 1 \cdot 2 \cdot 7$

We shall find the complete factorization of their GCD;

Certainly 1 is a factor of both 12 and 14. Another common factor is the number _____.

> 2

108. $12 = 1 \cdot 2 \cdot 2 \cdot 3$

$14 = 1 \cdot 2 \cdot 7$

Let us form the product of the factors common to 12 and 14:

$1 \cdot 2$

Since

$12 = (1 \cdot 2) \cdot (2 \cdot 3),$

$1 \cdot 2$ is a factor, and hence an exact divisor, of 12.

Since

$14 = (1 \cdot 2) \cdot 7,$

$1 \cdot 2$ is a factor, and hence an exact divisor, of 14.

Hence $1 \cdot 2$ is a _____ divisor of 12 and 14.

COMMON .

109. $12 = 1 \cdot 2 \cdot 2 \cdot 3$

$14 = 1 \cdot 2 \cdot 7$

$1 \cdot 2$ is a common divisor of 12 and 14. But no other factors of 12 and 14 are common. Hence no number larger than $1 \cdot 2$ can be a common factor, and so a common divisor, of 12 and 14.

Therefore $1 \cdot 2$ is the _____ of 12 and 14.

GCD

110. $12 = 1 \cdot 2 \cdot 2 \cdot 3$ $14 = 1 \cdot 2 \cdot 7$

The GCD of 12 and 14 has the complete factorization

$1 \cdot 2$

Observe that the complete factorization of the GCD contains the factor 1 and every prime factor which appears in the complete factorization of 12, and at the same time, appears in the complete factorization of 14.

111. $12 = 1 \cdot 2 \cdot 2 \cdot 3$

$14 = 1 \cdot 2 \cdot 7$

The GCD of 12 and 14 has the complete factorization

$1 \cdot 2$

Also note that the prime factor 2 appears two times in 12, only once in 14 and only _____ in the GCD;

ONCE

112. $12 = 1 \cdot 2 \cdot 2 \cdot 3$

$14 = 1 \cdot 2 \cdot 7$

And the GCD of 12 and 14 is, in simplest form,

$1 \cdot 2 =$ _____

2

113. Let us find the GCD of 8 and 20. It will be the largest number which is an exact divisor, and hence a _____, of 8 and also of 20.

FACTOR

114. The complete factorizations of 8 and 20 are

$8 = 1 \cdot 2 \cdot 2 \cdot 2$

$20 = 1 \cdot 2 \cdot 2 \cdot 5$

Note that 1 and 2 are common factors of 8 and 20. But note, too, that $8 = (1 \cdot 2 \cdot 2) \cdot 2$ and $20 = (1 \cdot 2 \cdot 2) \cdot 5.$

Hence

$1 \cdot 2 \cdot 2$

is a common factor, and so a _____ _____ of 8 and 20.

COMMON DIVISOR

115.　　$8 = 1 \cdot 2 \cdot 2 \cdot 2$

　　　$20 = 1 \cdot 2 \cdot 2 \cdot 5$

$1 \cdot 2 \cdot 2$ is a common divisor of 8 and 20. Since no other factors are common to 8 and 20, no larger number can be a common divisor of them.

Hence

　　$1 \cdot 2 \cdot 2$

is the _____ of 8 and 20.

116.　　$8 = 1 \cdot 2 \cdot 2 \cdot 2$

　　　$20 = 1 \cdot 2 \cdot 2 \cdot 5$

The GCD of 8 and 20 has the complete factorization

　　$1 \cdot 2 \cdot 2$

Again, note that the GCD contains 1 and only those prime factors which are in both 8 and 20, and that the repeated prime factor appears in the GCD the lesser number of times it appears in either 8 or 20.

Finally, in simplest form,

　　$1 \cdot 2 \cdot 2 = $ _____

117. These examples suggest a way to find the GCD of two numbers.

Obtain the complete factorizations of the numbers and form a product which includes only 1 and those prime factors found in _____ of the numbers.

118. And if a prime factor is repeated in one or both of the original numbers, in the GCD it appears only as often as in that number which contains the _____ occurrences of that factor.

119. Consider the numbers 24 and 36. Their complete factorizations are

　　$24 = 1 \cdot 2 \cdot 2 \cdot 2 \cdot 3$

　　$36 = 1 \cdot 2 \cdot 2 \cdot 3 \cdot 3$

Then their GCD has the complete factorization

_____ $\cdot$ _____ $\cdot$ _____ $\cdot$ _____

120. The GCD of 24 and 36 is, in simplest form,

　　$1 \cdot 2 \cdot 2 \cdot 3 = $ _____

121. The complete factorizations of 70 and 84 are

　　$70 = 1 \cdot 2 \cdot 5 \cdot 7$

　　$84 = 1 \cdot 2 \cdot 2 \cdot 3 \cdot 7$

Their GCD has the complete factorization:

_____ $\cdot$ _____ $\cdot$ _____

122. The GCD of 70 and 84 is, in simplest form,

　　$1 \cdot 2 \cdot 7 = $ _____

123. Find the complete factorization of the GCD of

$$63 = 1 \cdot 3 \cdot 3 \cdot 7$$

and

$$75 = 1 \cdot 3 \cdot 5 \cdot 5 \underline{\hspace{2cm}}$$

$1 \cdot 3$

124. Find the complete factorization of the GCD of the numbers

$$1 \cdot 2 \cdot 2 \cdot 2 \cdot 3 \cdot 5 \cdot 7 \cdot 7$$
$$1 \cdot 2 \cdot 2 \cdot 3 \cdot 3 \cdot 7 \underline{\hspace{2cm}}$$

$1 \cdot 2 \cdot 2 \cdot 3 \cdot 7$

125. We can also find the GCD of three (or more) numbers in this way.

$$40 = 1 \cdot 2 \cdot 2 \cdot 2 \cdot 5$$
$$52 = 1 \cdot 2 \cdot 2 \cdot 13$$
$$60 = 1 \cdot 2 \cdot 2 \cdot 3 \cdot 5$$

The GCD of 40, 52, and 60 has the complete factorization

$$\underline{\hspace{1.5cm}} \cdot \underline{\hspace{1.5cm}} \cdot \underline{\hspace{1.5cm}}$$

$1 \cdot 2 \cdot 2$

126. Find the complete factorization of the GCD of

$$63 = 1 \cdot 3 \cdot 3 \cdot 7$$
$$147 = 1 \cdot 3 \cdot 7 \cdot 7 \underline{\hspace{2cm}}$$

$1 \cdot 3 \cdot 7$

127. Find the complete factorization of the GCD of

$$108 = 1 \cdot 2 \cdot 2 \cdot 3 \cdot 3 \cdot 3$$

and

$$270 = 1 \cdot 2 \cdot 3 \cdot 3 \cdot 3 \cdot 5 \underline{\hspace{2cm}}$$

$1 \cdot 2 \cdot 3 \cdot 3 \cdot 3$

128. Find the complete factorization of the GCD of

$$100 = 1 \cdot 2 \cdot 2 \cdot 5 \cdot 5$$
$$120 = 1 \cdot 2 \cdot 2 \cdot 2 \cdot 3 \cdot 5$$
$$220 = 1 \cdot 2 \cdot 2 \cdot 5 \cdot 11 \underline{\hspace{2cm}}$$

$1 \cdot 2 \cdot 2 \cdot 5$

129. For two (or more) numbers, the LCM is the smallest of their common $\underline{\hspace{2cm}}$ and the GCD is the largest of their common $\underline{\hspace{2cm}}$.

MULTIPLES;   DIVISORS

130. To find the LCM of two different numbers, we can list the multiples of each and choose the S$\underline{\hspace{2cm}}$ number found in $\underline{\hspace{2cm}}$ lists.

SMALLEST;   BOTH

131. 20, 40, 60, 80, 100, 120, 140, 160, 180, 200, 220, 240, 260, 280, 300,...are multiples of 20.

56, 112, 168, 224, 280, 336,...are multiples of 56.

The LCM of 20 and 56 is $\underline{\hspace{1.5cm}}$.

280

132. And the LCM of two different numbers will never be smaller than the $\underline{\hspace{2cm}}$ of the two numbers.

GREATER

133. To find the GCD of two different numbers, we can list the exact divisors of each and choose the _____ number found in _____ lists.

LARGEST; BOTH

134. The exact divisors of 120 are

1, 2, 3, 4, 5, 6, 8, 10, 12, 15, 20, 24, 30, 40, 60, 120

The exact divisors of 140 are

1, 2, 4, 5, 7, 10, 14, 20, 28, 35, 70, 140

The GCD of 120 and 140 is _____.

20

135. And the GCD of two different numbers will never be larger than the _____ of the two numbers.

SMALLER

136. Both the LCM and the GCD of two numbers can be obtained from the complete factorizations of the two numbers.

In forming the _____, 1 and all prime factors found in either or both of the two numbers are used.

In forming the _____, only 1 and those prime factors found in both of the two numbers are used.

LCM; GCD

137. The complete factorizations of 180 and 2100 are

$$180 = 1 \cdot 2 \cdot 2 \cdot 3 \cdot 3 \cdot 5$$

$$2100 = 1 \cdot 2 \cdot 2 \cdot 3 \cdot 5 \cdot 5 \cdot 7$$

The LCM of 180 and 2100 has the complete factorization _____.

The GCD of 180 and 2100 has the complete factorization _____.

$1 \cdot 2 \cdot 2 \cdot 3 \cdot 3 \cdot 5 \cdot 5 \cdot 7$; $1 \cdot 2 \cdot 2 \cdot 3 \cdot 5$

Problems A (Answers on page 508)

For each pair of numbers below, list the first ten multiples of each number and select the LCM of each pair from the lists.

Example: 6 and 10.

Answer: 6: 6, 12, 18, 24, 30, 36, 42, 48, 56, 60
           10: 10, 20, 30, 40, 50, 60, 70, 80, 90, 100
           LCM: 30

1. 4 and 6

2. 10 and 14

3. 8 and 12

4. 7 and 10

5. 6 and 8

For each pair of numbers below, list all the exact divisors of each number and select the GCD of each pair from the lists.

Example: 20 and 50.

Answer: 20: 1, 2, 4, 5, 10, 20
           50: 1, 2, 5, 10, 25, 50
           GCD: 10

6. 4 and 6

7. 14 and 21

8. 9 and 12

9. 15 and 16

10. 7 and 21

In each of the following, the complete factorizations of a pair of numbers are given. Give the complete factorization of the LCM and of the GCD of each pair.

Example: $1 \cdot 2 \cdot 2 \cdot 3$ and $1 \cdot 2 \cdot 3 \cdot 3 \cdot 7$.

Answer: LCM: $1 \cdot 2 \cdot 2 \cdot 3 \cdot 3 \cdot 7$ and
         GCD: $1 \cdot 2 \cdot 3$

11. $1 \cdot 2 \cdot 3 \cdot 3$ and $1 \cdot 2 \cdot 3 \cdot 5$

12. $1 \cdot 2 \cdot 2 \cdot 2$ and $1 \cdot 2 \cdot 3 \cdot 5$

13. $1 \cdot 2 \cdot 3 \cdot 5 \cdot 5$ and $1 \cdot 3 \cdot 5 \cdot 5$

14. $1 \cdot 2 \cdot 5 \cdot 7$ and $1 \cdot 3 \cdot 3 \cdot 3$

15. $1 \cdot 2 \cdot 2 \cdot 3 \cdot 7$ and $1 \cdot 2 \cdot 3 \cdot 7$

Note that in each pair of numbers below, one number is a multiple of the other. Use this fact to find the LCM and the GCD of each pair.

16. 4 and 12

17. 5 and 25

18. 1 and 11

19. 3 and 36

20. 7 and 56

Write the complete factorization of each number in the following pairs. Use these to find, in simplest form, the LCM and the GCD of each pair of numbers. (The results of problems 11–20 for Chapter 9 will be useful here.)

Example: 100 and 105.

Answer: 100: $1 \cdot 2 \cdot 2 \cdot 5 \cdot 5$
           105: $1 \cdot 3 \cdot 5 \cdot 7$
           LCM: $1 \cdot 2 \cdot 2 \cdot 3 \cdot 5 \cdot 5 \cdot 7 = \underline{2100}$
           GCD: $1 \cdot 5 = \underline{5}$

21. 16 and 36

22. 40 and 44

23. 50 and 54

24. 69 and 100

25. 100 and 260

Problems B

For each pair of numbers below, list the first ten multiples of each number and select the LCM of each pair from the lists.

1. 6 and 9

2. 8 and 10

3. 9 and 12

4. 5 and 7

5. 4 and 16

For each pair of numbers below, list all the exact divisors of each number and select the GCD of each pair from the lists.

6. 6 and 8

7. 10 and 16

8. 12 and 30

9. 13 and 14

10. 8 and 40

In each of the following, the complete factorizations of a pair of numbers are given. Give the complete factorization of the LCM and of the GCD of each pair.

11. $1 \cdot 3 \cdot 5 \cdot 5$ and $1 \cdot 2 \cdot 5 \cdot 7$

12. $1 \cdot 5 \cdot 5 \cdot 7 \cdot 7$ and $1 \cdot 2 \cdot 3 \cdot 5$

13. $1 \cdot 3 \cdot 3 \cdot 3$ and $1 \cdot 3 \cdot 3 \cdot 3 \cdot 11$

14. $1 \cdot 5 \cdot 11 \cdot 13$ and $1 \cdot 2 \cdot 2 \cdot 2 \cdot 3$

15. $1 \cdot 5 \cdot 5 \cdot 11 \cdot 11 \cdot 11$ and $1 \cdot 3 \cdot 5 \cdot 5 \cdot 5 \cdot 5 \cdot 11$

Note that in each pair of numbers below, one number is a multiple of the other. Use this fact to find the LCM and the GCD of each pair.

16. 6 and 54

17. 14 and 42

18. 1 and 100

19. 11 and 121

20. 49 and 294

Write the complete factorization of each number in the following pairs. Use these to find, in simplest form, the LCM and the GCD of each pair of numbers. (The results of problems 11–20 for Chapter 9 will be useful here.)

21. 18 and 32

22. 48 and 72

23. 250 and 360

24. 250 and 1000

25. For each of the problems 21–24, compute the product of the given pair of numbers. In each case, also compute the product of the LCM and the GCD of each pair of numbers. Compare these products. What do you find in each case?

POWERS OF NUMBERS

1. Every natural number can be expressed, in just one way, as a product of the number 1 and of prime factors arranged in order. The product is called the _____ _____ of the number.

> COMPLETE FACTORIZATION

2. The complete factorizations of the first ten composite numbers are

$$4 = 1 \cdot 2 \cdot 2$$
$$6 = 1 \cdot 2 \cdot 3$$
$$8 = 1 \cdot 2 \cdot 2 \cdot 2$$
$$9 = 1 \cdot 3 \cdot 3$$
$$10 = 1 \cdot 2 \cdot 5$$
$$12 = 1 \cdot 2 \cdot 2 \cdot 3$$
$$14 = 1 \cdot 2 \cdot 7$$

_____

_____

_____

> $15 = 1 \cdot 3 \cdot 5;$ $16 = 1 \cdot 2 \cdot 2 \cdot 2 \cdot 2;$
> $18 = 1 \cdot 2 \cdot 3 \cdot 3$

3. Of course, the prime numbers also have complete factorizations. But the complete factorization of each prime contains only _____ factors. The first is the number _____ and the second is the prime number, itself.

> TWO;   1

4. The LCM of a set of natural numbers is the _____ number which is a _____ _____ of the numbers.

> SMALLEST;   COMMON MULTIPLE

5. The LCM of a set of numbers can be determined from their complete factorizations. For the numbers

$$1 \cdot 2 \cdot 2 \cdot 3 \cdot 5 \cdot 5$$
$$1 \cdot 3 \cdot 5 \cdot 5 \cdot 11$$
$$1 \cdot 3 \cdot 3 \cdot 3 \cdot 5$$

the complete factorization of the LCM is _____ .

> $1 \cdot 2 \cdot 2 \cdot 3 \cdot 3 \cdot 3 \cdot 5 \cdot 5 \cdot 11$

6. The GCD of a set of natural numbers is the _____ number which is a _____ _____ of the num-bers.

7. The GCD of a set of numbers, too, can be determined from their complete factoriza-tions. For the numbers

$1 \cdot 2 \cdot 3 \cdot 5 \cdot 5 \cdot 11$

$1 \cdot 2 \cdot 2 \cdot 3 \cdot 3 \cdot 5 \cdot 5 \cdot 11 \cdot 11$

$1 \cdot 2 \cdot 5 \cdot 5 \cdot 5$

the complete factorization of the GCD is _____.

$1 \cdot 2 \cdot 5 \cdot 5$

8. Let us introduce a notation to simplify the writing of certain products.

We shall write $2 \cdot 2 = 2^2$ and note that $2 \cdot 2 = 4$.

We shall write $2 \cdot 2 \cdot 2 = 2^3$ and note that $2 \cdot 2 \cdot 2 = 8$,

We shall write $2 \cdot 2 \cdot 2 \cdot 2 = $ _____ and note that $2 \cdot 2 \cdot 2 \cdot 2 = $ _____.

2^4; 16

9. $2^2 = 2 \cdot 2 = 4$

$2^3 = 2 \cdot 2 \cdot 2 = 8$

$2^4 = 2 \cdot 2 \cdot 2 \cdot 2 = 16$

Similarly,

$2^5 = 2 \cdot 2 \cdot 2 \cdot 2 \cdot 2 = 32$

and

$2^6 = $ _____ $\cdot$ _____ $\cdot$ _____ $\cdot$ _____ $\cdot$ _____ $\cdot$ _____ $=$ _____

$2^6 = 2 \cdot 2 \cdot 2 \cdot 2 \cdot 2 \cdot 2 = 64$

10. We call each of the expressions

2^2, 2^3, 2^4, 2^5, and 2^6

a POWER OF 2.

2^2 is called the SECOND POWER OF 2.

2^3 is called the THIRD POWER OF 2.

And 2^4 is called the _____

_____ _____ _____.

FOURTH POWER OF 2

11. $2^5 = 2 \cdot 2 \cdot 2 \cdot 2 \cdot 2 = 32$ is called the FIFTH POWER OF 2.

In the expression 2^5, we call the number 2 the BASE;

$2^6 = 2 \cdot 2 \cdot 2 \cdot 2 \cdot 2 \cdot 2 = 64$ is called the _____ _____ OF 2.

In the expression 2^6, we call the number 2 the _____.

SIXTH POWER; BASE

12. 2^5 is called the fifth power of 2 and

$2^5 = 2 \cdot 2 \cdot 2 \cdot 2 \cdot 2 = 32$

In the expression 2^5, we call the number 5 the EXPONENT.

2^6 is called the sixth power of 2 and

$2^6 = 2 \cdot 2 \cdot 2 \cdot 2 \cdot 2 \cdot 2 = 64$.

In the expression 2^6, we call the number 6 the _____.

EXPONENT

13. $2^5 = 2 \cdot 2 \cdot 2 \cdot 2 \cdot 2$

Note that the base, 2, is used as a factor the number of times indicated by the exponent, 5.

$2^6 = 2 \cdot 2 \cdot 2 \cdot 2 \cdot 2 \cdot 2$

Again, note that the base, 2, is used as a _____ the number of times indicated by the exponent, 6.

FACTOR

14. We call 2^7 the _____ _____ _____ _____ and

$2^7 = $ _____ $= $ _____,

in simplest form.

SEVENTH POWER OF 2;
$2 \cdot 2 \cdot 2 \cdot 2 \cdot 2 \cdot 2 \cdot 2$; 128

15. $2^7 = 2 \cdot 2 \cdot 2 \cdot 2 \cdot 2 \cdot 2 \cdot 2 = 128$

We call 2^7 a power of 2. 2 is called the _____, and 7 is called the _____.

BASE; EXPONENT

16. $2^7 = 2 \cdot 2 \cdot 2 \cdot 2 \cdot 2 \cdot 2 \cdot 2 = 128$

Note that the base, 2, is used as a factor 7 times, and 7 is the exponent.

Higher powers of 2 are defined in a similar way. In each, the base, 2, is used as a _____ the number of times indicated by the _____.

FACTOR; EXPONENT

17. We shall also define a POWER OF 3.

3^2 is called the SECOND POWER OF 3, and $3^2 = 3 \cdot 3 = 9$

3^3 is called the THIRD POWER OF 3, and $3^3 = 3 \cdot 3 \cdot 3 = 27$

3^4 is called the _____ _____ _____ _____, and

$3^4 = $ _____ $= $ _____,

in simplest form.

FOURTH POWER OF 3; $3 \cdot 3 \cdot 3 \cdot 3$; 81

18. $3^4 = 3 \cdot 3 \cdot 3 \cdot 3 = 81$

In the expression 3^4, we call _____ the base and _____ the exponent.

3; 4

19. $3^4 = 3 \cdot 3 \cdot 3 \cdot 3 = 81$

Note that the base, 3, is used as a factor 4 times, and 4 is the exponent.

Powers of any whole number are defined in a similar way. Thus

$4^3 = $ _____ $\cdot$ _____ $\cdot$ _____ $= $ _____

$5^2 = $ _____ $\cdot$ _____ $= $ _____

$1^6 = $ _____ $\cdot$ _____ $\cdot$ _____ $\cdot$ _____ $\cdot$ _____ $\cdot$ _____ $= $ _____

$4^3 = 4 \cdot 4 \cdot 4 = 64$; $5^2 = 5 \cdot 5 = 25$;
$1^6 = 1 \cdot 1 \cdot 1 \cdot 1 \cdot 1 \cdot 1 = 1$

20. We call 4^3 the third power of 4.

We call 5^2 the _____ _____ _____ _____.

We call 1^6 the _____ _____ _____ _____.

SECOND POWER OF 5;
SIXTH POWER OF 1

21. $4^3 = 4 \cdot 4 \cdot 4 = 64$

Note that the base, 4, is used as a factor 3 times, and 3 is the exponent.

$5^2 = 5 \cdot 5 = 25$

Again, the _____, 5, is used as a _____ 2 times, and 2 is the exponent.

BASE;   FACTOR

22. $1^6 = 1 \cdot 1 \cdot 1 \cdot 1 \cdot 1 \cdot 1 = 1$

The base, 1, is used as a factor _____ times, and 6 is the _____.

6;   EXPONENT

23. $3^5 = $ _____ $\cdot$ _____ $\cdot$ _____ $\cdot$ _____ $\cdot$ _____
    = _____
    $4^2 = $ _____ $\cdot$ _____ = _____
    $0^4 = $ _____ $\cdot$ _____ $\cdot$ _____ $\cdot$ _____
    = _____
    $1^5 = $ _____ $\cdot$ _____ $\cdot$ _____ $\cdot$ _____
    = _____

$3^5 = 3 \cdot 3 \cdot 3 \cdot 3 \cdot 3 = 243$;
$4^2 = 4 \cdot 4 = 16$;
$0^4 = 0 \cdot 0 \cdot 0 \cdot 0 = 0$;
$1^5 = 1 \cdot 1 \cdot 1 \cdot 1 \cdot 1 = 1$

24. $5^3 = $ _____ = _____
    $1^4 = $ _____ = _____
    $6^2 = $ _____ = _____
    $0^3 = $ _____ = _____

$5^3 = 5 \cdot 5 \cdot 5 = 125$;
$1^4 = 1 \cdot 1 \cdot 1 \cdot 1 = 1$
$6^2 = 6 \cdot 6 = 36$;
$0^3 = 0 \cdot 0 \cdot 0 = 0$

25. If a represents any whole number, and if n represents any natural number greater than 1, we call

a^n

the nth _____ of _____.

POWER;   a

26. a^n is called the nth power of a.

We call a the _____ and n the _____.

BASE;   EXPONENT

27. In the expression a^n, the base a is used as a _____ exactly _____ times.

FACTOR;   n

28. a^n has been defined for any base, a, and for an exponent, n, which is a natural number greater than 1. For the sake of completeness, let us also define FIRST POWERS of any number.

0^1 is defined to be 0

1^1 is defined to be 1

2^1 is defined to be _____

3^1 is defined to be _____

2;   3

29. Similarly, we define

$4^1 = 4$

$5^1 =$ _____

$6^1 =$ _____

$7^1 =$ _____

$8^1 =$ _____

5;   6;   7;   8

30. First powers of any whole number are defined in a similar way.

If a represents any whole number,

$a^1 =$ _____

a

31. For any whole number, a, the first power of a, a^1, is simply a itself.

$19^1 =$ _____

$55^1 =$ _____

$107^1 =$ _____

$0^1 =$ _____

19;   55;   107;   0

32. The first power of any whole number is that number itself. For this reason, we shall not usually write an exponent 1. But remember, we can use the exponent 1 if we wish. Hence

$7 = 7^1$

$11 = 11^1$

$13 =$ _____

$17 =$ _____

_____ $= 19^1$

13^1; 17^1;   19

33. Let us use our new notation to simplify writing the complete factorizations of numbers.

$1 = 1$

$2 = 1 \cdot 2$

$3 = 1 \cdot 3$

$4 = 1 \cdot 2 \cdot 2 = 1 \cdot 2^2$

$5 = 1 \cdot 5$

$6 = 1 \cdot 2 \cdot 3$

$7 = 1 \cdot 7$

$8 = 1 \cdot 2 \cdot 2 \cdot 2 = 1 \cdot$ _____

$9 = 1 \cdot 3 \cdot 3 = 1 \cdot$ _____

2^3; 3^2

34. $8 = 1 \cdot 2^3$

$9 = 1 \cdot 3^2$

$10 = 1 \cdot 2 \cdot 5$

$11 = 1 \cdot 11$

$12 = 1 \cdot 2 \cdot 2 \cdot 3 = 1 \cdot 2^2 \cdot 3$

$13 = 1 \cdot 13$

$14 = 1 \cdot 2 \cdot 7$

$15 = 1 \cdot 3 \cdot 5$

$16 = 1 \cdot 2 \cdot 2 \cdot 2 \cdot 2 = 1 \cdot$ _____

$17 = 1 \cdot 17$

$18 = 1 \cdot 2 \cdot 3 \cdot 3 =$ _____

2^4; $1 \cdot 2 \cdot 3^2$

35. $19 = 1 \cdot 19$

$20 = 1 \cdot 2 \cdot 2 \cdot 5 = 1 \cdot 2^2 \cdot 5$

$21 = 1 \cdot 3 \cdot 7$

$22 = 1 \cdot 2 \cdot 11$

$23 = 1 \cdot 23$

$24 = 1 \cdot 2 \cdot 2 \cdot 2 \cdot 3 =$ _____

$25 = 1 \cdot 5 \cdot 5 =$ _____

$1 \cdot 2^3 \cdot 3$; $1 \cdot 5^2$

36. Remember that every number can be considered as a first power of itself. Then we can say that the complete factorization of a natural number expresses the number as a product whose first factor is 1 and whole remaining factors are powers of _____ numbers, in order.

PRIME

37. The complete factorizations of 45 and 150 are

$$45 = 1 \cdot 3 \cdot 3 \cdot 5$$
$$150 = 1 \cdot 2 \cdot 3 \cdot 5 \cdot 5$$

The LCM of 45 and 150 can be found as the product of 1 and all prime factors found in either 45 or 150 or both. Repeated prime factors are used only as often as they occur in the number with the _____ number of occurrences.

GREATER

38. $$45 = 1 \cdot 3 \cdot 3 \cdot 5$$
$$150 = 1 \cdot 2 \cdot 3 \cdot 5 \cdot 5$$

The complete factorization of the LCM of 45 and 150 is _____.

$1 \cdot 2 \cdot 3 \cdot 3 \cdot 5 \cdot 5$

39. Let us use the power notation and restate these results;

$$45 = 1 \cdot 3^2 \cdot 5$$
$$150 = 1 \cdot 2 \cdot 3 \cdot 5^2$$

The LCM of 45 and 150 can be written _____.

$1 \cdot 2 \cdot 3^2 \cdot 5^2$ (See Frame 38)

40. $$45 = 1 \cdot 3^2 \cdot 5$$
$$150 = 1 \cdot 2 \cdot 3 \cdot 5^2$$

The LCM of 45 and 150 is $1 \cdot 2 \cdot 3^2 \cdot 5^2$.

Note that the LCM contains 1 and every prime factor in either 45 or 150 or both. And, in the LCM, the power of any prime factor is the G_____ power of that prime factor which appears in 45 or 150.

GREATER

41. The complete factorizations of 245 and 525 are

$$245 = 1 \cdot 5 \cdot 7 \cdot 7$$
$$525 = 1 \cdot 3 \cdot 5 \cdot 5 \cdot 7$$

The LCM of 245 and 525 has the complete factorization _____.

$1 \cdot 3 \cdot 5 \cdot 5 \cdot 7 \cdot 7$

42. Again, using the power notation,

$$245 = 1 \cdot 5 \cdot 7^2$$
$$525 = 1 \cdot 3 \cdot 5^2 \cdot 7$$

and the LCM of 245 and 525 has the complete factorization _____.

$1 \cdot 3 \cdot 5^2 \cdot 7^2$

43. $$245 = 1 \cdot 5 \cdot 7^2$$
$$525 = 1 \cdot 3 \cdot 5^2 \cdot 7$$

The LCM of 245 and 525 can be written

$1 \cdot 3 \cdot 5^2 \cdot 7^2$

Note that the LCM contains 1 and all prime factors found in either 245 or 525 or both, and, for prime factors, the LCM contains exactly the G_____ power found in either number.

GREATER

44. Consider the numbers whose complete factorizations are

$$1 \cdot 3^3 \cdot 5^2$$

$$1 \cdot 3 \cdot 5^4 \cdot 11$$

The complete factorization of the LCM of these numbers is

_____ · _____ · _____ · _____

$$1 \cdot 3^3 \cdot 5^4 \cdot 11$$

45. The LCM of three (or more) numbers can be found in a similar way.

$$8 = 1 \cdot 2^3$$

$$20 = 1 \cdot 2^2 \cdot 5$$

$$42 = 1 \cdot 2 \cdot 3 \cdot 7$$

The complete factorization of the LCM of 8, 20, and 42 is _____.

$$1 \cdot 2^3 \cdot 3 \cdot 5 \cdot 7$$

46. $$8 = 1 \cdot 2^3$$

$$20 = 1 \cdot 2^2 \cdot 5$$

$$42 = 1 \cdot 2 \cdot 3 \cdot 7$$

Their LCM can be written $1 \cdot 2^3 \cdot 3 \cdot 5 \cdot 7$.

Again, 1 and _____ prime factor in any of the original numbers is a factor of the LCM. And in the LCM, the power of any prime factor is the G _____ power of that factor in any of the numbers.

EVERY;   GREATEST

47. Find the complete factorization of the LCM of the following numbers:

$$1 \cdot 2^4 \cdot 5 \cdot 11$$

$$1 \cdot 2 \cdot 3^2 \cdot 11$$

$$1 \cdot 3^3 \cdot 5^2 \cdot 17 \quad \text{_____}$$

$$1 \cdot 2^4 \cdot 3^3 \cdot 5^2 \cdot 11 \cdot 17$$

48. The complete factorizations of 60 and 72 are

$$60 = 1 \cdot 2 \cdot 2 \cdot 3 \cdot 5$$

$$72 = 1 \cdot 2 \cdot 2 \cdot 2 \cdot 3 \cdot 3$$

The GCD of 60 and 72 can be formed as the product of 1 and only those prime factors found in both 60 and 72. Repeated prime factors are used only as often as they occur in the number with the F _____ occurrences.

FEWER

49. $$60 = 1 \cdot 2 \cdot 2 \cdot 3 \cdot 5$$

$$72 = 1 \cdot 2 \cdot 2 \cdot 2 \cdot 3 \cdot 3$$

The complete factorization of the GCD of 60 and 72 is _____.

$$1 \cdot 2 \cdot 2 \cdot 3$$

50. Again, let us use the power notation and restate these results.

$$60 = 1 \cdot 2^2 \cdot 3 \cdot 5$$

$$72 = 1 \cdot 2^3 \cdot 3^2$$

The GCD of 60 and 72 can be written _____.

$$1 \cdot 2^2 \cdot 3 \quad \text{(See Frame 49)}$$

51. $$60 = 1 \cdot 2^2 \cdot 3 \cdot 5$$

$$72 = 1 \cdot 2^3 \cdot 3^2$$

The GCD of 60 and 72 is $1 \cdot 2^2 \cdot 3$.

Note that the GCD contains 1 and only those prime factors in both 60 and 72, and that, in it, powers of all prime factors equal the S _____ power of each such factor which appears.

SMALLER

52. The complete factorizations of 425 and 2475 are

$$425 = 1 \cdot 3 \cdot 5 \cdot 5 \cdot 7$$

$$2475 = 1 \cdot 3 \cdot 3 \cdot 5 \cdot 5 \cdot 11$$

The GCD of 425 and 2475 has the complete factorization _____ .

$$1 \cdot 3 \cdot 5 \cdot 5$$

53. Again, using the power notation,

$$425 = 1 \cdot 3 \cdot 5^2 \cdot 7$$

$$2475 = 1 \cdot 3^2 \cdot 5^2 \cdot 11$$

and the GCD of 425 and 2475 has the complete factorization _____ .

$$1 \cdot 3 \cdot 5^2$$

54. $$425 = 1 \cdot 3 \cdot 5^2 \cdot 7$$

$$2475 = 1 \cdot 3^2 \cdot 5^2 \cdot 11$$

The GCD of 425 and 2475 can be written $1 \cdot 3 \cdot 5^2$

Note that the GCD contains 1 and only those prime factors found in both 425 and 2475, and, for prime factors, it contains only the S_____ power found in either number.

SMALLER

55. Consider the numbers whose complete factorizations are

$$1 \cdot 2^3 \cdot 5^3 \cdot 7$$

$$1 \cdot 2^5 \cdot 5^2 \cdot 7^2 \cdot 13$$

The complete factorization of the GCD of these numbers is

_____ . _____ . _____ . _____ .

$$1 \cdot 2^3 \cdot 5^2 \cdot 7$$

56. The GCD of three (or more) numbers can be found in a similar way.

$$12 = 1 \cdot 2^2 \cdot 3$$

$$20 = 1 \cdot 2^2 \cdot 5$$

$$36 = 1 \cdot 2^2 \cdot 3^2$$

$$40 = 1 \cdot 2^3 \cdot 5$$

The complete factorization of the GCD of 12, 20, 36, and 40 is _____ .

$$1 \cdot 2^2$$

57. $$12 = 1 \cdot 2^2 \cdot 3$$

$$20 = 1 \cdot 2^2 \cdot 5$$

$$36 = 1 \cdot 2^2 \cdot 3^2$$

$$40 = 1 \cdot 2^3 \cdot 5$$

The GCD of these numbers can be written $1 \cdot 2^2$.

Note that 1 and only those prime factors found in _____ of the original numbers are factors of the GCD, and in the GCD, the power of any prime factor is the S_____ power of that factor found in any of the numbers.

ALL;   SMALLEST

58. Find the complete factorization of the GCD of the following numbers:

$$1 \cdot 3^3 \cdot 5 \cdot 7$$

$$1 \cdot 2^3 \cdot 3^2 \cdot 7$$

$$1 \cdot 2 \cdot 3^2 \cdot 7^4 \cdot 13$$ _____

$$1 \cdot 3^2 \cdot 7$$

59. $$11 = 1 \cdot 11$$

$$19 = 1 \cdot 19$$

The GCD of 11 and 19 is _____ .

1

60. $13 = 1 \cdot 13$

    $24 = 1 \cdot 2^3 \cdot 3$

    The GCD of 13 and 24 is _____ .

    1

61. $15 = 1 \cdot 3 \cdot 5$

    $28 = 1 \cdot 2^2 \cdot 7$

    The GCD of 15 and 28 is _____ .

    1

62. The GCD of 11 and 19 is 1.

    The GCD of 13 and 24 is 1.

    The GCD of 15 and 28 is 1.

    Whenever two numbers have 1 as their greatest common divisor, they are said to be RELATIVELY PRIME.

    The GCD of 11 and 19 is 1. Hence 11 and 19 are _____ _____ .

    RELATIVELY PRIME

63. Note that 11 and 19 are relatively prime and that 11 and 19 are both _____ natural numbers.

    PRIME

64. The GCD of 13 and 24 is 1. Hence 13 and 24 are _____ _____ .

    RELATIVELY PRIME

65. Note that 13 and 24 are relatively prime, but that 13 is a _____ number, whereas 24 is a _____ number.

    PRIME;   COMPOSITE

66. And 15 and 28 are relatively prime since their _____ is 1.

    Yet both 15 and 28 are _____ numbers.

    GCD;   COMPOSITE

67. To state that two numbers are relatively prime means that their GCD is 1. The numbers can be primes or composites.

    Which of the following pairs of numbers are relatively prime ?

    a) 4 and 10

    b) 1 and 12

    c) 2 and 9

    d) 16 and 25 _____

    b, c, and d

68. Recall that if

    $c = ab$

    a is an exact divisor of c. But then a is also a _____ of c.

    FACTOR

69. The exact divisors of 70 are, in order,

    1, 2, 5, 7, 10, 14, 35, 70

    Then each of these numbers is also a _____ of 70.

    FACTOR

70. The exact divisors of 84 are, in order,

1, 2, 3, 4, 6, 7, 12, 14, 21, 28, 42, 84

and so each of these numbers is also a
_____ of 84.

71. The numbers 1, 2, 7, and 14 are common divisors of 70 and 84. But each is also a factor of 70 and also of 84. We shall say, then, that 1, 2, 7, and 14 are COMMON FACTORS of _____ and _____ .

72. Indeed, every common divisor of two (or more) numbers is also a _____ _____ of those numbers.

73. 1, 2, 7, and 14 are common factors of 70 and 84, as well as common divisors of these numbers.

And the HIGHEST COMMON FACTOR of 70 and 84 is _____ .

74. The highest common factor of 70 and 84 is 14.

Since 14 is also the largest of their common divisors, 14 is the _____ of 70 and 84.

75. In fact, since every common divisor of two or more numbers is also a common factor of those numbers, their greatest common divisor is also their highest _____ .

76. We use the letters HCF to represent "highest common factor." For any numbers, the HCF is equal to the _____ .

77. Finally, the numbers whose complete factorizations are

$1 \cdot 2^5 \cdot 3^2 \cdot 5$

$1 \cdot 2 \cdot 3^3 \cdot 5 \cdot 7^2$

have an LCM whose complete factorization is _____ , and a GCD whose complete factorization is _____ .

78. $0^2 = 0 \cdot 0 = 0$

$1^2 = 1 \cdot 1 = 1$

$2^2 = 2 \cdot 2 = 4$

$3^2 = 3 \cdot 3 = $ _____

$4^2 = 4 \cdot 4 = $ _____

$5^2 = 5 \cdot 5 = $ _____

$6^2 = 6 \cdot 6 = $ _____

79. The expression 2^2 is called the second power of 2. It will also be called the SQUARE OF 2.

The expression 3^2 is called the _____ power _____ . It will also be called the _____ _____ _____ .

SECOND;   OF 3;   SQUARE OF 3

80. Similarly 5^2 is sometimes called the square of 5, and 8^2 can be called the _____ of 8.

And

$8^2 = $ _____ · _____ = _____

in simplest form.

SQUARE; $8^2 = 8 \cdot 8 = 64$

81. The square of 7 is $7^2 = 7 \cdot 7 = 49$.

The square of 9 is _____ = _____ · _____ = _____ , in simplest form.

$9^2 = 9 \cdot 9 = 81$

82. Every whole number, then, has a square. The square of a number is merely the _____ power of that number.

SECOND

83. $0^3 = 0 \cdot 0 \cdot 0 = 0$
        $1^3 = 1 \cdot 1 \cdot 1 = 1$
        $2^3 = 2 \cdot 2 \cdot 2 = $ _____
        $3^3 = 3 \cdot 3 \cdot 3 = $ _____
        $4^3 = 4 \cdot 4 \cdot 4 = $ _____
        $5^3 = 5 \cdot 5 \cdot 5 = $ _____

8;   27;   64;   125

84. The expression 2^3 is called the third power of 2. It will also be called the CUBE OF 2.

The expression 3^3 is called the _____ power _____ . It will also be called the _____ _____ _____ .

THIRD;   OF 3;   CUBE OF 3

85. Similarly, 5^3 is sometimes called the cube of 5, and 6^3 can be called the _____ of 6.

And

$6^3 = $ _____ · _____ · _____ = _____

in simplest form.

CUBE; $6^3 = 6 \cdot 6 \cdot 6 = 216$

86. The cube of 7 is $7^3 = 7 \cdot 7 \cdot 7 = 343$.

The cube of 8 is _____ = _____ · _____ · _____ = _____ , in simplest form.

$8^3 = 8 \cdot 8 \cdot 8 = 512$

87. Every whole number has a cube. The cube of a number is merely the _____ _____ of that number.

THIRD POWER

88. There are no special names for other powers of numbers.

Two numbers have rather uninteresting powers.

$0^1 = 0$

$0^2 = 0 \cdot 0 = 0$

$0^3 = 0 \cdot 0 \cdot 0 = 0$

$0^4 = 0 \cdot 0 \cdot 0 \cdot 0 = $ _____

$0^5 = 0 \cdot 0 \cdot 0 \cdot 0 \cdot 0 = $ _____

0;   0

89. Every power of the number 0 is equal to _____.

Also.

$1^1 = 1$

$1^2 = 1 \cdot 1 = 1$

$1^3 = 1 \cdot 1 \cdot 1 = 1$

$1^4 = 1 \cdot 1 \cdot 1 \cdot 1 = $ _____

$1^5 = 1 \cdot 1 \cdot 1 \cdot 1 \cdot 1 = $ _____

0;   1;   1

90. And every power of the number 1 is equal to _____.

1

91. Find

$1^{17} = $ _____

$0^{55} = $ _____

$0^{100} = $ _____

$17^1 = $ _____

1;   0;   0;   17

92. Find

$1^{22} = $ _____

$0^{101} = $ _____

$1^{99} = $ _____

$3^3 = $ _____

1;   0;   1;   27

93. Find

$2 \cdot 3^3 \quad = $ _____

$(2 \cdot 3)^3 = $ _____

$(2 + 3)^3 = $ _____

$2 + 3^3 \quad = $ _____

54;   216;   125;   29   (Go on to the next frame.)

94. As the last few examples indicate, the problem of finding the value of an expression involving several numbers and operations must be approached carefully.

Let us establish a convention regarding the order in which the various operations will be performed.

95. We have already agreed that when a problem involves only the operation of addition, the numbers can be added in any order.

Thus

$6 + 4 + 9 + 13 = 32$

$5 + 7 + 4 + 2 + 11 = $ _____

$6 + 8 + 23 + 40 = $ _____

29;   77

96. We have also agreed that when a problem involves only the operation of multiplication, the numbers can be multiplied in any order.

Thus

$$4 \cdot 3 \cdot 2 \cdot 5 \cdot 7 = 840$$

$$5 \cdot 5 \cdot 6 \cdot 2 \cdot 3 = \underline{\hphantom{XXX}}$$

$$7 \cdot 2 \cdot 5 \cdot 7 \cdot 1 = \underline{\hphantom{XXX}}$$

900;   490

97. When a problem involves both addition and multiplication, we have agreed that, unless there are parentheses to indicate a departure from the normal order, all multiplications will be performed before any additions.

Thus

$$4 \cdot 3 + 5 \cdot 5 = 12 + 25 = 37$$

$$6 \cdot 6 + 1 \cdot 7 + 2 \cdot 2 \cdot 3 = 36 + 7 + 12 = \underline{\hphantom{XXX}}$$

$$4 \cdot 4 \cdot 4 + 2 \cdot 2 \cdot 2 \cdot 2 \cdot 2 + 7 \cdot 5 = \underline{\hphantom{XXX}}$$
$$+ \underline{\hphantom{XXX}} + \underline{\hphantom{XXX}} = \underline{\hphantom{XXX}}$$

55;   64;   32;   35;   131

98. The expressions

$$12 - 4 - 3$$

$$15 + 7 - 2$$

$$20 - 5 + 18$$

have no meaning at present, for there are no symbols to indicate which operation is to be performed first, and we have established no convention regarding the procedure to be followed.

99. When a problem involves more than two numbers and only the operation of subtraction, or addition and subtraction, let us agree to proceed from left to right, two numbers at a time, unless grouping symbols indicate otherwise.

Thus

$$12 - 4 - 3 = 8 - 3 = 5$$

$$15 + 7 - 2 = \underline{\hphantom{XXX}} - 2 = \underline{\hphantom{XXX}}$$

$$20 - 5 + 18 = \underline{\hphantom{XXX}} + \underline{\hphantom{XXX}} = \underline{\hphantom{XXX}}$$

22;   20;   15;   18;   33

100. Find

$$6 + 9 + 20 - 13 - 2 = \underline{\hphantom{XXX}}$$

$$34 + 5 - 25 - 6 + 2 = \underline{\hphantom{XXX}}$$

$$1 + 1 + 19 - 10 - 4 = \underline{\hphantom{XXX}}$$

$$35 - 2 - 3 - 6 - 4 = \underline{\hphantom{XXX}}$$

$$6 + 9 + 20 - 13 - 2 = 15 + 20 - 13 - 2$$
$$= 35 - 13 - 2 = 22 - 2 = 20$$
$$34 + 5 - 25 - 6 + 2 = 39 - 25 - 6 + 2$$
$$= 14 - 6 + 2 = 8 + 2 = 10$$
$$1 + 1 + 19 - 10 - 4 = 2 + 19 - 10 - 4$$
$$= 21 - 10 - 4 = 11 - 4 = 7$$
$$35 - 2 - 3 - 6 - 4 = 33 - 3 - 6 - 4$$
$$= 30 - 6 - 4 = 24 - 4 = 20$$

101. When a problem involves more than two numbers, and only the operations of multiplication and division, let us agree to perform all <u>divisions first</u>, unless grouping symbols indicate otherwise.

Thus

$$6 \cdot 2 \cdot \frac{15}{3} = 6 \cdot 2 \cdot 5 = 60$$

$$\frac{14}{2} \cdot 7 \cdot 3 = 7 \cdot 7 \cdot 3 = \underline{\hphantom{XXX}}$$

$$5 \cdot \frac{84}{4} \cdot 6 = \underline{\hphantom{XXX}} \cdot \underline{\hphantom{XXX}} \cdot \underline{\hphantom{XXX}}$$
$$= \underline{\hphantom{XXX}}$$

147;   5;   21;   6;   630

102. Find

$$\frac{12}{4} \cdot 3 \cdot 2 = \underline{\hspace{2cm}}$$

$$4 \cdot \frac{27}{3} \cdot 5 = \underline{\hspace{2cm}}$$

$$\frac{16}{2} \cdot \frac{70}{5} = \underline{\hspace{2cm}}$$

$$2 \cdot 3 \cdot 4 \cdot \frac{20}{4} = \underline{\hspace{2cm}}$$

$$\frac{12}{4} \cdot 3 \cdot 2 = 3 \cdot 3 \cdot 2 = \underline{18}$$

$$4 \cdot \frac{27}{3} \cdot 5 = 4 \cdot 9 \cdot 5 = \underline{180}$$

$$\frac{16}{2} \cdot \frac{70}{5} = 8 \cdot 14 = \underline{112}$$

$$2 \cdot 3 \cdot 4 \cdot \frac{20}{4} = 2 \cdot 3 \cdot 4 \cdot 5 = \underline{120}$$

103. But let us agree that when a problem involves additions or subtractions and also multiplications or divisions, and there are no grouping symbols to indicate otherwise, all divisions, and then all multiplications, will be performed first.

Thus

$$6 + 2 \cdot 3 + \frac{24}{6} = 6 + 2 \cdot 3 + 4 = 6 + 6 + 4 = 16$$

$$\frac{30}{6} + 9 + 2 \cdot 3 = 5 + 9 + 2 \cdot 3 = 5 + 9 +$$

$$\underline{\hspace{1.5cm}} = \underline{\hspace{1.5cm}}$$

$$7 \cdot 2 + \frac{26}{2} + 3 \cdot 8 = 7 \cdot 2 + 13 + 3 \cdot 8$$

$$= \underline{\hspace{1.5cm}} + 13 + \underline{\hspace{1.5cm}} = \underline{\hspace{1.5cm}}$$

6;   20;   14;   24;   51

104. Find

$$6 + 2 \cdot 9 + 5 \cdot 7 - 4 = \underline{\hspace{2cm}}$$

$$\frac{12}{3} + \frac{38}{2} - \frac{24}{6} = \underline{\hspace{2cm}}$$

$$5 \cdot 8 \cdot 7 - 2 \cdot 3 \cdot 4 = \underline{\hspace{2cm}}$$

$$1 + 2 \cdot 3 - \frac{6}{3} + 8 = \underline{\hspace{2cm}}$$

$$6 + 2 \cdot 9 + 5 \cdot 7 - 4 = 6 + 18 + 35 - 4 = \underline{55}$$

$$\frac{12}{3} + \frac{38}{2} - \frac{24}{6} = 4 + 19 - 4 = \underline{19}$$

$$5 \cdot 8 \cdot 7 - 2 \cdot 3 \cdot 4 = 280 - 24 = \underline{256}$$

$$1 + 2 \cdot 3 - \frac{6}{3} + 8 = 1 + 2 \cdot 3 - 2 + 8 =$$

$$1 + 6 - 2 + 8 = \underline{13}$$

105. When there are no symbols to indicate otherwise, let us find the powers of all numbers before performing any of the operations of addition, subtraction, multiplication, or division.

Thus

$$4^3 \cdot 5^2 = 64 \cdot 25 = 1600$$

$$3^4 + 6^2 = 81 + 36 = 117$$

$$5 \cdot 2^4 = \underline{\hspace{1cm}} \cdot \underline{\hspace{1cm}} = \underline{\hspace{1.5cm}}$$

$$7^2 - 3^3 = \underline{\hspace{1cm}} - \underline{\hspace{1cm}} = \underline{\hspace{1cm}}$$

$$5 \cdot 2^4 = \underline{5} \cdot \underline{16} = \underline{80}; \quad 7^2 - 3^3 = \underline{49} - \underline{27} = \underline{22}$$

106. Find

$$8^3 / 2^4 = \underline{\hspace{2cm}}$$

$$5^2 + 5^3 = \underline{\hspace{2cm}}$$

$$16^2 + 3 = \underline{\hspace{2cm}}$$

$$120 - 8^2 = \underline{\hspace{2cm}}$$

$$\frac{8^3}{2^4} = \frac{512}{16} = \underline{32}$$

$$5^2 + 5^3 = 25 + 125 = \underline{150}$$

$$16^2 + 3 = 256 + 3 = \underline{259}$$

$$120 - 8^2 = 120 - 64 = \underline{56}$$

107. Of course, the appearance of parentheses in a problem may change the order in which operations are performed. The parentheses indicate that the operations within are to be performed _____ .

108. Thus $2 \cdot 3^3 = 2 \cdot 27 = 54$

 but $(2 \cdot 3)^3 = (6)^3 = 216$

 and $2 + 3^3 = 2 + 27 = 29$

 while $(2 + 3)^3 = (5)^3 = 125$

 Find $2 + 3^2 \cdot 5 = 2 + 9 \cdot 5 = 2 +$ _____

 = _____

 $(2 + 3)^2 \cdot 5 = (5)^2 \cdot 5 =$ _____ $\cdot 5$

 = _____

109. Find

 $(6 + 3)^2$ = _____

 $6^2 + 3^2$ = _____

 $6 + 3^2$ = _____

 $(6 \cdot 3)^2$ = _____

110. $4^2 + 8 \cdot 2 =$ _____

 $(4 + 8)^2 \cdot 2 =$ _____

 $16 \cdot (3^2 + 2) =$ _____

 $(4^2 - 3^2)5 =$ _____

111. There is another grouping symbol which is used to indicate "first." This is the horizontal BAR written above, or below, an expression. Thus $(4 + 3) \cdot 8$ can also be written:

$$\overline{4 + 3} \cdot 8 = 7 \cdot 8 = 56$$

or

$$\underline{4 + 3} \cdot 8 = 7 \cdot 8 = 56$$

We shall not use this symbol except in division problems where the bar is also used as a _____ symbol.

112. Hence in $\dfrac{6 + 4}{2}$ the bar has two meanings. First, it groups the $(6 + 4)$; it instructs us to first add 6 and 4. Second, it is a division symbol; it tells us to divide $(6 + 4)$ by 2.

 Hence

$$\frac{6 + 4}{2} = \frac{10}{2} = 5.$$

 Similarly

$$\frac{84}{5 + 9} = \frac{84}{} = \underline{}.$$

113. Find

$$\frac{4 \cdot 2 \cdot 3}{6} = \text{_____}$$

$$\frac{12 + 20}{6 - 2} = \text{_____}$$

$$\frac{2^2 + 3^2}{13} = \text{_____}$$

$$\frac{14 + 10}{2 \cdot 4} = \text{_____}$$

$$\frac{4 \cdot 2 \cdot 3}{6} = \frac{24}{6} = \underline{4}$$

$$\frac{12 + 20}{6 - 2} = \frac{32}{4} = \underline{8}$$

$$\frac{2^2 + 3^2}{13} = \frac{4 + 9}{13} = \frac{13}{13} = \underline{1}$$

$$\frac{14 + 10}{2 \cdot 4} = \frac{24}{8} = \underline{3}$$

114. Find

$$12 + \frac{5 + 9}{2} - 2 = \text{_____}$$

$$16 - (8 - 4 + 1) = \text{_____}$$

$$14 + (3^2 + 1) = \text{_____}$$

$$\frac{(2 + 5)^2 + 1}{2} = \text{_____}$$

$$12 + \frac{5 + 9}{2} - 2 = 12 + \frac{14}{2} - 2 = 12 + 7 - 2$$
$$= \underline{17}$$

$$16 - (8 - 4 + 1) = 16 - (5) = \underline{11}$$
$$14 + (3^2 + 1) = 14 + (9 + 1) = 14 + (10) = \underline{24}$$
$$\frac{(2 + 5)^2 + 1}{2} = \frac{(7)^2 + 1}{2} = \frac{49 + 1}{2} = \frac{50}{2} = \underline{25}$$

115. Find

$$21 - 2 \cdot 3 + 4 = \text{_____}$$

$$3^2 + 4^2 - 5^2 = \text{_____}$$

$$3 \cdot (7 + 2) - 2 \cdot (7 - 2) = \text{_____}$$

$$13 - \frac{2 + 16}{3} + 5^2 = \text{_____}$$

$$21 - 2 \cdot 3 + 4 = 21 - 6 + 4 = \underline{19}$$
$$3^2 + 4^2 - 5^2 = 9 + 16 - 25 = \underline{0}$$
$$3 \cdot (7 + 2) - 2(7 - 2) = 3 \cdot (9) - 2 \cdot (5)$$
$$= 27 - 10 = \underline{17}$$
$$13 - \frac{2 + 16}{3} + 5^2 = 13 - \frac{18}{3} + 5^2$$
$$= 13 - \frac{18}{3} + 25 = 13 - 6 + 25 = \underline{32}$$

116. Let us summarize the rules concerning order of performing operations:

1) First perform all operations set off by grouping symbols.
2) Next find all indicated powers of numbers.
3) Then perform all divisions called for.
4) Perform all multiplications indicated.
5) Finally, moving from left to right, perform any remaining additions or subtractions.

Chapter 11

Problems A (Answers on page 509)

Write each of the following as a product without exponents. Do not compute any products.

1. 2^4

2. $2 \cdot 3^3$

3. $2^2 \cdot 3^3 \cdot 5^1$

4. $3^4 \cdot 5^3 \cdot 7$

5. $2^2 \cdot 3^3 \cdot 5^4 \cdot 7^5$

Use exponents to simplify the writing of each of the following products. Do not compute any products.

6. $2 \cdot 2 \cdot 2 \cdot 3 \cdot 3$

7. $2 \cdot 3 \cdot 3 \cdot 3 \cdot 3 \cdot 5 \cdot 5$

8. $3 \cdot 3 \cdot 5 \cdot 5 \cdot 5 \cdot 7 \cdot 11 \cdot 11 \cdot 11 \cdot 11$

9. $2 \cdot 2 \cdot 3 \cdot 3 \cdot 5 \cdot 5 \cdot 7 \cdot 7 \cdot 7 \cdot 11$

10. $5 \cdot 5 \cdot 5 \cdot 11 \cdot 11 \cdot 13 \cdot 17 \cdot 17 \cdot 17 \cdot 17$

Find the simplest form of each of the following natural numbers.

11. 3^4

12. $2 \cdot 3^2 \cdot 5$

13. $3^3 \cdot 5^2$

14. $2 \cdot 3 \cdot 5^3 \cdot 7$

15. $2^2 \cdot 3^3 \cdot 5^2 \cdot 11$

Find the complete factorization of each of the following. Use exponents whenever a factor is repeated. (The results of problems 11–20 for Chapter 9 will be useful here.)

16. 16

17. 36

18. 40

19. 44

20. 50

21. 54

22. 69

23. 100

24. 260

25. 23,100

For each of the following lists of numbers, give the complete factorization of their LCM and of their GCD. Use exponents whenever a factor is repeated.

26. $1 \cdot 2^3 \cdot 3$ and $1 \cdot 2^2 \cdot 3^2$

27. $1 \cdot 2 \cdot 3^3 \cdot 5$ and $1 \cdot 3^2 \cdot 5^2$

28. $1 \cdot 5^2 \cdot 7^3$ and $1 \cdot 5 \cdot 7^2$

29. $1 \cdot 2^2 \cdot 3 \cdot 5^2$, $1 \cdot 2 \cdot 3^2 \cdot 5 \cdot 7$ and $1 \cdot 2^3 \cdot 3 \cdot 7^2$

30. $1 \cdot 2^2 \cdot 3 \cdot 7$, $1 \cdot 2 \cdot 5 \cdot 7^2$ and $1 \cdot 3^2 \cdot 5$

List, in order, all the natural numbers less than 15 which are relatively prime to each of the following.

Example: 28. Answer: $28 = 1 \cdot 2^2 \cdot 7$
$$\underline{1, \ 3, \ 5, \ 9, \ 11, \ 13}$$

31. 8

32. 9

33. 12

34. 15

35. 42

Find the simplest form of each of the following. Be sure to perform operations in the correct order.

36. $36 - 4 \cdot 5 + 2$

37. $125 - 14/2 + 2 \cdot 3$

38. $2 \cdot 5^2 - 4$

39. $(3^2 - 2^3) \cdot 5 - 10/2$

40. $38 - 6^2 + (12 - 8)^3$

41. $4 \cdot 9 + 3 \cdot 9 - 7 \cdot 8 - 2 \cdot 0$

42. $175/5 - 81/27 + 6/6$

43. $1 + 5^2 \cdot 6$

44. $(1 + 5)^2 \cdot 6$

45. $(1 + 5^2) \cdot 6$

Problems B

Write each of the following as a product without exponents. Do not compute any products.

1. 3^5

2. $5^2 \cdot 7^3 \cdot 11$

3. $2^3 \cdot 5^3 \cdot 17$

4. $2^2 \cdot 5^3 \cdot 11^4 \cdot 13^5$

5. $2 \cdot 3 \cdot 5^3 \cdot 11^2 \cdot 13^1$

Use exponents to simplify the writing of each of the following products. Do not compute any products.

6. $2 \cdot 2 \cdot 3 \cdot 3 \cdot 3 \cdot 5 \cdot 5 \cdot 7 \cdot 7 \cdot 7$

7. $2 \cdot 3 \cdot 3 \cdot 5 \cdot 5 \cdot 5 \cdot 7 \cdot 7 \cdot 7 \cdot 7 \cdot 11 \cdot 11$

8. $3 \cdot 3 \cdot 3 \cdot 3 \cdot 3 \cdot 3 \cdot 5 \cdot 5 \cdot 5$

9. $2 \cdot 3 \cdot 5 \cdot 7 \cdot 5 \cdot 7 \cdot 5 \cdot 7 \cdot 3$

10. $2 \cdot 3 \cdot 2 \cdot 3 \cdot 2 \cdot 5 \cdot 2 \cdot 7 \cdot 2 \cdot 7$

Find the simplest form of each of the following natural numbers.

11. 5^4

12. $3^2 \cdot 5^2$

13. $2^2 \cdot 3^4 \cdot 5^2$

14. $2 \cdot 5^3 \cdot 7 \cdot 11$

15. $2^2 \cdot 3^3 \cdot 5^2 \cdot 7^2$

Find the complete factorization of each of the following. Use exponents whenever a factor is repeated. (The results of problems 11–20 for Chapter 9 will be useful here.)

16. 18

17. 32

18. 48

19. 72

20. 250

21. 360

22. 1000

23. 728

24. 1320

25. 10,000

For each of the following lists of numbers, give the complete factorization of their LCM and of their GCD. Use exponents whenever a factor is repeated.

26. $1 \cdot 3^2 \cdot 5^3$ and $1 \cdot 3 \cdot 5^2 \cdot 7$

27. $1 \cdot 2^4 \cdot 5^3$ and $1 \cdot 2^3 \cdot 5^4$

28. $1 \cdot 2 \cdot 3^4 \cdot 5^2$ and $1 \cdot 3^2 \cdot 5^2 \cdot 11$

29. $1 \cdot 2^2 \cdot 3 \cdot 5^2$, $1 \cdot 2^3 \cdot 3^3 \cdot 5 \cdot 13$, and $1 \cdot 2 \cdot 3 \cdot 11$

30. $1 \cdot 3 \cdot 5^3 \cdot 7$, $1 \cdot 2^2 \cdot 3^4$, and $1 \cdot 2^3 \cdot 5^2 \cdot 7^2$

List, in order, all the natural numbers greater than 20 but less than 31 which are relatively prime to each of the following.

31. 4

32. 15

33. 16

34. 34

35. 63

Find the simplest form of each of the following. Be sure to perform operations in the correct order.

36. $(4 + 7) \cdot (2 + 9)$

37. $17 - 15 + 19 \cdot 2$

38. $36/9 - 24/8 + 9 \cdot 3$

39. $4^2 + 5^2$

40. $(7 - 2)^2 + 6^2$

41. $5 + 8^2 \cdot 3$

42. $(5 + 8)^2 \cdot 3$

43. $(2^3 + 3^2) + (3^3 + 2^2)$

44. $(12 - 6 + 3)^3$

45. $5 \cdot 6 + 6^2 - 4 \cdot 6$

FRACTIONS AND QUOTIENT NUMBERS

1. So far we have considered only the natural numbers and zero. The symbols 1, 2, 3, 4, ... are used to represent the _____ _____, while _____ is the symbol used to represent zero.

   NATURAL NUMBERS;   0

2. Zero is defined to be the size of the _____ _____. A natural number is a property shared by _____ of the same _____.

   EMPTY SET;   SETS;   SIZE

3. A FRACTION is a symbol of the form a/b, where a and b are symbols which represent natural numbers.

4. Then 2/3, 5/6, 8/5, 12/2 are all examples of _____.

   FRACTIONS

5. For the fraction, 2/3, we call 2 the NUMERATOR. The numerator of 5/6 is _____.

   5

6. For 8/3 we call 8 the _____ and 3 the DENOMINATOR.

   NUMERATOR

7. The fractions 5/7 and 5/2 have the same _____, but different denominators.

   NUMERATOR

8. Although 2/5 and 8/5 have different numerators, they have the same _____.

   DENOMINATOR

9. An expression such as 5/8 is called a _____. We say that 5 is the _____ and 8 is the _____.

   FRACTION;   NUMERATOR; DENOMINATOR

10. In the fraction a/b, we call a the _____ and b the _____.

NUMERATOR;   DENOMINATOR

11. Both the numerator and denominator of a fraction must be _____ which represent natural numbers.

SYMBOLS

12. Since 0 does not represent a _____ _____, the expression 0/2 is not a _____.

NATURAL NUMBER;   FRACTION

13. Neither the numerator nor the denominator of a fraction may be _____.

0

14. Which of these are fractions?
    2/7,   0/3,   4/0,   0/0 _____

Only 2/7

15. A fraction is a _____ of the form a/b, where both a and b represent _____ _____.

SYMBOL;   NATURAL NUMBERS

16. We say that the fractions 2/3 and 4/6 are equal and write
    2/3 = 4/6
    Notice that
    $2 \cdot 6 = 3 \cdot 4$

17. Also $4/6 = 6/9$ and $4 \cdot 9 = 6 \cdot$ _____.

6

18. Similarly $3/4 = 6/8$ and $3 \cdot 8 = 4 \cdot$ _____.

6

19. Observe the following:
    $\dfrac{1}{3} = \dfrac{4}{12}$ and $1 \cdot 12 = 3 \cdot 4$

    $\dfrac{2}{5} = \dfrac{4}{10}$ and $2 \cdot$ _____ $= 5 \cdot 4$

    $\dfrac{5}{4} = \dfrac{10}{8}$ and $5 \cdot 8 =$ _____ $\cdot$ _____

10; $4 \cdot 10$

20. In general we say that
    $a/b = c/d$ whenever $a \cdot d = b \cdot c$
    Thus
    $3/2 = 9/6$ since $3 \cdot 6 =$ _____ $\cdot$ _____
    $6/10 = 3/5$ since   _____ $\cdot$ _____
    $= 10 \cdot$ _____

$2 \cdot 9$; $6 \cdot 5 = 10 \cdot 3$

21. We have defined the fractions a/b and c/d to be equal whenever
    $a \cdot d =$ _____ $\cdot$ _____.

$b \cdot c$

22. Does 2/3 = 4/6? _____

5/8 = 10/16? _____

5/12 = 4/9? _____

YES;   YES;   NO

23. 5/12 does not equal 4/9, since 5 · 9 does not equal _____ · _____.

12 · 4

24. a/b = c/d only when
_____ · _____ = b · _____.

a · d = b · c

25. We have defined a/b = c/d to mean that ad = bc. Later we will show why this is a reasonable definition.

26. Notice that 2/3 = 30/45 since
2 · _____ = _____ · _____.

2 · 45 = 3 · 30

27. Which of the following fractions are equal to 2/3?

4/6,   6/9,   8/12,   10/15

_____

ALL ARE

28. There are other fractions equal to 2/3.

2/3 = _____/18,   since   2 · 18 = 3 · 12

2/3 = _____/21,   since   2 · 21
= 3 · _____

12;   14;   14

29. We have observed that

2/3,   4/6,   6/9,   8/12,   10/15,
12/18,   14/21,   30/45

are all equal fractions. Are there other fractions which are also equal to 2/3? _____

YES

30. In fact there is no limit to the collection of fractions which equal 2/3. Imagine the set of all fractions equal to 2/3. The property which is shared by all these fractions is called the QUOTIENT NUMBER TWO-THIRDS.

31. Remember, a natural number is a property shared by _____ of the same size, but a quotient number is a property shared by _____ which are equal.

SETS;   FRACTIONS

32. Which of these fractions equal 1/2?

2/4,   3/6,   4/8,   5/12,   10/20

_____

ALL EXCEPT 5/12

33. The property shared by 1/2, 2/4, 3/6, 4/8, 5/10, 10/20 and all other fractions equal to 1/2 is another _____ number.

QUOTIENT

34. The property shared by all fractions equal to 1/2 is called the _____ NUMBER ONE-HALF.

QUOTIENT

35. The property shared by {a, b, c}, {x, y, z}, {1, 2, 3}, {π, √, +}, and all other sets of the same size is called a _____ number.

> NATURAL

36. The quotient number two-thirds is the property shared by 2/3 and all other _____ equal to 2/3.

> FRACTIONS

37. The quotient number two-thirds may be represented by the fraction 2/3 or by any other fraction which is _____ to 2/3. We call each of these fractions a REPRESENTATIVE of two-thirds.

> EQUAL

38. Is 4/6 a representative of two-thirds?

_____

Is 12/18 a representative of two-thirds?

_____

> YES;   YES

39. In fact any fraction that equals 2/3 is called a _____ of two-thirds.

> REPRESENTATIVE

40. Then, 2/3, 4/6, 6/9, 8/12 are all called _____ of two-thirds.

> REPRESENTATIVES

41. A quotient number is a property shared by equal _____, any one of which is said to be a _____ of the quotient number.

> FRACTIONS;   REPRESENTATIVE

42. Every fraction determines a quotient number. For example, 2/5 determines the quotient number which is the property shared by 2/5, 4/10, 6/15, 8/20, and all other fractions equal to 2/5.

Is 10/25 a representative of this quotient number? _____

> YES

43. Which of these are representatives of the quotient number determined by 3/12?

1/4,   2/8,   4/16,   5/20   _____

> ALL ARE   (since all are equal to 3/12)

44. Recall that the product of any two natural numbers is a natural number, but the quotient of two natural numbers is not always a _____ _____.

> NATURAL NUMBER

45. We have used the expression 4/2 to represent the quotient of 4 divided by 2. Similarly, an expression which represents 12 divided by 3 is _____.

> 12/3

46. And we have said that

$$12/3 = 4 \quad \text{since} \quad 12 = 4 \cdot \underline{\hspace{2cm}}$$

3

47. Similarly

$$10/2 = 5 \quad \text{since} \quad 10 = 5 \cdot 2$$
$$8/4 = \underline{\hspace{2cm}} \quad \text{since} \quad 8 = 2 \cdot 4$$
$$15/3 = \underline{\hspace{2cm}} \quad \text{since}$$
$$15 = \underline{\hspace{1.5cm}} \cdot \underline{\hspace{1.5cm}}$$

2;   5; $15 = \underline{5} \cdot \underline{3}$

48. In general, we say that the natural number a divided by the natural number b is the natural number q, such that a = q · b, provided such a natural number q can be found.

In symbols, a/b = q such that a = _____.

q · b

49. Until now we have said that it is not possible to divide 5 by 2, since no natural number can be found whose product with 2 equals _____.

5

50. Since 8/2 represents the quotient of 8 divided by 2, it seems quite natural to represent the quotient of 5 divided by 2 with the expression _____.

5/2

51. But 5/2 is what we now call a fraction, and hence it determines some _____ number.

QUOTIENT

52. We define the quotient of 5 divided by 2 to be the quotient number which can be represented by the fraction _____.

5/2

53. Similarly, we say that the quotient of 2 divided by 3 is the quotient number represented by _____.

2/3

54. In fact we can define the quotient of any two natural numbers, a and b, to be the quotient number represented by the fraction _____.

a/b

55. But we have previously defined the quotient of 8 divided by 2 to be the natural number _____.

4

56. Yet now we say that the quotient of 8 divided by 2 is the _____ number represented by the fraction 8/2.

QUOTIENT

57. To avoid a contradiction, we must agree that the _____ number 4 and the _____ number represented by 8/2 are the same number.

NATURAL;   QUOTIENT

58. Of course, the natural number 4 and the quotient number represented by 8/2 were not originally defined in the same way. The natural number 4 was defined as the property shared by all _____ of the same size as {a, b, c, d}, while the corresponding quotient number was defined as the property shared by all _____ equal to 8/2.

SETS;   FRACTIONS

59. But the natural number 4 and the quotient number represented by 8/2 are equal. Hence the natural number 4 is also a _____ number.

QUOTIENT

60. Similarly, 12/4 represents a quotient number as well as the natural number 3. Hence we say that the quotient number represented by 12/4 is also a _____ number.

NATURAL

61. Since 2 = 10/5 we see that 2 is a _____ _____ as well as a natural number.

QUOTIENT NUMBER

62. Is 5 both a natural number and a quotient number? _____

YES   (5 = 15/3, for example)

63. Are the natural numbers 6, 7, 8, 9, 10 also quotient numbers? _____

YES

64. In fact, every natural number is also a _____ _____.

QUOTIENT NUMBER

65. For convenience, we will speak of the quotient number 2/3, when what we mean is the quotient number represented by the fraction 2/3. Is the quotient number 15/3 also a natural number? _____

YES

66. However, the quotient numbers 2/5, 3/4, 8/7 are not also natural numbers. Which of these are natural numbers?

   5/10,   25/5,   4/1,   8/3
   _____

25/5   and   4/1

67. Then while every natural number is also a _____ _____ we see that some _____ _____ are not natural numbers.

QUOTIENT NUMBER;   QUOTIENT NUMBERS

68. Recall that if A and B are sets, and if every member of A is also a member of B, we say that A is a _____ of B.

SUBSET

69. Then since every natural number is also a quotient number, we can say that the set of all natural numbers is a _____ of the set of all quotient numbers.

SUBSET

70. Which of these represent quotient numbers?

2/3,   8/3,   10/5,   4,   5/1

_____

ALL DO

71. Which of these represent natural numbers?

2/3,   8/3,   10/5,   4,   5/1

_____

10/5,   4,   5/1

72. The set of natural numbers is a subset of the set of _____ _____.

QUOTIENT NUMBERS

73. The quotient of 3 and 4 is the _____ _____ represented by $\overline{3/4}$. The quotient of 6 and 2 is both the natural number _____ and the quotient number represented by the fraction _____.

QUOTIENT NUMBER;   3;   6/2

74. We have said that a/b = c/d whenever $a \cdot d$ = _____.

b · c

75. We will now show that this is a reasonable definition. Observe that 12/4 and 6/2 both represent the natural number 3, and so it is reasonable to write 12/4 = 6/2.

And notice that $12 \cdot 2 = 4 \cdot$ _____.

6

76. 20/4 equals the natural number _____.

10/2 equals the natural number _____.

5;   5

77. Notice 20/4 and 10/2 represent the same natural number. Does $20 \cdot 2 = 4 \cdot 10$? _____

YES

78. Do 12/6 and 8/2 represent the same natural number? _____

Does $12 \cdot 2 = 6 \cdot 8$? _____

NO;   NO

79. Does 10/5 = 6/3?   _____

Does $10 \cdot 3 = 5 \cdot 6$?   _____

Does 12/4 = 8/2?   _____

Does $12 \cdot 2 = 4 \cdot 8$?   _____

YES;   YES;   NO;   NO

80. We see that for fractions which represent natural numbers, the definition we have used for equality seems reasonable. In fact, we can show that if a/b and c/d are any two fractions which represent the same natural number, then

$$a \cdot d = \underline{\hspace{2cm}}$$

b · c

81. For suppose that a/b and c/d both represent the natural number q. That is,

$$a/b = q \quad \text{and} \quad c/d = q$$

From the definition of division we know that for the expression a/b = q, the dividend, a, is the product of the divisor, b, and the quotient, q.

Hence $a = b \cdot \underline{\hspace{1.5cm}}$.

q

82. $a/b = q$

$a = bq$

Hence $a \cdot d = (bq) \cdot \underline{\hspace{1.5cm}}$.

d

83. $a/b = q$

$a = bq$

$ad = (bq)d$

But by the associative property of multiplication

$$(bq)d = b(\underline{\hspace{1.5cm}}).$$

qd

84. $a/b = q$

$a = bq$

$ad = (bq)d = b(qd)$

But c/d = q also, and so, by the definition of division,

$$c = q \cdot \underline{\hspace{1.5cm}}.$$

d

85. $c/d = q$

$c = qd$

But we already have seen that

$ad = b(qd)$

Hence we can write

$$ad = b \underline{\hspace{1.5cm}}.$$

c

86. We began with the assumption that a/b and c/d were two fractions which represented the same natural number, q. Hence we can write

$$a/b \underline{\hspace{1.5cm}} c/d$$

=

87. We have seen that

$a/b = q \qquad c/d = q$

$a = bq \qquad c = dq$

Hence $ad = (bq)d = b(qd) = bc$

For fractions representing natural numbers, if

$$a/b = c/d, \quad \text{then} \quad \underline{\hspace{2cm}}$$

ad = bc

88. But we have not demonstrated this result when a/b and c/d represent quotient numbers which are not also natural numbers. We shall not attempt to do this, but will assume that the same rule holds for all fractions, whether or not they represent natural numbers. That is, we assume that if a/b = c/d, then _____ .

> ad = bc

89. We call this the CROSS PRODUCT test of equality.

Hence 3/10 = 6/20,* since the cross products, 3 · 20 and _____ , are equal.

> 10 · 6

90. 4/12 = 1/3 since the cross products _____ and 12 · 1 are equal.

> 4 · 3

91. 5/15 = 1/3 since the _____ products 5 · 3 and 15 · 1 are equal.

> CROSS

*The fact that these are cross products may be more easily seen by writing

$$\frac{3}{10} = \frac{6}{20}$$

Notice that the products 3 · 20 and 10 · 6 are both 60, and that the two fractions 3/10 and 6/20 are equal. It may be helpful for the reader to re-write fractions using the horizontal bar in subsequent frames in which reference is made to cross products.

92. We have previously observed that 4/6, 6/9, 8/12, and 10/15 are each equal to 2/3. Notice also that

$$\frac{4}{6} = \frac{2 \cdot 2}{3 \cdot 2} \qquad \frac{8}{12} = \frac{2 \cdot}{3 \cdot 4}$$

$$\frac{6}{9} = \frac{2 \cdot 3}{3 \cdot 3} \qquad \frac{10}{15} = \frac{2 \cdot}{3 \cdot}$$

> $$\frac{8}{12} = \frac{2 \cdot 4}{3 \cdot 4}; \qquad \frac{10}{15} = \frac{2 \cdot 5}{3 \cdot 5}$$

93. Then $\frac{2 \cdot 2}{3 \cdot 2}, \frac{2 \cdot 3}{3 \cdot 3}, \frac{2 \cdot 4}{3 \cdot 4}, \frac{2 \cdot 5}{3 \cdot 5}$, are all equal to 2/3, and we may write

$$\frac{2 \cdot 2}{3 \cdot 2} = \frac{2}{3} \qquad \frac{2 \cdot 4}{3 \cdot 4} = \frac{2}{3}$$

$$\frac{2 \cdot 3}{3 \cdot 3} = \frac{2}{3} \qquad \frac{2 \cdot 5}{3 \cdot 5} = \underline{\quad}$$

> 2;   2/3

94. Similarly,

$$\frac{2 \cdot 6}{3 \cdot 6} = \frac{2}{3}$$

$$\frac{2 \cdot 7}{3 \cdot 7} = \underline{\quad}$$

> 2/3

95. When we write 2 · 7 = 14, we say that 14 is the product of 2 and 7, and we call the numbers 2 and 7 the _____ of this product.

> FACTORS

96. Then since (2 · 7)/(3 · 7) = 2/3, we say that 7, which is a factor of both the numerator and denominator of the fraction (2 · 7)/(3 · 7), can be CANCELLED.

97. What <u>factor</u> can be cancelled in the fraction $(2 \cdot 8)/(3 \cdot 8)$? _____

8

98. Now observe carefully. We know that $(2 \cdot 8)/(3 \cdot 8) = 2/3$ because the cross products $(2 \cdot 8)3$ and $(3 \cdot 8)2$ are both equal to the number _____.

48

99. It is interesting to observe that if the factor 8 is cancelled from both the numerator and denominator, then $(2 \cdot 8)/(3 \cdot 8)$
= _____.

2/3

100. We will show that this is always the case. If any fraction contains a factor common to both the numerator and the denominator, then the fraction which results from cancelling this factor is equal to the original one.

101. In symbols, we express this by writing $ax/bx = a/b$. Now to show that two fractions are equal we must show that their cross _____ are equal.

PRODUCTS

102. Hence to show $ax/bx = a/b$, we must show that $(ax)b =$ _____.

(bx)a

103. We want to show that $(ax)b = (bx)a$.

Now $(ax)b = a(xb)$ by the _____ property of multiplication.

ASSOCIATIVE

104. We are showing that $(ax)b = (bx)a$.

We have

$(ax)b = a(xb)$

$= a(bx)$

by the _____ property of multiplication.

COMMUTATIVE

105. We are showing that $(ax)b = (bx)a$.

We have seen that

$(ax)b = a(xb) = a(bx)$

And again by the commutative property of multiplication,

$a(bx) = (bx)$_____

a

106. Hence we have shown that the cross products

$(ax)b = (bx)a$

and so the fractions

ax/bx and a/b are _____.

EQUAL

107. Thus if we are given any fractions, we can form equal fractions by cancelling any factor common to both the numerator and denominator.

108. Then we see that, without making use of the cross product test, we have

$$\frac{3 \cdot 5}{4 \cdot 5} = \frac{3}{4}$$

$$\frac{5 \cdot 7}{6 \cdot 7} = \underline{\qquad}$$

5/6

109. Also

$$\frac{6}{8} = \frac{3 \cdot 2}{4 \cdot 2} = \underline{\qquad}$$

$$\frac{10}{15} = \underline{\qquad} = \frac{2}{3}$$

$$\frac{3}{4}; \qquad \frac{10}{15} = \frac{2 \cdot 5}{3 \cdot 5} = \frac{2}{3}$$

110.

$$\frac{12}{18} = \frac{2 \cdot}{3 \cdot 6} = \frac{2}{3}$$

$$\frac{9}{12} = \frac{3 \cdot}{4 \cdot} = \frac{3}{4}$$

$$\frac{12}{18} = \frac{2 \cdot 6}{3 \cdot 6} = \frac{2}{3}; \qquad \frac{9}{12} = \frac{3 \cdot 3}{4 \cdot 3} = \frac{3}{4}$$

111. The fractions 2/3, 4/6, 6/9, 8/12, 10/15 all represent the same _____ number.

QUOTIENT

112. We say that 2/3 is the SIMPLEST FORM of this quotient number, since it is the representative fraction with smallest possible numerator and denominator.

113. Which of these is the simplest form of the quotient number all represent?

8/16, 4/8, 1/2, 2/4

_____

1/2

114. The simplest form of the quotient number 3/9 is _____.

The simplest form of the quotient number 6/15 is _____.

1/3;   2/5

115. Recall that some quotient numbers are also _____ numbers.

NATURAL

116. The quotient number 6/2 is also the natural number _____.

3

117. We agree that when a quotient number is also a natural number, its simplest form will be one of the symbols 1, 2, 3, ...

Then the simplest form of 6/2 is 3, and the simplest form of 15/3 is _____.

5

118. Find the simplest form of each.

80/10 = _____
20/10 = _____
7/1 = _____
39/13 = _____

8;   2;   7;   3

119. And we agree that when a quotient number is not also a natural number, we call the fraction whose numerator and denominator are as small as possible the representation in S_____ form.

SIMPLEST

120. But the numerator and denominator of a fraction will be as small as possible when no factor of each, greater than 1, can be
C_____.

CANCELLED

121. That is, the numerator and denominator of a fraction will be as small as possible if they have no _____ factor greater than 1.

COMMON

122. But if two numbers have no common factor greater than 1, then 1 is their _____ common factor.

HIGHEST

123. Hence the numerator and denominator of a fraction will be as small as possible if their HCF is 1. We call any two numbers whose HCF is 1 _____ prime.

RELATIVELY

124. So we can say that a fraction is in simplest form when its _____ and _____ are relatively prime.

NUMERATOR;   DENOMINATOR
(either order)

125. Which of these pairs of numbers are relatively prime?

   15 and 12

   27 and 10

   21 and 7

   6 and 1 _____

27 and 10;   6 and 1

126. Which of these fractions are in simplest form?

   5/10,   26/30,   1/6,   87/101
   _____

1/6   and   87/101

127. How could we represent the quotient of zero divided by 3? _____

0/3

128. Is 0/3 a fraction? _____

NO

129. Since 0/3 is not a fraction, we may say that 0/3 does not represent a _____ number.

QUOTIENT

130. But 0/3 = 0, since 0 = _____ · 3.

0

131. And since 0/3 = 0, we see that while 0/3 does not represent a quotient number, it does represent a _____ number.

> WHOLE

132. And the symbol, 0, is the simplest form of the whole number, zero. Then while 0/7 does not represent a quotient number, it does represent a whole number whose simplest form is _____ .

> 0

133. Each of the expressions

   0/1,   0/2,   0/3,   0/4,   0/5,   . . .

   is a representation of the number whose simplest form is _____ . This number is neither a natural number nor a _____ number, but it is a _____ number.

> 0;   QUOTIENT;   WHOLE

134. To summarize:

   If a quotient number is also a natural number, its simplest form is one of the symbols 1, 2, 3, 4, ... But if a quotient number must be represented by a fraction, the simplest form is that fraction, among its possible representatives, whose numerator and denominator are relatively _____ .

> PRIME

135. Let us agree that, unless otherwise instructed, we will always represent a quotient number by its _____ form.

> SIMPLEST

136. A natural number is a property shared by _____ of the same _____ .

> SETS;   SIZE

137. A quotient number is a property shared by equal _____ .

> FRACTIONS

138. Two fractions are equal if their cross _____ are equal.

> PRODUCTS

139. a/b = c/d means that _____ .

> ad = bc

140. But also ax/bx = a/b since the cross products (ax)b and (bx)a are equal. And hence a _____ in the numerator of a fraction may be cancelled with a common factor in the denominator.

> FACTOR

141. Every natural number is also a _____ number.

> QUOTIENT

142. Hence the set of _____ numbers is a subset of the set of _____ numbers.

| NATURAL;   QUOTIENT |

Chapter 12

Problems A (Answers on page 509)

Use the cross-product test to decide whether the fractions in each pair below are equal or not equal. Insert in each case one of the symbols = or ≠ to indicate your decision.

1. 3/12 _____ 5/20
2. 11/15 _____ 33/45
3. 8/10 _____ 28/35
4. 12/15 _____ 9/11
5. 16/3 _____ 25/4

Use the cancellation property, ax/bx = a/b, to replace each fraction by an equal one.

6. $(5 \cdot 7)/(8 \cdot 7)$ = _____
7. $(12 \cdot 9)/(7 \cdot 9)$ = _____
8. 15/25 = _____/5
9. 91/130 = _____/10
10. 236/177 = 4/_____

Write each of the following in simplest form.

11. 16/32   15. 3/1
12. 36/15   16. 63/35
13. 72/18   17. 56/88
14. 7/7   18. 17/31

143. Some quotient numbers are also natural numbers. The simplest form of a quotient number is either 1, 2, 3, 4, . . . , if possible, or a fraction whose numerator and denominator are _____ _____.

| RELATIVELY PRIME |

19. 792/504   20. 1225/175

Problems B

Between the two fractions in each of the pairs below, insert one of the symbols = or ≠ so as to form a true statement.

1. 3/4 _____ 15/20
2. 8/3 _____ 56/21
3. 5/8 _____ 7/11
4. 14/3 _____ 17/4
5. 18/12 _____ 12/8

Find the simplest form of each of the following.

6. 4/12   13. 26/39
7. 8/20   14. 91/77
8. 15/9   15. 26/74
9. 21/7   16. 84/77
10. 15/15   17. 65/91
11. 55/11   18. 560/720
12. 13/65   19. 504/936
                  20. 539/231

MULTIPLICATION AND ADDITION OF QUOTIENT NUMBERS

1. A property which is shared by equal fractions is called a _____ number.

   QUOTIENT

2. A quotient number will usually, but not always, be represented in S _____ form.

   SIMPLEST

3. The simplest form of a quotient number which is also a natural number is one of the symbols _____ .

   1, 2, 3, . . .

4. A quotient number which is not a natural number must be represented by a _____ .

   FRACTION

5. A fraction is in simplest form when its numerator and denominator are relatively _____ .

   PRIME

6. A _____ which is common to both the numerator and denominator of a fraction may be cancelled.

   FACTOR

7. Express in simplest form:

   15/18 = _____

   24/8 = _____

   5/6;   3

8. The product of two fractions is indicated by using the dot, just as with natural numbers. For example, the product of 3/4 and 5/8 is indicated by writing $\frac{3}{4} \cdot \frac{5}{8}$.

   Indicate the product of 2/3 and 8/3.

   _____

   $\frac{2}{3} \cdot \frac{8}{3}$

9. When multiplying two fractions we multiply their numerators and denominators.

Thus

$$\frac{2}{5} \cdot \frac{3}{7} = \frac{2 \cdot 3}{5 \cdot 7} = \frac{6}{35}$$

$$\frac{5}{8} \cdot \frac{3}{4} = \frac{5 \cdot 3}{8 \cdot 4} = \underline{\hspace{3cm}}$$

15/32

10. Multiply

$$\frac{3}{7} \cdot \frac{5}{4} = \underline{\hspace{3cm}}$$

$$\frac{6}{13} \cdot \frac{1}{5} = \underline{\hspace{3cm}}$$

15/28;   6/65

11. Observe the following example.

$$\frac{2}{7} \cdot \frac{3}{2} = \frac{2 \cdot 3}{7 \cdot 2} = \frac{3}{7}$$

Notice that the factor 2 contained in both the numerator and denominator was cancelled.

Find

$$\frac{5}{8} \cdot \frac{8}{9} = \underline{\hspace{3cm}}$$

$$\frac{5 \cdot 8}{8 \cdot 9} = \frac{5}{9}$$

12. The process of cancelling can be very helpful in reducing a product to simplest form after multiplication. A _____ which is common to both the numerator and the denominator of a fraction may be cancelled.

FACTOR

13. But to see which factor may be cancelled it is sometimes necessary to write the numerator and denominator of a fraction in factored form. Thus

$$\frac{6}{7} \cdot \frac{5}{3} = \frac{6 \cdot 5}{7 \cdot 3} = \frac{2 \cdot 3 \cdot 5}{7 \cdot 3}$$

The factor that may be cancelled is _____.

3

14. $$\frac{6}{7} \cdot \frac{5}{3} = \frac{6 \cdot 5}{7 \cdot 3} = \frac{2 \cdot 3 \cdot 5}{7 \cdot 3} = \frac{}{7}$$

If we had written

$$\frac{6}{7} \cdot \frac{5}{3} = \frac{30}{21}$$

it would not have been so obvious that the factor _____ may be cancelled.

10;   3

15. Consider

$$\frac{4}{7} \cdot \frac{21}{11} = \frac{4 \cdot 21}{7 \cdot 11}$$

Since $21 = 3 \cdot 7$, we see that the factor _____ is common to both the numerator and denominator of $(4 \cdot 21)/(7 \cdot 11)$.

7

16. Then

$$\frac{4}{7} \cdot \frac{21}{11} = \frac{4 \cdot 21}{7 \cdot 11} = \frac{4 \cdot 3 \cdot 7}{7 \cdot 11} = \underline{\hspace{3cm}}$$

Again, if we had written

$$\frac{4}{7} \cdot \frac{21}{11} = \frac{84}{77}$$

it would not have been so obvious that 7 is a factor which may be _____.

12/11;   CANCELLED

17. Another example is

$$\frac{2}{9} \cdot \frac{6}{5} = \frac{2 \cdot 6}{9 \cdot 5}$$

Since $6 = 2 \cdot 3$ and $9 = 3 \cdot 3$, we see that the factor _____ may be cancelled.

> 3

18. Then

$$\frac{2}{9} \cdot \frac{6}{5} = \frac{2 \cdot 6}{9 \cdot 5} = \frac{2 \cdot 2 \cdot 3}{3 \cdot 3 \cdot 5} = \text{_____}$$

> 4/15

19. Find the factor which may be cancelled and reduce these products to simplest form.

$$\frac{10}{7} \cdot \frac{4}{15} = \frac{10 \cdot 4}{7 \cdot 15} = \text{_____}$$

$$\frac{8}{5} \cdot \frac{7}{12} = \frac{8 \cdot 7}{5 \cdot 12} = \text{_____}$$

> 8/21;   14/15

20. Reduce each product to simplest form by cancelling factors.

$$\frac{8}{15} \cdot \frac{3}{4} = \frac{8 \cdot 3}{15 \cdot 4} = \text{_____}$$

$$\frac{40}{77} \cdot \frac{21}{4} = \frac{40 \cdot 21}{77 \cdot 4} = \text{_____}$$

> $$\frac{8 \cdot 3}{15 \cdot 4} = \frac{2 \cdot 4 \cdot 3}{5 \cdot 3 \cdot 4} = \frac{2}{5};$$
>
> $$\frac{40 \cdot 21}{77 \cdot 4} = \frac{4 \cdot 10 \cdot 3 \cdot 7}{11 \cdot 7 \cdot 4} = \frac{10 \cdot 3}{11} = \frac{30}{11}$$

21. When multiplying fractions, first indicate the products of the numerators and denominators and then look for a _____ which may be cancelled.

> FACTOR

22. Indicate the product and find the factor which may be cancelled to reduce the product to simplest form.

$$\frac{3}{29} \cdot \frac{10}{3} = \text{_____}$$

$$\frac{1}{10} \cdot \frac{15}{2} = \text{_____}$$

$$\frac{4}{3} \cdot \frac{3}{8} = \text{_____}$$

> 10/29;   3/4;   1/2

23. Another way to indicate the product of two fractions is

$$\left(\frac{2}{5}\right)\left(\frac{15}{7}\right) = \frac{2}{5} \cdot \frac{15}{7} = \frac{2 \cdot 15}{5 \cdot 7} = \frac{}{7}$$

$$\left(\frac{3}{2}\right)\left(\frac{4}{3}\right) = \text{_____}$$

> 6;   2

24. Express all products in simplest form.

$$\frac{5}{12} \cdot \frac{4}{5} = \text{_____}$$

$$\left(\frac{18}{5}\right)\left(\frac{5}{18}\right) = \text{_____}$$

$$\left(\frac{6}{1}\right)\left(\frac{2}{3}\right) = \text{_____}$$

> 1/3;   1;   4

25. Every natural number is also a quotient number. Hence every natural number can be expressed as a fraction.

$$5 = 15/3$$
$$8 = \underline{\hspace{1cm}}/2$$
$$4 = \underline{\hspace{1cm}}/1$$

16;   4

26. $5 = 15/3$

We can also write $5 = 10/2$ and $5 = 5/1$.

$$8 = 16/2$$

We can also write $8 = 32/4$ and $8 = 8/1$.

The simplest <u>fraction</u> we can use to represent 5 is _____, and the simplest <u>fraction</u> we can use to represent 8 is _____.

5/1;   8/1

27. To form the product of a natural number and a fraction we can first express the natural numbers as a fraction in <u>simplest</u> form.

$$(5)\left(\frac{2}{3}\right) = \frac{5}{1} \cdot \frac{2}{3} = \underline{\hspace{2cm}}$$

$$\frac{3}{4} \cdot 8 = \frac{3}{4} \cdot \frac{8}{1} = \underline{\hspace{2cm}}$$

10/3;   6

28. Express the following products in simplest form.

$$\frac{8}{25} \cdot \frac{50}{6} = \underline{\hspace{2cm}}$$

$$12 \cdot \frac{3}{8} = \underline{\hspace{2cm}}$$

$$\frac{2}{5} \cdot 20 = \underline{\hspace{2cm}}$$

8/3;   9/2;   8

29. Recall that every quotient number can be represented by a _____.

FRACTION

30. We define the product of two quotient numbers as the quotient number determined by multiplying any two representative fractions.

Hence the product of the quotient numbers represented by 3/5 and 7/8 is the quotient number represented by _____.

21/40

31. And the product of the quotient numbers represented by 8 and 6/7 is the quotient number represented by _____.

48/7

32. We previously defined the product of zero and any natural number to be _____.

ZERO

33. Similarly, we define the product of zero and any quotient number to be _____.

ZERO

34. Find the following products:

$$\frac{12}{5} \cdot 10 = \underline{\hspace{1cm}}$$

$$0 \cdot \frac{3}{4} = \underline{\hspace{1cm}}$$

$$(100)\left(\frac{3}{10}\right) = \underline{\hspace{1cm}}$$

> 24;   0;   30

35. The cross products of the fractions 2/5 and 3/8 are

2·8 and _____.

> 5·3

36. Write the sum of the cross products of each pair of fractions.

3/5 and 2/8	3·8 + 5·2
5/9 and 2/5	5·5 + _____
1/3 and 1/2	_____

> 9·2;   1·2 + 3·1

37. Addition of fractions is not so simple as multiplication. We illustrate the rule for addition by example.

$$\frac{2}{3} + \frac{1}{4} = \frac{2 \cdot 4 + 3 \cdot 1}{3 \cdot 4}$$

Notice that the numerator of the result, 2·4 + 3·1, is the sum of the cross _____ of the original fractions.

> PRODUCTS

38. The numerator of the sum of two fractions is obtained by adding the _____ _____ of the fractions.

> CROSS PRODUCTS

39. Thus

$$\frac{3}{8} + \frac{2}{5} = \frac{3 \cdot 5 +}{8 \cdot 5}$$

$$\frac{6}{5} + \frac{2}{9} = \frac{+}{5 \cdot 9}$$

> 8·2;   6·9 + 5·2

40.

$$\frac{1}{2} + \frac{3}{5} = \frac{+}{2 \cdot 5}$$

$$\frac{5}{9} + \frac{3}{20} = \frac{+}{9 \cdot 20}$$

> 1·5 + 2·3;   5·20 + 9·3

41. Recall that in an expression involving both multiplication and addition, unless there are symbols of grouping to indicate otherwise, the _____ is performed first.

> MULTIPLICATION

42. In the expression

2·3 + 5·7

the operation to perform first is

_____.

> MULTIPLICATION

43. Then

$$2 \cdot 3 + 5 \cdot 7 = 6 + \underline{\hspace{1cm}}.$$

> 35

44. And

$$3 \cdot 7 + 4 \cdot 8 = \underline{\hspace{1cm}} + \underline{\hspace{1cm}}.$$

> 21;　32

45. Hence

$$3 \cdot 7 + 4 \cdot 5 = \underline{\hspace{1cm}} + \underline{\hspace{1cm}} = \underline{\hspace{1cm}}.$$

> 21;　20;　41

46. Then

$$\frac{2}{5} + \frac{1}{3} = \frac{2 \cdot 3 + 5 \cdot 1}{5 \cdot 3} = \frac{+}{15} = \underline{\hspace{1cm}}.$$

> $\underline{6} + \underline{5}$;　11/15

47.

$$\frac{1}{4} + \frac{2}{5} = \frac{+}{20} = \underline{\hspace{1cm}}$$

$$\frac{3}{7} + \frac{1}{2} = \frac{}{14}$$

> $\underline{5} + \underline{8}$;　13/20;　13

48.

$$\frac{6}{5} + \frac{2}{9} = \frac{6 \cdot 9 + 5 \cdot 2}{5 \cdot 9}$$

Notice that the denominator of the sum, namely $5 \cdot 9$, is the _____ of the denominators of the original fractions.

> PRODUCT

49.

$$\frac{1}{4} + \frac{2}{3} = \frac{1 \cdot 3 + 4 \cdot 2}{12} = \frac{3 + 8}{12} = \frac{11}{12}$$

> $4 \cdot 3$

50. Add the following:

$$\frac{3}{2} + \frac{4}{5} = \frac{+}{10} = \underline{\hspace{1cm}}$$

$$\frac{3}{5} + \frac{2}{9} = \frac{27 + 10}{} = \underline{\hspace{1cm}}$$

> $\underline{15} + \underline{8}$;　23/10;　45;　37/45

51. Add

$$\frac{3}{7} + \frac{1}{2} = \underline{\hspace{1cm}}$$

$$\frac{7}{5} + \frac{2}{9} = \underline{\hspace{1cm}}$$

$$\frac{1}{11} + \frac{1}{5} = \underline{\hspace{1cm}}$$

> 13/14;　73/45;　16/55

52. When adding two fractions which are not in simplest form, it is sometimes, but not always, easier first to reduce them to simplest form.

Thus

$$\frac{5}{10} + \frac{3}{9} = \frac{1}{2} + \frac{1}{3} = \underline{\hspace{1cm}}$$

> 5/6

53. Reduce to simplest form before adding.

$$\frac{8}{12} + \frac{21}{14} = \underline{\hspace{3cm}}$$

$$\frac{35}{40} + \frac{55}{44} = \underline{\hspace{3cm}}$$

$$\frac{8}{12} + \frac{21}{14} = \frac{2}{3} + \frac{3}{2} = \frac{4+9}{6} = \frac{13}{6};$$

$$\frac{35}{40} + \frac{55}{44} = \frac{7}{8} + \frac{5}{4} = \frac{28+40}{32} = \frac{68}{32} = \frac{17}{8}$$

54. Add the following fractions:

$$\frac{2}{4} + \frac{1}{5} = \underline{\hspace{3cm}}$$

$$\frac{4}{1} + \frac{1}{2} = \underline{\hspace{3cm}}$$

7/10;   9/2

55. When adding two fractions we form the _____ of their cross products for the numerator of the result, and the _____ of their denominators for the denominator of the result.

SUM;   PRODUCT

56. In symbols, we indicate the rule for adding fractions by writing

$$\frac{a}{b} + \frac{c}{d} = \frac{ad+bc}{}$$

bd

57. You may remember a rule for adding fractions which is different from the one given here. Later we will show why the two rules are actually equivalent, and show that sometimes the rule given here is not the easiest possible one to use.

58. The rule we use here is called the CROSS PRODUCT RULE FOR ADDITION OF FRACTIONS and we represent it in symbols by writing

$$\frac{a}{b} + \frac{c}{d} = \underline{\hspace{2cm}}.$$

$$\frac{ad+bc}{bd}$$

59. Express the following sums in simplest form. Simplify before adding, when possible.

$$\frac{5}{8} + \frac{2}{3} = \underline{\hspace{3cm}}$$

$$\frac{6}{18} + \frac{3}{4} = \underline{\hspace{3cm}}$$

$$\frac{3}{1} + \frac{2}{3} = \underline{\hspace{3cm}}$$

31/24;   13/12;   11/3

60. In the last example we noted that

$$\frac{3}{1} + \frac{2}{3} = \frac{9+2}{1 \cdot 3} = \frac{11}{3}$$

Similarly,

$$2 + \frac{3}{4} = \frac{2}{1} + \frac{3}{4} = \frac{}{4}$$

11

61. Then we see that to add a natural number and a fraction, we first change the natural number to a _____.

FRACTION

62. Add

$$\frac{3}{10} + 2 = \frac{3}{10} + \frac{2}{1} = \frac{}{10}$$

$$5 + \frac{1}{3} = \underline{\hspace{2cm}}$$

$$4 + \frac{1}{4} = \underline{\hspace{2cm}}$$

23;   16/3;   17/4

63. Add or multiply as indicated:

$$(6)\left(\frac{2}{3}\right) = \underline{\hspace{2cm}}$$

$$3 + \frac{2}{5} = \underline{\hspace{2cm}}$$

$$\frac{3}{9} + 2 = \underline{\hspace{2cm}}$$

4;   17/5   7/3
(remember to reduce to simplest form)

64. Recall that 0 is the additive identity. That is, if a is any whole number then

$$a + 0 = 0 + a = \underline{\hspace{1.5cm}}.$$

a

65. Similarly, when adding zero and any fraction we define the sum to be the original fraction. Thus

$$2/3 + 0 = 2/3 \qquad 0 + 5/9 = \underline{\hspace{1.5cm}}$$

$$2/3 \cdot 0 = \underline{\hspace{1.5cm}}.$$

5/9;   0   (this is a product!)

66. Perform the indicated operation.

$$\frac{2}{5} + \frac{3}{4} = \underline{\hspace{2cm}}$$

$$18 \cdot \frac{2}{3} = \underline{\hspace{2cm}}$$

$$\left(\frac{2}{5}\right)\left(\frac{3}{4}\right) = \underline{\hspace{2cm}}$$

$$9 + \frac{4}{3} = \underline{\hspace{2cm}}$$

23/20;   12;   3/10;   31/3

67. In symbols, the product of any two fractions is indicated by

$$\frac{a}{b} \cdot \frac{c}{d} = \frac{ac}{}$$

bd

68. The sum is the more complicated expression.

$$\frac{a}{b} + \frac{c}{d} = \frac{}{bd}$$

ad + bc

69. Frequently a factor may be cancelled from both the numerator and the denominator of a fraction.

Thus

$$\frac{a \cdot x}{b \cdot x} = \underline{\hspace{2cm}}.$$

a/b

70. We have defined addition of any two fractions and of any natural number or zero and a fraction. Then addition of quotient numbers is also defined in the obvious way. The sum of any two quotient numbers is the quotient number determined by adding _____ which represent those quotient numbers.

FRACTIONS

71. The expression $5\frac{2}{3}$ is an abbreviation for the sum, $5 + \frac{2}{3}$. Similarly, the sum $3 + \frac{1}{2}$ can be shortened to _____.

$3\frac{1}{2}$

72. Hence

$4\frac{1}{3}$ or $4 + \frac{1}{3} = \frac{4}{1} + \frac{1}{3} = \frac{}{3}$.

13

73. And

$3\frac{3}{4} = \frac{3}{1} + \frac{3}{4} = \frac{}{4}$

$9\frac{2}{5} = \frac{}{5}$

15;   47

74. Expressions like $5\frac{2}{3}$ are called MIXED NUMBERS. Frequently we will prefer to write a number like $5\frac{2}{3}$ as a fraction, namely

$5\frac{2}{3} = \frac{}{3}$

17

75. Change the following mixed numbers to fractions:

$4\frac{1}{5} =$ _____

$8\frac{4}{9} =$ _____

$1\frac{2}{7} =$ _____

21/5;   76/9;   9/7

76. A fraction whose numerator is equal to or larger than its denominator is sometimes called an IMPROPER FRACTION, whereas a fraction whose numerator is smaller than its denominator is called a P_____ fraction.

PROPER

77. 8/3, 5/2, 7/7, 9/8 are all examples of _____ fractions.

IMPROPER

78. Every mixed number can be changed to a fraction.

$5\frac{3}{4} = \frac{}{4}$ $1\frac{1}{2} = \frac{}{2}$ $80\frac{1}{3} = \frac{}{3}$

23;   3;   241

79. Notice that whenever a mixed number is written as a fraction, it is an_____ fraction.

IMPROPER

80. An improper fraction is one in which the denominator is equal to or _____ than the numerator.

LESS

81. But there is nothing "improper" about an improper fraction. In fact, we shall usually prefer to use improper fractions, in simplest form, rather than mixed numbers.

82. The addition and multiplication of natural numbers were defined in such a way that several rather interesting properties would be true. The fact that

$$5 + 7 = 7 + 5$$

is an example of the _____ property of _____ for natural numbers.

COMMUTATIVE;   ADDITION

83. And if a and b are any natural numbers the fact that

$$ab = ba$$

symbolizes the _____ property of _____ for natural numbers.

COMMUTATIVE;   MULTIPLICATION

84. Let us show that the commutative property of addition also holds for quotient numbers. Let a/b and c/d be any two representative fractions. Then we want to show that

$$\frac{a}{b} + \frac{c}{d} = \frac{c}{d} + \underline{\hspace{1cm}}$$

a/b

85. We want to show that

$$\frac{a}{b} + \frac{c}{d} = \frac{c}{d} + \frac{a}{b}$$

Now by the cross product rule

$$\frac{a}{b} + \frac{c}{d} = \frac{\underline{\hspace{1.5cm}}}{bd}$$

ad + bc

86. We can see that

$$\frac{a}{b} + \frac{c}{d} = \frac{ad + bc}{bd}$$

But also by the cross product rule

$$\frac{c}{d} + \frac{a}{b} = \frac{cb + \underline{\hspace{0.8cm}}}{db}$$

da

87. We want to show that

$$\frac{a}{b} + \frac{c}{d} = \frac{c}{d} + \frac{a}{b}$$

We have $\frac{a}{b} + \frac{c}{d} = \frac{ad + bc}{bd}$ and

$$\frac{c}{d} + \frac{a}{b} = \frac{cb + da}{db}$$

Hence we need only show that

$$\frac{ad + bc}{bd} = \frac{\underline{\hspace{1cm}}}{db}$$

cb + da

88. We want to show that

$$\frac{ad + bc}{bd} = \frac{cb + da}{db}$$

But a, b, c, and d represent natural numbers. And, by the commutative property of multiplication for natural numbers, we can write

cb = bc
da = _____
db = _____

ad;   bd

89. Since cb = bc, da = ad, and db = bd, we can write

$$\frac{cb + da}{db} = \frac{bc + ad}{}$$

bd

90. We have

$$\frac{cb + da}{db} = \frac{bc + ad}{bd}$$

But bc + ad = ad + bc

because of the _____ property of _____ for natural numbers.

COMMUTATIVE;   ADDITION

91. We have shown that

$$\frac{cb + da}{db} = \frac{bc + ad}{bd} \quad \text{and} \quad bc + ad = ad + bc$$

Hence we can conclude that

$$\frac{cb + da}{db} = \frac{bc + ad}{bd} = \frac{}{bd}$$

ad + bc

92. Thus we have shown that

$$\frac{ad + bc}{bd} = \frac{cb + da}{db}$$

But we had previously shown that this is equivalent to

$$\frac{a}{b} + \frac{c}{d} = \underline{\hspace{2cm}}$$

$$\frac{c}{d} + \frac{a}{b}$$

93. We have established, therefore, the commutative property of addition for quotient numbers. This property is illustrated by writing

$$\frac{5}{6} + \frac{2}{7} = \frac{2}{7} + \underline{\hspace{2cm}}$$

5/6

94. We shall not do so here, but one can also verify the associative property of addition for quotient numbers. And for multiplication of quotient numbers, too, both _____ and _____ properties can be demonstrated.

COMMUTATIVE;   ASSOCIATIVE
(either order)

95. $$\frac{2}{3} + \left(\frac{3}{4} + \frac{1}{2}\right) = \left(\frac{2}{3} + \frac{3}{4}\right) + \frac{1}{2}$$

illustrates the _____ property of _____ for quotient numbers.

$$\frac{5}{8} \cdot \frac{11}{3} = \frac{11}{3} \cdot \frac{5}{8}$$

illustrates the _____ property of _____ for quotient numbers.

ASSOCIATIVE;   ADDITION;   COMMUTATIVE;   MULTIPLICATION

96. The property symbolized by writing

a(b + c) = ab + ac

is called the _____ property.

DISTRIBUTIVE

97. It can be shown that this property, also, holds for quotient numbers. Thus

$$\frac{3}{4}\left(\frac{1}{5} + \frac{2}{7}\right) = \frac{3}{4} \cdot \frac{1}{5} + \underline{\hspace{2cm}}.$$

$$\frac{3}{4} \cdot \frac{2}{7}$$

98. Review. Every quotient number can be represented by a _____.

FRACTION

99. To multiply two quotient numbers we multiply any _____ which represent these numbers.

FRACTIONS

100. The product of the fractions a/b and c/d is the fraction _____.

ac/bd

101. The sum of two quotient numbers is found by _____ fractions which represent these quotient numbers.

ADDING

102. And

$$\frac{a}{b} + \frac{c}{d} = \underline{\hspace{2cm}}.$$

$$\frac{ad + bc}{bd}$$

103. To add a natural number and a fraction we first write the natural number as a _____.

FRACTION

104. Hence

$$10 + \frac{3}{4} = \underline{\hspace{2cm}}.$$

43/4

105. Fractions like 2/5, 3/7, 9/10, 1/2 are called _____ fractions, while 5/3, 8/5, 4/4 100/1 are called _____ fractions.

PROPER;   IMPROPER

106. The sum of a natural number and a fraction may be indicated without using the plus sign. Thus $8 + \frac{2}{3}$ can be written simply $8\frac{2}{3}$ and is called a _____ number.

MIXED

107. But every mixed number may also be written as an _____ fraction, and we usually prefer the latter form.

IMPROPER

108. Then we prefer to write

$$8\frac{2}{3} = \frac{26}{3} \quad \text{and}$$

$$10\frac{3}{8} = \underline{\hspace{1.5cm}}$$

83/8

109. Find

$$(18)\left(\frac{1}{6}\right) = \underline{\hspace{1cm}}$$

$$5\tfrac{2}{3} = \underline{\hspace{1cm}}$$

$$\left(\frac{3}{4}\right)(16) = \underline{\hspace{1cm}}$$

3;   17/3;   12

110. Addition and multiplication of quotient numbers have been defined in such a way that certain properties of natural numbers are also valid for quotient numbers. These properties are the distributive, associative, and _____ properties.

COMMUTATIVE

Chapter 13

Problems A (Answers on page 509)

Multiply. Reduce products to simplest form by cancelling factors.

1. $\dfrac{3}{8} \cdot \dfrac{20}{7}$

2. $\dfrac{15}{4} \cdot \dfrac{2}{5}$

3. $\dfrac{21}{44} \cdot \dfrac{11}{35}$

4. $\dfrac{36}{35} \cdot \dfrac{65}{99}$

5. $\dfrac{63}{35} \cdot \dfrac{20}{9}$

Add or multiply, as indicated. Write answers in simplest form.

6. $\dfrac{1}{4} + \dfrac{2}{3}$

7. $\dfrac{8}{5} \cdot \dfrac{3}{4}$

8. $\dfrac{3}{8} + \dfrac{5}{12}$

9. $\dfrac{2}{15} \cdot \dfrac{5}{4}$

10. $\dfrac{9}{4} + \dfrac{2}{3}$

11. $5 + \dfrac{1}{3}$

12. $(6)\left(\dfrac{1}{3}\right)$

13. $6\frac{1}{3}$

14. $\left(\dfrac{2}{5}\right)(15)$

15. $15\frac{2}{5}$

16. $(1)\left(\dfrac{3}{4}\right)$

17. $1 + \dfrac{3}{4}$

18. $1\frac{3}{4}$

19. $(0)\left(\dfrac{3}{4}\right)$

20. $0 + \dfrac{3}{4}$

For quotient numbers parentheses mean "first," just as for natural numbers. Compute the following, as indicated. Write answers in simplest form.

Example: $\dfrac{2}{3} + \left(\dfrac{1}{2} + \dfrac{3}{5}\right)$. Solution: $\dfrac{2}{3} + \left(\dfrac{1}{2} + \dfrac{3}{5}\right)$

$$= \dfrac{2}{3} + \dfrac{11}{10} = \dfrac{53}{30}$$

21. $\left(\dfrac{3}{5} + \dfrac{1}{4}\right) + \dfrac{1}{3}$

22. $\dfrac{3}{5} + \left(\dfrac{1}{4} + \dfrac{1}{3}\right)$

23. Examine the expressions in problems 21 and 22 and the results obtained. What property of quotient numbers is illustrated by these two problems?

24. Show that

$$\dfrac{1}{2}\left(\dfrac{2}{3} + \dfrac{1}{5}\right) \quad \text{and} \quad \left(\dfrac{1}{2} \cdot \dfrac{2}{3}\right) + \left(\dfrac{1}{2} \cdot \dfrac{1}{5}\right)$$

are equal. What property does this illustrate?

25. Use only the definition of multiplication for quotient numbers and properties of natural numbers to show that if

   $a/b \quad$ and $\quad c/d$

are any two quotient numbers, then

$$\dfrac{a}{b} \cdot \dfrac{c}{d} = \dfrac{c}{d} \cdot \dfrac{a}{b}$$

Problems B

Add or multiply, as indicated. Write answers in simplest form.

1. $\dfrac{2}{3} \cdot \dfrac{4}{5}$

2. $\dfrac{5}{12} + \dfrac{1}{5}$

3. $\dfrac{6}{5} \cdot \dfrac{10}{3}$

4. $\dfrac{3}{8} \cdot \dfrac{4}{9}$

5. $\dfrac{17}{3} + \dfrac{3}{17}$

6. $\dfrac{2}{9} + 4$

7. $\left(\dfrac{2}{9}\right)(4)$

8. $(12)\left(\dfrac{3}{8}\right)$

9. $12 + \dfrac{3}{8}$

10. $12\frac{3}{8}$

11. $0 + \dfrac{5}{7}$

12. $(0)\left(\dfrac{5}{7}\right)$

13. $\dfrac{8}{7} \cdot \dfrac{21}{20}$

14. $\dfrac{33}{24} \cdot \dfrac{28}{11}$

15. $\dfrac{63}{65} \cdot \dfrac{26}{49}$

16. $36\left(\dfrac{5}{63}\right)$

17. $\left(\dfrac{3}{77}\right)(22)$

18. $\dfrac{91}{12} \cdot \dfrac{36}{13}$

19. $\dfrac{34}{65} \cdot \dfrac{26}{51}$

20. $\dfrac{7}{36} \cdot \dfrac{9}{14}$

Multiply in the order indicated.

21. $\left(\dfrac{5}{6} \cdot \dfrac{7}{8}\right) \cdot \dfrac{5}{2}$

22. $\dfrac{5}{6} \cdot \left(\dfrac{7}{8} \cdot \dfrac{5}{2}\right)$

23. What property of quotient numbers is illustrated by problems 21 and 22?

24. Let a/b, c/d, e/f, be <u>any</u> three quotient numbers. Write a general statement of the associative property of multiplication for quotient numbers.

25. Use only the definition of multiplication for quotient numbers and properties of natural numbers to prove the associative property of multiplication for quotient numbers.

AN ALTERNATIVE RULE FOR ADDITION

1. Addition of fractions has been defined in terms of cross _____. That is, we define

$$\frac{a}{b} + \frac{c}{d} = \underline{\hspace{3cm}}$$

> PRODUCTS; $\dfrac{ad + bc}{bd}$.

2. Then

$$\frac{2}{5} + \frac{4}{9} = \frac{ + }{45} = \underline{\hspace{2cm}}.$$

> 18;   20;   38/45

3. Similarly,

$$\frac{2}{7} + \frac{3}{7} = \frac{ + }{49} = \frac{35}{49} = \frac{5 \cdot 7}{7 \cdot 7} = \underline{\hspace{2cm}}$$

> 14;   21;   5/7

4. $\dfrac{2}{7} + \dfrac{3}{7} = \dfrac{5}{7}$

   Note that each term has the same denominator, 7. And observe that this number is also the _____ of the sum.

> DENOMINATOR

5. Use the cross product rule to find the following sum in simplest form.

$$\frac{2}{9} + \frac{5}{9} = \underline{\hspace{2cm}}$$

> $\dfrac{2}{9} + \dfrac{5}{9} = \dfrac{18 + 45}{9 \cdot 9} = \dfrac{63}{9 \cdot 9} = \dfrac{7 \cdot 9}{9 \cdot 9} = \dfrac{7}{9}$

6. $\dfrac{2}{9} + \dfrac{5}{9} = \dfrac{7}{9}$

   Note that the terms have numerators which are 2 and 5. And observe that the numerator of the sum is the _____ of these numbers.

> SUM

7. Using the cross product rule, and simplifying, we have

$$\frac{1}{12} + \frac{7}{12} = \frac{12 + 84}{144} = \frac{96}{144} = \frac{2 \cdot 48}{3 \cdot 48} = \underline{\hspace{2cm}}$$

   But note that $1 + 7 = 8$ and

$$\frac{1}{12} + \frac{7}{12} = \frac{1 + 7}{12} = \frac{8}{12} = \frac{2 \cdot 4}{3 \cdot 4} = \underline{\hspace{2cm}}$$

> 2/3;   2/3

8. Use the method illustrated in the previous frames to find the simplest form of each of the following.

$$\frac{2}{3} + \frac{5}{3} = \frac{2+5}{3} = \text{_____}$$

$$\frac{3}{10} + \frac{4}{10} = \text{_____}$$

$$\frac{8}{15} + \frac{6}{15} = \text{_____}$$

7/3;   7/10;   14/15

9. Find the simplest form of each of the following using the short method illustrated.

$$\frac{5}{12} + \frac{8}{12} = \text{_____}$$

$$\frac{13}{5} + \frac{3}{5} = \text{_____}$$

$$\frac{2}{9} + \frac{5}{9} = \text{_____}$$

$$\frac{12}{117} + \frac{3}{117} = \text{_____}$$

13/12;   16/5;   7/9;   15/117 = 5/39

10. We shall show that whenever the denominators of two fractions are equal, then their sum can be more easily found by adding their _____ and not changing the common denominator.

NUMERATORS

11. Let a/b and c/b represent any two fractions whose _____ are equal.

DENOMINATORS

12. Then we want to show that

$$\frac{a}{b} + \frac{c}{b} = \frac{\text{_____}}{b} .$$

a + c

13. Now we have defined the addition of fractions in terms of their cross _____.

PRODUCTS

14. By the cross product rule, $\frac{a}{b} + \frac{c}{d} = \frac{\text{_____}}{bd}$.

ad + bc

15. We want to show now that $\frac{a}{b} + \frac{c}{b} = \frac{a+c}{b}$.

By the cross product rule, $\frac{a}{b} + \frac{c}{b} = \frac{ab + \text{\_\_\_\_}}{b \cdot b}$.

bc

16. $$\frac{a}{b} + \frac{c}{b} = \frac{ab + bc}{b \cdot b}$$

But by the commutative property of multiplication

$$ab + bc = b \text{_____} + bc .$$

a

17. We have

$$\frac{a}{b} + \frac{c}{b} = \frac{ab + bc}{b \cdot b} \quad \text{and} \quad ab + bc = ba + bc .$$

Hence

$$\frac{a}{b} + \frac{c}{b} = \frac{ba + bc}{\text{_____}} .$$

b·b

18. We have shown that

$$\frac{a}{b} + \frac{c}{b} = \frac{ba + bc}{b \cdot b} \ .$$

But by the distributive property

$$ba + bc = b(\underline{\quad} + \underline{\quad}).$$

a;   c

19. We have

$$\frac{a}{b} + \frac{c}{b} = \frac{ba + bc}{b \cdot b} \quad \text{and} \quad ba + bc = b(a + c)$$

Hence

$$\frac{a}{b} + \frac{c}{b} = \frac{b(a + c)}{\underline{\qquad}}$$

b · b

20. $$\frac{a}{b} + \frac{c}{b} = \frac{b(a + c)}{b \cdot b}$$

But the factor b may be cancelled, and so

$$\frac{a}{b} + \frac{c}{b} = \frac{a + c}{\underline{\qquad}}$$

b

21. $$\frac{a}{b} + \frac{c}{b} = \frac{a + c}{b}$$

We have proved that, for the special case where two fractions have equal denominators, their sum may be found most easily by _____ their numerators.

ADDING

22. Hence

$$\frac{5}{21} + \frac{3}{21} = \underline{\qquad}$$

$$\frac{3}{7} + \frac{1}{7} = \underline{\qquad}$$

$$\frac{9}{10} + \frac{3}{10} = \frac{12}{10} = \frac{}{5}$$

8/21;   4/7;   6

23. But when the denominators of the two fractions are not equal, we cannot use this method. Thus, to add 3/5 and 4/9 we use the cross product rule.

$$\frac{3}{5} + \frac{4}{9} = \underline{\qquad}$$

$$\frac{27 + 20}{45} = \frac{47}{45}$$

24. Use an appropriate method to add

$$\frac{8}{3} + \frac{2}{3} = \underline{\qquad}$$

$$\frac{4}{9} + \frac{1}{2} = \underline{\qquad}$$

$$\frac{5}{6} + \frac{3}{8} = \underline{\qquad}$$

10/3;   17/18;   58/48 = 29/24

25. Find the indicated sum or product:

$$3 + \frac{2}{5} = \underline{\qquad}$$

$$\left(\frac{2}{5}\right)\left(\frac{1}{2}\right) = \underline{\qquad}$$

$$\frac{3}{10} + \frac{2}{10} = \underline{\qquad}$$

$$5\frac{1}{6} = \underline{\qquad}$$

17/5;   1/5;   1/2;   31/6

26. Remember $5\frac{1}{6}$ means the _____ of 5 and $\frac{1}{6}$.

27. But $(5)\left(\frac{1}{6}\right)$ represents the _____ of 5 and $\frac{1}{6}$ and equals _____ .

28. Express each of the following in simplest form:

$(10)\left(\frac{3}{2}\right)$ = _____

$8 + \frac{3}{4}$ = _____

$4\frac{2}{3}$ = _____

$\frac{3}{110} + \frac{4}{110}$ = _____

29. A fraction is in simplest form when its _____ and _____ are as small as possible.

30. And we have seen that a fraction will be in simplest form when its numerator and denominator are relatively _____ .

31. When reducing a fraction to simplest form, we have cancelled a _____ which is common to both the numerator and denominator.

32. Then the fraction $(5 \cdot 13)/(12 \cdot 13)$ can be reduced to simplest form by cancelling the common factor _____ .

33. To change 15/18 to simplest form we write

$\frac{15}{18} = \frac{5 \cdot 3}{6 \cdot 3} = $ _____ .

34.   15/18 = 5/6

In changing 15/18 to its simplest form, 5/6, we cancelled the common factor, _____ .

35. Express in simplest form:

36/45 = _____

27/9 = _____

16/12 = _____

36.   16/12 = 4/3

To obtain this result, we can write

16/12 = $(4 \cdot 4)/(3 \cdot 4)$

and then cancel the _____ factor 4.

37. $\frac{16}{12} = \frac{4 \cdot 4}{3 \cdot 4} = \frac{4}{3}$

We have cancelled the common factor 4. Note that while 4 is not the only common factor of the numerator, 16, and the denominator, 12, it is their H_____ common factor.

38. $\frac{16}{12} = \frac{4 \cdot 4}{3 \cdot 4} = \frac{4}{3}$

In effect then we reduce 16/12 to simplest form by cancelling the HCF of the numerator and denominator.

But the HCF of any two numbers is also their greatest common _____.

39. $\frac{16}{12} = \frac{4 \cdot 4}{3 \cdot 4} = \frac{4}{3}$

Since the number we have cancelled, 4, is the GCD of 16 and 12, then 4 must be a common divisor of 16 and 12, and

16/4 = _____   12/4 = _____

40. $\frac{16}{12} = \frac{4 \cdot 4}{3 \cdot 4} = \frac{4}{3}$ $\frac{16}{4} = 4$ $\frac{12}{4} = 3$

Then cancelling the factor 4 from the numerator and denominator of the fraction 16/12 is equivalent to dividing each by 4.

We could say that the fraction 16/12 can be reduced to simplest form by dividing the numerator and denominator by their G_____.

41. The example of the last few frames illustrates a general principle. We have said that when the numerator and denominator of a fraction contain a common _____, it can be cancelled.

42. In symbols ax/bx = _____.

43. Since x is a factor of ax, then x is also an exact _____ of ax.

44. And the quotient of ax and x, represented by ax/x, equals _____, since the product of _____ and x equals ax.

45. Then

ax/x = a

Similarly bx is divisible by x, and bx/x = _____.

46. $\dfrac{ax}{bx} = \dfrac{a}{b}$ by cancelling.

But when ax and bx are each divided by x, the quotients are also a and b.

In general, cancelling a factor of the numerator and denominator of a fraction is equivalent to _____ both by that common factor.

DIVIDING

47. Every common factor of two numbers is also a common divisor. And cancelling a common F_____ of the numerator and denominator of a fraction is equivalent to dividing the numerator and denominator by a common D_____.

FACTOR;   DIVISOR

48. Furthermore, the resulting fraction will always be in simplest form if we C_____ the HCF or D _____ by the GCD of the numerator and denominator.

CANCEL;   DIVIDE

49. Hence

36/45 = _____

in simplest form, and this result can be obtained by either cancelling the _____, 9, in the numerator and denominator, or dividing each by 9.

4/5;   FACTOR

50. Cancelling allows us to write

ax/bx = _____.

a/b

51. Consider the fraction $3/(4 \cdot 3)$.

Is 3 a factor of the numerator and denominator of this fraction?

YES

52. $3/(4 \cdot 3)$

3 is a factor of both the numerator and denominator here. Can we cancel 3 from each?_____

NO!   (see next frame)

53. $3/(4 \cdot 3)$

We cannot cancel the 3 in the numerator and denominator of this fraction as it now stands. Since the numerator is not expressed as a product, we cannot use the cancelling rule.

However, we can write $3 = 1 \cdot$ _____.

3

54. Since

$3 = 1 \cdot 3$

we can write

$3/(4 \cdot 3) = (1 \cdot 3)/(4 \cdot 3)$

Can we cancel the 3 in the numerator and denominator now?_____

YES

55. And $(1 \cdot 3)/(4 \cdot 3) =$ _____.

Let us return to the original fraction $3/(4 \cdot 3)$.

Is 3 an exact divisor of both the numerator and denominator?_____

1/4;   YES

56. $3/(4 \cdot 3)$

The numerator and denominator are both divisible by 3. When we divide, we get the quotients _____ and _____, respectively.

> 1;   4

57. And, as we have seen,

$$3/(4 \cdot 3) = 1/4$$

Hence, for some fractions we may be able to divide numerator and denominator by a common divisor even though we cannot cancel a common factor without first changing the form of the fractions.

58. Consider the fraction 2/3.

If the numerator and denominator are each multiplied by 8, the resulting products are, respectively.

$$2 \cdot 8 = \underline{\qquad} \quad \text{and} \quad 3 \cdot 8 = \underline{\qquad}$$

> 16;   24

59. We can use the cross product test to see that

$$2/3 \underline{\qquad} 16/24$$

> =

60. Then

$$\frac{2}{3} = \frac{2 \cdot 8}{3 \cdot 8} = \frac{16}{24}.$$

Similarly, if we consider the fraction 4/5 and multiply both the numerator and denominator by 9, the resulting fraction, _____, is _____ to 4/5.

> 36/45;   EQUAL

61. $$\frac{4}{5} = \frac{4 \cdot 9}{5 \cdot 9} = \frac{36}{45}$$

In fact, we can obtain an equal fraction from any fraction by either _____ or _____ both the numerator and the denominator by the same natural number.

> MULTIPLYING;   DIVIDING
> (either order)

62. Change each fraction to an equal fraction by multiplying both numerator and denominator by 3.

$$5/6 = \underline{\qquad}$$
$$1/2 = \underline{\qquad}$$
$$8/5 = \underline{\qquad}$$

> 15/18;   3/6;   24/15

63. When the numerator and denominator of the fraction 5/6 are both multiplied by _____, the resulting equal fraction is 10/12.

> 2

64. By what must the numerator and denominator of 3/4 be multiplied to give the equal fraction 15/20? _____

> 5

65. In each case, determine the number by which both the numerator and denominator have been multiplied.

$$3/4 = 21/28 \underline{\qquad}$$
$$1/9 = 9/81 \underline{\qquad}$$
$$6/5 = 120/100 \underline{\qquad}$$

> 7;   9;   20

66. Find the numerator which makes these fractions equal.

$1/3 =$ _____ $/15$

> 5

67. $1/3 = [\ \ ]/15$

Since the denominator, 3, has been multiplied by 5, to give 15, then the numerator, 1, must also be multiplied by _____ .

> 5

68. Find the numerator.

$1/5 =$ _____ $/20$

> 4

69. In each case, find the numerator.

$1/2 =$ _____ $/20$
$1/7 =$ _____ $/42$
$2/3 =$ _____ $/12$

> 10;   6;   8

70. $2/3 = [\ \ ]/12$

Notice that since 3 is multiplied by _____ to give 12, we must also multiply 2 by _____ .

> 4;   4

71. Find the numerator.

$5/8 =$ _____ $/40$

> 25

72. Supply the missing numerator.

a) $2/9 =$ _____ $/18$ b) $3/7 =$ _____ $/28$
c) $8/3 =$ _____ $/9$ d) $4/5 =$ _____ $/65$

> a) 4;   b) 12;   c) 24;   d) 52

73. If 2/3 is changed to a fraction whose denominator is 12, the result is _____ .

> 8/12

74. Change 2/5 to an equivalent fraction whose denominator is the same as for the fraction 3/20.

$2/5 =$ _____

> 8/20

75. Write each of these as a fraction whose denominator is the same as for the fraction 7/30.

$1/2 =$ _____
$5/6 =$ _____
$8/15 =$ _____

> 15/30;   25/30;   16/30

76. Write 2/3 as a fraction whose denominator is 6.

$2/3 =$ _____

> 4/6

77. Since $2/3 = 4/6$, the sum of 2/3 and 1/6 is the same as the sum of 4/6 and 1/6, and $4/6 + 1/6 =$ _____ .

> 5/6

78. Then

$$\frac{2}{3} + \frac{1}{6} = \frac{4}{6} + \frac{1}{6} = \text{_____} \, ,$$

5/6

79. By the cross product rule for adding,

$$\frac{2}{3} + \frac{1}{6} = \frac{\text{\_\_} + \text{\_\_}}{18} = \frac{\text{\_\_}}{18} = \frac{\text{\_\_}}{6}$$

12 + 3;   15;   5

80. Hence, to add 2/3 and 1/6 we may either change 2/3 to 4/6 and use a short method, or we may use the _____ _____ rule.

CROSS PRODUCT

81. To use the short method to find 1/2 + 3/8, we should change 1/2 to an equal fraction whose denominator is the same as that of the fraction _____ .

3/8

82. Then to find 1/2 + 3/8, we first write 1/2 = _____ .

4/8

83. Thus

$$\frac{1}{2} + \frac{3}{8} = \frac{4}{8} + \frac{3}{8} = \text{_____} .$$

7/8

84. To find 2/3 + 5/12, we could change the fraction _____ to an equal one whose denominator is the same as that for the fraction 5/12.

2/3

85. Hence

$$\frac{2}{3} + \frac{5}{12} = \frac{\text{\_\_}}{12} + \frac{5}{12} = \frac{13}{12}$$

8

86. To add 8/5 and 7/20, we should change the fraction _____ to an equal fraction whose denominator is _____ .

8/5;   20

87. Then

$$\frac{8}{5} + \frac{7}{20} = \text{_____} + \frac{7}{20} = \text{_____} .$$

32/20;   39/20

88. $$\frac{8}{5} + \frac{7}{20} = \frac{32}{20} + \frac{7}{20} = \frac{39}{20}$$

But if we use the cross product rule,

$$\frac{8}{5} + \frac{7}{20} = \frac{160 + \text{\_\_}}{100} = \frac{195}{100} = \frac{39 \cdot 5}{20 \cdot 5} = \text{_____}$$

35;   39/20

89. Notice that, of course, the result of adding 8/5 and 7/20 is the same whichever method is used.

90. One method of finding the sum of 2/7 and 3/35 is

$$\frac{2}{7} + \frac{3}{35} = \frac{10}{35} + \frac{3}{35} = \underline{\hspace{1cm}}$$

We call this the method of COMMON DE-NOMINATORS.

13/35

91. Use the method of common denominators to find

$$\frac{3}{8} + \frac{1}{16} = \frac{}{16} + \frac{1}{16} = \underline{\hspace{1cm}}$$

$$\frac{1}{5} + \frac{7}{10} = \underline{\hspace{1cm}}$$

$$\frac{5}{12} + \frac{2}{3} = \underline{\hspace{1cm}}$$

6;   7/16;   9/10;   13/12

92. Change 2/5 to a fraction whose denominator is the same as that of the fraction 7/15.

$$2/5 = \underline{\hspace{1cm}}$$

6/15

93. Change 1/2 to a fraction whose denominator is the same as that of the fraction 3/5.

$$1/2 = \underline{\hspace{1cm}} /5$$

IMPOSSIBLE   (see next frame)

94.   1/2 = [   ]/5

This is impossible, since there is no natural number whose product with 2 equals _____.

5

95. Since there is no natural number whose product with 2 is 5, we say that 5 is not divisible by 2 or that 5 is not a M_____ of 2.

MULTIPLE

96. Is 15 a multiple of 3? _____

Is 12 a multiple of 8? _____

YES;   NO

97. In each of the following pairs of fractions, is the denominator of one a multiple of the other?

1/2 and 3/8   Yes, 8 is a multiple of 2.

5/6 and 3/10   _____

7/18 and 2/3   _____

NO;   YES, 18 IS A MULTIPLE OF 3

98. We are not able to change 1/2 to a fraction whose denominator is 5 since 5 is not a _____ of 2.

MULTIPLE

99. Is it possible to change 3/4 to a fraction whose denominator is

9? _____

12? _____

100? _____

70? _____

NO;   YES;   YES;   NO

100. We have used the method of common denominators to add fractions only when one denominator is a _____ of the other.

101. The method of common denominators may be used in other cases, but with more difficulty.

Consider the problem $1/2 + 1/5$.

By the method of common denominators we should try to change $1/2$ to a fraction whose _____ is the same as that for the fraction $1/5$.

102. But we cannot change $1/2$ to a fraction whose denominator is the same as $1/5$, since 5 is not a _____ of 2.

103. Consider the least common multiple of 2 and 5. The LCM of 2 and 5 is _____.

104. Is 10 a multiple of 2? _____
Is 10 a multiple of 5? _____

105. Since 10 is a multiple of both 2 and 5, it is possible to change both $1/2$ and $1/5$ to fractions with a common denominator, _____.

106. $1/2 =$ _____ $/10$ $1/5 =$ _____ $/10$

107. Then since

$1/2 = 5/10$

$1/5 = 2/10$

to add $1/2$ and $1/5$ we may instead add $5/10$ and _____.

108. Thus

$$\frac{1}{2} + \frac{1}{5} = \frac{5}{10} + \frac{}{10} = \frac{}{10}$$

109. When we write

$$\frac{1}{2} + \frac{1}{5} = \frac{5}{10} + \frac{2}{10} = \frac{7}{10},$$

we have used the method of _____ _____.

110. Use the cross product rule to add

$$\frac{1}{2} + \frac{1}{5} = \frac{+}{2 \cdot 5} = \text{_____}.$$

111. By the common denominator method:

$$\frac{1}{2} + \frac{1}{5} = \frac{5}{10} + \frac{2}{10} = \frac{5+2}{10} = \frac{7}{10}$$

By the cross product method:

$$\frac{1}{2} + \frac{1}{5} = \frac{1 \cdot 5 + 2 \cdot 1}{2 \cdot 5} = \frac{5+2}{10} = \frac{7}{10}$$

These examples show certain similarities between the two methods, but they do not show that one method is preferable to the other.

In general, it is easier to use the common denominator method when one denominator is equal to or a multiple of the other. But when this is not the case, the choice of method is not clear.

112. The common denominator method is to be preferred in which of the following problems?

a) $\frac{8}{29} + \frac{2}{29}$ b) $\frac{3}{17} + \frac{4}{5}$

c) $\frac{12}{5} + \frac{3}{20}$ d) $\frac{12}{7} + \frac{2}{9}$ _____

> a and c

113. Use either method to find each of the following in simplest form:

$$\frac{8}{3} + \frac{5}{6} = \underline{\hspace{1cm}}$$

$$\frac{6}{5} + \frac{3}{2} = \underline{\hspace{1cm}}$$

$$\frac{1}{25} + \frac{2}{5} = \underline{\hspace{1cm}}$$

$$\frac{173}{37} + \frac{21}{37} = \underline{\hspace{1cm}}$$

> $21/6 = 7/2$; $27/10$; $11/25$; $194/37$

114. Originally we defined the sum of two fractions with the _____ _____ rule.

> CROSS PRODUCT

115. But in this chapter we have shown that this is equivalent to the method of _____ _____.

> COMMON DENOMINATORS

116. Either the cross product rule or the method of common denominators may be used to find the sum of any two fractions, but it will generally be easier to use the method of common denominators whenever the denominators are equal, or when one is a _____ of the other.

> MULTIPLE

Chapter 14

Problems A (Answers on page 510)

Find the simplest form of the missing numerator.

Example: $\frac{3}{8} = \frac{}{72}$. Solution: $\frac{3}{8} = \frac{3 \cdot 9}{8 \cdot 9} = \frac{27}{72}$

Example: $\frac{2}{3 \cdot 5} = \frac{}{2 \cdot 3 \cdot 3 \cdot 5}$

Solution: $\frac{2}{3 \cdot 5} = \frac{2 \cdot 2 \cdot 3}{2 \cdot 3 \cdot 3 \cdot 5} = \frac{12}{90}$

1. $\frac{1}{4} = \frac{}{28}$

2. $\frac{7}{3} = \frac{}{36}$

3. $\frac{5}{8} = \frac{}{104}$

4. $\frac{4}{3 \cdot 7} = \frac{}{2 \cdot 3 \cdot 7}$

5. $\frac{5}{2 \cdot 3} = \frac{}{2 \cdot 2 \cdot 3 \cdot 5}$

6. $\frac{6}{15} = \frac{}{40}$ (Hint: First simplify 6/15)

7. $\frac{35}{14} = \frac{}{8}$

Use either the method of common denominators or the cross product rule to add. Write answers in simplest form.

8. $\frac{9}{7} + \frac{3}{4}$ 13. $\frac{12}{7} + \frac{1}{2}$

9. $\frac{4}{3} + \frac{1}{4}$ 14. $\frac{9}{16} + \frac{5}{8}$

10. $3 + \frac{2}{3}$ 15. $\frac{4}{5} + \frac{5}{8}$

11. $1 + \frac{2}{5}$ 16. $\frac{165}{46} + \frac{17}{23}$

12. $\frac{13}{18} + \frac{5}{9}$

Add or multiply, as indicated. Write answers in simplest form.

17. $\frac{8}{17} \cdot \frac{17}{4}$ 19. $0 \cdot \frac{11}{5}$

18. $4\frac{2}{9}$ 20. $\frac{12}{7} + 1$

Find the quotient number that answers each of the following.

Example:

The enrollment at a certain college is 3840. On a certain day 1/6 of the student body was absent because of illness and 1/10 was absent for other reasons.

a) How many students were absent because of illness?

b) What fractional part of the student body was absent for all reasons?

c) How many students attended classes?

Solution:

a) (1/6)(3840) = 640
   640 students were absent for illness.

b) $\frac{1}{6} + \frac{1}{10} = \frac{10 + 6}{60} = \frac{16}{60} = \frac{8}{30}$
   8/30 of the student body was absent.

c) $\left(\frac{8}{30}\right)(3840) = \frac{8 \cdot 3840}{30} = \frac{8 \cdot 30 \cdot 128}{30}$

   $= 8 \cdot 128 = 1024$

   1024 students were absent
   3840 − 1024 = 2816
   2816 students attended classes.

21. The membership of the United States House of Representatives is 435. If 3/5 of the House was present for a certain vote, how many were present?

22. If all members of the House are present (see problem 21) and a 2/3 vote is required to override a Presidential veto, how many votes are required?

23. During their Freshman year 1/3 of the students at a certain college dropped out of school. If there were 2148 freshmen at the beginning of the year, how many were left at the end of the year?

24. Mr. Jones spent 1/5 of his income for rent and 1/4 for food. What fractional part did he spend for both food and rent?

25. If Mr. Jones' income was $8000 per year (see problem 24) how much did he spend for rent and food together?

Problems B

Add or multiply, as indicated. Write answers in simplest form.

1. $\dfrac{3}{8} + \dfrac{5}{2}$

2. $\dfrac{5}{12} + \dfrac{5}{6}$

3. $\dfrac{5}{8} + \dfrac{8}{5}$

4. $\dfrac{8}{3} + \dfrac{3}{8}$

5. $\dfrac{15}{8} \cdot \dfrac{4}{5}$

6. $\dfrac{5}{7} + 2$

7. $4 + \dfrac{2}{9}$

8. $4 \cdot \dfrac{2}{9}$

9. $\dfrac{3}{5} + 1$

10. $\dfrac{12}{7} \cdot 1$

11. $\dfrac{4}{15} + \dfrac{3}{10}$

12. $8 + \dfrac{3}{4}$

13. $0 + \dfrac{11}{5}$

14. $\dfrac{11}{15} + \dfrac{2}{3}$

15. $\dfrac{69}{25} \cdot \dfrac{15}{23}$

16. $11 + \dfrac{5}{2}$

17. $\dfrac{14}{9} \cdot \dfrac{3}{56}$

18. $\dfrac{7}{3} + \dfrac{2}{21}$

19. $\dfrac{13}{49} + \dfrac{6}{35}$

20. $\dfrac{19}{65} + \dfrac{4}{13}$

21. A baseball team won 2/3 of its games during a season. If the team played 147 games, how many did it win?

22. An athlete ran for 2 minutes. During the first minute he ran 1/4 of a mile and during the second minute he ran 3/16 of a mile. How far did he run altogether?

23. If 8/10 of those eligible to vote actually voted in an election and 5/9 of those who voted supported the winning candidate, what fractional part of the eligible vote did he receive?

24. There are 500,000 college students in California. 1/8 of them attend the University of California, 1/5 attend a state college, 1/5 attend private colleges, and the remainder attend the junior colleges. How many attend a junior college?

25. The United States Senate contains 100 members. If 4/5 of the members were present and 9/16 of those present voted for a certain bill, how many voted for the bill?

CHAPTER 15

ORDERING OF QUOTIENT NUMBERS

1. A symbol of the form a/b with certain restrictions on a and b is called a _____.

   FRACTION

2. If a/b is a fraction, then both a and b must be _____ which represent natural numbers.

   SYMBOLS

3. That is, both the _____ and _____ of a fraction must represent a _____ _____.

   NUMERATOR;   DENOMINATOR
   (either order);   NATURAL NUMBER

4. To determine if two fractions are equal, we use the _____ product test of equality.

   CROSS

5. That is, a/b = c/d means that _____ = _____.

   ad = bc

6. Many fractions are equal. In fact, the fractions

   6/12,   5/10,   4/8,   3/6,   2/4

   and 1/2

   are all equal. The property shared by all these equal fractions is called a _____ _____.

   QUOTIENT NUMBER

7. Every quotient number may be represented by a _____.

   FRACTION

8. Some quotient numbers may also be represented by the symbols 1, 2, 3, 4, ... , and hence are also _____ _____.

   NATURAL NUMBERS

9. The natural numbers can be arranged in order. In fact, we arrange the natural numbers in the order in which we _____ .

> COUNT

10. And when the natural numbers are arranged in the order 1, 2, 3, 4, 5, ..., it happens that each number is _____ than every number that follows it.

> LESS

11. Then, 2 is less than 3, and we indicate this in symbols by writing 2 _____ 3.

> <

12. Which of the following statements are true?

   a) $5 < 9$

   b) $2 < 5$

   c) $14 < 8$

   d) $12 < 12$ _____

> a and b

13. We know that $5 < 9$, since there is a natural number 4, such that _____ + 4 = _____ .

> $\underline{5} + 4 = \underline{9}$

14. When we write an expression like $12 > 3$, we mean 3 _____ 12.

> <

15. Which of the following are true?

   a) $9 > 6$ d) $9 > 9$

   b) $13 < 10$ e) $27 < 28$

   c) $1 > 5$ _____

> a and e

16. Recall that for any two natural numbers a and b exactly one of the following is true.

   $a < b$

   $a = b$

   a _____ b

> >

17. Then for any two natural numbers either the first is less than the second, the first is equal to the second, or the first is _____ than the second.

> GREATER

18. Since this is true, one says that the natural numbers are ordered. We will show that the quotient numbers are also _____ .

> ORDERED

19. Every quotient number can be represented by a _____ .

> FRACTION

20. Two fractions a/b and c/d are equal if _____ .

> ad = bc

21. Hence 2/5 = 14/35, because
2·35 = _____ · _____.

> 5·14

22. We shall say that 2/5 < 7/17, since
2·17 < 5·7. Notice that the cross product
2·17 = 34, while 5·7 = 35, and

34 _____ 35.

> <

23. Similarly, we say that 3/7 < 4/9, since
3·9 _____ 7·4

> <

24. 5/8 < 9/14, since 5·14 < _____.

> 8·9

25. 2/3 < 5/7, since 2·_____
< _____ · _____.

> 2·7 < 3·5

26. Consider the fractions 3/7 and 7/16.
Since
3·16 = 48
7·7 = 49,
and
3·16 < 7·7
it follows that
3/7 _____ 7/16

> <

27. The cross products determine when one fraction is less than another. In symbols,

a/b < c/d, whenever ad < _____.

> bc

28. Which of these statements are true?
a) 2/5 < 5/12   b) 3/8 < 4/11
c) 5/9 < 6/11   _____

> ONLY a IS TRUE

29. In fact,
3/8 > 4/11   since   3·11 _____ 8·4.

> >

30. And 5/9 > 6/11   since
_____ > _____.

> 5·11 > 9·6

31. In symbols, a/b > c/d whenever
_____.

> ad > bc

32. Which of these is true?
a) 5/7 > 7/10   b) 8/3 > 5/2
c) 4/11 > 3/8   _____

> a and b

33. Which of these is true?

    a) 3/8 < 5/13   b) 12/7 > 7/4

    c) 6/1 > 52/9   _____

      a and c

34. Consider the two fractions 5/11 and 4/9.
The cross products are

$$5 \cdot 9 = 45 \quad \text{and} \quad \underline{\quad} \cdot \underline{\quad} = \underline{\quad}$$

      11 · 4 = 44

35. 5/11   and   4/9

    5 · 9 _____ 11 · 4

      >

36. 5/11   and   4/9

    Since 5 · 9 > 11 · 4, it follows that
5/11 _____ 4/9.

      >

37. In general, for any two fractions a/b and c/d,
if ad < bc, then a/b _____ c/d, and if
ad > bc, then _____ .

      < ;   a/b > c/d

38. Of course, if ad = bc, then

    a/b _____ c/d

      =

39. Determine the sign, < , >, or =, in each case.

    3/11 _____ 4/15

    12/5 _____ 7/3

    9/4 _____ 7/3

    8/3 _____ 16/6

      > ;   > ;   < ;   =

40. To determine which of two fractions is larger
we need only compare their _____
products.

      CROSS

41. And since the cross products of two fractions
are always _____ numbers, it will
always be possible to determine which is
larger, or if they are equal.

      NATURAL

42. Then, given any two fractions a/b and c/d,
exactly one of the following is true.

    a/b < c/d   a/b = c/d   a/b _____ c/d

      >

43. Given any two fractions we can always tell
which, if either, is larger. Determine the
sign < , >, or =.

    2/15 _____ 4/15

    8/15 _____ 3/15

    17/15 _____ 1/15

      < ;   > ;   >

44. Notice that the fractions in the previous frame all have the same denominator.

$$2/15 < 4/15 \qquad 8/15 > 3/15$$

$$17/15 > 1/15$$

When fractions have the same denominator we need not compare their cross _____ to tell which is larger.

45. In fact, for fractions with the same denominators, the larger fraction is the one with the larger _____.

46. Note that, in each pair, the fractions have the same denominator. Use this fact to write:

$$9/17 < 10/17 \qquad 13/75 > 8/75$$

$$12/7 \underline{\qquad} 18/7 \qquad 133/9 \underline{\qquad} 125/9$$

<; >

47. $133 > 125$

and so we have concluded that

$$133/9 > 125/9$$

We can, of course, show that this is so by means of the cross product test.

$$133 \cdot 9 = 1197 \qquad 9 \cdot 125 = 1125$$

and

$$133 \cdot 9 \underline{\qquad} 9 \cdot 125$$

48. But these problems are more easily completed by using the fact that the fractions have the same denominator. Compare

$$125/64 \underline{\qquad} 139/64,$$

$$512/833 \underline{\qquad} 509/833,$$

$$51/92 \underline{\qquad} 175/92$$

49. Whenever two fractions have the same D _____, the larger fraction will be the one with the _____ numerator.

50. Use the cross product rule to compare:

$$8/3 \underline{\qquad} 8/5,$$

$$8/1 \underline{\qquad} 8/9,$$

$$8/7 \underline{\qquad} 8/4$$

51. These fractions have the same numerator.

$$8/3 > 8/5, \qquad 8/1 > 8/9, \qquad 8/7 < 8/4$$

To determine the larger fraction we need compare only the _____.

52. For fractions that have the same numerators, the larger fraction has the _____ denominator.

53. Compare. Note that in each pair the fractions have the same numerators.

12/7 _____ 12/9,

17/25 _____ 17/23,

173/96 _____ 173/105

>;   <;   >

54. The _____ _____ rule can always be used to compare two fractions, but it is easier not to use it whenever the fractions contain the same numerator or the same denominator.

CROSS PRODUCT

55. Notice that 2 < 3 and also 3 < 4.

We shorten this by writing 2 < 3 < 4.

Similarly, since 5 < 6 and 6 < 7, we may write

_____ < _____ < _____

5 < 6 < 7

56. Write these statements in the shorter form.

2 < 7   and   7 < 12   2 < 7 < _____

9 < 15   and   15 < 16

9 < _____ < _____

2/3 < 3/4 and 3/4 < 5/6   _____

12;   15 < 16;   2/3 < 3/4 < 5/6

57. Since 4 < 5 < 6, we say that 5 is BETWEEN 4 and 6.

Similarly, since 8 < 9 < 10 we say that _____ is between _____ and 10.

9;   8

58. Consider 5 and 8. There are two natural numbers between 5 and 8. They are _____ and _____ .

6;   7   (either order)

59. Precisely, when we say that 6 and 7 are both between 5 and 8, we mean that both 5 < 6 < 8, and also 5 < _____ < 8.

7

60. How many natural numbers are there between 3 and 9? _____

FIVE   (4, 5, 6, 7, 8)

61. How many natural numbers are there between 12 and 13? _____

NONE

62. Since there are no natural numbers between 12 and 13, and since 13 > 12, we say that 13 is the SUCCESSOR of _____ .

12

63. Similarly _____ is the successor of 9.

10

64. If one natural number is the successor of another, then there are _____ natural numbers between the two.

NO

65. Then given any two natural numbers it may or may not be possible to find another natural number which is _____ them.

BETWEEN

66. But this is not true for fractions. In fact, given any two fractions we can always find another _____ which is between them.

FRACTION

67. Consider the fractions 1/2 and 4/5. Note that 1/2 _____ 4/5.

<

68. $1/2 < 4/5$

There are many fractions between 1/2 and 4/5. One way of finding a fraction between 1/2 and 4/5 is first to notice that

$$1/2 = 5/10, \qquad 4/5 = \underline{\quad}/10$$

8

69. $1/2 = 5/10 \quad$ and $\quad 4/5 = 8/10$

It is clear that both 6/10 and _____/10 are fractions which are between 5/10 and 8/10, and hence are between 1/2 and 4/5.

7

70. Also $1/2 = 10/20, \qquad 4/5 = 16/20$.

And we see that 11/20, 12/20, _____, _____ are all between 1/2 and 4/5.

13/20; 14/20; 15/20

71. We could continue:

$$1/2 = 50/100, \qquad 4/5 = 80/100$$

Now we see that there are, indeed, many fractions between 1/2 and 4/5. In fact, 51/100, 52/100, 53/100, ... , 78/100, 79/100 are all _____ 1/2 and 4/5.

BETWEEN

72. Consider the fractions 1/3 and 1/2.

It is curious to note that the fraction 2/5 is between 1/3 and 1/2. That is,

$$1/3 < 2/5, \qquad \text{since} \qquad 1 \cdot 5 < 3 \cdot 2$$

and

$$2/5 < 1/2, \qquad \text{since} \qquad \underline{\quad} < \underline{\quad}$$

$\underline{2 \cdot 2} < \underline{5 \cdot 1}$

73. $1/3 < 2/5 < 1/2$

It is curious that

$$2 = 1 + 1$$
$$5 = 3 + 2$$

That is, the numerator of 2/5 is the sum of the numerators of 1/3 and 1/2, while the _____ of 2/5 is the _____ of the denominators of 1/3 and 1/2.

DENOMINATOR;   SUM

74. Consider 1/4 and 1/3.

If we add the numerators and denominators, the resulting fraction is _____.

2/7

75. Is 2/7 between 1/4 and 1/3? _____

YES $(1/4 < 2/7$ and $2/7 < 1/3)$

76. Consider 1/5 and 2/3.

Adding numerators and denominators gives the fraction _____ .

> 3/8

77. And $1/5 < 3/8$, since $1 \cdot 8 <$ _____ , while $3/8 < 2/3$, since _____ $<$ _____ .

> $5 \cdot 3;$ $\underline{3 \cdot 3} < \underline{8 \cdot 2}$

78. Then by adding numerators and denominators we again obtained a fraction which is _____ the original two fractions.

> BETWEEN

79. This process of adding numerators and denominators will always give a fraction which is between the two original fractions, although we shall not prove this fact.

80. This if $a/b < c/d$, one example of a fraction between a/b and c/d is

$$\frac{a + c}{}$$

> b + d

81. This is an important result. Given <u>any</u> two fractions which are unequal, we can <u>always</u> find another fraction which is _____ the two.

> BETWEEN

82. Then since $2/5 < 3/7$, we know that _____/12 is between 2/5 and 3/7.

> 5

83. Then $2/5 < 5/12 < 3/7$.

But also 7/17 is between 2/5 and 5/12, while _____ is between 5/12 and 3/7.

> 8/19

84. Then 7/17, 5/12, and 8/19 are all between 2/5 and 3/7.

Continuing, between 2/5 and 7/17 is the fraction 9/22.

Between 7/17 and 5/12 is _____ .

Between 5/12 and 8/19 is _____ .

Between 8/19 and 3/7 is _____ .

> 12/29;   13/31;   11/26

85. Then we have found seven fractions all of which are between 2/5 and 3/7. We could continue without stopping. There is no end to the list of fractions which are between 2/5 and 3/7. We say that there are INFINITELY many such fractions.

86. Similarly, if we had begun with 1/2 and 3/4, we could have shown that there are I _____ many fractions between 1/2 and 3/4.

> INFINITELY

87. Indeed, had we begun with <u>any</u> two unequal fractions, we could have shown that there are infinitely many _____ between the two.

> FRACTIONS

88. Recall that we said that 27 is the
_____ of 26, since there are no natural numbers between 26 and 27, and 27 > 26.

SUCCESSOR

89. Since there is always another fraction between any two we consider, a fraction can
have no S_____.

SUCCESSOR

90. And it is impossible to arrange all the fractions in such a way that each one is less than
every fraction which comes after it in the
list, as we did with the _____ numbers.

NATURAL

91. Since 36 is the successor of 35, we say that
35 and 36 are CONSECUTIVE natural numbers. Similarly, 15 and _____ are consecutive natural numbers.

16

92. Give four consecutive natural numbers beginning with 9. _____

9, 10, 11, 12

93. The numbers 15, 16, 17, and 18 are said to
be _____ natural numbers.

CONSECUTIVE

94. To compare a natural number with a fraction, we may first write the natural number
as a _____.

FRACTION

95. Is 2/5 < 3?

Since we can write 3 = 3/1, we need only ask
if 2/5 < 3/1. Our cross product test tells us
that

$2 \cdot 1$ _____ $5 \cdot 3$

and hence

$2/5$ _____ $3/1$

<;   <

96. Compare

15/11 _____ 2

6 _____ 23/4

2/3 _____ 1

<   (since $15 \cdot 1 < 11 \cdot 2$)

>   (since $6 \cdot 4 > 1 \cdot 23$)

<   (since $2 \cdot 1 < 3 \cdot 1$)

97. Remember that $5\frac{2}{3}$ means

$5 + \frac{2}{3}$,   and $5 + \frac{2}{3} = \frac{}{3}$

17

98. Note also that 5 < 17/3, since
$5 \cdot 3 < 1 \cdot$ _____.

17

99. And $17/3 < 6$, or $17/3 < 6/1$, since $17 \cdot 1 <$ _____.

$3 \cdot 6$

100. In the previous frames we have shown that

$5 < 17/3 < 6$

and hence we see that $17/3$ is _____ 5 and 6.

BETWEEN

101. Similarly, $3\frac{3}{4} =$ _____ $/4$.

15

102. Note that $15/4 = 3\frac{3}{4}$ and $3 < 15/4 < 4$, since $3 \cdot 4 < 1 \cdot 15$ and $15 \cdot 1 <$ _____.

$4 \cdot 4$

103. Change $12/5$ to a mixed number.

$12/5 =$ _____

$2\frac{2}{5}$

104. $12/5 = 2\frac{2}{5}$, and $2 < 12/5 < 3$.
We see that $12/5$ or $2\frac{2}{5}$ is between the consecutive natural numbers _____ and 3.

2

105. Find two consecutive natural numbers such that $26/5$ is between them. _____

5 AND 6

106. The symbol $0/1$ does not represent a fraction, since its _____ does not represent a _____ number.

NUMERATOR;   NATURAL

107. But the symbol $0/1$ does represent the _____ of 0 and 1.

QUOTIENT

108. And we know that $0/1 =$ _____ in simplest form, since _____ $\cdot 1 = 0$

0;   0

109. We may also use cross products to compare the number represented by $0/1$ with any fraction. Then $0/1$ _____ $2/3$, since $0 \cdot 3$ _____ $1 \cdot 2$.

$<$; $<$

110. And since $0 = 0/1$, it follows that 0 _____ $2/3$.

$<$

111. Similarly,

$$0 \underline{\hspace{1.5cm}} 3/4$$
$$0 \underline{\hspace{1.5cm}} 5/6$$
$$0 \underline{\hspace{1.5cm}} 1/100$$
$$0 \underline{\hspace{1.5cm}} 15/4$$

$$<; \quad <; \quad <; \quad <$$

112. In fact 0 is _____ than any fraction.

LESS

113. Can you find consecutive <u>natural</u> numbers such that 2/3 is between the two? _____

NO

114. But 2/3 is between 0 and 1. In fact, any P_____ fraction is between 0 and 1.

PROPER

115. Is 15/3 <u>between</u> consecutive natural numbers? _____

NO

116. In fact, 15/3 = 5.

And while 5 is between 4 and 6, 4 and 6 are not _____ natural numbers.

CONSECUTIVE

117. But any improper fraction that does not equal a natural number is _____ two _____ natural numbers.

BETWEEN; CONSECUTIVE

118. The easiest way to determine these numbers is to change the improper fraction to a mixed number.

For example, $39/8 = 4\frac{7}{8}$, so we see that 39/8 is between _____ and _____.

4; 5

119. Similarly,

$17/7 = 2\frac{3}{7}$ and is between _____ and _____.

27/36 is between _____ and _____.

63/10 is between _____ and _____.

<u>2</u> and <u>3</u>; <u>0</u> and <u>1</u>; <u>6</u> and <u>7</u>

120. We had previously ordered the whole numbers; now we have ordered the fractions. We shall order the quotient numbers in the obvious way.

To determine which of two quotient numbers is larger, we compare any _____ which represent them.

FRACTIONS

121. And if p and q represent quotient numbers, then exactly one of the following is true:

$$p < q \quad p = q \quad p \underline{\hspace{1.5cm}} q$$

$$>$$

122. To determine which of two quotient numbers is larger we compare fractions which are _____ of these quotient numbers.

And to compare fractions, we compare their _____ _____.

REPRESENTATIVES; CROSS PRODUCTS

123. Between any two natural numbers there may or may not be another natural number, but there is always a _____ number.

QUOTIENT

124. And there is always another _____ number between any two quotient numbers.

QUOTIENT

125. In fact, between any two quotient numbers there are _____ _____ other quotient numbers.

INFINITELY MANY

126. And every quotient number which is not a natural number is either between 0 and 1, or between _____ natural numbers.

CONSECUTIVE

Problems A (Answers on page 510)

For each of the following pairs of fractions, insert either $<$ or $>$ between the fractions so as to form a true statement.

1. 3/8 _____ 5/13

2. 11/3 _____ 7/2

3. 5/3 _____ 17/10

4. 2/19 _____ 5/48

5. 126/65 _____ 33/17

Arrange each group of fractions in increasing order.

Example: 2/5, 3/4, 1/2, 3/7.

Solution: $2/5 < 3/7 < 1/2 < 3/4$

6. 3/8, 4/7, 4/9

7. 5/11, 3/7, 4/9

8. 12/5, 7/3, 9/4

9. 12/17, 9/17, 8/17, 10/17, 11/17

10. 11/9, 11/5, 11/7, 11/8, 11/6

Find two consecutive natural numbers such that the given quotient number is between them.

Example: 53/9. Solution: $53/9 = 5\frac{8}{9}$. 53/9 is between 5 and 6.

11. 5/2

12. 17/3

13. 65/14

14. 173/15

15. 261/76

List, in increasing order, all the natural numbers which are between the two given quotient numbers.

Example: 8/3 and 17/2. Solution: $8/3 = 2\frac{2}{3}$. $17/2 = 8\frac{1}{2}$. Then 3, 4, 5, 6, 7, 8 are between 8/3 and 17/2.

16. 5/2 and 23/3

17. 1/3 and 11/4

18. 14/9 and 20/7

19. 11/7 and 15/9

20. 53/5 and 91/7

Answer the following questions.

Example: Mr. Jones earns $700 per month and spends $200 for food. Mr. Smith earns $500 per month and spends $150 per month on food. Who spends the larger fractional part of his income on food?

Solution: $200/700 = 2/7$
Mr. Jones spends 2/7 of his income on food.

$150/500 = 3/10$
Mr. Smith spends 3/10 of his income on food.

Mr. Smith spends the larger fractional part of his income on food.

21. Jane typed 436 words during a 10-minute typing test and Mary typed 473 words on the same test, but by mistake she typed for 11 minutes. Which girl is the faster typist?

22. In a history class of 31 students, 27 passed the course. In an English class of 23 students, 3 did not pass. In which class did the higher fractional part pass the course?

23. One automobile traveled 173 miles on 9 gallons of gasoline, while a second automobile traveled 98 miles on 5 gallons of gasoline. Which automobile was more economical of gasoline?

24. In a sample of 600 engine parts, an inspector found 7 defective parts. After making certain changes in the production process 9 defective parts were found in a sample of 800. Did the change improve production quality?

25. During a 10-year period the population of Florida increased from 3,000,000 to 5,000,000 approximately, while during the same period the population of California increased from 11,000,000 to 17,000,000. Which state had the larger fractional increase?

Problems B

For each of the following pairs of fractions, insert either < or > between the fractions so as to form a true statement.

1. 4/7 _____ 8/15
2. 9/4 _____ 12/5
3. 11/7 _____ 7/4
4. 13/18 _____ 4/5
5. 181/317 _____ 4/7

Arrange each group of fractions in increasing order.

6. 3/4, 2/3, 1/2
7. 2/3, 3/5, 4/7
8. 5/8, 3/4, 6/11, 5/9
9. 4/23, 7/23, 6/23, 1/23 9/23, 17/23
10. 17/3, 17/5, 17/16, 17/21, 17/8, 17/7

Find two consecutive natural numbers such that the given quotient number is between them.

11. 15/4
12. 37/5
13. 83/9
14. 117/12
15. 437/24

List, in increasing order, all natural numbers which are between the two given quotient numbers.

16. 7/2 and 19/3
17. 2/5 and 11/3
18. 37/9 and 53/12
19. 8/2 and 39/7
20. 16/3 and 21/3

Answer the following.

21. At school A, 81 graduates out of a class of 112 went on to college; at school B, 52 of 70 graduates continued with college. At which school did the higher fractional portion go on to college?

22. John weighs 150 pounds and can press 130 pounds while Bill weighs 220 pounds and can press 190 pounds. The grade in a body development class is determined by the fractional part of one's body weight that one can press. Which student earned the higher grade?

23. A group of 34 children brushed every day with brand X toothpaste, and at the end of the test period the group had a total of 23 new cavities. A second group of 81 children brushed daily with brand Y toothpaste for the same period, and this group developed 52 new cavities. Based on this evidence, which brand of toothpaste was more effective in reducing cavities?

24. A farmer counted 53 eggs laid by his hens during a 12-day period. After changing the type of feed, he counted 27 eggs laid by the same group of hens in a 7-day period. Was egg production better with the old type of feed or the new?

25. During Easter vacation, 6 out of 11 tourists at Ft. Lauderdale beach are girls, while at Daytona Beach 8 out of 15 are girls. At which beach would a group of fraternity men be more likely to enjoy themselves?

CHAPTER 16

MIXED NUMBERS

1. The property shared by all fractions that are equal to some particular fraction is called a _____ number.

> QUOTIENT

2. Every quotient number may be represented by some _____ .

> FRACTION

3. Some quotient numbers may also be represented by the symbols 1, 2, 3, 4, ... , and hence are also _____ _____ .

> NATURAL NUMBERS

4. But the simplest form of a quotient number which is not also a natural number is a _____ .

> FRACTION

5. When the numerator of a fraction is equal to or greater than its denominator we say it is an _____ fraction.

> IMPROPER

6. And every quotient number which can be represented by an improper fraction is either a natural number or is between _____ natural numbers.

> CONSECUTIVE

7. Also, we can say that if a quotient number may be represented by a fraction whose numerator is greater than its denominator, then this quotient number is _____ than 1.

> GREATER

8. Which of these are greater than 1?
   a) 4/3   b) 5/5   c) 17/18   d) 1/3
   e) 19/18   _____

> a AND e

9. An improper fraction represents a quotient number which is either equal to 1 or _____ than 1.

> GREATER

10. When the numerator of a fraction is less than its denominator, we say it is a _____ fraction.

PROPER

11. Which of these are proper fractions?

    a) 8/8   b) 3/7   c) 1/3   d) 5/6
    e) 12/10   _____

b, c, d

12. Then a proper fraction is between _____ and _____.

0;   1

13. And every proper fraction represents a quotient number which is _____ than 1.

LESS

14. A quotient number which may be represented by an improper fraction is either equal to 1 or _____ than 1, while a quotient number which may be represented by a proper fraction is always _____ than 1.

GREATER;   LESS

15. Which of these are less than 1?

    a) 15/17   b) 17/15   c) 1/5   d) 12/12
    _____

a and c

16. $4/7 = 8/14$ since $4 \cdot 14 =$ _____ .

$7 \cdot 8$

17. And $3/8 < 2/5$ since _____ $<$ _____ .

$3 \cdot 5 < 8 \cdot 2$

18. Also $9/10 > 8/9$ since _____ $>$ _____ .

$9 \cdot 9 > 10 \cdot 8$

19. Insert $<$, $>$, or $=$ so as to form a true statement:

    8/15 _____ 1
    15/9 _____ 3/2
    16/11 _____ 1
    9/5 _____ 15/8

$<;$ $>;$ $>;$ $<$

20. If $ab = c$, we say that c is the _____ of a and b.

PRODUCT

21. $5 \cdot 7 = 35$

    The product is _____, while the factors are _____ and _____ .

35;   5 and 7   (either order)

22. $5 \cdot 7 = 35$

Notice that the product, 35, is G _____ than either of the factors, 5 and 7.

GREATER

23. $3 \cdot 6 = 18$

Is the product greater than either of the factors? _____

YES

24.   Will the product of two natural numbers always be greater than either of the factors? _____

NO!   (see next frame)

25. $1 \cdot 3 = 3$

The product, 3, is not greater than the factor _____.

3

26.   But we can say that the product of two natural numbers is greater than either factor unless one of the factors is _____.

1

27.   And when one factor is 1, the product will always _____ the other factor.

EQUAL

28.   If we multiply a first natural number by a second natural number that is greater than 1, the resulting product will be _____ than the first number.

GREATER

29.   Consider the following:

$$\frac{2}{5} \cdot \frac{3}{2} = \frac{3}{5}$$

The product is _____ ; the first factor is 2/5, and the second factor is _____ .

3/5;   3/2

30. $\frac{2}{5} \cdot \frac{3}{2} = \frac{3}{5}$

Is $3/5 > 3/2$? _____
Is $3/5 > 2/5$? _____

NO;   YES

31. $\frac{2}{5} \cdot \frac{3}{2} = \frac{3}{5}$

We see that the product, 3/5, is greater than one factor, but less than the other. Notice also that 2/5 is _____ than 1, while 3/2 is _____ than 1.

LESS;   GREATER

32. $\frac{2}{5} \cdot \frac{3}{2} = \frac{3}{5}$

$3/2 > 1$ and $3/5 > 2/5$

Notice than when the factor 2/5 is multiplied by the factor 3/2 (which is _____ than 1), the resulting product, 3/5, is _____ than the factor 2/5.

GREATER;   GREATER

33. Also,

$$\frac{3}{2} \cdot \frac{2}{5} = \frac{3}{5}$$

$$2/5 < 1 \quad \text{and} \quad 3/5 < 3/2$$

Here we see that when the factor 3/2 is multiplied by the factor 2/5 (which is _____ than 1), the resulting product, 3/5, is _____ than the factor 3/2.

LESS;　　LESS

34. Consider

$$\frac{3}{8} \cdot \frac{2}{3} = \frac{1}{4}, \quad \frac{3}{8} \cdot \frac{4}{3} = \text{_____}$$

1/2

35. 　$$\frac{3}{8} \cdot \frac{2}{3} = \frac{1}{4} \quad \frac{3}{8} \cdot \frac{4}{3} = \frac{1}{2}$$

In the first example 3/8 is multiplied by 2/3, a fraction less than _____, while in the second example the same factor 3/8 is multiplied by 4/3, a fraction greater than _____.

1;　　1

36. 　$$\frac{3}{8} \cdot \frac{2}{3} = \frac{1}{4} \quad \frac{3}{8} \cdot \frac{4}{3} = \frac{1}{2}$$

And when 3/8 is multiplied by a fraction _____ than 1, the resulting product, 1/4, is _____ than 3/8. But when 3/8 is multiplied by a fraction greater than _____, the resulting product, 1/2, is greater than _____.

LESS;　　LESS;　　1;　　3/8

37. It can be shown that this is always the case. When a number is multiplied by a fraction less than _____, the resulting product will always be _____ than the first number. But when a number is multiplied by a fraction greater than _____, the resulting product is _____ than the first number.

1;　　LESS;　　1;　　GREATER

38. Consider the product

$$\frac{3}{4} \cdot \frac{5}{2} = [\quad]$$

Since 5/2 > 1, we know that the product will be greater than _____.

3/4

39. 　$$\frac{3}{4} \cdot \frac{5}{2} = \frac{5}{2} \cdot \frac{3}{4} = [\quad]$$

But since 3/4 < 1, we know that the product will be less than _____.

5/2

40. 　$$\frac{3}{4} \cdot \frac{5}{2} = [\quad]$$

The product is greater than _____ but less than _____.

3/4;　　5/2

41. 　$$\frac{3}{4} \cdot \frac{5}{2} = [\quad]$$

One factor is less than 1, the other factor is greater than 1, and the product is B_____ the two factors.

BETWEEN

42. When one factor is less than _____ and the other factor is greater than _____, their product is between the two factors.

> 1;   1

43. Consider

$$\frac{2}{3} \cdot \frac{5}{8} = [\quad]$$

Since $5/8 < 1$, the product is less than 2/3.

Since $2/3 < 1$, the product is also less than _____.

> 5/8

44. Then the product of two fractions which are each less than _____ will be _____ than either factor.

> 1;   LESS

45. Consider

$$\frac{4}{3} \cdot \frac{7}{5} = [\quad]$$

Since $7/5 > 1$, the product is greater than _____.

Since $4/3 > 1$, the product is greater than _____.

> 4/3;   7/5

46. Thus the product of two factors which are both greater than _____, is _____ than either factor.

> 1;   GREATER

47. We should remember that the product of two quotient numbers will not always be greater than the factors. Rather, it will depend on whether the factors are greater than _____ or less than _____.

> 1;   1

48. We have said that an expression like $3\frac{2}{3}$ represents the _____ of 3 and 2/3.

> SUM

49. Then $3\frac{2}{3} =$ _____ /3.

> 11

50. $3\frac{2}{3} = 11/3$

Each of the expressions $3\frac{2}{3}$ and $11/3$ represents a _____ number.

> QUOTIENT

51. Although we will not do so frequently, we can also call the expression, $3\frac{2}{3}$, a M _____ number. $11/3$ is an _____ fraction.

> MIXED;   IMPROPER

52. Mixed numbers may always be written as improper fractions, and we will usually do so. Then

$$5\frac{3}{4} = \underline{\quad}/4 \qquad 8\frac{2}{3} = \underline{\quad}$$

> 23;   26/3

53. The expression

$$(2\tfrac{3}{4})(3\tfrac{1}{2})$$

represents the product of $2\tfrac{3}{4}$ and $3\tfrac{1}{2}$. Similarly, the product of $5\tfrac{1}{3}$ and $6\tfrac{3}{4}$ may be represented by _____ .

$$(5\tfrac{1}{3})(6\tfrac{3}{4})$$

54. Recall that to multiply two quotient numbers we multiply any two _____ which represent them.

FRACTIONS

55. Then, since a mixed number is a representative of a quotient number, the product of two mixed numbers may be found by multiplying any _____ which also represent these quotient numbers.

FRACTIONS

56. $2\tfrac{3}{4} =$ _____ $/4$ $3\tfrac{1}{2} =$ _____

11;   7/2

57. $2\tfrac{3}{4} = 11/4$ $3\tfrac{1}{2} = 7/2$
Then

$$(2\tfrac{3}{4})(3\tfrac{1}{2}) = \frac{11}{4} \cdot \text{_____} .$$

7/2

58. Hence

$$(2\tfrac{3}{4})(3\tfrac{1}{2}) = \frac{11}{4} \cdot \frac{7}{2} = \text{_____} .$$

$$\frac{77}{8}$$

59. $(2\tfrac{3}{4})(3\tfrac{1}{2}) = 77/8$

There is no reason to write $77/8$ as a mixed number, and we will not do so. Answers will be written in simplest form, and we consider the simplest form of a mixed number to be an _____ fraction.

IMPROPER

60. Multiply

$$(4\tfrac{5}{6})(2\tfrac{4}{5}) = 29/6 \cdot \text{_____} = \text{_____}$$

14/5;   203/15

61. Remember, to multiply two mixed numbers, we first change them to improper fractions.

$$(6\tfrac{1}{2})(1\tfrac{1}{3}) = \text{_____}$$
$$(4\tfrac{2}{3})(3/11) = \text{_____}$$

26/3;   14/11

62. $(4\tfrac{2}{3})\left(\dfrac{3}{11}\right) = \dfrac{14}{3} \cdot \dfrac{3}{11} = \dfrac{14}{11}$

Of course, if one factor is already a fraction, so much the better.

$$(5/6)(2\tfrac{1}{2}) = \text{_____}$$
$$(1\tfrac{1}{2})(2/3) = \text{_____}$$
$$(10\tfrac{2}{3})(2\tfrac{5}{8}) = \text{_____}$$

25/12;   1;   28

63. We may represent the sum of $3\tfrac{1}{2}$ and $4\tfrac{2}{3}$ by

$$3\tfrac{1}{2} + 4\tfrac{2}{3} .$$

And to add two mixed numbers we may first change them to _____ .

FRACTIONS

64. Thus

$$3\tfrac{1}{2} + 4\tfrac{2}{3} = 7/2 + \underline{\hspace{2cm}}.$$

14/3

65. And

$$3\tfrac{1}{2} + 4\tfrac{2}{3} = \frac{7}{2} + \frac{14}{3} = \frac{21 + \underline{\hspace{0.8cm}}}{6} = \underline{\hspace{2cm}}.$$

28;　49/6

66. Find the sums.

$$1\tfrac{1}{2} + 2\tfrac{3}{4} = 3/2 + \underline{\hspace{2cm}} = \underline{\hspace{2cm}}$$

$$3\tfrac{2}{5} + 4\tfrac{1}{2} = \underline{\hspace{2cm}}$$

11/4;　17/4;　79/10

67. Find the sum or product as indicated.

$$(2\tfrac{1}{2})(3\tfrac{1}{2}) = \underline{\hspace{2cm}}$$

$$2\tfrac{1}{2} + 3\tfrac{1}{4} = \underline{\hspace{2cm}}$$

$$(5/6)(4\tfrac{1}{3}) = \underline{\hspace{2cm}}$$

$$5/6 + 4\tfrac{1}{3} = \underline{\hspace{2cm}}$$

35/4;　23/4;　65/18;　31/6

68. Consider the sum $215\tfrac{1}{4} + \dfrac{2}{3}$.

This is the sum of a mixed number and a fraction, and may be found by first writing $215\tfrac{1}{4}$ as a fraction.

$$215\tfrac{1}{4} = \underline{\hspace{2cm}}$$

861/4

69. $215\tfrac{1}{4} = 861/4$

Hence

$$215\tfrac{1}{4} + \frac{2}{3} = \underline{\hspace{2cm}} + \frac{2}{3}$$

861/4

70. $215\tfrac{1}{4} + \dfrac{2}{3} = \dfrac{861}{4} + \dfrac{2}{3} = \dfrac{861 \cdot 3 + 4 \cdot 2}{4 \cdot 3} = \underline{\hspace{1.5cm}}$

2591/12

71. But remember that $215\tfrac{1}{4}$ represents the sum of \underline{\hspace{1.5cm}} and \underline{\hspace{1.5cm}}.

215;　1/4　(either order)

72. Then we can write $215\tfrac{1}{4} = \underline{\hspace{1.5cm}} + \underline{\hspace{1.5cm}}.$

215;　1/4　(either order)

73. Hence $215\tfrac{1}{4} + \dfrac{2}{3}$ could also be written

$$\left(215 + \frac{1}{4}\right) + \underline{\hspace{1.5cm}}.$$

2/3

74. But $\left(215 + \dfrac{1}{4}\right) + \dfrac{2}{3} = 215 + \left(\dfrac{1}{4} + \underline{\hspace{1.5cm}}\right).$

2/3

75. $215\tfrac{1}{4} + \dfrac{2}{3} = 215 + \left(\dfrac{1}{4} + \dfrac{2}{3} \right)$

And

$\dfrac{1}{4} + \dfrac{2}{3} = $ _____

11/12

76. Hence

$215\tfrac{1}{4} + \dfrac{2}{3} = 215 + \dfrac{11}{12} = \dfrac{}{12} \cdot$

2591

77. If you compare the result of the previous frame with the result obtained by working the same problem by first changing the mixed number to a fraction, you will, of course, find that the results are the same. When adding a large mixed number, it may not be easiest to first change it to a _____.

FRACTION

78. Thus

$316\tfrac{2}{7} + 117\tfrac{3}{7} = (316 + 117) + \left(\dfrac{2}{7} + \dfrac{3}{7} \right)$
$= 433 + $ _____.

5/7

79. And

$316\tfrac{2}{7} + 117\tfrac{3}{7} = 433 + \dfrac{5}{7} = \dfrac{}{7}$

3036

80. Add

$35\tfrac{5}{6} + 21\tfrac{2}{3} = 56 + \left(\dfrac{5}{6} + \dfrac{2}{3} \right) = 56 + $ _____

$= \dfrac{}{2} \cdot$

3/2;   115

81. Find the sum.

$212\tfrac{3}{4} + 94\tfrac{5}{8} = $ _____

2459/8

82. Consider the product

$(2\tfrac{2}{3})(4\tfrac{1}{2})$

If we change these mixed numbers to fractions, we see that

$(2\tfrac{2}{3})(4\tfrac{1}{2}) = (8/3)(9/2) = $ _____

12

83. Then

$(2\tfrac{2}{3})(4\tfrac{1}{2}) = \dfrac{8}{3} \cdot \dfrac{9}{2} = 12.$

A careless student might think that

$(2\tfrac{2}{3})(4\tfrac{1}{2}) = (2)(4) + \left(\dfrac{2}{3} \right)\left(\dfrac{1}{2} \right)$

But notice that

$(2)(4) + \left(\dfrac{2}{3} \right)\left(\dfrac{1}{2} \right) = 8 + $ _____

1/3

84. $(2\frac{2}{3})(4\frac{1}{2}) = \frac{8}{3} \cdot \frac{9}{2} = 12$

The careless solution would give

$(2\frac{2}{3})(4\frac{1}{2}) = 8\frac{1}{3},$ which is <u>not</u> correct.

Hence, when multiplying mixed numbers, we must first change them to _____ .

FRACTIONS

85. But when adding, we may either change mixed numbers to fractions first, or not, whichever is easier.

86. Find the sum or product by any method.

$92\frac{1}{5} + 75\frac{2}{5}$ = _____

$(8\frac{1}{3})(2\frac{2}{5})$ = _____

$(60\frac{1}{2})(75\frac{1}{4})$ = _____

838/5;   20;   36,421/8

87. Recall that the distributive property for quotient numbers justifies our writing

$p(q + r) = p \cdot q + $ _____

for any quotient numbers p, q, and r.

p · r

88. Then

$\frac{3}{4}\left(\frac{1}{2} + \frac{2}{3}\right) = \frac{3}{4} \cdot \frac{1}{2} + $ _____ .

$\frac{3}{4} \cdot \frac{2}{3}$

89. But every natural number is also a quotient number, and hence

$6\left(\frac{1}{2} + \frac{2}{3}\right) = 6 \cdot \frac{1}{2} + $ _____

$6 \cdot \frac{2}{3}$

90. $6\left(\frac{1}{2} + \frac{2}{3}\right) = 6 \cdot \frac{1}{2} + 6 \cdot \frac{2}{3}$

And

$6 \cdot \frac{1}{2} = \frac{6}{1} \cdot \frac{1}{2} = 3$

$6 \cdot \frac{2}{3} = \frac{6}{1} \cdot \frac{2}{3} = $ _____

4

91. Then

$6\left(\frac{1}{2} + \frac{2}{3}\right) = 3 + $ _____ = _____

4;   7

92. Similarly, the distributive property may be used to calculate

$15\left(\frac{1}{5} + \frac{2}{3}\right) = 15 \cdot \frac{1}{5} + 15 \cdot \frac{2}{3} = 3 + $ _____

= _____

10;   13

93. Use the distributive property to find

$20\left(\frac{3}{10} + \frac{2}{5}\right) = $ _____ + _____ = _____

$30\left(\frac{4}{15} + \frac{7}{10}\right) = $ _____ + _____ = _____

6 + 8 = 14;   8 + 21 = 29

94. From the previous frame, by the distributive property,

$$30\left(\frac{4}{15} + \frac{7}{10}\right) = 30 \cdot \frac{4}{15} + 30 \cdot \frac{7}{10} = 8 + 21 = 29$$

But also

$$\frac{4}{15} + \frac{7}{10} = \frac{4 \cdot 10 + 15 \cdot 7}{15 \cdot 10} = \frac{}{150} = \underline{\hspace{2cm}}$$

> 145;   29/30

95. $$30\left(\frac{4}{15} + \frac{7}{10}\right) = 8 + 21 = 29$$

Also

$$\frac{4}{15} + \frac{7}{10} = \frac{40 + 105}{150} = \frac{145}{150} = \frac{29}{30}.$$

Hence

$$30\left(\frac{4}{15} + \frac{7}{10}\right) = 30\left(\underline{\hspace{2cm}}\right) = 29.$$

> 29/30

96. We see that the same result is obtained in either method of computing

$$30\left(\frac{4}{15} + \frac{7}{10}\right) = 29.$$

But use of the distributive property simplifies the solution somewhat.

97. Compute

$$20\left(\frac{3}{10} + \frac{4}{5}\right) = \underline{\hspace{2cm}}$$

$$60\left(\frac{5}{12} + \frac{7}{30}\right) = \underline{\hspace{2cm}}$$

> 6 + 16 = <u>22</u>;   25 + 14 = <u>39</u>

98. The product of two quotient numbers need not always be greater than the factors. In fact, the product will be less than either factor if both factors are less than _____.

> 1

99. If one factor is less than 1, while the other factor is greater than 1, the product will be _____ the factors.

> BETWEEN

100. It is only when each factor is _____ than _____ that the product is greater than either factor.

> GREATER;   1

101. When multiplying mixed numbers, we should first write them as _____.

> FRACTIONS

102. But when we are _____ mixed numbers which are large, it may be easier, and also correct, not to change them to fractions.

> ADDING

103. Sometimes the _____ property simplifies finding the product of a natural number and the sum of two fractions.

> DISTRIBUTIVE

Chapter 16

Change the mixed numbers to fractions and multiply. Write answers in simplest form.

1. $\left(\frac{2}{3}\right)\left(5\frac{2}{3}\right)$

2. $\left(\frac{42}{5}\right)\left(6\frac{1}{2}\right)$

3. $\left(4\frac{4}{5}\right)\left(1\frac{7}{8}\right)$

4. $(32)\left(16\frac{1}{3}\right)$

5. $\left(3\frac{1}{7}\right)\left(2\frac{1}{2}\right)$

Find the following sums by any method. Write answers in simplest form.

6. $1\frac{7}{8} + \frac{2}{3}$

7. $13\frac{1}{3} + 7\frac{2}{3}$

8. $14\frac{2}{3} + 133$

9. $101\frac{3}{10} + 256\frac{1}{2}$

10. $606\frac{4}{6} + 289\frac{1}{3}$

Without finding the number x, decide for each problem whether the second statement is true or false.

Example: $\frac{4}{3} \cdot \frac{12}{13} = x$ $x < 12/13$

Solution: False (since $4/3 > 1$)

Example: $\frac{2}{5} \cdot x = \frac{3}{5}$ $x > 1$

Solution: True (since $3/5 > 2/5$)

11. $7 \cdot \frac{3}{5} = x$ $x > 7$

12. $15 \cdot \frac{6}{10} = x$ $x < 15$

13. $x \cdot \frac{4}{13} = 10$ $x < 1$

14. $\frac{3}{8} \cdot x = \frac{3}{8}$ $x = 1$

15. $\frac{5}{6} \cdot x = \frac{6}{5}$ $x > 5/6$

16. $x \cdot \frac{8}{3} = 5$ $x > 5$

17. $\left(3\frac{1}{2}\right) \cdot x = \frac{1}{3}$ $x < \frac{1}{3}$

18. $x \cdot x = \frac{3}{2}$ $x < 1$

Use the distributive property to compute each of the following.

Example: $42\left(\frac{4}{7} + \frac{2}{3}\right)$

Solution: $42\left(\frac{4}{7} + \frac{2}{3}\right) = 42 \cdot \frac{4}{7} + 42 \cdot \frac{2}{3} = 24 + 28$
$= 52$

19. $16\left(\frac{3}{4} + \frac{7}{8}\right)$

20. $40\left(\frac{7}{10} + \frac{7}{8}\right)$

Answer the following questions.

21. On two successive plays a football team gains $4\frac{3}{4}$ yards and $5\frac{1}{2}$ yards. Was this enough for a "first down"? (ten yards)

22. If it takes $22\frac{2}{3}$ yards of carpet to cover a living room and $17\frac{1}{4}$ yards to cover a dining room, how many yards of carpet will cover both rooms?

23. A small size box of detergent contains $8\frac{3}{4}$ ounces. How much do six boxes of this size contain?

24. A recipe that will serve eight persons requires $3\frac{3}{4}$ cups of flour. How much flour is required for a recipe that will serve four?

25. An automobile can travel $18\frac{1}{5}$ miles on a gallon of gasoline. If its tank holds $17\frac{1}{3}$ gallons, how far can the car travel on a full tank?

Problems B

Perform the indicated operation and write answers in simplest form.

1. $\left(\frac{8}{7}\right)\left(12\frac{1}{3}\right)$

2. $\frac{15}{16} + 5\frac{3}{4}$

3. $\left(13\frac{1}{3}\right)\left(\frac{7}{8}\right)$

4. $\left(2\frac{2}{3}\right)\left(12\frac{1}{5}\right)$

5. $6\frac{7}{8} + 12\frac{5}{6}$

6. $13\frac{2}{3} + \frac{7}{8}$

7. $(3\frac{3}{10})(10)$

8. $\frac{47}{12} + 5\frac{2}{3}$

9. $7\frac{2}{3} + 2\frac{3}{7}$

10. $(5\frac{1}{2})(5\frac{1}{2})$

Use the distributive property to find the following in simplest form.

11. $21\left(\frac{5}{7} + \frac{8}{3}\right)$

12. $84\left(\frac{5}{12} + \frac{9}{4}\right)$

Without finding the number x, decide for each problem whether the second statement is true or false.

13. $\frac{3}{4} \cdot (4\frac{1}{2}) = x \qquad x > 3/4$

14. $(5\frac{1}{3}) \cdot (2\frac{1}{2}) = x \qquad x < 5\frac{1}{3}$

15. $\left(\frac{3}{8}\right) \cdot \cdot x = 2\frac{1}{2} \qquad x < 1$

16. $\left(\frac{3}{8}\right) \cdot x = 2\frac{1}{2} \qquad x > 3/8$

17. $\left(\frac{3}{8}\right) \cdot x = 2\frac{1}{2} \qquad x < 2\frac{1}{2}$

18. $x \cdot \frac{3}{4} = x \qquad x < 1$

19. $x \cdot \frac{3}{4} = \frac{3}{4} \qquad x = 1$

20. $x \cdot x = x \qquad x > 1$

21. A common stock listed on the New York Exchange sells for $81\frac{3}{4}$. After a general market advance the stock went up $5\frac{7}{8}$. What is the new price of the stock?

22. A coffee cup holds $5\frac{1}{2}$ ounces. How many ounces of coffee are required for 12 cups?

23. If $2\frac{1}{2}$ cups of water are required to cook one cup of rice, how many cups of water are necessary for $1\frac{3}{4}$ cups of rice?

24. If ground beef sells for 69¢ per pound, how much will $1\frac{1}{3}$ pounds cost?

25. A farmer who owned $42\frac{1}{8}$ acres of land enlarged his farm by buying $17\frac{1}{3}$ acres of adjacent property. How large was his new farm?

CHAPTER 17

SUBTRACTION OF QUOTIENT NUMBERS

1. 12 − 7 = _____

   since

   7 + _____ = 12

   5;   5

2. In the subtraction problem 12 − 7 = 5, we call 12 the minuend, 7 the _____, and 5 the _____.

   SUBTRAHEND;   DIFFERENCE

3. 12 − 7 = 5   since   7 + 5 = 12

   In a subtraction problem the difference is a number which when added to the _____ equals the _____.

   SUBTRAHEND;   MINUEND

4. In general, if a, b, and d represent whole numbers,

   a − b = d

   if

   _____ + d = _____.

   b;   a

5. a − b = d   if   b + d = a

   Now if d is a natural number, then b + d = a means that b is _____ than a.

   LESS

6. a − b = d   if   b + d = a

   And if d is the number 0, then b + d = b + 0 = a means that b is _____ _____ a.

   EQUAL TO

7. In fact, for whole numbers a and b, we define the difference a − b only when

   b _____ a   or   b _____ a

   <;   =   (either order)

8. If b < a, we say that a − b is the natural number d, such that

   _____ + d = _____

   b;   a

[17:8]

SUBTRACTION OF QUOTIENT NUMBERS   259

9. While if b = a, we say that a − b = _____, since b + 0 = b = a.

> 0

10. But when b > a there is no whole number, d, such that b + d = a, and hence we say that the _____ of a and b is not defined.

> DIFFERENCE

11. Which of these expressions is defined?
    a) 7 − 3   b) 12 − 12   c) 3 − 7
    d) 4 − 0   _____

> a, b and d

12. Remember, the difference of the natural numbers 7 and 3 is the natural number which, when added to 3, equals 7. Similarly, the difference of the quotient numbers 5/7 and 3/7 is the quotient number which, when added to 3/7, equals _____.

> 5/7

13. We indicate the difference of 5/7 and 3/7 by writing $\frac{5}{7} − \frac{3}{7}$; it is the quotient number which when added to _____ equals _____.

> 3/7;   5/7

14. Then
$$\frac{5}{7} − \frac{3}{7} = \underline{\hspace{1cm}}$$
since
$$\frac{3}{7} + \underline{\hspace{1cm}} = \frac{5}{7}$$

> 2/7;   2/7

15. Similarly
$$\frac{7}{12} − \frac{6}{12} = \underline{\hspace{1cm}}$$
since
$$\frac{6}{12} + \underline{\hspace{1cm}} = \frac{7}{12}$$

> 1/12;   1/12

16. Find the difference.
$$\frac{8}{9} − \frac{3}{9} = \underline{\hspace{1cm}}$$
$$\frac{12}{7} − \frac{3}{7} = \underline{\hspace{1cm}}$$
$$\frac{15}{27} − \frac{10}{27} = \underline{\hspace{1cm}}$$

> 5/9;   9/7;   5/27

17. $\frac{8}{9} − \frac{3}{9} = \frac{5}{9}$,   since $\frac{3}{9} + \underline{\hspace{1cm}} = \frac{8}{9}$

$\frac{12}{7} − \frac{3}{7} = \frac{9}{7}$,   since

$\frac{3}{7} + \underline{\hspace{1cm}} = \underline{\hspace{1cm}}$

$\frac{15}{27} − \frac{10}{27} = \frac{5}{27}$,   since

$\underline{\hspace{1cm}} + \underline{\hspace{1cm}} = \underline{\hspace{1cm}}$

> $\frac{5}{9}$; $\frac{3}{7} + \frac{9}{7} = \frac{12}{7}$; $\frac{10}{27} + \frac{5}{27} = \frac{15}{27}$

18. In general, the difference of two distinct quotient numbers is a quotient number which, when added to the _____, gives the _____ as a result.

> SUBTRAHEND;   MINUEND

19. Find the sum

$$\frac{4}{13} + 0 = \underline{\qquad}$$

> 4/13

20. Then, since $\frac{4}{13} + 0 = \frac{4}{13}$, we conclude that

$$\frac{4}{13} - \frac{4}{13} = \underline{\qquad}$$

> 0

21. Similarly $\frac{17}{3} - \frac{17}{3} = \underline{\qquad}$ since

$$\frac{17}{3} + \underline{\qquad} = \frac{17}{3}.$$

> 0;   0

22. Find the difference.

$$\frac{53}{12} - \frac{53}{12} = \underline{\qquad}$$

$$\frac{3}{74} - \frac{3}{74} = \underline{\qquad}$$

$$\frac{21}{22} - \frac{21}{22} = \underline{\qquad}$$

> 0;   0;   0

23. $\frac{53}{12} - \frac{53}{12} = 0$ since $\frac{53}{12} + \underline{\qquad} = \frac{53}{12}$

$\frac{3}{74} - \frac{3}{74} = 0$ since

$$\frac{3}{74} + \underline{\qquad} = \underline{\qquad}$$

$\frac{21}{22} - \frac{21}{22} = 0$ since

$$\underline{\qquad} + \underline{\qquad} = \underline{\qquad}$$

> 0; $\frac{3}{74} + \underline{0} = \frac{3}{74}$; $\frac{21}{22} + \underline{0} = \frac{21}{22}$

24. In fact the difference of any quotient number and itself is not a _____ number, but is the number _____.

> QUOTIENT;   ZERO

25. $\dfrac{5}{8} - \dfrac{5}{8} = \underline{\qquad}$

$\dfrac{3}{7} - \dfrac{9}{21} = \underline{\qquad}$

> 0;   0

26. $\dfrac{8}{3} - \dfrac{4}{3} = \underline{\qquad}$

$\dfrac{9}{10} - \dfrac{6}{10} = \underline{\qquad}$

> 4/3;   3/10

27. Consider

$$\frac{3}{8} - \frac{6}{8} = [\quad]$$

If this problem has a solution, then there must be a quotient number which when added to 6/8 equals _____.

> 3/8

28. $\frac{3}{8} - \frac{6}{8} = [\quad]$

is defined if the problem $\frac{6}{8} + [\quad] = \frac{3}{8}$ has a solution. Does this latter problem have a solution? _____

NO

29. Since $\frac{6}{8} + [\quad] = \frac{3}{8}$ has no solution, we conclude that neither does $\frac{3}{8} - \frac{6}{8} = [\quad]$.

Notice that $3/8 < 6/8$.

30. In fact, whenever the minuend is less than the subtrahend, it will be impossible to find the _____ of the two quotient numbers.

DIFFERENCE

31. Find the difference, where possible.

$\frac{8}{9} - \frac{6}{9} =$ _____

$\frac{3}{17} - \frac{3}{17} =$ _____

$\frac{12}{5} - \frac{15}{5} =$ _____

2/9;   0;   IMPOSSIBLE

32. $\frac{8}{9} - \frac{6}{9} = \frac{2}{9}$ and $\frac{6}{9} < \frac{8}{9}$

$\frac{3}{17} - \frac{3}{17} = 0$ and $\frac{3}{17}$ _____ $\frac{3}{17}$

$\frac{12}{5} - \frac{15}{5}$ is impossible   and

$\frac{15}{5}$ _____ $\frac{12}{5}$

=;   >

33. So, for quotient numbers, too, we define their difference only when the subtrahend is the same as the minuend or when it is _____ than the minuend.

LESS

34. We have shown in the previous frames that

$\frac{5}{7} - \frac{3}{7} = \frac{2}{7}$ $\frac{12}{7} - \frac{3}{7} = \frac{9}{7}$

$\frac{7}{12} - \frac{6}{12} = \frac{1}{12}$ $\frac{15}{27} - \frac{10}{27} = \frac{5}{27}$

$\frac{8}{9} - \frac{3}{9} = \frac{5}{9}$ $\frac{8}{9} - \frac{6}{9} = \frac{2}{9}$

In each case we have considered the _____ of two fractions whose _____ are the same.

DIFFERENCE;   DENOMINATORS

35. If a/b and c/b are any two fractions with the same denominator, we see that

$\frac{a}{b} - \frac{c}{b} = \frac{\rule{1.5cm}{0.4pt}}{b}$

a − c

36. $\frac{a}{b} - \frac{c}{b} = \frac{a - c}{b}$

When two fractions have the same _____, we may find their difference by _____ their numerators and keeping the same denominator.

DENOMINATOR;   SUBTRACTING

37. Use the rule

$$\frac{a}{b} - \frac{c}{b} = \frac{a-c}{b}$$

to find each difference.

$$\frac{12}{5} - \frac{2}{5} = \underline{\hspace{2cm}}$$

$$\frac{143}{74} - \frac{140}{74} = \underline{\hspace{2cm}}$$

$$\frac{831}{173} - \frac{820}{173} = \underline{\hspace{2cm}}$$

$$\frac{10}{5} = 2; \qquad \frac{3}{74}; \qquad \frac{11}{173}$$

38. Consider the difference

$$\frac{1}{2} - \frac{3}{10}$$

Since these two fractions do not have the same denominator, we cannot use the previous rule. But 1/2 = 5/10, so

$$\frac{1}{2} - \frac{3}{10} = \frac{5}{10} - \frac{3}{10} = \underline{\hspace{2cm}}$$

in simplest form.

$$\frac{2}{10} = \frac{1}{5}$$

39. $\frac{2}{3} - \frac{2}{9}$

In order to use the rule we must first write 2/3 as a fraction whose denominator is

$$\underline{\hspace{1cm}}.$$

9

40. $\frac{2}{3} - \frac{2}{9}$

Since 2/3 = $\underline{\hspace{1cm}}$/9, we see that

$$\frac{2}{3} - \frac{2}{9} = \frac{\underline{}}{9} - \frac{2}{9} = \underline{\hspace{1cm}}.$$

6;   6;   4/9

41. $$\frac{2}{3} - \frac{2}{9} = \frac{6}{9} - \frac{2}{9} = \frac{4}{9}$$

We have found the difference here by the METHOD OF COMMON DENOMINATORS for subtraction of fractions.

42. To use the method of common denominators for $\frac{4}{3} - \frac{7}{12}$, we must first write

$$4/3 = \underline{\hspace{2cm}}$$

16/12

43. Since $\frac{4}{3} = \frac{16}{12}$, then $\frac{4}{3} - \frac{7}{12} = \underline{\hspace{2cm}} - \frac{7}{12}$

$$= \underline{\hspace{2cm}}, \text{ in simplest form.}$$

16/12; $\frac{9}{12} = \frac{3}{4}$

44. Similarly, by the method of common denominators,

$$\frac{13}{20} - \frac{3}{5} = \frac{13}{20} - \frac{\underline{}}{20} = \underline{\hspace{2cm}}$$

12; $\frac{1}{20}$

45. To find $\frac{23}{8} - \frac{3}{2}$ by the method of common denominators, we first write

$$3/2 = \underline{\hspace{2cm}}.$$

12/8

46. Then, since 3/2 = 12/8,

$$\frac{23}{8} - \frac{3}{2} = \frac{23}{8} - \underline{\hspace{2cm}} = \underline{\hspace{1cm}}$$

12/8;   11/8

47. Use the method of common denominators to find the difference.

$$\frac{5}{16} - \frac{1}{4} = \text{_____}$$

$$\frac{11}{6} - \frac{3}{2} = \text{_____}$$

$$\frac{4}{3} - \frac{7}{15} = \text{_____}$$

48. In each of the differences we have considered so far, either the denominators have been the same, or one denominator has been a multiple of the other. For differences of this type, the easiest solution is to use the method of
_____ _____.

COMMON DENOMINATORS

49. But when the denominators are different, and neither one is a _____ of the other, the method of common denominators is not quite so convenient.

MULTIPLE

50. When two fractions have unequal denominators, we may find their sum by the cross _____ method.

PRODUCT

51. Recall

$$\frac{a}{b} + \frac{c}{d} = \frac{ad + \text{\_\_}}{bd}$$

bc

52. Find the sum.

$$\frac{3}{8} + \frac{4}{5} = \frac{3 \cdot 5 + \text{_____}}{} = \text{_____}$$

$$\frac{9}{5} + \frac{2}{9} = \text{_____}$$

$$\frac{3 \cdot 5 + 8 \cdot 4}{8 \cdot 5} = \frac{47}{40}; \quad \frac{91}{45}$$

53. And to find the <u>difference</u> of two fractions with unequal denominators we may use a method <u>similar</u> to the method of _____ _____ for addition.

CROSS PRODUCTS

54. We will show that

$$\frac{a}{b} - \frac{c}{d} = \frac{ad - bc}{bd}$$

whenever

$$a/b > c/d$$

55. We will show that

$$\frac{a}{b} - \frac{c}{d} = \frac{ad - bc}{bd}$$

Notice that the numerator ad − bc is the _____ of the cross _____ of the fractions a/b and c/d.

DIFFERENCE;   PRODUCTS

56. We will show that

$$\frac{a}{b} - \frac{c}{d} = \frac{ad - bc}{bd}$$

The denominator, bd, is the _____ of the denominators of a/b and c/d.

PRODUCT

57. Consider the difference

$$\frac{a}{b} - \frac{c}{d} = [\quad]$$

Remember, the difference must be a quotient number which when _____ to c/d equals a/b.

ADDED

58. And we want to show that

$$\frac{a}{b} - \frac{c}{d} = \frac{}{bd}$$

whenever

a/b > c/d.

ad − bc

59. Now first we must show that (ad − bc)/bd is indeed a _____ number.

QUOTIENT

60. If ad − bc and bd are both _____ numbers, the expression (ad − bc)/bd will be a quotient number.

NATURAL

61. Remember that a/b > c/d, and hence ad _____ bc.

>

62. But if ad > bc, then ad − bc is a _____ number.

NATURAL

63. For the fractions a/b and c/d, the denominators must be _____ numbers.

NATURAL

64. Since both b and d are natural numbers, the product bd is also a _____ number.

NATURAL

65. We have said that whenever a/b > c/d, then ad > bc, and hence both ad − bc and bd are natural numbers.

Then (ad − bc)/bd is a _____ number.

QUOTIENT

66. Remember, we want to show that

$$\frac{a}{b} - \frac{c}{d} = \frac{ad - bc}{bd}$$

We have shown that, whenever a/b > c/d, then (ad − bc)/bd is a quotient number.

In the problem

$$\frac{a}{b} - \frac{c}{d} = \frac{ad - bc}{bd}$$

the minuend is _____ and the subtrahend is _____.

a/b;   c/d

67. We are showing that

$$\frac{a}{b} - \frac{c}{d} = \frac{ad - bc}{bd}$$

The minuend is a/b.

The subtrahend is c/d, and we are showing that the difference is _____.

(ad − bc)/bd

68. We have said that the difference of two quotient numbers is a quotient number which, when added to the _____, gives a result which equals the _____.

SUBTRAHEND; MINUEND

69. Remember, if $\dfrac{a}{b} - \dfrac{c}{d} = \dfrac{ad - bc}{bd}$, then

    "subtrahend + difference = minuend"

    or

    $\dfrac{c}{d} + \underline{\hspace{3cm}} = \dfrac{a}{b}$.

(ad − bc)/bd

70. Hence we want to show that

    $$\dfrac{c}{d} + \dfrac{ad - bc}{bd} = \dfrac{a}{b}$$

    We will use the method of common _____.

DENOMINATORS

71. For the fractions c/d and (ad − bc)/bd a common denominator is bd. Then c/d = ($\underline{\hspace{1.5cm}}$ · c)/(b · d)

b

72. Since c/d = bc/bd, then

    $$\dfrac{c}{d} + \dfrac{ad - bc}{bd} = \dfrac{bc}{bd} + \dfrac{ad - bc}{\underline{\hspace{1cm}}}$$

bd

73. But to add $\dfrac{bc}{bd} + \dfrac{ad - bc}{bd}$, which are fractions with the same denominator, we add their numerators.

    $$\dfrac{bc}{bd} + \dfrac{ad - bc}{bd} = \dfrac{\underline{\hspace{1cm}} + (ad - bc)}{bd}$$

bc

74. Now we have shown that

    $$\dfrac{c}{d} + \dfrac{ad - bc}{bd} = \dfrac{bc}{bd} + \dfrac{ad - bc}{bd} = \dfrac{bc + (ad - bc)}{bd}$$

    Consider the numerator bc + (ad − bc). The expression ad − bc is the _____ of ad and bc.

DIFFERENCE

75. ad − bc, the difference of ad and bc, is a number which when added to the subtrahend, _____, gives a result which equals the minuend, _____.

bc;   ad

76. We have said that the difference, ad − bc, is a number which when added to bc gives a result which equals ad.

    Consider

    bc + (ad − bc)

    Here the difference, ad − bc, is added to bc, and must give a result which equals _____.

ad

77. Then

$$bc + (ad - bc) = \underline{\hspace{1cm}}$$

Remember, the difference ad − bc is a number which when added to bc gives a result which equals ad.

ad

78. We were finding the sum of c/d and (ad − bc)/bd, and we said that

$$\frac{c}{d} + \frac{ad - bc}{bd} = \frac{bc}{bd} + \frac{ad - bc}{bd} = \frac{bc + (ad - bc)}{bd}$$

Now we have shown that the numerator bc + (ad − bc) = ad.

Then

$$\frac{c}{d} + \frac{ad - bc}{bd} = \frac{\underline{\hspace{0.5cm}}}{bd}$$

ad

79. Hence

$$\frac{c}{d} + \frac{ad - bc}{bd} = \frac{ad}{bd} = \frac{\underline{\hspace{0.3cm}}}{b}$$

a

80. We have shown that

$$\frac{c}{d} + \frac{ad - bc}{bd} = \frac{a}{b}$$

But this means that (ad − bc)/bd is the _____ of a/b and c/d.

DIFFERENCE

81. Thus we have shown that

$$\frac{a}{b} - \frac{c}{d} = \frac{ad - bc}{bd}$$

We call this the cross _____ rule for subtraction of fractions.

PRODUCT

82. Use the cross product rule to subtract:

$$\frac{3}{4} - \frac{1}{3} = \frac{3 \cdot 3 - 4 \cdot 1}{4 \cdot 3} = \frac{\underline{\hspace{0.3cm}}}{12}$$

5

83. Subtract

$$\frac{8}{5} - \frac{2}{3} = \frac{}{15} = \underline{\hspace{1cm}}$$

$$\frac{6}{11} - \frac{1}{2} = \underline{\hspace{1cm}}$$

$$\frac{8}{5} - \frac{2}{3} = \frac{24 - 10}{15} = \frac{14}{15}; \quad \frac{1}{22}$$

84. Remember, it is impossible to subtract quotient numbers when the subtrahend is _____ than the minuend.

GREATER

85. But if one forgets this and attempts to use the cross product rule,

$$\frac{3}{4} - \frac{7}{8} = \frac{24 - 28}{32}$$

notice that 24 − 28 is impossible with whole numbers, and hence the difference

$$\frac{3}{4} - \frac{7}{8}$$

is also _____.

IMPOSSIBLE

86. Subtract, where possible.

$$\frac{3}{8} - \frac{1}{5} = \underline{\hspace{2cm}}$$

$$\frac{12}{5} - \frac{7}{3} = \underline{\hspace{2cm}}$$

$$\frac{8}{11} - \frac{3}{4} = \underline{\hspace{2cm}}$$

> 7/40; 1/15; IMPOSSIBLE

87. Use either the method of common denominators or the cross product rule to subtract.

$$\frac{15}{8} - \frac{7}{8} = \underline{\hspace{2cm}}$$

$$\frac{4}{4} - \frac{1}{4} = \underline{\hspace{2cm}}$$

$$\frac{7}{1} - \frac{8}{3} = \underline{\hspace{2cm}}$$

> 1; 3/4; 13/3

88. Use the common denominator method:

$$\frac{5}{5} - \frac{2}{5} = \underline{\hspace{2cm}}$$

Use the cross product rule:

$$\frac{1}{1} - \frac{2}{5} = \underline{\hspace{2cm}}$$

> 3/5; 3/5

89. $$\frac{5}{5} - \frac{2}{5} = \frac{5-2}{5} = \frac{3}{5}$$

Also

$$\frac{1}{1} - \frac{2}{5} = \frac{1 \cdot 5 - 1 \cdot 2}{1 \cdot 5} = \frac{5-2}{5} = \frac{3}{5}$$

Observe that both 5/5 and 1/1 represent the natural number _____.

> 1

90. Then to subtract $1 - \frac{2}{5}$ we may either think of this as

$$\frac{5}{5} - \frac{2}{5} = \underline{\hspace{2cm}}$$

or

$$\frac{1}{1} - \frac{2}{5} = \frac{1 \cdot 5 - 1 \cdot 2}{1 \cdot 5} = \underline{\hspace{2cm}}$$

> 3/5; 3/5

91. To use the method of common denominators we write

$$1 - \frac{3}{8} = \frac{8}{8} - \frac{3}{8} = \underline{\hspace{2cm}}$$

To use the cross product rule we write

$$1 - \frac{3}{8} = \frac{1}{1} - \frac{3}{8} = \frac{-}{1 \cdot 8} = \underline{\hspace{2cm}}$$

> $\frac{5}{8}$; $1 - \frac{3}{8} = \frac{1}{1} - \frac{3}{8} = \frac{8-3}{8} = \frac{5}{8}$

92. Use either method to subtract:

$$1 - \frac{11}{15} = \underline{\hspace{2cm}}$$

$$1 - \frac{73}{100} = \underline{\hspace{2cm}}$$

$$1 - \frac{9}{8} = \underline{\hspace{2cm}}$$

> 4/15; 27/100; IMPOSSIBLE

93. $1 - \frac{9}{8}$ is impossible since $1 < 9/8$. Consider

$$2 - \frac{9}{8} = \frac{2}{1} - \frac{9}{8} = \frac{2 \cdot 8 -}{8} = \underline{\hspace{2cm}}.$$

> 1 · 9; 7/8

94. By the cross product rule

$$2 - \frac{9}{8} = \frac{16 - 9}{8} = \frac{7}{8}$$

We can also use the method of common denominators.

$$2 - \frac{9}{8} = \frac{}{8} - \frac{9}{8} = \frac{7}{8}$$

> 16

95. Use any method to subtract:

$$3 - \frac{4}{5} = \underline{\hspace{1.5cm}}$$

> 11/5

96. $$3 - \frac{4}{5} = \frac{15}{5} - \frac{4}{5} = \frac{11}{5}$$

$$3 - \frac{4}{5} = \frac{3}{1} - \frac{4}{5} = \frac{15 - 4}{5} = \frac{11}{5}$$

Here, we have used the two methods already explained. Note, also, that since $3 = 2 + 1$, we may write

$$3 - \frac{4}{5} = (2 + 1) - \frac{4}{5} = 2 + \left(1 - \frac{4}{5}\right)$$

$$= 2 + \underline{\hspace{1.5cm}}$$

> 1/5

97. $$3 - \frac{4}{5} = 2 + \frac{1}{5} = \frac{}{5}$$

Similarly,

$$25 - \frac{2}{3} = (24 + 1) - \frac{2}{3} = 24 + \left(1 - \frac{2}{3}\right)$$

$$= 24 + \underline{\hspace{1.5cm}} = \underline{\hspace{1.5cm}}$$

> 11;   1/3;   73/3

98. This last method is particularly useful when the natural number is large. Consider

$$836 - \frac{3}{5} = (835 + 1) - \frac{3}{5} = 835 + \left(1 - \frac{3}{5}\right)$$

$$= 835 + \underline{\hspace{1.5cm}}$$

> 2/5

99. $$836 - \frac{3}{5} = 835 + \frac{2}{5} = \frac{}{5}$$

> 4177

100. Subtract by any method.

$$\frac{8}{3} - 2 = \underline{\hspace{1.5cm}}$$

> 2/3

101. $$\frac{8}{3} - 2 = \frac{8}{3} - \frac{6}{3} = \frac{2}{3}$$

or $$\frac{8}{3} - 2 = \frac{8}{3} - \frac{2}{1} = \frac{8 - 6}{3} = \frac{2}{3}$$

Find $\frac{83}{9} - 9 = \underline{\hspace{1.5cm}}$

> 2/9

102. Consider

$$5\tfrac{2}{3} - 3.$$

Remember that $5\tfrac{2}{3}$ means $\underline{\hspace{1.5cm}} + \underline{\hspace{1.5cm}}$.

> $5 + \frac{2}{3}$

103. Then

$$5\tfrac{2}{3} - 3 = 5 + \frac{2}{3} - 3 = \underline{\hspace{2cm}} + \frac{2}{3}$$

2

104. $5\tfrac{2}{3} - 3 = 2 + \frac{2}{3} = \dfrac{}{3}$

8

105. Similarly

$$817\tfrac{7}{10} - 317 = 817 + \frac{7}{10} - 317$$

$$= \underline{\hspace{2cm}} + \frac{7}{10} = \dfrac{}{10}$$

500;   5007

106. Also $6 - 3\tfrac{1}{2} = 6 - \left(3 + \frac{1}{2}\right)$

But $6 - \left(3 + \frac{1}{2}\right) = 6 - 3 - \frac{1}{2}$

And $6 - 3 - \frac{1}{2} = \underline{\hspace{2cm}} - \frac{1}{2}$

3

107. $6 - 3\tfrac{1}{2} = 3 - \frac{1}{2} = \frac{6}{2} - \frac{1}{2} = \underline{\hspace{2cm}}$

5/2

108. Similarly

$$23 - 5\tfrac{2}{3} = 18 - \underline{\hspace{2cm}} = \dfrac{}{3}$$

2/3;   52

109. $31 - 15\tfrac{3}{4} = \underline{\hspace{2cm}} - \frac{3}{4} = \dfrac{}{4}$

16;   61

110. Subtract. Express answer in simplest form.

$$12\tfrac{2}{3} - 8 = \underline{\hspace{2cm}}$$

$$11 - 5\tfrac{1}{2} = \underline{\hspace{2cm}}$$

$$16\tfrac{5}{8} - \frac{1}{4} = \underline{\hspace{2cm}}$$

14/3;   11/2;   131/8

111. Next consider the difference of two mixed numbers.

$$4\tfrac{1}{2} - 3\tfrac{2}{3}$$

We may change each to a fraction.

$$4\tfrac{1}{2} - 3\tfrac{2}{3} = \frac{9}{2} - \dfrac{}{3}$$

11

112. $4\tfrac{1}{2} - 3\tfrac{2}{3} = \frac{9}{2} - \frac{11}{3}$

And by the cross product rule

$$\frac{9}{2} - \frac{11}{3} = \dfrac{}{6}$$

5

113. Change to fractions and subtract.

$$3\tfrac{3}{4} - 2\tfrac{1}{2} = \underline{\hspace{2cm}} \qquad 35\tfrac{3}{4} - 29\tfrac{1}{2} = \underline{\hspace{2cm}}$$

5/4;   25/4

114.

But there is an easier way to compute $35\frac{3}{4} - 29\frac{1}{2}$.

Remember

$$35\frac{3}{4} = 35 + \frac{3}{4} \quad \text{and} \quad 29\frac{1}{2} = 29 + \frac{1}{2}$$

Then

$$35\frac{3}{4} - 29\frac{1}{2} = \left(35 + \frac{3}{4}\right) - \left(29 + \frac{1}{2}\right)$$
$$= (35 - 29) + \left(\frac{3}{4} - \underline{\qquad}\right)$$

1/2

115.

Then

$$35\frac{3}{4} - 29\frac{1}{2} = (35 - 29) + \left(\frac{3}{4} - \frac{1}{2}\right)$$
$$= 6 + \underline{\qquad} = \frac{25}{4}$$

1/4

116.

Similarly,

$$15\frac{3}{5} - 8\frac{2}{5} = (15 - 8) + \left(\underline{\qquad} - \underline{\qquad}\right)$$

3/5;   2/5

117.

Hence

$$15\frac{3}{5} - 8\frac{2}{5} = 7 + \underline{\qquad} = \frac{\underline{\qquad}}{5}$$

1/5;   36

118.

Subtract. Express results in simplest form.

$$19\frac{5}{6} - 11\frac{2}{3} = \underline{\qquad}$$
$$265\frac{1}{2} - 264\frac{1}{4} = \underline{\qquad}$$

49/6;   5/4

119.

In this chapter we have defined the difference of two quotient numbers to be the number which, when _____ to the subtrahend, gives a result which equals the _____.

ADDED;   MINUEND

120.

But such a number cannot be found when the _____ is larger than the _____, and in this case we say the difference is not defined.

SUBTRAHEND;   MINUEND

121.

And when the difference of two quotient numbers is defined, we may always use the _____ _____ rule to find the difference.

CROSS PRODUCT

122.

In symbols the cross product rule for subtraction is

$$\frac{a}{b} - \frac{c}{d} = \underline{\qquad}$$

$$\frac{ad - bc}{bd}$$

123.

But when the denominators of the two quotient numbers are the same, it is easier not to use the cross product rule. In fact, when the denominators are the same we may write

$$\frac{a}{b} - \frac{c}{b} = \frac{\underline{\qquad}}{b}$$

a − c

124. And if one denominator is a multiple of the other, it is easier first to change one of the fractions so that it will have the same _____ as the other fraction, and then use the method of _____ _____.

DENOMINATOR; COMMON DENOMINATORS

Problems A (Answers on page 511)

Use the definition of subtraction to change each statement of subtraction to an equivalent statement of addition and each statement of addition to a pair of equivalent statements of subtraction.

Example: $5\frac{3}{4} - 2\frac{1}{2} = 3\frac{1}{4}$.

Solution: $2\frac{1}{2} + 3\frac{1}{4} = 5\frac{3}{4}$

Example: $18\frac{7}{8} + 5\frac{1}{2} = 24\frac{3}{8}$.

Solution: $24\frac{3}{8} - 5\frac{1}{2} = 18\frac{7}{8}$

$24\frac{3}{8} - 18\frac{7}{8} = 5\frac{1}{2}$

1. $\dfrac{7}{12} - \dfrac{3}{10} = \dfrac{17}{60}$

2. $24 - 5\frac{1}{3} = \dfrac{56}{3}$

3. $\dfrac{5}{6} + \dfrac{2}{7} = \dfrac{47}{42}$

4. $\dfrac{45}{4} + \dfrac{100}{3} = \dfrac{535}{12}$

5. $22\frac{1}{2} - 6\frac{3}{16} = \dfrac{261}{16}$

6. $3\frac{1}{7} + 2\frac{7}{8} = 6\frac{1}{56}$

7. $\dfrac{89}{12} - 6\frac{5}{12} = 1$

Use the method of common denominators to find the difference. Express answers in simplest form.

8. $\dfrac{15}{8} - \dfrac{3}{8}$

9. $\dfrac{24}{155} - \dfrac{9}{155}$

10. $\dfrac{44}{5} - \dfrac{7}{15}$

11. $\dfrac{19}{60} - \dfrac{1}{12}$

12. $\dfrac{17}{35} - \dfrac{4}{105}$

Use the cross product method to find the difference. Express answers in simplest form.

13. $\dfrac{7}{12} - \dfrac{4}{7}$

14. $\dfrac{5}{8} - \dfrac{1}{10}$

15. $\dfrac{16}{3} - \dfrac{17}{4}$

16. $\dfrac{6}{25} - \dfrac{4}{100}$

17. $\dfrac{5}{6} - \dfrac{5}{9}$

Use any method to find the difference. Write answers in simplest form.

18. $12\frac{1}{3} - 5$

19. $45 - 16\frac{2}{3}$

20. $7\frac{1}{2} - 3\frac{1}{3}$

21. $322\frac{5}{6} - 116\frac{7}{10}$

22. $5\frac{7}{12} - \dfrac{47}{10}$

23. $\dfrac{88}{3} - 5\frac{1}{6}$

24. $\dfrac{115}{8} - 9$

25. $56 - \dfrac{157}{3}$

Problems B

Perform the indicated operation. Write answers in simplest form.

1. $\dfrac{47}{3} - \dfrac{43}{3}$

2. $\dfrac{22}{17} - \dfrac{17}{17}$

3. $\dfrac{23}{16} - \dfrac{3}{4}$

4. $\dfrac{166}{101} - \dfrac{23}{101}$

5. $5 - \dfrac{17}{7}$

6. $8\frac{2}{3} - \dfrac{11}{2}$

7. $5\frac{2}{5} + \dfrac{8}{3}$

8. $(2\frac{3}{8})(4\frac{5}{6})$

9. $11\frac{5}{6} - \dfrac{25}{3}$

10. $\dfrac{437}{29} + \dfrac{27}{29}$

11. $139\frac{1}{4} + 253\frac{1}{2}$

12. $846\frac{1}{2} - 514\frac{1}{5}$

13. $215\frac{2}{3} - 174\frac{1}{6}$

14. $(18\frac{3}{4})(5\frac{1}{3})$

15. $\frac{115}{4} - 14\frac{3}{8}$

16. $12 + \frac{1}{3}$

17. $12\frac{3}{7} + 0$

18. $2\frac{1}{2} - 0$

19. $18 - 5\frac{1}{3}$

20. $13\frac{3}{8} - 5\frac{1}{2}$

Express answers to the following as mixed numbers or natural numbers.

21. The gasoline tank of a certain automobile holds $17\frac{3}{4}$ gallons when full. If $15\frac{1}{2}$ gallons more are needed to fill the tank, how many does it hold at the present time?

22. An investor bought some stock priced at $117\frac{3}{8}$. A month later the stock was selling for $120\frac{7}{8}$. What was the investor's gain on each share?

23. A carpenter wants to cut a board which is $12\frac{1}{3}$ feet long from a 16-foot length of lumber. How much should he saw off the end of the lumber?

24. On Monday a horse raced for $1\frac{1}{4}$ miles and on the following Thursday he raced for $7/8$ mile. How far did he race during the week?

25. A product that normally sells at 3 cans for 47¢ is on sale at 2 cans for 29¢. How much is saved on each can during the sale?

DIVISION OF QUOTIENT NUMBERS

1. By the cross product rule

   $$\frac{a}{b} - \frac{c}{d} = \underline{\hspace{2cm}}$$

   (ad − bc)/bd

2. Use the cross product rule to subtract

   $$\frac{3}{4} - \frac{2}{3} = \underline{\hspace{2cm}} \qquad 3 - \frac{5}{2} = \underline{\hspace{2cm}}$$

   1/12;   1/2

3. Mixed numbers may be first changed to fractions.

   $$2\frac{1}{2} - 1\frac{3}{5} = \frac{5}{2} - \frac{8}{5} = \underline{\hspace{2cm}}$$

   Similarly,

   $$3\frac{2}{3} - 2\frac{3}{4} = \underline{\hspace{2cm}}$$

   9/10;   11/12

4. Sometimes it is easier not to change mixed numbers to fractions.

   $$8\frac{3}{4} - 3 = (8 - 3) + \frac{3}{4} = 5 + \frac{3}{4} = \underline{\hspace{2cm}}$$

   Similarly,

   $$112\frac{3}{7} - 12 = \underline{\hspace{2cm}}$$

   23/4;   703/7

5. Do not change to fractions before subtracting.

   $$73\frac{3}{4} - 13\frac{1}{4} = (73 - 13) + \left(\frac{3}{4} - \frac{1}{4}\right) = \underline{\hspace{2cm}}$$

   121/2

6. Subtract:

   $$185\frac{5}{7} - 85\frac{4}{7} = \underline{\hspace{2cm}}$$

   701/7

7. Consider

$$3\tfrac{1}{3} - \frac{2}{3} = [\quad]$$

If we do not change to fractions, we could write

$$3\tfrac{1}{3} - \frac{2}{3} = \left(3 + \frac{1}{3}\right) - \frac{2}{3} = 3 + \left(\underline{} - \frac{2}{3}\right)$$

> 1/3

8. $3\tfrac{1}{3} - \frac{2}{3} = 3 + \left(\frac{1}{3} - \frac{2}{3}\right)$

But $1/3 - 2/3$ is impossible, since $1/3 < 2/3$. However, we can instead write

$$3\tfrac{1}{3} = 2 + 1 + \frac{1}{3} = 2 + \frac{}{3}$$

> 4

9. $3\tfrac{1}{3} = 2 + \frac{4}{3}$

Hence

$$3\tfrac{1}{3} - \frac{2}{3} = 2 + \frac{4}{3} - \frac{2}{3} = 2 + \underline{}$$

> 2/3

10. Similarly

$$5\tfrac{1}{5} - \frac{3}{5} = 4 + 1 + \frac{1}{5} - \frac{3}{5} = 4 + \underline{} - \frac{3}{5}$$

> 6/5

11. Then

$$5\tfrac{1}{5} - \frac{3}{5} = 4 + \frac{6}{5} - \frac{3}{5} = 4 + \underline{} = \frac{}{5}$$

> 3/5;   23

12. $12\tfrac{2}{7} - \frac{4}{7} = 11 + \underline{} - \frac{4}{7}$

Remember,

$$12\tfrac{2}{7} = 11 + 1 + \frac{2}{7}$$

> 9/7

13. Then

$$12\tfrac{2}{7} - \frac{4}{7} = 11 + \frac{9}{7} - \frac{4}{7} = \frac{}{7}$$

> 82

14. Subtract, using the method illustrated in the preceding frames.

$$9\tfrac{1}{4} - \frac{3}{4} = \underline{} \qquad 15\tfrac{2}{7} - \frac{6}{7} = \underline{}$$

> 17/2;   101/7

15. Also, we may subtract mixed numbers as follows:

$$3\tfrac{1}{4} - 1\tfrac{3}{4} = 2 + \underline{} - 1\tfrac{3}{4}$$

> 5/4

16. Then

$$3\tfrac{1}{4} - 1\tfrac{3}{4} = 2\tfrac{5}{4} - 1\tfrac{3}{4} = 1\tfrac{2}{4} = \frac{}{2}$$

> 3

17. And

$$6\tfrac{2}{5} - 3\tfrac{4}{5} = 5\tfrac{7}{5} - 3\tfrac{4}{5} = \underline{}$$

> $2\tfrac{3}{5} = 13/5$

18. Remember, if the fractional part of the subtrahend is larger than the fractional part of the minuend, we may first rewrite the minuend.

Then

$$4\tfrac{2}{3} = 3 + \frac{}{3}$$

> 5

19. Complete the following.

$$10\tfrac{1}{5} = 9 + \frac{}{5}$$

$$175\tfrac{2}{3} = 174 + \frac{}{3}$$

$$301\tfrac{9}{10} = 300 + \frac{}{10}$$

> 6;   5;   19

20. Then

$$12\tfrac{1}{4} - 3\tfrac{3}{4} = 11 + \frac{}{4} - 3\tfrac{3}{4}$$

> 5

21. And

$$12\tfrac{1}{4} - 3\tfrac{3}{4} = 11\tfrac{5}{4} - 3\tfrac{3}{4} = \underline{}$$

> $8\tfrac{2}{4} = 8\tfrac{1}{2} = 17/2$

22. Subtract. Write your answers as mixed numbers.

$$73\tfrac{2}{5} - 12\tfrac{4}{5} = \underline{}$$

$$175\tfrac{1}{7} - 63\tfrac{5}{7} = \underline{}$$

$$35\tfrac{1}{3} - 21\tfrac{3}{4} = \underline{}$$

> $60\tfrac{3}{5}$; $111\tfrac{3}{7}$; $13\tfrac{7}{12}$

23. Of course we may always write mixed numbers as fractions before subtracting.

$$4\tfrac{1}{3} - 2\tfrac{3}{4} = \frac{13}{3} - \frac{11}{4} = \frac{}{12}$$

$$6\tfrac{1}{5} - 1\tfrac{2}{3} = \underline{}$$

> 19;   68/15

24. But when the mixed numbers are large, it is easier not to change to fractions. Subtract, leaving the answer as a mixed number.

$$826\tfrac{1}{4} - 175\tfrac{2}{5} = \underline{}$$

> $650\tfrac{17}{20}$

25. Recall that we indicate the quotient of two natural numbers a and b, by writing a/b. Sometimes this quotient is another natural number. If so, then

$$a/b = q$$

where q is a natural number, and $q \cdot b = \underline{}$.

> a

26. If the quotient of the natural numbers a and b is a natural number q, we write a/b = q or q·b = a.

Then we say that a is _____ by b, and b is an exact _____ of a.

> DIVISIBLE;   DIVISOR

27. If there is no natural number, q, such that a/b = q, then we say that a is not _____ by b or b is not an exact _____ of a.

> DIVISIBLE;   DIVISOR

28. If there is no natural number, q, such that a/b = q, we define the quotient of a and b to be simply the quotient number represented by the fraction _____.

> a/b

29. Then the quotient of 12 and 3 is 4, since 4·3 = 12, while the quotient of 12 and 5 is the quotient number which may be represented by the fraction _____.

> 12/5

30. If a/b = q, we say that a is the dividend, b is the _____ and q is the _____.

> DIVISOR;   QUOTIENT

31. And if a/b = q, then q·b = _____.

> a

32. If a/b = q, then q·b = a.

That is, the quotient, q, is a number whose product with the divisor, b, equals the _____, a.

> DIVIDEND

33. And when we say that the quotient of a and b is the quotient number represented by the fraction a/b, we are indicating that a is the dividend, b is the _____ and a/b is the _____.

> DIVISOR;   QUOTIENT

34. a is the dividend.
b is the divisor.
a/b is the quotient.

What is the product of the quotient and the divisor?

> a   (see next frame)

35. a is the dividend.
b is the divisor.
a/b is the quotient.

And the product of the quotient and the divisor

$$\frac{a}{b} \cdot b = \frac{a}{b} \cdot \frac{b}{1} = \frac{ab}{b \cdot 1} = \frac{a}{1} = a$$

Then the product of the quotient and the divisor equals the _____.

> DIVIDEND

36. In fact, this is how we have defined the quotient of two natural numbers. The quotient of two natural numbers is a number (sometimes a natural number, sometimes a quotient number) whose product with the _____ equals the _____.

> DIVISOR;   DIVIDEND

37. And we define the quotient of two quotient numbers in the same way. That is, the quotient of two quotient numbers is the quotient number whose _____ with the divisor equals the dividend.

> PRODUCT

38. Then the quotient of two quotient numbers is defined in terms of a product. This is why we say division is the inverse of _____.

> MULTIPLICATION

39. We indicate the quotient of 2/3 and 5/8 by writing

$$\frac{2}{3} \div \frac{5}{8}$$

Similarly, we may indicate the quotient of 1/2 and 3/4 by _____ .

$$\frac{1}{3} \div \frac{3}{4}$$

40. $\frac{1}{2} \div \frac{3}{4} = [\quad]$

In this problem the dividend is 1/2 and the divisor is _____ .

3/4

41. $\frac{1}{2} \div \frac{3}{4} = [\quad]$

The dividend is 1/2.
The divisor is 3/4.

The quotient is not known, but, by definition, the _____ of the quotient and the divisor is equal to the dividend.

PRODUCT

42. $\frac{1}{2} \div \frac{3}{4} = [\quad]$

The product of the quotient and the divisor equals the dividend. Then the quotient must be 2/3, since

$$\frac{2}{3} \cdot \text{_____} = \frac{1}{2}$$

Remember, the divisor is 3/4.

3/4

43. Since

$$\frac{2}{3} \cdot \frac{3}{4} = \frac{1}{2}$$

we know that 2/3 is the quotient of 1/2 and _____ .

3/4

44. That is, since $\frac{2}{3} \cdot \frac{3}{4} = \frac{1}{2}$, we know that

$$\frac{1}{2} \div \frac{3}{4} = \text{_____}$$

2/3

45. $\frac{1}{2} \div \frac{3}{4} = \frac{2}{3}$ since $\frac{2}{3} \cdot \frac{3}{4} = \frac{1}{2}$

The product of the quotient, 2/3, and the divisor, _____ , equals the _____ , 1/2.

3/4;   DIVIDEND

46. Any two _____ numbers may be represented by a/b and c/d.

QUOTIENT

47. Then the quotient of a/b and c/d may be represented by _____ .

$$\frac{a}{b} \div \frac{c}{d}$$

48. In the expression

$$\frac{a}{b} \div \frac{c}{d}$$

a/b is the _____ and c/d is the _____.

DIVIDEND;   DIVISOR

49. We will show that

$$\frac{a}{b} \div \frac{c}{d} = \frac{ad}{bc}$$

In this problem, the dividend is a/b, the divisor is c/d, and the quotient is _____.

ad/bc

50. We will show that

$$\frac{a}{b} \div \frac{c}{d} = \frac{ad}{bc}$$

Of course, by the definition of division, the product of the _____ and the divisor equals the _____.

QUOTIENT;   DIVIDEND

51. We will show that

$$\frac{a}{b} \div \frac{c}{d} = \frac{ad}{bc}$$

We must show that the product of the quotient and the divisor equals the dividend. Then we must show that

$$\frac{ad}{bc} \cdot \frac{c}{d} = \underline{\hspace{1.5cm}}$$

a/b

52. In order to show that $\frac{a}{b} \div \frac{c}{d} = \frac{ad}{bc}$

we must show that $\frac{ad}{bc} \cdot \frac{c}{d} = \frac{a}{b}$

But $\frac{ad}{bc} \cdot \frac{c}{d} = \frac{(ad)c}{\underline{\hspace{1cm}}}$

(bc)d

53. Then

$$\frac{ad}{bc} \cdot \frac{c}{d} = \frac{(ad)c}{(bc)d}$$

$$= \frac{a(cd)}{b(cd)}$$

$$= \frac{\underline{\hspace{0.6cm}}}{b}$$

a

54. Hence we have shown that

$$\frac{ad}{bc} \cdot \frac{c}{d} = \frac{a}{b}$$

Then ad/bc is a number whose _____ with c/d equals a/b.

PRODUCT

55. And since ad/bc is a number whose product with c/d is a/b, we say that ad/bc is the _____ of a/b and c/d.

QUOTIENT

56. Hence

$$\frac{a}{b} \div \frac{c}{d} = \frac{ad}{bc}$$

since

$$\frac{ad}{bc} \cdot \frac{c}{d} = \underline{\hspace{2cm}}$$

a/b

57. We have shown that

$$\frac{a}{b} \div \frac{c}{d} = \frac{ad}{bc}$$

Notice that the cross products of a/b and c/d are ad and _____ .

bc

58. $\frac{a}{b} \div \frac{c}{d} = \frac{ad}{bc}$

Then the numerator and denominator of the quotient, ad/bc, are the cross products of _____ and _____ .

a/b;   c/d

59. Hence

$$\frac{2}{3} \div \frac{5}{8} = \frac{2 \cdot 8}{\underline{\hspace{1cm}}} = \frac{16}{15}$$

3·5

60. Similarly,

$$\frac{3}{4} \div \frac{1}{3} = \frac{3 \cdot 3}{\underline{\hspace{1cm}}} = \underline{\hspace{1.5cm}}$$

4·1;   9/4

61. Divide:

$$\frac{5}{8} \div \frac{1}{3} = \frac{5 \cdot 3}{8 \cdot 1} = \underline{\hspace{2cm}}$$

$$\frac{8}{9} \div \frac{2}{5} = \underline{\hspace{2cm}}$$

$$\frac{3}{5} \div \frac{8}{3} = \underline{\hspace{2cm}}$$

15/8;   40/18 = 20/9;   9/40

62. Note that

$$3 \div \frac{2}{5} = \frac{3}{1} \div \frac{2}{5} = \frac{15}{\underline{\hspace{0.5cm}}}$$

2

63. And

$$7 \div \frac{1}{2} = \frac{7}{1} \div \frac{1}{2} = \frac{7 \cdot 2}{1 \cdot 1} = 14$$

Similarly,

$$12 \div \frac{1}{4} = \frac{12}{1} \div \frac{1}{4} = \underline{\hspace{2cm}}$$

$$20 \div \frac{2}{3} = \underline{\hspace{2cm}}$$

48;   30

64. And

$$\frac{2}{5} \div 3 = \frac{2}{5} \div \frac{3}{1} = \frac{2}{\underline{\hspace{0.5cm}}}$$

15

65. Divide:

$$\frac{6}{5} \div \frac{1}{2} = \underline{\hspace{2cm}}$$

$$4 \div \frac{5}{3} = \underline{\hspace{2cm}}$$

$$\frac{6}{11} \div 3 = \underline{\hspace{2cm}}$$

12/5;   12/5; $\frac{6}{11} \div 3 = \frac{6}{11} \div \frac{3}{1} = \frac{6}{33} = \frac{2}{11}$

66. To divide mixed numbers, we must first write them as fractions.

$$3\frac{1}{2} \div 1\frac{1}{3} = \frac{7}{2} \div \frac{4}{3} = \underline{\hspace{2cm}}$$

21/8

67. Change to fractions and divide:

$$\frac{3}{4} \div 5\frac{1}{2} = \underline{\hspace{2cm}} \qquad 8\frac{2}{3} \div 3\frac{3}{4} = \underline{\hspace{2cm}}$$

3/22;   · 104/45

68. Multiply or divide as indicated:

a) $\frac{3}{4} \cdot \frac{2}{5} = \underline{\hspace{2cm}}$ b) $\frac{9}{16} \div \frac{3}{4} = \underline{\hspace{2cm}}$

c) $8\frac{2}{3} \cdot 1\frac{1}{2} = \underline{\hspace{2cm}}$ d) $5 \div 2\frac{1}{2} = \underline{\hspace{2cm}}$

a) 3/10;   b) 3/4;   c) 13;   d) 2

69. Recall that the quotient of 12 and 3 is indicated by 12/3. And we see that

12/3 = 4,   since   4 · 3 = 12.

What is the quotient of 4 and 0?

_____

IT IS UNDEFINED   (see next frame)

70. 4/0 is not defined, since the product of 0 and any number is 0. That is, we cannot find any number whose _____ with the divisor 0 equals the dividend 4.

PRODUCT

71. We say that division of natural numbers by zero is impossible. Is division of quotient numbers by zero possible? That is, can we find a quotient number whose product with zero equals the dividend? _____

NO

72. In fact, we have defined the product of 0 and any quotient number to be _____.

0

73. Consider

$$\frac{2}{3} \div 0 = [\quad]$$

The quotient, when multiplied by the divisor, must equal the _____.

DIVIDEND

74. $\frac{2}{3} \div 0 = [\quad]$

But no matter what the quotient is, when it is multiplied by the divisor 0 the result is _____.

0

75. Hence, division of quotient numbers by zero is also impossible. Find the quotient where possible.

$$\frac{3}{4} \div 5 = \underline{\hspace{2cm}}$$

$$2\frac{1}{2} \div 0 = \underline{\hspace{2cm}}$$

$$5\frac{1}{2} \div 3\frac{1}{2} = \underline{\hspace{2cm}}$$

> 3/20;   IMPOSSIBLE;   11/7

76. Consider the quotient of 0 and 1. We indicate this by 0/1, and we see that

$$0/1 = \underline{\hspace{1.5cm}}, \quad \text{since} \quad \underline{\hspace{1.5cm}} \cdot 1 = 0$$

> 0;   0

77. In fact, if 0 is divided by any natural number, the result is _____.

> 0

78. Consider

$$0 \div \frac{2}{3} = [\quad]$$

The quotient must be a number whose _____ with the divisor, 2/3, equals the dividend, 0.

> PRODUCT

79. $$0 \div \frac{2}{3} = [\quad]$$

Since the product of _____ with 2/3 equals 0, we know that $0 \div \overline{2/3} = \underline{\hspace{1cm}}$.

> 0;   0

80. Similarly,

$$0 \div \frac{5}{8} = \underline{\hspace{2cm}}$$

$$0 \div \frac{12}{7} = \underline{\hspace{2cm}}$$

$$0 \div 1753^{17}\!/_{36} = \underline{\hspace{2cm}}$$

> 0;   0;   0

81. In fact if zero is divided by any quotient number, the result is _____.

> ZERO

82. But it is always impossible for a quotient number to be divided by_____.

> ZERO

83. The dividend may be zero, but the _____ may not be zero.

> DIVISOR

84. Which of these are impossible?

a) $5\frac{2}{3} \div 0$

b) $0 \div \frac{1}{2}$

c) $4\frac{2}{3} \div 0$

d) $0 \div 0$

e) $\frac{0}{4}$ _____

> a, c, d

85. Which of these are equal to zero?

    a) $5\frac{2}{5} \div 0$

    b) $\frac{0}{3}$

    c) $0 \div 5\frac{1}{2}$

    d) $0 \div 0$

    e) $\frac{4}{0}$ _____

> **b, c**

86. Multiply or divide, if possible.

    a) $\frac{3}{4} \cdot 2\frac{1}{2} =$ _____   b) $7\frac{2}{3} \div 0 =$ _____

    c) $3\frac{1}{2} \div 1\frac{2}{3} =$ _____ d) $0 \div 3\frac{1}{4} =$ _____

> **a) 15/8;   b) IMPOSSIBLE;   c) 21/10;**
> **d) 0**

87. Recall that a/b < c/d if ad < _____ .

> **bc**

88. Insert the sign $<$, $>$, or =.

    a) $\frac{3}{8}$ _____ $\frac{5}{13}$ b) $3\frac{1}{2}$ _____ $3\frac{1}{4}$

    c) $\frac{9}{5}$ _____ 1   d) $\frac{3}{4}$ _____ 1

> **a) $<$;   b) $>$;   c) $>$;   d) $<$**

89. Consider

$$\frac{3}{4} \cdot \frac{2}{3} = \frac{1}{2}$$

The factor 3/4 is multiplied by 2/3, which is _____ than 1, and the product, 1/2, is _____ than 3/4.

> **LESS;   LESS**

90. $\frac{3}{4} \cdot \frac{8}{3} = 2$

Here the factor 3/4 is multiplied by a number greater than _____ , and the resulting product, 2, is _____ than 3/4.

> **1;   GREATER**

91. Then sometimes the product is greater than the first factor, and sometimes the product is less than the first factor. It depends on whether the second factor is greater than, or less than, _____ .

> **1**

92. Consider

$$\frac{3}{4} \div \frac{1}{3} = \frac{9}{4}$$

The divisor is _____ , a number less than 1. The quotient is 9/4, a number _____ than the dividend 3/4.

> **1/3;   GREATER**

93. $\frac{6}{5} \div \frac{2}{5} = 3$

Again, when the divisor is _____ than 1, the quotient is _____ than the dividend.

> **LESS;   GREATER**

94. But

$$\frac{2}{3} \div \frac{4}{3} = \frac{1}{2}$$

Here the divisor is _____ than 1, while the quotient is _____ than the dividend.

> **GREATER;   LESS**

95. Then for division of quotient numbers, the quotient may be either less than or greater than the dividend. If the divisor is less than 1, the quotient is _____ than the dividend. But if the divisor is greater than _____, the quotient is less than the _____.

GREATER; 1; DIVIDEND

96. $\frac{5}{8} \div \frac{2}{3} = [\quad]$

Since the divisor is _____ than 1, the quotient is _____ than the dividend, 5/8.

LESS; GREATER

97. $\frac{5}{8} \div \frac{3}{2} = [\quad]$

Since the _____ is greater than 1, the quotient is _____ than the dividend.

DIVISOR; LESS

98. $5\frac{2}{3} \div 2\frac{1}{2} = [\quad]$
The quotient is _____ than $5\frac{2}{3}$.

LESS

99. $6\frac{3}{4} \div \frac{5}{8} = [\quad]$

The quotient is _____ than $6\frac{3}{4}$.

GREATER ·

100. In this chapter we have defined the quotient of two quotient numbers. We have said that the quotient is a number whose _____ with the divisor equals the _____.

PRODUCT; DIVIDEND

101. And we proved that

$\frac{a}{b} \div \frac{c}{d} = $ _____.

ad/bc

102. Mixed numbers should always be changed to _____ before dividing or multiplying.

FRACTIONS

103. But for large mixed numbers it is correct and may be easier not to change to fractions when _____ or _____.

ADDING; SUBTRACTING
(either order)

104. If a quotient number is multiplied by a factor greater than 1, the resulting product is _____ than the number. But if a quotient number is divided by a divisor greater than 1, the resulting quotient is _____ than the dividend.

GREATER; LESS

105. If a quotient number is multiplied by a factor less than _____, the resulting product is _____ than the number. But if a quotient number is divided by a divisor less than 1, the resulting quotient is _____ than the dividend.

1; LESS; GREATER

Chapter 18

Problems A (Answers on page 511)

Use the cross product rule to divide. Write answers in simplest form.

1. $\dfrac{7}{12} \div \dfrac{5}{6}$

2. $\dfrac{22}{7} \div \dfrac{1}{3}$

3. $\dfrac{2}{3} \div \dfrac{7}{16}$

4. $\dfrac{5}{3} \div \dfrac{2}{7}$

5. $\dfrac{5}{8} \div \dfrac{5}{8}$

Perform the indicated operation. Write answers in simplest form.

6. $3\frac{1}{2} - 1\frac{1}{4}$

7. $5\frac{2}{3} + 4\frac{5}{6}$

8. $4 \div 9$

9. $4 - 2\frac{1}{3}$

10. $\dfrac{2}{3} \cdot \dfrac{7}{16}$

11. $63\frac{5}{8} - 28\frac{11}{12}$

12. $7\frac{7}{8} \div 4$

13. $2\frac{1}{2} \cdot \dfrac{4}{5}$

14. $8\frac{1}{5} - 5\frac{3}{5}$

15. $0 \div \dfrac{5}{21}$

16. $4\frac{1}{3} \div 2\frac{1}{3}$

17. $48 \div \dfrac{3}{8}$

18. $9\frac{2}{3} - 5\frac{8}{9}$

19. $50\frac{1}{3} \div 40\frac{2}{3}$

20. $\dfrac{16}{3} \cdot 0$

Without finding the number, x, decide whether the second statement is true or false.

Example: $\dfrac{5}{8} \div x = 1 \qquad x < 1$

Solution: True (When the divisor is less than 1, the quotient is greater than the dividend.)

21. $\dfrac{5}{6} \div \dfrac{2}{3} = x \qquad x > 5/6$

22. $1\frac{2}{3} \div \dfrac{7}{12} = x \qquad x > 7/12$

23. $x \div \dfrac{5}{7} = \dfrac{6}{7} \qquad x > 6/7$

24. $x \cdot \dfrac{9}{10} = 1 \qquad x > 9/10$

25. $0 \div \dfrac{7}{5} = x \qquad x > 0$

26. $\dfrac{3}{8} \div x = \dfrac{1}{2} \qquad x < 1$

27. $5 \div x = 3/4 \qquad x < 1$

28. $x \div \dfrac{5}{6} = \dfrac{17}{3} \qquad x < 17/3$

29. $x \div 24 = x \qquad x > 1$

30. $\dfrac{5}{6} \div x = \dfrac{6}{7} \qquad x > 7/6$

Problems B

Perform the indicated operation. Write answers in simplest form.

1. $\dfrac{3}{5} \div \dfrac{20}{21}$

2. $\dfrac{5}{7} \div \dfrac{12}{5}$

3. $\dfrac{12}{5} \cdot \dfrac{15}{28}$

4. $2\frac{1}{2} \div 5\frac{1}{3}$

5. $1\frac{3}{4} + 4\frac{7}{8}$

6. $8\frac{1}{3} - 4\frac{5}{6}$

7. $\dfrac{14}{15} \div \dfrac{15}{14}$

8. $\dfrac{14}{15} \cdot \dfrac{15}{14}$

9. $2\frac{3}{8} \cdot 0$

10. $\dfrac{27}{4} - 5\frac{2}{3}$

11. $\dfrac{1}{100} \div \dfrac{5}{6}$

12. $\dfrac{7}{2} \div \dfrac{13}{3}$

13. $137\frac{1}{4} - 93\frac{1}{8}$

14. $493\frac{1}{6} - 277\frac{1}{2}$

15. $0 \div 436\frac{3}{16}$

Answer the following without determining x.

16. If $3\frac{7}{8} \div x = 2/3$, is $x < 3\frac{7}{8}$? Explain.

17. If $x \div 19\frac{3}{7} = 15$, is $x > 19\frac{3}{7}$? Explain.

18. Can the sum of two quotient numbers, each less than 1, be greater than 1? Explain.

19. Can the difference of two quotient numbers, each less than 1, be greater than 1? Explain.

20. Must the product of two quotient numbers, each greater than 1, be greater than 1? Explain.

21. Must the quotient of two quotient numbers, each greater than 1, be less than 1? Explain.

22. A 50-gallon tank is to be filled with water by repeated pourings from a bucket which holds $3\frac{1}{3}$ gallons. How many times must the bucket be used?

23. A camper estimates that his daily food ration weighs $1\frac{7}{8}$ pounds. How many full-days' ration can he carry, if the total weight of food must not be greater than 21 pounds?

24. How many shares of stock priced at $51\frac{3}{4}$ dollars each can be purchased for 1000 dollars?

25. The total capacity of a tank is $17\frac{3}{4}$ gallons. If the gage shows that the tank is 3/8 full, how many gallons must be added to fill the tank?

CHAPTER 19

COMPLEX FRACTIONS

1. The quotient of two quotient numbers is a quotient number whose _____ with the divisor equals the dividend.

> PRODUCT

2. And we say that D_____ and _____ are inverse operations.

> DIVISION;   MULTIPLICATION

3. If a/b and c/d are quotient numbers, then

$$\frac{a}{b} \div \frac{c}{d} = \underline{\hspace{1cm}}$$

> ad/bc

4. Divide:

$$\frac{3}{5} \div \frac{2}{3} = \underline{\hspace{1cm}} \qquad \frac{7}{8} \div \frac{5}{3} = \underline{\hspace{1cm}}$$

> 9/10;   21/40

5. The rule

$$\frac{a}{b} \div \frac{c}{d} = \frac{ad}{bc}$$

gives the quotient of two fractions in terms of their cross _____.

> PRODUCTS

6. We call

$$\frac{a}{b} \div \frac{c}{d} = \frac{ad}{bc}$$

the CROSS PRODUCT RULE FOR DIVISION

7. There are also cross product rules for addition and subtraction, which are symbolized by

$$\frac{a}{b} + \frac{c}{d} = \underline{\hspace{2cm}}$$

$$\frac{a}{b} - \frac{c}{d} = \underline{\hspace{2cm}}$$

> (ad + bc)/bd;   (ad − bc)/bd

8. But multiplication of fractions does not involve their cross products. In fact,

$$\frac{a}{b} \cdot \frac{c}{d} = \underline{\hspace{1cm}}$$

> ac/bd

9. Multiply.

$$\frac{3}{5} \cdot \frac{5}{4} = \underline{\qquad}$$

$$\frac{2}{3} \cdot \frac{3}{2} = \underline{\qquad}$$

$$\frac{5}{2} \cdot \frac{4}{1} = \underline{\qquad}$$

3/4;   1;   10

10. Find the product.

$$\frac{3}{8} \cdot \frac{8}{3} = \underline{\qquad} \qquad \frac{4}{5} \cdot \frac{5}{4} = \underline{\qquad}$$

$$7 \cdot \frac{1}{7} = \underline{\qquad} \qquad \frac{1}{3} \cdot 3 = \underline{\qquad}$$

1;   1;   1;   1

11. Observe that each product in the previous frame is 1.

$$\frac{3}{4} \cdot \frac{4}{3} = \underline{\qquad} \qquad \frac{2}{3} \cdot \underline{\qquad} = 1$$

1;   3/2

12. Find the missing factor.

$$\frac{3}{8} \cdot \underline{\qquad} = 1$$

$$\underline{\qquad} \cdot \frac{5}{3} = 1$$

$$\frac{1}{5} \cdot \underline{\qquad} = 1$$

8/3;   3/5;   5

13. Find a factor which makes the product 1.

$$\frac{4}{9} \cdot \underline{\qquad} = 1$$

$$\underline{\qquad} \cdot \frac{1}{3} = 1$$

$$4 \cdot \underline{\qquad} = 1$$

9/4;   3;   1/4

14. When the product of two quotient numbers is 1, we say that each factor is the MULTIPLICATIVE INVERSE of the other.

Then since $\frac{2}{3} \cdot \frac{3}{2} = 1$, we say that 2/3 is the multiplicative inverse of _____.

3/2

15. Since $2 \cdot \frac{1}{2} = 1$, we say that 1/2 is the multiplicative inverse of 2, and also 2 is the multiplicative inverse of_____. Similarly, the multiplicative inverse of 1/3 is _____.

1/2;   3

16. Find the multiplicative inverse of:

2/5 _____   4 _____   1/9 _____

5/2;   1/4;   9

17. Since $\frac{3}{4} \cdot \frac{4}{3} = 1$, we say that 4/3 is the multiplicative _____ of 3/4.

INVERSE

18. The multiplicative inverse of 3 is _____.
The multiplicative inverse of 1 is _____.

1/3;   1   (since 1·1 = 1)

19. 5 is the _____ _____
of 1/5.

20. Find the missing factor, if possible.

$4 \cdot$ _____ $= 1$

$1 \cdot$ _____ $= 1$

$0 \cdot$ _____ $= 1$

21. $0 \cdot [\quad] = 1$

This problem is impossible, since the product of 0 and any quotient number is _____.

22. Then 0 does not have a _____ inverse.

23. But   every   quotient   number   has   a _____ _____. It is the number whose product with the given number is 1.

24. The numbers 5/8 and 8/5 are called multiplicative _____ since their _____ is 1.

25. Another word for multiplicative inverse is RECIPROCAL. Then the reciprocal of 2/9 is 9/2, and the reciprocal of 5 is _____ .

26. 3/8 is the _____ of 8/3.

3/8 is also the _____
_____ of 8/3.

27. Since

$$\frac{a}{b} \cdot \frac{b}{a} = 1$$

we say that a/b is the _____ of b/a, and b/a is the _____ of a/b.

28. If c/d represents any quotient number, then the reciprocal of c/d can be represented by _____.

29. By the cross product rule

$$\frac{a}{b} \div \frac{c}{d} = \frac{ad}{bc}$$

We have just said that the reciprocal of c/d is d/c. Consider the product of a/b and the reciprocal of c/d.

$$\frac{a}{b} \cdot \frac{d}{c} = \text{_____}$$

30. Observe carefully:

$$\frac{a}{b} \div \frac{c}{d} = \frac{ad}{bc} \qquad \frac{a}{b} \cdot \frac{d}{c} = \frac{ad}{bc}$$

Notice that the quotient of a/b and c/d is the same as the _____ of a/b and the reciprocal of c/d.

> PRODUCT

31. Then, to find the quotient of two quotient numbers, we may _____ the dividend by the reciprocal of the divisor.

> MULTIPLY

32. Then $\frac{2}{3} \div \frac{4}{5}$ is also the product of 2/3 and _____.

> 5/4

33. Division may be performed by finding the product of the dividend and the _____ of the _____.

> RECIPROCAL;   DIVISOR

34. When we divide by finding the product of the dividend and the reciprocal of the divisor, we are using the RECIPROCAL RULE FOR DIVISION. Another way of stating this rule is to say that division can be performed by multiplying the dividend by the _____ _____ of the divisor.

> MULTIPLICATIVE INVERSE

35. By the reciprocal rule

$$\frac{3}{5} \div \frac{2}{3} = \frac{3}{5} \cdot \frac{3}{2} = \underline{\hspace{2cm}}$$

$$\frac{9}{7} \div 2 = \frac{9}{7} \cdot \underline{\hspace{1.5cm}} = \underline{\hspace{1.5cm}}$$

$$3 \div \frac{1}{4} = \underline{\hspace{1.5cm}} \cdot \underline{\hspace{1.5cm}} = \underline{\hspace{1.5cm}}$$

> $\frac{9}{10}$; $\frac{9}{7} \div 2 = \frac{9}{7} \cdot \frac{1}{2} = \frac{9}{14}$;
>
> $3 \div \frac{1}{4} = 3 \cdot 4 = 12$

36. Perform the special divisions below. Note that the divisor is a natural number. Use the reciprocal rule. Be sure to reduce to simplest form.

$$\frac{8}{3} \div 2 = \frac{8}{3} \cdot \frac{1}{2} = \frac{4}{3}$$

$$\frac{10}{3} \div 2 = \underline{\hspace{2cm}}$$

$$\frac{16}{3} \div 2 = \underline{\hspace{2cm}}$$

$$\frac{22}{3} \div 2 = \underline{\hspace{2cm}}$$

> 5/3;   8/3;   11/3

37. Notice.

$$\frac{8}{3} \div 2 = \frac{4}{3} \qquad \frac{10}{3} \div 2 = \frac{5}{3}$$

$$\frac{16}{3} \div 2 = \frac{8}{3} \qquad \frac{22}{3} \div 2 = \frac{11}{3}$$

In each case the numerator of the quotient is the result of dividing the numerator of the dividend by _____.

> 2

38. Thus, to divide a fraction by 2, we may merely divide its numerator by 2. Then

$$\frac{50}{37} \div 2 = \frac{25}{37}$$

$$\frac{44}{81} \div 2 = \frac{}{81}$$

$$\frac{162}{77} \div 2 = \underline{\hspace{1cm}}$$

39. Similarly, we may shorten the division of fractions by other natural numbers.

$$\frac{15}{37} \div 3 = \frac{5}{37}$$

$$\frac{16}{29} \div 4 = \frac{}{29}$$

$$\frac{30}{17} \div 5 = \underline{\hspace{1cm}}$$

40. But sometimes the numerator is not divisible by the natural number which is the divisor. However:

$$\frac{3}{5} \div 2 = \frac{3}{5} \cdot \frac{1}{2} = \frac{3}{10}$$

$$\frac{7}{5} \div 2 = \frac{7}{5} \cdot \frac{1}{2} = \underline{\hspace{1cm}}$$

$$\frac{17}{5} \div 2 = \underline{\hspace{1cm}}$$

41. $\frac{3}{5} \div 2 = \frac{3}{10}$ $\frac{7}{5} \div 2 = \frac{7}{10}$ $\frac{17}{5} \div 2 = \frac{17}{10}$

In each case the denominator of the quotient is the result of _____ the denominator of the dividend by 2.

42. Similarly,

$$\frac{8}{5} \div 3 = \frac{8}{15} \qquad \frac{12}{7} \div 5 = \frac{12}{35} \qquad \frac{9}{4} \div 7 = \frac{9}{28}$$

To divide a fraction by a natural number we may _____ the denominator of the dividend by that natural number.

43. Use the short method described in the previous frame to divide.

$$\frac{3}{4} \div 5 = \frac{3}{20} \qquad \frac{5}{8} \div 4 = \frac{5}{} \qquad \frac{7}{12} \div 3 = \underline{\hspace{1cm}}$$

44. Then to divide a fraction by a natural number, we may either _____ the numerator or _____ the denominator of that fraction by the natural number.

45. Divide, using the short method. Express results in simplest form.

a) $\frac{5}{8} \div 3 = \underline{\hspace{1cm}}$ b) $\frac{12}{7} \div 4 = \underline{\hspace{1cm}}$

c) $\frac{15}{8} \div 5 = \underline{\hspace{1cm}}$ d) $\frac{4}{9} \div 7 = \underline{\hspace{1cm}}$

46. The reciprocal rule for division states that the quotient of two quotient numbers is equal to the _____ of the dividend and the reciprocal of the divisor.

47. If a/b and c/d represent quotient numbers, then their product can be represented by _____.

ac/bd

48. $$\frac{a}{b} \cdot \frac{c}{d} = \frac{ac}{bd}$$

Since a/b and c/d are quotient numbers, their numerators and denominators, a, b, c, and d, are symbols which represent _____ _____.

NATURAL NUMBERS

49. $$\frac{a}{b} \cdot \frac{c}{d} = \frac{ac}{bd}$$

But if a and c are natural numbers, their product, ac, is also a natural number, and if b and d are natural numbers, their product, bd, is also a _____ _____.

NATURAL NUMBER

50. $$\frac{a}{b} \cdot \frac{c}{d} = \frac{ac}{bd}$$

Hence the numerator and denominator of the product, ac/bd, are both natural numbers and so we may see that this product is a _____ number.

QUOTIENT

51. $$\frac{a}{b} \cdot \frac{c}{d} = \frac{ac}{bd}$$

The product of any two quotient numbers is also a quotient number. We see, then, that the set of quotient numbers is _____ under the operation of multiplication.

CLOSED

52. If c/d represents a quotient number, then c and d represent natural numbers. But then the reciprocal of c/d, _____, must also be a _____ number.

d/c;   QUOTIENT

53. If c/d is a quotient number, its reciprocal, d/c, is also a quotient number. But the reciprocal rule for division of quotient numbers changes each division problem to a _____ of the dividend and the reciprocal of the divisor.

PRODUCT

54. Then, since products of quotient numbers are always quotient numbers, the quotient of two such numbers must also be a quotient number. The set of quotient numbers is also _____ under the operation of division.

CLOSED

55. Both the product and the quotient of any two quotient numbers will be quotient numbers, and so we say that the set of quotient numbers is closed with respect to both _____ and _____.

MULTIPLICATION;   DIVISION
(either order)

56. Similarly, the sum of two quotient numbers is always a quotient number, so the quotient numbers are also closed with respect to _____.

ADDITION

57. But the difference of two quotient numbers will be a quotient number only when the subtrahend is _____ than the minuend. For this reason we say that the quotient numbers are not _____ with respect to _____.

> LESS;   CLOSED;   SUBTRACTION

58. Every natural number may be written as a _____, and hence is also a quotient number.

> FRACTION

59. In fact we say that the set of all natural numbers is a _____ of the set of all quotient numbers.

> SUBSET

60. Usually, the product of a natural number and a quotient number is a quotient number, which is <u>not</u> also a natural number. For instance,

$$7 \cdot \frac{2}{3} = \text{_____} \qquad \frac{4}{3} \cdot 8 = \text{_____}$$

> 14/3;   32/3

61. But sometimes the product of a natural number and a quotient number is a natural number.

$$12 \cdot \frac{2}{3} = 8 \qquad \text{a) } 15 \cdot \frac{3}{5} = \text{_____}$$

$$\text{b) } \frac{2}{9} \cdot 9 = \text{_____} \qquad \text{c) } \frac{1}{3} \cdot 3 = \text{_____}$$

> a) 9;   b) 2;   c) 1

62. Observe

$$\frac{2}{3} \cdot 3 = 2 \qquad \frac{2}{3} \cdot 6 = 4$$

$$\frac{2}{3} \cdot 9 = 6 \qquad \frac{2}{3} \cdot 12 = 8$$

when 2/3 is multiplied by a multiple of its _____, the product is a natural number.

> DENOMINATOR

63. $\frac{3}{8} \cdot 16 = 6 \qquad \frac{4}{5} \cdot 15 = 12$

$\frac{2}{3} \cdot 3 = 2 \qquad \frac{3}{25} \cdot 50 = 6$

In each case one factor is a _____ of the denominator of the fraction.

> MULTIPLE

64. Then the product of a fraction and any multiple of its _____ will be a natural number.

> DENOMINATOR

65. Consider the fractions 2/3 and 3/4.

The LCM of the denominators, 3 and 4, is 12. Then 12 is a multiple of both _____ and _____.

> 3;   4   (either order)

66. Consider 2/3 and 3/4.

Since 12 is a multiple of both denominators, the product of 12 and either 2/3 and 3/4 will be a _____ number.

In fact,

$\frac{2}{3} \cdot 12 = $ _____ $\frac{3}{4} \cdot 12 = $ _____

NATURAL;   8;   9

67. When we multiply each of two fractions by the LCM of their _____, the resulting products will be natural numbers.

DENOMINATORS

68. Thus, if 2/5 and 3/10 are both multiplied by _____, the LCM of 5 and 10, the resulting products will be natural numbers.

10

69. What is the smallest natural number whose product with both 3/8 and 5/12 is a natural number? _____

(Remember, this is the LCM of 8 and 12.)

24

70. What is the smallest natural number whose product with both 5/6 and 3/10 is a natural number? _____

(Remember, this is the LCM of the denominators.)

30

71. If a and b represent natural numbers, we call a/b a fraction. Then

2/5 $\frac{(3 \cdot 5)}{7}$ $\frac{8}{(1 + 4)}$

are all fractions. Let us agree that a fraction whose numerator and denominator are both the simplest forms of natural numbers is called a SIMPLE FRACTION. Then since neither $3 \cdot 5$ nor $1 + 4$ is the simplest form of a natural number, we shall say that the only simple fraction above is _____.

2/5

72. Which of the following are simple fractions?

a) $\frac{2 \cdot 3 + 5}{7}$ c) $\frac{1 + 2}{1 + 2}$

b) 5/9   d) 1875/354

b and d

73. We will also want to consider symbols of the form x/y when x and y are symbols which represent quotient numbers. We will say that any such symbol which is not a simple fraction is a COMPLEX FRACTION. Both

2/3 $\frac{3/4}{7}$

are symbols of this type, and we see that 2/3 is a _____ fraction, while $\frac{3/4}{7}$ is a _____ fraction.

SIMPLE;   COMPLEX

74. There are many other examples of complex fractions. All except one of the following is a complex fraction.

$$\frac{2\frac{2}{5}}{5} \qquad \frac{1}{3/4} \qquad \frac{2/5}{3\frac{1}{4}} \qquad \frac{7}{8} \qquad \frac{6/5}{3/8}$$

The one which is not a complex fraction is _____. We call it a _____ fraction.

7/8;   SIMPLE

75. The expressions

$$\frac{2/3}{8} \qquad \frac{5}{3/4} \qquad \frac{4/3}{2/5} \qquad \frac{3\frac{1}{2}}{5\frac{2}{3}} \qquad \frac{9}{6\frac{1}{2}}$$

all are called _____ fractions.

COMPLEX

76. Each of the following is either a simple fraction or a complex fraction.

a) $\frac{5}{8}$ b) $\frac{2 + 1/2}{7}$ c) $\frac{4/3}{5\frac{1}{2}}$ d) $\frac{3\frac{2}{7}}{5\frac{5}{8}}$ e) $\frac{15}{3/5}$

Which of these are complex fractions?

_____

b, c, d, and e

77. A complex fraction also has a numerator and a denominator. For the complex fraction

$$\frac{2/3}{5/8}$$

we call 2/3 the numerator and _____ the denominator.

5/8

78. For the complex fraction

$$\frac{3\frac{1}{5}}{4}$$

the numerator is _____, and the denominator is 4.

$3\frac{1}{5}$

79. $\frac{5/3}{8}$ is not a _____ fraction since its _____ is not the simplest form of a natural number.

SIMPLE;   NUMERATOR

80. $\frac{4}{3/8}$ is a _____ fraction, since its _____ is not the simplest form of a natural number

COMPLEX;   DENOMINATOR

81. In the expression

$$\frac{6/3}{8}$$

the numerator, 6/3, represents a natural number, but not the simplest form of this natural number. Then this expression is not a _____ fraction.

SIMPLE

82. One of the properties of (simple) fractions which was proved earlier is

ax/bx = _____

whenever x is a natural number.

a/b

83. And, later, we interpreted this to mean that if both the numerator and the denominator of a fraction are either _____ or divided by the same natural number, the resulting fraction will equal the original one.

MULTIPLIED

84. It can be shown that the same property is true for complex fractions. That is, both the numerator and the denominator of a complex fraction may be multiplied by the same _____ number.

NATURAL

85. In fact, the numerator and denominator may be multiplied by any quotient number, but we will usually be multiplying by _____ numbers.

NATURAL

86. Consider

$$\frac{2/3}{3/4}$$

The numerator is 2/3, and the denominator is _____.

3/4

87. $\frac{2/3}{3/4}$

When the numerator is multiplied by 12, the product is

$$\frac{2}{3} \cdot 12 = \text{_____}$$

And if the denominator is also multiplied by 12, the product is

$$\frac{3}{4} \cdot 12 = \text{_____}$$

8;   9

88. Then

$$\frac{2/3}{3/4} = \frac{\frac{2}{3} \cdot 12}{\frac{3}{4} \cdot 12} = \frac{8}{9}$$

8

89. This is a surprising result!

$$\frac{2/3}{3/4} = \frac{8}{9}$$

The complex fraction, $\frac{2/3}{3/4}$, is equal to the _____ fraction, 8/9.

SIMPLE

90. Similarly,

$$\frac{3/8}{1/4} = \frac{\frac{3}{8} \cdot 8}{\frac{1}{4} \cdot 8} = \text{_____}$$

3/2

91. Consider

$$\frac{3/8}{5/12}$$

To change this complex fraction to a simple fraction, we can multiply both the numerator and denominator by the smallest natural number whose product with both 3/8 and 5/12 is a _____ number.

NATURAL

92. $\frac{3/8}{5/12}$

But the smallest natural number whose product with both 3/8 and 5/12 is a natural number is the LCM of the denominators, 8 and _____.

12

93.
$$\frac{3/8}{5/12}$$

Since the LCM of 8 and 12 is _____, this is the smallest natural number by which we can multiply both 3/8 and 5/12 so that both products will be natural numbers.

24

94. Then

$$\frac{3/8}{5/12} = \frac{\frac{3}{8} \cdot 24}{\frac{5}{12} \cdot 24} = \frac{}{10}$$

9

95. The complex fraction

$$\frac{1/2}{3/4}$$

may be changed to a simple fraction if we multiply both its numerator and denominator by _____, the LCM of 2 and 4.

4

96. Thus

$$\frac{1/2}{3/4} = \frac{\frac{1}{2} \cdot 4}{\frac{3}{4} \cdot 4} = \underline{\hspace{1cm}}$$

2/3

97. Similarly, to change

$$\frac{2/3}{5/6}$$

to a simple fraction, we multiply both the numerator and denominator by _____, the LCM of 3 and 6.

6

98. Then

$$\frac{2/3}{5/6} = \frac{\frac{2}{3} \cdot 6}{\frac{5}{6} \cdot 6} = \underline{\hspace{1cm}}$$

4/5

99. To reduce

$$\frac{3/8}{7/10}$$

to a simple fraction we multiply both 3/8 and 7/10 by _____. Remember, this should be the _____ of 8 and 10.

40;   LCM

100. Hence

$$\frac{3/8}{7/10} = \frac{\frac{3}{8} \cdot 40}{\frac{7}{10} \cdot 40} = \underline{\hspace{1cm}}$$

15/28

101. Reduce to a simple fraction:

$$\frac{3/4}{7/10} = \frac{}{14}$$

Remember, multiply by the LCM of _____ and _____.

15;   4 and 10   (either order)

102. Change to a simple fraction in simplest form.

$$\frac{2/15}{4/9} = \underline{\hspace{1cm}}$$

$$\frac{\frac{2}{15} \cdot 45}{\frac{4}{9} \cdot 45} = \frac{6}{20} = \frac{3}{10}$$

103. Sometimes a complex fraction may have a mixed number in either its numerator or denominator. Then we may write

$$\frac{3\frac{1}{2}}{2/3} = \frac{7/2}{2/3} = \frac{}{4}$$

> 21

104. Change mixed numbers to fractions and then reduce the complex fraction to a simple fraction.

$$\frac{4\frac{2}{5}}{1\frac{3}{10}} = \underline{}$$

> $$\frac{4\frac{2}{5}}{1\frac{3}{10}} = \frac{22/5}{13/10} = \frac{44}{13}$$

105. Consider

$$\frac{2 + \frac{1}{3}}{3/4}$$

Notice that the numerator of this complex fraction is $2 + \frac{1}{3}$ while the denominator is _____.

> 3/4

106. $$\frac{2 + \frac{1}{3}}{3/4}$$

The LCM of 3 and 4, the denominators of 1/3 and 3/4, is 12, and we may multiply both $2 + \frac{1}{3}$ and 3/4 by 12. Then

$$12(2 + \frac{1}{3}) = 12 \cdot 2 + 12 \cdot \frac{1}{3} = 24 + \underline{}$$
$$= \underline{}$$

> 4; 28

107. $$\frac{2 + \frac{1}{3}}{3/4}$$

Note that the product of 12 and the numerator is

$$12(2 + \frac{1}{3}) = 24 + 4 = 28$$

The product of 12 and the denominator is

$$12 \cdot \frac{3}{4} = \underline{}.$$

> 9

108. Then

$$\frac{2 + \frac{1}{3}}{3/4} = \frac{12(2 + \frac{1}{3})}{12(3/4)} = \frac{}{9}$$

> 28

109. Similarly, we may reduce

$$\frac{3 + \frac{1}{2}}{5 + \frac{3}{4}} = \frac{4(3 + \frac{1}{2})}{4(5 + \frac{3}{4})} = \frac{12 + 2}{ + } = \underline{}$$

> $\underline{20} + \underline{3}$;   14/23

110. And

$$\frac{100 + \frac{3}{8}}{50 + \frac{1}{12}} = \frac{24(100 + \frac{3}{8})}{24(50 + \frac{1}{12})} = \frac{2400 + }{1200 + } = \underline{}$$

> $$\frac{2400 + 9}{1200 + 2} = \frac{2409}{1202}.$$

111. Express as a simple fraction in simplest form.

$$\frac{70\frac{2}{3}}{25\frac{1}{6}} = \frac{70 + \frac{2}{3}}{25 + \frac{1}{6}} = \frac{6(70 + \frac{2}{3})}{6(25 + \frac{1}{6})} = \underline{}$$

> $$\frac{420 + 4}{150 + 1} = \frac{424}{151}$$

112. Consider

$$\frac{\frac{1}{2} + \frac{3}{4}}{5/8}$$

We may reduce this to a simple fraction if we multiply both the numerator and denominator by the LCM of 2, 4, and 8, which is _____.

8

113. Then

$$\frac{\frac{1}{2} + \frac{3}{4}}{5/8} = \frac{8\left(\frac{1}{2} + \frac{3}{4}\right)}{8(5/8)} = \frac{4 + \underline{}}{5} = \underline{}$$

6;   2

114. $$\frac{\frac{1}{2} + \frac{3}{4}}{5/8} = \frac{8\left(\frac{1}{2} + \frac{3}{4}\right)}{8(5/8)} = \frac{4 + 6}{5} = \frac{10}{5} = 2$$

Then a complex fraction may equal a _____ _____.

NATURAL NUMBER

115. To reduce

$$\frac{\frac{3}{4} + \frac{1}{3}}{5/6}$$

to a simple fraction, we should multiply the numerator and denominator by the LCM of 4, 3, and 6, which is _____.

12

116. Then

$$\frac{\frac{3}{4} + \frac{1}{3}}{5/6} = \frac{12\left(\frac{3}{4} + \frac{1}{3}\right)}{12(5/6)} = \underline{}$$

13/10

117. Consider

$$\frac{3}{4/5}$$

Here we should multiply by 5, and

$$\frac{3}{4/5} = \frac{3 \cdot 5}{\frac{4}{5} \cdot 5} = \underline{}$$

15/4

118. Reduce to a simple fraction or a natural number.

$$\frac{5}{2/3} = \underline{}$$

$$\frac{2\frac{1}{3}}{1/6} = \underline{}$$

$$\frac{\frac{1}{2} + \frac{1}{5}}{3/10} = \underline{}$$

15/2;   14;   7/3

119. The examples illustrate that every complex fraction may be reduced to a _____ fraction or a natural number.

SIMPLE

120. And, since every simple fraction or natural number represents a _____ number, we know that every complex fraction also represents a _____ number.

QUOTIENT;   QUOTIENT

Chapter 19

Problems A   (Answers on page 511)

Express, in simplest form, the multiplicative inverse of each of the following:

1. 3/8
2. 9/4
3. 12
4. 1/9
5. 1
6. $1\frac{1}{2}$
7. $4\frac{2}{3}$
8. $175\frac{1}{4}$

Use the reciprocal rule to divide. Write answers in simplest form.

9. $\frac{3}{8} \div \frac{5}{9}$

10. $\frac{2}{5} \div \frac{5}{4}$

11. $\frac{8}{3} \div \frac{4}{3}$

12. $3\frac{1}{2} \div \frac{1}{7}$

13. $\frac{5}{6} \div 1\frac{1}{3}$

14. $8\frac{1}{3} \div 2\frac{1}{2}$

15. $9\frac{3}{5} \div 1\frac{2}{3}$

Find each of the following quotients in simplest form.

16. $\frac{3}{8} \div 4$

17. $\frac{10}{3} \div 5$

18. $\frac{16}{5} \div 8$

19. $\frac{2}{3} \div 5$

20. $7\frac{1}{3} \div 11$

Simplify each of the following complex fractions by multiplying both the numerator and denominator by an appropriate natural number. Write answers in simplest form.

21. $\frac{2/3}{5/6}$

22. $\frac{3/8}{7/6}$

23. $\frac{11/12}{5/9}$

24. $\frac{5}{3/8}$

25. $\frac{2/5}{11}$

26. $\frac{\frac{1}{2} + \frac{1}{3}}{4}$

27. $\frac{5}{\frac{2}{5} + \frac{1}{4}}$

28. $\frac{3\frac{1}{2}}{\frac{1}{3} + \frac{2}{9}}$

29. $\frac{5\frac{2}{3} + 2\frac{3}{4}}{5}$

30. $\frac{\frac{3}{8} + 7\frac{1}{3}}{1\frac{5}{6}}$

Problems B

Express, in simplest form, the multiplicative inverse of each of the following:

1. 4/3
2. 5
3. 1/3
4. $3\frac{1}{4}$
5. $19\frac{2}{3}$
6. $\frac{1}{2} + \frac{1}{3}$

Find each of the following quotients in simplest form.

7. $\frac{3}{8} \div \frac{4}{9}$

8. $\frac{4}{15} \div \frac{8}{5}$

9. $\frac{23}{7} \div \frac{19}{21}$

10. $\frac{91}{19} \div \frac{13}{28}$

11. $4\frac{6}{7} \div \frac{17}{14}$

12. $2\frac{3}{8} \div 4\frac{3}{4}$

13. $15 \div 2\frac{1}{7}$

14. $\frac{16}{7} \div 8$

15. $\frac{5}{8} \div 21$

16. $\frac{52}{7} \div 13$

Write each of the following as a simple fraction or natural number in simplest form.

17. $\frac{3/7}{5}$

18. $\frac{12}{6/5}$

19. $\frac{5/3}{4/9}$

20. $\frac{3\frac{1}{4}}{26}$

21. $\frac{5\frac{1}{2}}{3\frac{1}{7}}$

22. $\frac{\frac{1}{4} + \frac{3}{2}}{5}$

23. $\frac{2\frac{1}{2} + 3}{3\frac{1}{3}}$

24. $\frac{4\frac{2}{3} + 5\frac{1}{2}}{5/6}$

25. $\frac{\frac{3}{8} + 2}{3\frac{5}{12}}$

CHAPTER 20

ORDER OF OPERATIONS; PERCENT

1. An expression like $\dfrac{2/3}{1/4}$ is called a
_____ _____ .

> COMPLEX FRACTION

2. But the complex fraction

$$\dfrac{2/3}{1/4}$$

may be changed to a simple fraction by multiplying both its numerator and denominator by _____, the LCM of 3 and 4.

> 12

3. Then

$$\dfrac{\dfrac{2}{3}}{\dfrac{1}{4}} = \dfrac{\dfrac{2}{3} \cdot 12}{\dfrac{1}{4} \cdot 12} = \text{_____}$$

> 8/3

4. Similarly,

$$\dfrac{3/8}{7/10}$$

may be changed to the simple fraction _____ if we multiply both its numerator and denominator by 40, the LCM of 8 and 10.

> 15/28

5. To change

$$\dfrac{5/12}{4/9}$$

to a simple fraction we multiply both its numerator and denominator by the _____ of 12 and 9, which is _____.

> LCM;   36

6. Then multiplying both the numerator and denominator by 36, we obtain

$$\dfrac{5/12}{4/9} = \text{_____}$$

> 15/16

7. Change to a simple fraction:

$$\frac{4/15}{5/9} = \underline{\hspace{2cm}}$$

12/25

8. We represent the quotient of 15 and 3 by writing 15/3, and say that 15/3 = _____, since _____ · 3 = 15.

· 5;   5

9. Although we have not done so until now, we may also represent the quotient of 15 and 3 by writing 15 ÷ 3. And, in simplest form,

15 ÷ 3 = _____

5

10. The quotient of two numbers is a number whose _____ with the divisor equals the dividend.

PRODUCT

11. Then, 20 ÷ 4 is the _____ of 20 and 4, and

20 ÷ 4 = _____

QUOTIENT;   5

12. 20 ÷ 4 = 5

since the product of _____ and _____ equals 20.

4;   5   (either order)

13. Then there are two ways to represent the quotient of 36 and 4. We may either write

36 ÷ 4   or   _____ /4

36

14. Similarly, we represent the quotient of 5 and 2 by writing either 5/2 or _____.

5 ÷ 2

15. 5 ÷ 2 = 5/2

Let us think of this as a division problem in which 5/2 is the quotient, 2 is the divisor, and 5 is the _____.

DIVIDEND

16. 5 ÷ 2 = 5/2

Remember, the _____ of the quotient and the divisor equals the dividend.

PRODUCT

17. 5 ÷ 2 = 5/2

The product of the quotient, 5/2, and the divisor, 2, is $\frac{5}{2} \cdot 2 = $ _____, the dividend.

5

18. The quotient of 2/3 and 5/6 may be represented by $\frac{2}{3} \div \frac{5}{6}$. By the cross product rule,

$\frac{2}{3} \div \frac{5}{6} = $ _____, in simplest form.

· 12/15 = 4/5   ·

19. $\frac{2}{3} \div \frac{5}{6} = \frac{4}{5}$

In this problem the dividend is 2/3, the divisor is _____, and the quotient is _____.

5/6;   4/5

20. $\frac{2}{3} \div \frac{5}{6} = \frac{4}{5}$

The quotient, 4/5, was found by the cross product rule, but notice, also, that the product of the quotient and the divisor is

$\frac{4}{5} \cdot \frac{5}{6} =$ _____,   the dividend.

2/3

21. Then the cross product rule for division is only a means of finding a quotient whose product with the _____ equals the _____.

DIVISOR;   DIVIDEND

22. The quotient of 2/3 and 5/6 has been represented by $\frac{2}{3} \div \frac{5}{6}$. We may also represent this quotient by $\frac{2/3}{5/6}$.

Similarly the quotient, $\frac{1}{2} \div \frac{3}{4}$, may be written _____.

$\frac{1/2}{3/4}$

23. $\frac{1}{2} \div \frac{3}{4} = \frac{1/2}{3/4}$

We can also write $\frac{2/5}{3/2} =$ _____ $\div$ _____

2/5;   3/2

24. Then

$\frac{2/5}{3/2} = \frac{2}{5} \div \frac{3}{2}$,

which, by the cross product rule, equals _____.

4/15

25. $\frac{3/4}{2/3}$

represents the _____ of 3/4 and 2/3, and may also be written _____ $\div$ _____.

QUOTIENT;   3/4;   2/3

26. Hence, by the cross product rule,

$\frac{3/4}{2/3} = \frac{3}{4} \div \frac{2}{3} =$ _____

9/8

27. Use the cross product rule to find the quotient.

$\frac{3/8}{5/12} =$ _____ $\div$ _____ $=$ _____,

in simplest form.

$\frac{3}{8} \div \frac{5}{12} = \frac{36}{40} = \frac{9}{10}$

28. The expression

$$\frac{3/8}{5/12}$$

represents the quotient of 3/8 and 5/12, just as the expression 6/11 represents the quotient of _____ and _____ .

> 6;   11

29. But

$$\frac{3/8}{5/12}$$

is also a _____ fraction.

> COMPLEX

30. To change a complex fraction to a simple fraction we may multiply both its numerator and denominator by the smallest natural number whose product with both the numerator and denominator is a _____ number.

> NATURAL

31. Then, to change the complex fraction

$$\frac{3/8}{5/12}$$

to a simple fraction, we may multiply by the LCM of 8 and _____ , which is _____ .

> 12;   24

32. Hence

$$\frac{3/8}{5/12} = \frac{\frac{3}{8} \cdot 24}{\frac{5}{12} \cdot 24} = \underline{\hspace{2cm}}$$

> 9/10

33. We have shown that

$$\frac{3/8}{5/12} = \frac{\frac{3}{8} \cdot 24}{\frac{5}{12} \cdot 24} = \frac{9}{10}$$

But previously we showed that

$$\frac{3/8}{5/12} = \frac{3}{8} \div \frac{5}{12} = \frac{36}{40} = \frac{9}{10}$$

34. Then an alternate method for simplifying a complex fraction is to consider it as a _____ of two numbers and then use the cross product rule for division.

> QUOTIENT

35. Hence

$$\frac{3/8}{3/4} = \frac{3}{8} \div \frac{3}{4} = \underline{\hspace{1.5cm}}, \text{ in simplest form.}$$

$$\frac{2/5}{7/8} = \underline{\hspace{1cm}} \div \underline{\hspace{1cm}} = \underline{\hspace{1cm}}$$

> $\frac{12}{24} = \frac{1}{2}$; $\frac{2}{5} \div \frac{7}{8} = \frac{16}{35}$

36. Similarly

$$\frac{3/4}{5} = \underline{\hspace{1.5cm}} \div \underline{\hspace{1.5cm}}$$

> $\frac{3}{4}$;   5

37. $$\frac{3/4}{5} = \frac{3}{4} \div 5$$

Recall that to divide a fraction by a natural number we may _____ the denominator of that fraction by the natural number.

> MULTIPLY

38. Then

$$\frac{3/4}{5} = \frac{3}{4} \div 5 = \frac{3}{\underline{}}$$

20

39. Similarly

$$\frac{2/3}{7} = \frac{2}{3} \div 7 = \underline{}$$

2/21

40. Notice that since $\frac{3/5}{8}$ represents the quotient of 3/5 and 8, and since we may find the quotient of a fraction and a natural number by multiplying the denominator by that natural number, we may shorten this result by writing

$$\frac{3/5}{8} = \frac{3}{5 \cdot 8} = \frac{3}{40}$$

Similarly

$$\frac{2/3}{5} = \frac{2}{\underline{}} = \frac{2}{15}$$

3 · 5

41. And

$$\frac{5/8}{3} = \frac{5}{8 \cdot 3} = \frac{5}{24}$$

$$\frac{6/5}{7} = \frac{6}{\underline{}} = \frac{6}{35}$$

$$\frac{4/9}{3} = \frac{4}{\underline{}}$$

5·7;   27

42. Sometimes the resulting simple fraction must still be reduced to simplest form. Thus

$$\frac{6/5}{3} = \frac{6}{5 \cdot 3} = \frac{}{5}$$

$$\frac{9/10}{3} = \frac{9}{10 \cdot 3} = \underline{}$$

$$\frac{12/5}{4} = \underline{}$$

2;   3/10;   3/5

43. When a problem involves both addition and subtraction of natural numbers, we have agreed to combine the numbers _____ at a time from left to right, if there are no symbols to indicate otherwise.

TWO

44. Thus

$$8 + 9 - 12 = \underline{} - 12 = \underline{}$$

17;   5

45. Compute.

$$3 + 27 - 10 = \underline{}$$

$$27 - 8 - 2 = \underline{}$$

20;   17

46. But where there are symbols to indicate otherwise, we do not necessarily combine from left to right. Thus

$$27 - 8 - 2 = 19 - 2 = 17$$

But

$$27 - (8 - 2) = 27 - \underline{} = 21$$

6

47. The parentheses indicate "first." Then

$$15 - 8 - 5 = \underline{\hspace{2cm}}$$

While

$$15 - (8 - 5) = \underline{\hspace{2cm}}$$

2; 12

48. When multiplications are included with additions and subtractions in the same problem, all the _____ are performed first, unless grouping symbols indicate some other order of performance.

MULTIPLICATIONS

49. Thus

$$3 + 7 \cdot 4 = 3 + \underline{\hspace{2cm}} = 31$$

And

$$8 + 4 \cdot 2 - 9 = 8 + \underline{\hspace{2cm}} - 9 = \underline{\hspace{2cm}}$$

28;   8;   7

50. Similar conventions are used for quotient numbers.

Thus to add

$$\frac{2}{3} + \frac{3}{4} + \frac{5}{8}$$

we may first add

$$\frac{2}{3} + \frac{3}{4} = \frac{8+9}{12} = \frac{17}{12}.$$

We next find the sum of 17/12 and _____.

5/8

51. Hence, using the cross product rule,

$$\frac{2}{3} + \frac{3}{4} + \frac{5}{8} = \frac{17}{12} + \frac{5}{8} = \underline{\hspace{2cm}}, \text{ in simplest form.}$$

$$\frac{17}{12} + \frac{5}{8} = \frac{17 \cdot 8 + 12 \cdot 5}{12 \cdot 8} = \frac{136 + 60}{12 \cdot 8} = \frac{196}{96} = \frac{49}{24}$$

52. Similarly,

$$\frac{1}{2} + \frac{3}{5} - \frac{3}{8}$$

can be found by first adding 1/2 and 3/5.

$$\frac{1}{2} + \frac{3}{5} = \frac{}{10}$$

11

53. Thus

$$\frac{1}{2} + \frac{3}{5} - \frac{3}{8} = \frac{11}{10} - \frac{3}{8}$$

And, by the cross product rule for subtraction,

$$\frac{11}{10} - \frac{3}{8} = \underline{\hspace{2cm}}, \text{ in simplest form.}$$

$$\frac{11}{10} - \frac{3}{8} = \frac{88 - 30}{80} = \frac{58}{80} = \frac{29}{40}$$

54. Combine the fractions two at a time from left to right, using the cross product rule.

$$\frac{8}{3} - \frac{1}{2} - \frac{3}{4} = \underline{\hspace{2cm}}$$

17/12

55. We have computed

$$\frac{8}{3} - \frac{1}{2} - \frac{3}{4} = \frac{13}{6} - \frac{3}{4} = \frac{34}{24} = \frac{17}{12}$$

by using the method of cross products and taking the fractions two at a time.

But we may also use the method of common _____ .

DENOMINATORS

56. $\frac{8}{3} - \frac{1}{2} - \frac{3}{4}$

The LCM of 3, 2, and 4 is _____ .

12

57. $\frac{8}{3} - \frac{1}{2} - \frac{3}{4}$

If we change each fraction to one whose denominator is 12, we have

$$\frac{8}{3} = \frac{32}{12} \qquad \frac{1}{2} = \frac{}{12} \qquad \frac{3}{4} = \frac{}{12}$$

6;   9

58. Since

$$\frac{8}{3} = \frac{32}{12} \qquad \frac{1}{2} = \frac{6}{12} \qquad \frac{3}{4} = \frac{9}{12}$$

we may compute

$$\frac{8}{3} - \frac{1}{2} - \frac{3}{4} = \frac{32}{12} - \frac{6}{12} - \frac{9}{12} = \frac{32 - 6 - 9}{12} =$$
_____

17/12

59. Similarly, to find

$$\frac{5}{6} + \frac{1}{8} - \frac{3}{4}$$

we may change each fraction to one whose denominator is _____ , the LCM of 6, 8 and 4.

24

60. Thus

$$\frac{5}{6} + \frac{1}{8} - \frac{3}{4} = \frac{20}{24} + \frac{}{24} - \frac{}{24} = \text{_____}$$

3;   18;   5/24

61. Use the method of common denominators to find

$$\frac{3}{2} + \frac{1}{4} - \frac{4}{3} - \frac{1}{6} = \text{_____} ,\qquad \text{in simplest}$$
form.

$$\frac{3}{2} + \frac{1}{4} - \frac{4}{3} - \frac{1}{6} = \frac{18}{12} + \frac{3}{12} - \frac{16}{12} - \frac{2}{12} = \frac{3}{12} = \frac{1}{4}$$

62. When parentheses are used, we first perform operations within them.

Thus

$$\frac{9}{5} - \left(\frac{1}{2} + \frac{1}{10} \right)$$

indicates that first we must find the sum

$$\frac{1}{2} + \frac{1}{10} = \text{_____}$$

3/5

63. Then

$$\frac{9}{5} - \left(\frac{1}{2} + \frac{1}{10} \right) = \frac{9}{5} - \frac{3}{5} = \text{_____}$$

6/5

64. Compute

$$\frac{3}{4} - \left(\frac{5}{6} - \frac{2}{3}\right) = \underline{\hspace{1cm}}, \quad \text{in simplest form.}$$

$$\frac{3}{4} - \left(\frac{5}{6} - \frac{2}{3}\right) = \frac{3}{4} - \left(\frac{5}{6} - \frac{4}{6}\right) = \frac{3}{4} - \frac{1}{6} =$$

$$= \frac{18 - 4}{24} = \frac{14}{24} = \frac{7}{12}$$

65. When multiplication is included with addition and subtraction of quotient numbers, the multiplication is performed first, unless there are symbols to indicate otherwise.

$$\frac{7}{8} + \frac{1}{2} \cdot \frac{3}{4} = \frac{7}{8} + \underline{\hspace{1.5cm}} = \underline{\hspace{1.5cm}}, \quad \text{in}$$

simplest form.

    3/8;   5/4

66. Compute

$$\frac{4}{3} - \frac{1}{3} \cdot \frac{3}{2} = \frac{4}{3} - \underline{\hspace{1.5cm}} = \underline{\hspace{1.5cm}}$$

$$\frac{2}{5} \cdot \frac{3}{2} - \frac{1}{5} = \underline{\hspace{1.5cm}}$$

    1/2;   5/6;   2/5

67. $\dfrac{3}{4} + \dfrac{1}{2} \cdot \dfrac{2}{3} - \dfrac{1}{6} = \underline{\hspace{1cm}}$

$$\frac{3}{4} + \frac{1}{2} \cdot \frac{2}{3} - \frac{1}{6} = \frac{3}{4} + \frac{1}{3} - \frac{1}{6} = \frac{9}{12} + \frac{4}{12} - \frac{2}{12} = \frac{11}{12}$$

68. Recall that for natural numbers, when division is included with other operations, the divisions are performed first, then the _____, and finally the _____ and subtractions from left to right, unless there are symbols to indicate otherwise.

    MULTIPLICATIONS;   ADDITIONS

69. Thus

$$5 + 14 \div 2 - 8 = 5 + \underline{\hspace{1.5cm}} - 8 = \underline{\hspace{1.5cm}}$$

    7;   4

70. Also, with quotient numbers, we perform divisions first.

$$\frac{1}{2} + \frac{3}{4} \div \frac{1}{3} = \frac{1}{2} + \underline{\hspace{1.5cm}} = \underline{\hspace{1.5cm}}$$

    9/4;   11/4

71. $\dfrac{1}{2} + \dfrac{2}{3} \div \dfrac{8}{3} - \dfrac{1}{4} = \dfrac{1}{2} + \underline{\hspace{1.5cm}} - \dfrac{1}{4} = \underline{\hspace{1cm}}$

    1/4;   1/2

72. But parentheses indicate "first." And since $\dfrac{1}{2} + \dfrac{2}{3} = \dfrac{7}{6}$,

$$\left(\frac{1}{2} + \frac{2}{3}\right) \div \frac{2}{5} = \frac{7}{6} \div \frac{2}{5} = \underline{\hspace{1.5cm}}$$

    35/12

73. Calculate as indicated.

$$\left(\frac{3}{5} - \frac{1}{2}\right) \div \frac{2}{3} = \underline{\hspace{1.5cm}}$$

$$\frac{1}{3}\left(\frac{3}{2} + \frac{1}{3}\right) = \underline{\hspace{1.5cm}}$$

$$\frac{1}{3} \cdot \frac{3}{2} + \frac{1}{3} = \underline{\hspace{1.5cm}}$$

    3/20;   11/18;   5/6

74. The horizontal bar, used to indicate a fraction or a division, is also a symbol to indicate "first." That is, we could write

$$\frac{2 + 12}{7} = (2 + 12) \div 7 = \underline{\hspace{1cm}}$$

2

75. Similarly,

$$\frac{3 + 6}{3 + 2} = (3 + 6) \div (3 + 2) = 9 \div 5 = \frac{9}{5}$$

And

$$\frac{2 + 9}{5 + 4} = \frac{}{9}$$

11

76. And with quotient numbers the horizontal bar again means "first." Thus

$$\frac{\frac{1}{2} + \frac{1}{3}}{5} = \left(\frac{1}{2} + \frac{1}{3}\right) \div 5 = \underline{\hspace{1cm}} \div 5 = \underline{\hspace{1cm}}$$

5/6;   1/6

77. Although parentheses indicate that addition is performed first in the expression

$$6\left(\frac{1}{2} + \frac{1}{3}\right)$$

by the distributive property we may also write

$$6\left(\frac{1}{2} + \frac{1}{3}\right) = 6 \cdot \frac{1}{2} + 6 \cdot \frac{1}{3} = 3 + \underline{\hspace{1cm}} = \underline{\hspace{1cm}}$$

2;   5

78.
$$\frac{\frac{1}{2} + \frac{1}{3}}{5} = \left(\frac{1}{2} + \frac{1}{3}\right) \div 5 = \frac{5}{6} \div 5 = \frac{1}{6}$$

But $\dfrac{\frac{1}{2} + \frac{1}{3}}{5}$ is also a complex fraction, and it may be simplified by multiplying both its numerator and denominator by 6, the LCM of 2 and 3. Thus

$$\frac{\frac{1}{2} + \frac{1}{3}}{5} = \frac{6\left(\frac{1}{2} + \frac{1}{3}\right)}{6 \cdot 5} = \frac{3 + 2}{6 \cdot 5} = \underline{\hspace{1cm}}, \quad \text{in}$$

simplest form.

1/6

79. Recall that when two fractions are equal, their cross products are equal. Thus, if

$$a/b = c/d \qquad \text{then} \qquad \underline{\hspace{2cm}}$$

ad = bc

80. Recall, too, that if the numerator and the denominator of a fraction are each multiplied by the same nonzero number, the resulting fraction is equal to the original. Thus, if x is not zero,

$$ax/bx = \underline{\hspace{1cm}}$$

a/b

81. Then

$$\frac{4}{9} = \frac{4 \cdot 7}{9 \cdot 7}$$

$$\frac{11}{25} = \frac{}{25 \cdot 15}$$

$$\frac{4}{23} = \frac{4 \cdot 9}{}$$

$$\frac{5}{16} = \frac{}{16 \cdot 7}$$

11·15;   23·9;   5·7

82. What number must the numerator and denominator of each fraction be multiplied by to yield the given equal fraction?

$$4/3 = 32/24 \underline{\hspace{1.5cm}}$$

$$5/21 = 25/105 \underline{\hspace{1.5cm}}$$

$$7/12 = 56/96 \underline{\hspace{1.5cm}}$$

$$12/3 = 120/30 \underline{\hspace{1.5cm}}$$

8; 5; 8; 10

83. Consider the problem

$$5/6 = [\quad]/48$$

To determine the missing numerator, we can find the number the original denominator, 6, was multiplied by to give the final denominator, 48. Then we can obtain an equal fraction by \underline{\hspace{3cm}} the original numerator, 5, by this same number.

MULTIPLYING

84. $5/6 = [\quad]/48$

Since $6 \cdot 8 = 48$, we must find $5 \cdot 8 = 40$ and write

$$5/6 = 40/48$$

Find the missing numerator or denominator:

$$7/25 = \underline{\hspace{1.5cm}}/200$$

$$6/11 = 30/\underline{\hspace{1.5cm}}$$

$7 \cdot 8 = \underline{56}$; $11 \cdot 5 = \underline{55}$

85. Find the missing numerator or denominator:

$$1/8 = \underline{\hspace{1.5cm}}/24$$

$$5/12 = 60/\underline{\hspace{1.5cm}}$$

$$7/20 = \underline{\hspace{1.5cm}}/100$$

$$3/5 = \underline{\hspace{1.5cm}}/100$$

3; 144; 35; 60

86. Consider the problem

$$1/8 = [\quad]/100$$

We shall determine the missing numerator by multiplying 1 and 8 by some number. We can see from the denominators that the number used must, when multiplied by 8, give a product of 100. Since 100 is not divisible by 8, there is no \underline{\hspace{2.5cm}} number whose product with 8 is 100.

NATURAL

87. We are considering

$$1/8 = [\quad]/100$$

There is no natural number whose product with 8 is 100, but we note that

$$8 \cdot \frac{100}{8} = 100$$

Then there is a quotient number whose product with 8 is 100. It is \underline{\hspace{1.5cm}}.

100/8

88. $1/8 = [\quad]/100$

We have seen that $8 \cdot \frac{100}{8} = 100$. Since the denominator of 1/8 is multiplied by 100/8, the numerator, too, must be multiplied by 100/8, and

$$1 \cdot \frac{100}{8} = \frac{100}{8} = \frac{25}{2},$$

or written as a mixed number

$$25/2 = \underline{\hspace{1.5cm}}$$

$12\frac{1}{2}$

89. Then

$$\frac{1}{8} = \frac{1 \cdot \frac{100}{8}}{8 \cdot \frac{100}{8}} = \frac{12\frac{1}{2}}{100}$$

We began with a _____ fraction, 1/8, and we found an equal _____ fraction, $\frac{12\frac{1}{2}}{100}$.

SIMPLE;   COMPLEX

90. Next consider the problem

$$1/6 = [\quad]/100$$

Again there is no natural number whose product with 6 equals 100, but there is a quotient number with this property. In fact,

$$6 \cdot \underline{\hspace{1cm}} = 100$$

100/6

91. Then since $6 \cdot \frac{100}{6} = 100$, we may write

$$\frac{1}{6} = \frac{1 \cdot \frac{100}{6}}{6 \cdot \frac{100}{6}} = \frac{100/6}{100}$$

And if 100/6 is changed to a mixed number, we have 1/6 = _____ /100.

$16\frac{2}{3}$

92. $3/7 = [\quad]/100$

To find the missing numerator here we must first find a number whose product with 7 is 100. The number whose product with 7 equals 100 is _____ .

100/7

93. $3/7 = [\quad]/100$

Then if we multiply both the numerator and denominator of 3/7 by 100/7, we see that

$$\frac{3}{7} = \frac{3 \cdot \frac{100}{7}}{7 \cdot \frac{100}{7}} = \frac{300/7}{}$$

100

94.

$$\frac{3}{7} = \frac{3 \cdot \frac{100}{7}}{7 \cdot \frac{100}{7}} = \frac{300/7}{100}$$

But written as a mixed number, $300/7 = $ _____ .

Then with a mixed number for the missing numerator, we may write

$$3/7 = \underline{\hspace{1cm}} /100$$

$42\frac{6}{7}$; $42\frac{6}{7}$

95. Similarly, other simple fractions may be written as complex fractions with denominator 100 and a mixed number for the numerator:

$$\frac{2}{9} = \frac{2 \cdot \frac{100}{9}}{9 \cdot \frac{100}{9}} = \frac{200/9}{100} = \frac{}{100}$$

$22\frac{2}{9}$

96. Carry out the steps necessary to write the simple fraction as a complex fraction whose denominator is 100 and whose numerator is a mixed number.

$3/8 = \underline{\hspace{1cm}} /100$

$5/11 = \underline{\hspace{1cm}} /100$

$$\frac{3}{8} = \frac{3 \cdot \dfrac{100}{8}}{8 \cdot \dfrac{100}{8}} = \frac{300/8}{100} = \frac{37\frac{1}{2}}{100} \; ;$$

$$\frac{5}{11} = \frac{5 \cdot \dfrac{100}{11}}{11 \cdot \dfrac{100}{11}} = \frac{500/11}{100} = \frac{45\frac{5}{11}}{100}$$

97. Of course, sometimes a simple fraction may be changed to another simple fraction with denominator 100.

$1/2 = \underline{\hspace{1cm}} /100$

$3/4 = \underline{\hspace{1cm}} /100$

$4/5 = \underline{\hspace{1cm}} /100$

50;   75;   80

98. Change each fraction to an equal one whose denominator is 100. The resulting fraction may be complex.

$7/10 = \underline{\hspace{2cm}}$

$5/8 = \underline{\hspace{2cm}}$

$2/3 = \underline{\hspace{2cm}}$

$70/100; \quad \dfrac{62\frac{1}{2}}{100} ; \quad \dfrac{66\frac{2}{3}}{100}$

99. The expression $3/4$ represents a quotient number. But it also represents the \underline{\hspace{2cm}} of 3 and 4.

QUOTIENT

100. In fact, we may write

$3/4 = 3 \div 4$

Similarly, we see that

$$\frac{62\frac{1}{2}}{100} = \underline{\hspace{1.5cm}} \div \underline{\hspace{1.5cm}}$$

$62\frac{1}{2}$;   100

101. We have already seen that

$$\frac{1}{8} = \frac{12\frac{1}{2}}{100}$$

We may also write

$1/8 = \underline{\hspace{1.5cm}} \div 100$.

$12\frac{1}{2}$

102. Similarly, since

$1/6 = \dfrac{16\frac{2}{3}}{100} \qquad 1/6 = \underline{\hspace{1cm}} \div 100$

$3/7 = \dfrac{42\frac{6}{7}}{100} \qquad 3/7 = \underline{\hspace{1cm}} \div 100$

$2/3 = \dfrac{66\frac{2}{3}}{100} \qquad 2/3 = \underline{\hspace{1cm}} \div 100$

$16\frac{2}{3}; \quad 42\frac{6}{7}; \quad 66\frac{2}{3}$

103. Let us agree to use the symbol, %, as an abbreviation for "$\div 100$." Then since

$3/4 = 75/100 = 75 \div 100,$

we may write

$3/4 = \underline{\hspace{1.5cm}} \%$

75

104. We have already seen that

$$1/6 = 16\tfrac{2}{3} \div 100$$

$$3/7 = 42\tfrac{6}{7} \div 100$$

$$2/3 = 66\tfrac{2}{3} \div 100$$

Hence we can write

$$1/6 = \underline{\hphantom{XXXX}}\%$$

$$3/7 = \underline{\hphantom{XXXX}}\%$$

$$2/3 = \underline{\hphantom{XXXX}}\%$$

$16\tfrac{2}{3}; \qquad 42\tfrac{6}{7}; \qquad 66\tfrac{2}{3}$

105. Of course you are familiar with the symbol %, which is read "PERCENT." The symbol, %, means "÷ \underline{\hphantom{XXXX}}."

100

106. Then 40% means $\underline{\hphantom{XXXX}} \div 100 = \dfrac{}{100} = \dfrac{}{5}$

40; 40; 2

107. And

$$75\% = \dfrac{}{100} = \underline{\hphantom{XXXX}}$$

75; 3/4

108. Change each "percent" to a fraction in simplest form.

$$10\% = 10/100 = 1/10$$

$$30\% = \underline{\hphantom{XXXX}}$$

$$60\% = \underline{\hphantom{XXXX}}$$

$$66\tfrac{2}{3}\% = \underline{\hphantom{XXXX}}$$

3/10; 3/5; 2/3

109. Also

$$125\% = 125/100 = 5/4$$

$$150\% = \underline{\hphantom{XXXX}}$$

3/2

110. Change each "percent" to a fraction or a natural number in simplest form.

$$12\tfrac{1}{2}\% = \underline{\hphantom{XXXX}}$$

$$160\ \% = \underline{\hphantom{XXXX}}$$

$$100\ \% = \underline{\hphantom{XXXX}}$$

$$500\ \% = \underline{\hphantom{XXXX}}$$

$$1\ \% = \underline{\hphantom{XXXX}}$$

1/8; 8/5; 1; 5; 1/100

111. We have shown that

$$\frac{5}{8} = \frac{62\tfrac{1}{2}}{100} = 62\tfrac{1}{2}\%$$

Then to change a fraction to a "percent" we may first change the fraction to an equal one whose denominator is \underline{\hphantom{XXXX}}.

100

112. Carry out the steps necessary to change the fraction to a "percent."

$$1/3 = \underline{\hphantom{XXXX}}\%$$

$$\frac{1}{3} = \frac{1 \cdot \frac{100}{3}}{3 \cdot \frac{100}{3}} = \frac{100/3}{100} = \frac{33\tfrac{1}{3}}{100} = 33\tfrac{1}{3}\%$$

113. Change each fraction to a "percent."

$1/4 =$ _____ %

$7/8 =$ _____ %

$5/3 =$ _____ %

114. Let us review some of the important facts about quotient numbers. A simple fraction is an expression of the form a/b, where both a and b are the _____ _____ of _____ numbers.

SIMPLEST FORMS;   NATURAL

115. Two fractions a/b and c/d are equal if _____ .

ad = bc

116. The property shared by the members of a set which contains all fractions equal to a given fraction is called a _____ _____ .

QUOTIENT NUMBER

117. Then every _____ determines a quotient number, and since every natural number is equal to some _____ , every natural number may be thought of as a quotient number.

FRACTION;   FRACTION

118. Since every natural number is also a quotient number, we say that the set of natural numbers is a _____ of the set of quotient numbers.

SUBSET

119. For simplicity, we may speak of a fraction as actually being a quotient number, but strictly speaking it is not. To add, subtract, multiply, or divide two quotient numbers, we add, subtract, multiply or divide any _____ which represent them.

FRACTIONS

120. We may symbolize the rules for combining fractions as follows:

$$\frac{a}{b} + \frac{c}{d} = \frac{ad + bc}{bd}$$

$$\frac{a}{b} - \frac{c}{d} = \underline{\hspace{3cm}}$$

$$\frac{a}{b} \cdot \frac{c}{d} = \underline{\hspace{3cm}}$$

$$\frac{a}{b} \div \frac{c}{d} = \underline{\hspace{3cm}}$$

(ad − bc)/bd;   ac/bd;   ad/bc

121. Addition and subtraction of fractions may also be performed by the method of common denominators. In fact

$$\frac{a}{b} + \frac{c}{b} = \frac{a + c}{b} \qquad \frac{a}{b} - \frac{c}{b} = \underline{\hspace{3cm}}$$

(a − c)/b

122. In order to change the numerator or denominator of a fraction, we may use the result that

   ax/bx = _____

   a/b

123. ax/bx = a/b

   But this is only true when x is not zero. This result may be interpreted to mean that a _____ common to both the numerator and denominator of a fraction may be _____, provided that factor is not zero.

   FACTOR;   CANCELLED

124. ax/bx = a/b

   if x is not zero.

   But also, we may interpret this to mean that both the numerator and denominator of a fraction may be either _____ or _____ by the same number, provided that number is not zero.

   MULTIPLIED;   DIVIDED (either order)

125. If the product of two numbers is 1, we say that each factor is the _____ _____ of the other

   MULTIPLICATIVE INVERSE

126. Another word for multiplicative inverse is _____, and every quotient number has a _____.

   RECIPROCAL;   RECIPROCAL

127. The quotient of two fractions may also be found by _____ the dividend by the reciprocal of the _____.

   MULTIPLYING;   DIVISOR

128. If x and y represent quotient numbers, the symbol x/y is called a _____ fraction, unless it is a simple fraction.

   COMPLEX

129. A complex fraction may be reduced to a simple fraction either by multiplying its numerator and denominator by an appropriate natural number, or by considering the complex fraction as a problem in D_____.

   DIVISION

130. When several operations are to be performed with quotient numbers, unless there are symbols to indicate otherwise, the first operation performed is _____, then _____, and finally the _____ and _____ from left to right.

   DIVISION;   MULTIPLICATION;
   ADDITIONS;   SUBTRACTIONS

Chapter 20

Problems A (answers on page 511)

Perform the operations in the order indicated. Write answers in simplest form.

1. $\dfrac{1}{2} + \dfrac{3}{4} + \dfrac{2}{3}$

2. $\dfrac{5}{6} + \dfrac{1}{2} - \dfrac{3}{4}$

3. $\dfrac{2}{5} - \dfrac{1}{4} + \dfrac{3}{10}$

4. $3\frac{5}{8} - \left(\dfrac{1}{2} + \dfrac{3}{4}\right)$

5. $6\frac{1}{2} - \left(2\frac{3}{4} - 1\frac{1}{3}\right)$

6. $\dfrac{3}{8} + \dfrac{5}{6} \cdot \dfrac{3}{5}$

7. $4\frac{2}{3} - \dfrac{5}{8} \cdot \dfrac{4}{5} + \dfrac{1}{6}$

8. $7\frac{2}{3} + 9\frac{1}{2} \div 3$

9. $15 \div \left(\dfrac{1}{2} + \dfrac{1}{3}\right)$

10. $6\frac{3}{4} - \left(\dfrac{5}{8} - \dfrac{1}{3}\right) \div 2\frac{1}{2}$

Change each "percent" to a fraction in simplest form.

11. 87%

12. 56%

13. $37\frac{1}{2}\%$

14. 1/3%

15. $216\frac{2}{3}\%$

Change each fraction to a "percent." Write your answer as a natural number, where possible, or as a mixed number.

16. 2/5

17. 7/20

18. 9/4

19. 5/12

20. 3/16

21. A house is $47\frac{1}{2}$ feet wide and is exactly centered on a lot which is $93\frac{1}{4}$ feet wide. How many feet wide is the yard on each side of the house?

22. A taxi charges 25 cents for the first 1/5 mile and 5 cents for each additional 1/5 mile. What is the charge for a ride of $2\frac{3}{5}$ miles?

23. On a loan of $125, a loan company charges $20 interest. What percent interest is this?

24. One store advertises that its goods are "1/3 off the regular price." Another promises a "25% reduction." Which store is offering the larger discount?

25. A baseball player's batting average is equal to ten times his percent of hits per official times at bat. Thus a player who has hit successfully 28% of the time has a batting average of 280. If Willie Mays hit 54 singles, 18 doubles, 7 triples and 40 home runs during a season in which he had 340 official trips to the plate, what was his batting average?

Problems B

Find the simplest form of each of the following expressions.

1. $\dfrac{1}{3} + \dfrac{2}{5} + \dfrac{1}{2}$

2. $\dfrac{3}{8} - \dfrac{1}{4} + \dfrac{1}{2}$

3. $3\frac{3}{4} - \dfrac{7}{8} - 1\frac{2}{3}$

4. $7\frac{1}{4} - \left(2\frac{1}{2} + 1\frac{1}{4}\right)$

5. $\dfrac{3}{8} + \dfrac{1}{2} \cdot \dfrac{3}{4}$

6. $4\frac{1}{2} - \dfrac{2}{3} \div \dfrac{4}{9}$

7. $\left(3\frac{1}{3}\right)\left(\dfrac{4}{5} - \dfrac{1}{2}\right)$

8. $3\frac{1}{2} - \dfrac{1}{3} \cdot \dfrac{3}{4} - 2$

9. $9 \div \left(\dfrac{1}{2} + \dfrac{1}{4}\right)$

10. $5\frac{1}{3} - \left(\dfrac{3}{8} - \dfrac{1}{4}\right) \div 1\frac{3}{4}$

Change each "percent" to a fraction in simplest form.

11. 70%

12. 96%

13. 136%

14. $62\frac{1}{2}\%$

15. 1/2%

Change each fraction to a "percent." Write your answer as a natural number, where possible, or as a mixed number.

16. 4/5   19. 7/12

17. 7/8   20. 9/16

18. 5/4

21. An investor bought 40 shares of stock at 23⅜ dollars per share. Later he sold the same stock for 29 dollars per share. What was his profit on the transaction?

22. During the season a basketball player completed 75 shots from the free throw line and missed only 5. What percent of his shots were completed successfully?

23. On a flight from San Francisco to London a jet required 5¼ hours for the first leg to New York, spent 1/2 hour refueling at New York, and 6⅛ hours for the final leg to London. How long did it take for the complete trip?

24. In order to encourage shorter letters, one proposed postal rate calls for a charge of 5 cents for the first ounce, 3 cents for each half-ounce for the next three ounces, and 5 cents for each half-ounce thereafter. Under such a rate schedule, how much would it cost to mail a 7½-ounce letter?

25. During a recent survey it was determined that 4 million Americans were out of a job and looking for work. The population of the United States at that time was 180 million, but 1/3 of these were children or students, 20 million were retired, and 30 million more were wives or other adults not part of the "work force." What percent of the total population should be considered the "work force"? What percent of the "work force" was unemployed?

NUMERATION AND PLACE

1. We have agreed to call any collection of objects a _____.

   SET

2. A set is clearly defined if we can decide, for any object under consideration, whether or not it belongs to the set. We call those things which belong to the set _____ of the set.

   MEMBERS

3. If two sets have exactly the <u>same</u> members, the sets are called _____.

   EQUAL

4. Two sets may have different members, and so be unequal. Yet it may be possible to exactly pair the members of one set with the members of the other. Such sets are said to have the same _____.

   SIZE

5. For any given set, there may be an unlimited number of sets of the same size. The property common to all such sets is called a _____ _____.

   NATURAL NUMBER

6. Each such set, then, determines a natural number. It is the property shared by that set and all other sets of the _____ _____.

   SAME SIZE

7. And two unequal sets of different size each determine a different natural number. Sets of every size exist; there are an unlimited number of natural numbers.

   The set with no elements is called the _____ set.

   EMPTY

8. And we define the size of the empty set to be the number _____.

   ZERO

9. We have called the natural numbers and zero _____ numbers.

> **WHOLE**

10. The whole numbers are ordered. That is, if a and b represent any whole numbers, we say

    a < b

    if there is a natural number, d, such that

    _____

> **a + d = b**

11. And, in our ordering of the whole numbers, for any natural number a,

    0 _____ a

> **<**

12. The first natural number is _____ . The last natural number is _____ .

> **1;   THERE IS NO LAST NATURAL NUMBER!**

13. The simplest form of the number _____ is 0.

    The simplest form of a _____ _____ is one of the symbols 1, 2, 3, . . .

> **ZERO;   NATURAL NUMBER**

14. In simplest form:

    We represent the number zero by 0.

    We represent the first nine natural numbers, in order, by

    1, _____, _____, _____, _____, _____, _____, _____, _____

> **2, 3, 4, 5, 6, 7, 8, 9**

15. In simplest form, then, we represent the first ten whole numbers by the symbols

    0, 1, 2, 3, 4, 5, 6, 7, 8, 9.

    We shall call these ten symbols DIGITS.

16. We call the symbols

    0, 1, 2, 3, 4, 5, 6, 7, 8, 9

    _____ , and each represents a whole number.

> **DIGITS**

17. The digit 0 represents the number _____ . The remaining nine digits represent the first nine _____ _____ .

> **ZERO;   NATURAL NUMBERS**

18. The natural number ten can be represented by the two digits 0 and 1: 10.

    The natural number eleven can be represented by the single digit 1 used twice:

    _____

    The natural number twelve can be represented by the two digits 1 and 2: _____

> **11;   12**

19. The natural number seventeen can be represented by the two digits 1 and 7: _____

The natural number fifty-three can be represented by the two digits 5 and 3: _____

The natural number eighty-eight can be represented by the single digit 8 used twice:

_____

17;   53;   88

20. In fact, the simplest form of every natural number from 10 through 99 can be represented using only _____ digits at a time (not necessarily different from one another).

TWO

21. But to represent the number one hundred, we use three digits: 100.

We represent one hundred one by three digits: 101.

We represent one hundred two by three digits: _____

We represent two hundred fifty-seven by three digits: _____

And we represent nine hundred four by three digits: _____

102;   257;   904

22. Indeed, using only three digits at a time (not necessarily different), it is possible to represent the simplest form of every natural number from _____ through _____ .

100;   999

23. Similarly, the simplest form of every natural number from 1000 through 9999 can be represented using only _____ digits at a time, and using only five digits at a time, we can represent the simplest form of every natural number from _____ through _____ .

FOUR;   10000;   99999

24. Continuing in this way, we find that the simplest form of <u>every</u> natural number can be expressed by using only the ten symbols we have called _____, possibly with repetitions.

DIGITS

25. We sometimes describe a number by a count of the digits used to represent its simplest form. Thus, 17 is a 2-DIGIT NUMBER and 42,171 is a 5-DIGIT NUMBER.

Classify each of the following according to number of digits:

    3   _____ -digit number
    443   _____ -digit number
    5281   _____ -digit number
    98   _____ -digit number

1;   3;   4;   2

26. 0 and the natural numbers from 1 through 9 are all 1-digit numbers.

The natural numbers from 10 through 99 are all _____ -digit numbers.

The natural numbers from _____ through _____ are all 3-digit numbers.

2;   100;   999

27. A natural number of 4 digits cannot be less than _____ .

A natural number of 7 digits cannot be less than _____ .

1000;   1000000

28. We have been describing a system of NU-MERATION, a way of representing the whole numbers. We have represented these numbers using only _____ symbols, called digits, with no symbols of operation.

TEN

29. Because our representations of the whole numbers use only ten different symbols, we sometimes say that we have based our system of numeration on the number 10, or that our representations of the numbers is a BASE 10 system of numeration.

30. The number 57 is read "fifty-seven." The number 75 is read "_____."

SEVENTY-FIVE

31. 57 and 75 are two different natural numbers. Yet each is represented by means of the two digits, 5 and 7. The difference in their representation is the PLACE or position which the digits occupy.

    234 is read "two hundred thirty-four"

    423 is read "_____"

FOUR HUNDRED TWENTY-THREE

32. Again, the numbers 234 and 423 are different, even though the same three digits are used to represent each. And again, the difference is in the position or _____ in which the digits occur.

PLACE

33. The number 3711 is read "three thousand, seven hundred eleven."

The number 1371 is read "_____."

ONE THOUSAND, THREE HUNDRED SEVENTY-ONE

34. The digits 1, 1, 3, and 7 are used to express both numbers

    3711   and   1371

But the numbers are not the same because the digits occupy different positions in the representations of these numbers.

Indeed, in the representation of any natural number, the _____ a digit occupies is as important in determining the number as is the digit itself.

PLACE   or   POSITION

35. The first natural number is represented by only a single digit. We say that this digit is in the ONES PLACE.

The next eight natural numbers, 2 through 9, also require only a single digit for their representations. In each case, this digit appears in the _____ place.

ONES

36. The next natural number is represented by two digits: 10.

We continue to call the place where the digit 0 occurs the ones place, but we say that the digit 1 is in the TENS PLACE.

The next eighty-nine natural numbers, 11 through 99, also require two digits for their representation. In each case, we again say that the left digit is in the _____ place and the right digit is in the _____ place.

TENS;   ONES

37. Thus, in the number 57, the digit 5 occurs in the tens place and the digit 7 occurs in the ones place.

And in the number 75, the digit 7 occurs in the _____ place while the digit 5 occurs in the _____ place.

TENS;   ONES

38. In the number 99 the digit 9 is used in both places. But the L_____ 9 is in the tens place while the R_____ 9 is in the ones place.

LEFT;   RIGHT

39. The next natural number is represented by three digits: 100.

We say that the digit 1 is in the HUNDREDS PLACE, and we continue to call the places where the digits 0 occur, from left to right, the _____ place and the _____ place.

TENS;   ONES

40. And, following 100, the next eight hundred ninety-nine natural numbers, 101 through 999, all require three digits for their representation. For each, the left digit is in the _____ place.

HUNDREDS

41. In the number 472, the digit 4 is in the _____ place.

In the number 729, the digit 2 is in the _____ place.

In the number 883, the digit 3 is in the _____ place.

In the number 24, the digit 2 is in the _____ place.

HUNDREDS;   TENS;   ONES;   TENS

42. In the number 403, the digit 0 is in the _____ place.

In the number 987, the digit 9 is in the _____ place.

In the number 7, the digit 7 is in the _____ place.

In the number 330, the digit 0 is in the _____ place.

TENS;   HUNDREDS;   ONES;   ONES

43. In the number 999, the digit 9 is used three times. But the position of each 9 is different. From left to right, the digits 9 are in the _____, _____, and _____ places.

HUNDREDS;   TENS;   ONES

44. The next natural number is represented by four digits: 1000.

We now say that the digit 1 is in the THOUSANDS PLACE. The digits 0 are in places we continue to call, from left to right, _____, _____, and _____.

> HUNDREDS;   TENS;   ONES

45. Following the number 1000, the next eight thousand, nine hundred ninety-nine natural numbers, _____ through _____, all require four digits for their representation.

> 1001;   9999

46. For each number from 1001 through 9999, the left digit is in the _____ place.

> THOUSANDS

47. In the number 5280, the digit 2 is in the _____ place.

In the number 1729, the digit 2 is in the _____ place.

In the number 2400, the digit 2 is in the _____ place.

And in the number 102, the digit 2 is in the _____ place.

> HUNDREDS;   TENS;   THOUSANDS; ONES

48. In the number 3412:

The digit 3 is in the _____ place.

The digit 1 is in the _____ place.

_____ is the digit in the hundreds place.

_____ is the digit in the tens place.

> THOUSANDS;   TENS;   4;   1

49. In the number 49, the digit 9 is in the _____ place.

In the number 387, the digit 8 is in the _____ place.

In the number 1612, the digit 6 is in the _____ place.

In the number 9888, the digit 9 is in the _____ place.

> ONES;   TENS;   HUNDREDS; THOUSANDS

50. 9999 is the largest natural number that can be represented in simplest form using only four digits. We represent the next natural number by 10,000, and say that the digit 1 is in the TEN-THOUSANDS PLACE.

Also, every number from 10000 through 99999 can be represented using _____ digits.

> FIVE

51. Each natural number from 10000 through 99999 can be represented by means of five digits. In every case the left digit is in the _____ place.

> TEN-THOUSANDS

52. Natural numbers greater than 99999 can be represented by means of more than five digits. And, as the number of digits increases, new places occur.

From right to left, the names of the places in the simplest form of a whole number are:

ONES, TENS, HUNDREDS, THOUSANDS, TEN-THOUSANDS, HUNDRED-THOUSANDS, MILLIONS, ...

53. Name the place in which the underlined digit occurs:

42913   thousands place

5714   _____ place

227411   _____ place

1441716   _____ place

> HUNDREDS;   TEN-THOUSANDS;
> TENS

54. Name the place in which the underlined digit occurs:

5291675   _____ place

47738162   _____ place

2770000   _____ place

557541   _____ place

> HUNDRED-THOUSANDS;   ONES;
> MILLIONS;   THOUSANDS

55. From right to left, the first seven places a digit may occupy are called:

_____
_____
_____
_____
_____
_____
_____

> ONES; TENS, HUNDREDS, THOUSANDS,
> TEN-THOUSANDS,   HUNDRED-THOU-
> SANDS, MILLIONS

56. We sometimes use a COMMA as an aid in naming the place in which a digit occurs. When they are used, commas are inserted between the digits in the hundreds and the thousands place, and between the digits in the hundred-thousands and the millions place.

Thus, 4291775 could be written, using commas, as _____.

> 4,291,775

57. Insert commas in the proper places:

42713   42,713

561133   _____

6553421   _____

2138   _____

> 561,133;   6,553,421;   2,138

58. When a number is written using more than nine digits, commas are inserted after every third digit, counting from the right. We shall not often consider such large numbers. And for many problems, we shall not use commas at all in their representations.

Thus, we shall write

4,775   as   4775

231,667   as   _____

57,417,992 as   _____

> 231667;   57417992

59. There are two ways in which natural numbers are commonly read. One is to read the digits as they occur in the simplest form, from left to right. Thus

42091

can be read "four, two, zero, nine, one."

And

7054163

can be read "_____"

> SEVEN, ZERO, FIVE, FOUR, ONE, SIX, THREE

60. When a natural number is read by simply stating the digits, in order, it is very clear as to what each digit is and the order in which the digits occur. There is little chance for the reader to be misunderstood.

This method of reading is often used when it is essential that there be no mistake in understanding the number intended, or when a minimum number of words is used to describe a number.

61. Another method of reading natural numbers takes into account the place in which digits occur. In this method, the words "million," "thousand" and "hundred" are read following the digits in these places. Thus

3,400

can be read "three thousand, four hundred"

and

41,805

can be read "_____."

> FORTY-ONE THOUSAND, EIGHT HUNDRED FIVE

62. How would each of the following numbers be read, in this second way?

4,927   "_____"

7,250,000   "_____"

866   "_____"

217,548   "_____"

> FOUR THOUSAND, NINE HUNDRED TWENTY-SEVEN
> SEVEN MILLION, TWO HUNDRED FIFTY THOUSAND
> EIGHT HUNDRED SIXTY-SIX
> TWO HUNDRED SEVENTEEN THOUSAND, FIVE HUNDRED FORTY-EIGHT

63. And we would read, in this way,

63   as   "_____"

429   as   "_____"

5,761   as   "_____"

80,114 as   "_____"

> SIXTY-THREE
> FOUR HUNDRED TWENTY-NINE
> FIVE THOUSAND, SEVEN HUNDRED SIXTY-ONE
> EIGHTY THOUSAND, ONE HUNDRED FOURTEEN

64. In its simplest form the number 3 has only a single digit, 3, in the ones place. Of course, we could write $3 = 3 \cdot 1$.

And the number 8 has only a single digit, 8, in the ones place. It, too, can be written

$8 = \underline{\hspace{1cm}} \cdot 1$.

> 8

65. In fact, every one-digit number can be expressed as the product of itself and the number 1.

$$2 = \underline{\hspace{2cm}} \cdot 1$$

$$6 = \underline{\hspace{2cm}} \cdot 1$$

$$9 = \underline{\hspace{2cm}} \cdot 1$$

$$1 = \underline{\hspace{2cm}} \cdot 1$$

2; 6; 9; 1

66. The number 63 is read "sixty-three."

The tens digit of this number is 6 and the ones digit is 3. Note that $60 = 6 \cdot 10$ and $63 = 60 + 3 = 60 + 3 \cdot 1$.

Hence

$$63 = 6 \cdot 10 + 3 \cdot 1$$

The number 47 is read "forty-seven."

The tens digit of this number is 4 and the ones digit is 7. Also, $40 = 4 \cdot 10$ and $47 = 40 + 7 = 40 + 7 \cdot 1$.

Hence

$$47 = \underline{\hspace{1.5cm}} \cdot 10 + \underline{\hspace{1.5cm}} \cdot 1$$

$47 = \underline{4} \cdot 10 + \underline{7} \cdot 1$

67. The number 35 is read "thirty-five."

The tens digit of 35 is $\underline{\hspace{1.5cm}}$ and the ones digit is $\underline{\hspace{1cm}}$.

And

$$35 = 30 + 5 \cdot 1 = \underline{\hspace{1cm}} \cdot \underline{\hspace{1cm}} + \underline{\hspace{1cm}} \cdot \underline{\hspace{1cm}}$$

3; 5; $\underline{3} \cdot 10 + \underline{5} \cdot 1$

68. 81 is read "eighty-one."

The $\underline{\hspace{2.5cm}}$ digit of 81 is 8. The $\underline{\hspace{2.5cm}}$ digit of 81 is 1.

$$81 = 80 + 1 \cdot 1 = \underline{\hspace{2cm}}$$

TENS; ONES; $8 \cdot 10 + 1 \cdot 1$

69. The tens digit of 72 is 7. The ones digit of 72 is 2.

Is $72 = 7 \cdot 10 + 2 \cdot 1$? $\underline{\hspace{1.5cm}}$

The tens digit of 13 is 1. The ones digit of 13 is 3.

Is $13 = 1 \cdot 10 + 3 \cdot 1$? $\underline{\hspace{1.5cm}}$

YES; YES

70. As these examples show, it is possible to express a two-digit natural number as a special sort of sum:

a) One term in the sum is the product of 10 and the $\underline{\hspace{2cm}}$ digit of the original number.

b) The other term is the product of 1 and the $\underline{\hspace{2cm}}$ digit of the original number.

TENS; ONES

71. The number 429 is read "four hundred twenty-nine." The hundreds digit of this number is 4. Note that

$$400 = 4 \cdot 100 \qquad \text{and} \qquad 429 = 400 + 29.$$

Hence

$$429 = 4 \cdot 100 + 29$$

But we have seen that 29 can be written

$$29 = 2 \cdot 10 + 9 \cdot 1.$$

Therefore

$$429 = 4 \cdot 100 + \underline{\hspace{1.5cm}} \cdot 10 + \underline{\hspace{1.5cm}} \cdot 1$$

$429 = 4 \cdot 100 + \underline{2} \cdot 10 + \underline{9} \cdot 1$

72. The number 852 is read "eight hundred fifty-two." The hundreds digit of this number is 8. Now $800 = 8 \cdot 100$ and $852 = 800 + 52$. Hence

$$852 = 8 \cdot 100 + 52$$

But

$$52 = 5 \cdot 10 + 2 \cdot 1$$

Hence

$$852 = \underline{} \cdot \underline{} + \underline{} \cdot \underline{} + \underline{} \cdot \underline{}$$

$$852 = \underline{8} \cdot \underline{100} + \underline{5} \cdot \underline{10} + \underline{2} \cdot \underline{1}$$

73. The number 366 is read "three hundred sixty-six." The hundreds digit is 3 and $300 = 3 \cdot 100$. Hence

$$366 = 300 + 66$$
$$= \underline{} + \underline{} + \underline{}$$

$$366 = \underline{3} \cdot \underline{100} + \underline{6} \cdot \underline{10} + \underline{6} \cdot \underline{1}$$

74. The number 495 is read "four hundred ninety-five." The hundreds digit of this number is \underline{}, the tens digit is \underline{}, and the ones digit is \underline{}, and we can write

$$495 = 400 + 95$$
$$= \underline{} + \underline{} + \underline{}$$

$$4; \quad 9; \quad 5; \quad \underline{4 \cdot 100 + 9 \cdot 10 + 5 \cdot 1}$$

75. The number 183 is read "one hundred eighty-three." The \underline{} digit of 183 is 1, the \underline{} digit of 183 is 8, and the \underline{} digit of 183 is 3. And

$$183 = 100 + 83 = \underline{}$$

HUNDREDS; TENS; ONES;
$1 \cdot 100 + 8 \cdot 10 + 3 \cdot 1$

76. The hundreds digit of 607 is 6. The tens digit of 607 is 0. The ones digit of 607 is 7. Is

$$607 = 6 \cdot 100 + 0 \cdot 10 + 7 \cdot 1? \quad \underline{}$$

The hundreds digit of 448 is 4. The tens digit of 448 is 4. The ones digit of 448 is 8. Is

$$448 = 4 \cdot 100 + 4 \cdot 10 + 8 \cdot 1? \quad \underline{}$$

YES; YES

77. Again, the examples we have considered show that a three-digit number can also be written as a sum in which:

a) One term is the product of 100 and the \underline{} digit of the original number.

b) Another term is the product of 10 and the \underline{} digit of the original number.

c) The remaining term is the product of 1 and the \underline{} digit of the original number.

HUNDREDS; TENS; ONES

78. 4,175 is read "four thousand, one hundred seventy-five." The thousands digit is \underline{}, the hundreds digit is \underline{}, the tens digit is \underline{}, and the ones digit is \underline{}.

4; 1; 7; 5

79. And we can write $4,175 = 4000 + 175$.
Now $4000 = 4 \cdot 1000$ and
$175 = 1 \cdot 100 + 7 \cdot 10 + 5 \cdot 1$
Hence

$$4,175 = \underline{} \cdot 1000 + \underline{} \cdot 100 + \underline{} \cdot 10 + \underline{} \cdot 1$$

$$4,175 = \underline{4} \cdot 1000 + \underline{1} \cdot 100 + \underline{7} \cdot 10 + \underline{5} \cdot 1$$

80. And we can write

$$6{,}293 = \underline{\quad} \cdot \underline{\quad} + \underline{\quad} \cdot \underline{\quad} + \underline{\quad} \cdot \underline{\quad} + \underline{\quad} \cdot \underline{\quad}$$

$$6{,}293 = 6 \cdot 1000 + 2 \cdot 100 + 9 \cdot 10 + 3 \cdot 1$$

81. $7{,}067 = \underline{\qquad\qquad} + \underline{\qquad\qquad} + \underline{\qquad\qquad} + \underline{\qquad\qquad}$

$$7{,}067 = 7 \cdot 1000 + 0 \cdot 100 + 6 \cdot 10 + 7 \cdot 1$$

82. We can also express a four-digit number as a sum in which:

 a) One term is the product of $\underline{\qquad\qquad}$ and the thousands digit of the original number.

 b) A second term is the product of $\underline{\qquad}$ and the hundreds digit of the original number.

 c) A third term is the product of $\underline{\qquad}$ and the tens digit of the original number.

 d) The last term is the product of $\underline{\qquad}$ and the ones digit of the original number.

$$1000; \quad 100; \quad 10; \quad 1$$

83. Indeed, any natural number can be expressed as a sum in this way, no matter how many digits it contains. Each term in the sum is a product of a digit in the number and one of the numbers:

$$1, 10, 100, 1000, \ldots$$

Thus we can write

$$52719 = \underline{\quad} \cdot 10000 + \underline{\quad} \cdot 1000 + \underline{\quad} \cdot 100 + \underline{\quad} \cdot 10 + \underline{\quad} \cdot 1$$

$$5; \quad 2; \quad 7; \quad 1; \quad 9$$

84. $52{,}719 = 5 \cdot 10000 + 2 \cdot 1000 + 7 \cdot 100 + 1 \cdot 10 + 9 \cdot 1$

This is the EXPANDED DIGIT representation of 52,719.

Write the expanded digit representation of each number below:

$$429 = \underline{\qquad\qquad\qquad}$$
$$6{,}512 = \underline{\qquad\qquad\qquad}$$
$$22{,}479 = \underline{\qquad\qquad\qquad}$$
$$177{,}406 = \underline{\qquad\qquad\qquad}$$

$$429 = 4 \cdot 100 + 2 \cdot 10 + 9 \cdot 1$$
$$6{,}512 = 6 \cdot 1000 + 5 \cdot 100 + 1 \cdot 10 + 2 \cdot 1$$
$$22{,}479 = 2 \cdot 10000 + 2 \cdot 1000 + 4 \cdot 100 + 7 \cdot 10 + 9 \cdot 1$$
$$177{,}406 = 1 \cdot 100000 + 7 \cdot 10000 + 7 \cdot 1000 + 4 \cdot 100 + 0 \cdot 10 + 6 \cdot 1$$

85. Write the expanded digit form of each number:

$$3{,}062 = \underline{\qquad\qquad\qquad}$$
$$87 = \underline{\qquad\qquad}$$
$$5{,}192{,}774 = \underline{\qquad\qquad\qquad}$$
$$21{,}000 = \underline{\qquad\qquad\qquad}$$

$$3{,}062 = 3 \cdot 1000 + 0 \cdot 100 + 6 \cdot 10 + 2 \cdot 1$$
$$87 = 8 \cdot 10 + 7 \cdot 1$$
$$5{,}192{,}774 = 5 \cdot 1000000 + 1 \cdot 100000 + 9 \cdot 10000 + 2 \cdot 1000 + 7 \cdot 100 + 7 \cdot 10 + 4 \cdot 1$$
$$21{,}000 = 2 \cdot 10000 + 1 \cdot 1000 + 0 \cdot 100 + 0 \cdot 10 + 0 \cdot 1$$

86. Note that even when the simplest form of a number contains the digit 0, in the expanded digit representation we include a term for each 0. And in the expanded digit representation of a natural number, each term is a product of one of the digits in the original number and the numbers:

$$\underline{\qquad}, \underline{\qquad}, \underline{\qquad}, \underline{\qquad}, \ldots$$

$$1, 10, 100, 1000$$

87. Write the expanded digit representation of 6,543,210. _____

> 6 · 1000000 + 5 · 100000 + 4 · 10000 + 3 · 1000 + 2 · 100 + 1 · 10 + 0 · 1

88. In the number 6,543,217:

The digit 7 is in the ones place.

The digit 1 is in the tens place.

The digit 2 is in the hundreds place.

The digit 3 is in the _____ place.

The digit 4 is in the _____ place.

The digit 5 is in the _____ place.

The digit 6 is in the _____ place.

> THOUSANDS;   TEN-THOUSANDS;
> HUNDRED-THOUSANDS;   MILLIONS

89. 6,543,217 = 6 · 1000000 + 5 · 100000
        + 4 · 10000 + 3 · 1000 + 2 · 100 + 1 · 10 + 7 · 1

The digit 7 is in the ones place. In the expanded digit representation, the digit 7 is multiplied by 1.

The digit 1 is in the tens place. In the expanded digit representation, the digit 1 is multiplied by 10.

The digit 2 is in the hundreds place. In the expanded digit representation, the digit 2 is multiplied by 100.

The digit 3 is in the _____ place. In the expanded digit representation, the digit 3 is multiplied by _____.

> THOUSANDS;   1000

90. 6,543,217 = 6 · 1000000 + 5 · 100000
        + 4 · 10000 + 3 · 1000 + 2 · 100 + 1 · 10 + 7 · 1

The digit in the ten-thousands place is multiplied by 10000.

The digit in the hundred-thousands place is multiplied by _____.

The digit in the _____ place is multiplied by 1000000.

> 100000;   MILLIONS

91. Using the number 6,543,217 as an example, we have shown that the place in which a digit occurs and the number that digit multiplies in the expanded digit form are related. For any natural number we find this same relationship.

The ones digit multiplies the number 1 in the expanded digit form.

The tens digit multiplies the number 10 in the expanded digit form.

The hundreds digit multiplies the number _____ in the expanded digit form.

The _____ digit multiplies the number 1000 in the expanded digit form.

> 100;   THOUSANDS

92. Any digit multiplies a number whose name "agrees" with that of the place the digit occupies.

Indeed, it is this fact which accounts for the names assigned to the various places in a number.

93. We have seen that the whole numbers are ordered. Then

527	<	561
3915	<	20304
6541	____	30801
29567	____	313413

> <;   <

94. 6541 < 30801 since there is a natural number, 24260, which when added to 6541 yields a sum of 30801.

29567 < 313413 since there is a natural number, _____, which, when added to _____ yields a sum of _____.

> 283846;   29567;   313413

95. Also

2953   >   1527

64003   <   64013

22574   _____   50637

491237   _____   492237

> <;   <

96. 22574 < 50637 since there is a natural number, _____, which when added to 22574 yields a sum of 50637.

491237 < 492237 since there is a natural number, _____, which when added to 491237 yields a sum of 492237.

> 28063;   1000

97. There is another way to compare natural numbers in simplest form. Consider, again, the number 491237. This number has:

digit 4 in the hundred-thousands place,

digit 9 in the ten-thousands place,

digit _____ in the thousands place,

digit 2 in the _____ place,

digit 3 in the _____ place,

and digit _____ in the ones place.

> 1;   HUNDREDS;   TENS;   7

98. While the number 492237 has:

digit _____ in the hundred-thousands place,

digit 9 in the _____ place,

digit _____ in the thousands place,

digit _____ in the hundreds place,

digit _____ in the tens place,

and digit 7 in the _____ place.

> 4;   TEN-THOUSANDS;   2;   2;   3;
> ONES

99. Then the numbers 491237 and 492237 have the same digit in each place but the thousands. And in the thousands place the smaller number, 491237, has a _____ digit than has the number 492237.

> SMALLER

100. We have also seen that 64003 < 64013. Note that both numbers have the same digit in each place but the _____.

> TENS

101. 64003 < 64013

Both numbers have the same digit in each place but the tens. And in the tens place, the smaller number, 64003, has a _____ _____ than has the number 64013.

> SMALLER DIGIT

102. Compare the following pairs of natural numbers.

7432	<	7732
5197	>	5117
42735	_____	45735
291364	_____	391364
55417	_____	55410
7257737	_____	7256737

<;   <;   >;   >

103. Note that all that is needed to compare two natural numbers whose simplest forms have the same digit in each place but one, is to examine the digits in that place. In each case, the smaller number has the _____ digit in that place.

SMALLER

104. We have seen that 22574 < 50637. The number 22574 has digit _____ in the ten-thousands place; the number 50637 has digit _____ in the ten-thousands place.

2;   5

105. Of course 22574 and 50637 do not have the same digit in any place. But even if they had the same digit in every place but the ten-thousands, we would still be able to conclude that 22574 < 50637 since 2 _____ 5.

<

106. Compare the following pairs of natural numbers.

72913	>	45176
5013	_____	4933
2163741	_____	5719437
417722	_____	137727

>;   <;   >

107. Note that all that is needed to compare two natural numbers whose simplest forms have the same number of digits, but which begin with a different digit, is to examine their first digits. Again, the number with the _____ first digit is the smaller number.

SMALLER

108. Now consider the numbers 47356 and 47729. Since

47356 + 373 = 47729

we can write

47356 _____ 47729.

<

109. 47356 < 47729

Note that both numbers have digit 4 in the ten-thousands place and digit 7 in the thousands place. But in the hundreds place, the smaller number has digit _____ while the larger number has digit _____ .

3;   7

110. Compare the following pairs of natural numbers.

52319 $<$ 52735

4176 $>$ 4102

31255 _____ 34175

98727 _____ 98733

794121 _____ 794429

3388617 _____ 3388040

111. In fact, to compare two natural numbers whose simplest forms have the same number of digits, we need only examine the digits in the first place in which they differ. In every case, the smaller number has the

_____ _____ .

SMALLER DIGIT

112. Compare the following pairs of natural numbers.

41792 _____ 41533

216559 _____ 216638

4544 _____ 7344

1234566 _____ 1234655

113. Of course, if the simplest forms of two natural numbers each contain a different number of digits, then the comparison is even simpler.

42913 $>$ 5272

3842 _____ 1235579

44721 _____ 4472

2235566 _____ 11111111

<; >; <

114. When the simplest forms of two natural numbers each contain a different number of digits, the smaller number has _____ digits.

FEWER

115. Compare.

51293 _____ 477

38 _____ 5544927

212121 _____ 3232

969 _____ 100301

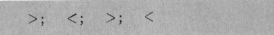

116. But when the simplest forms of two natural numbers each contain the same number of digits, the digit each contains in the _____ place in which they differ determines the order.

FIRST

117. Compare.

27291 _____ 27710

56251 _____ 66213

72947 _____ 19072

344556 _____ 344519

<; <; >; >

118. There are occasions when we shall wish to use one natural number to APPROXIMATE another. For example, if the population of a city is 724,792, we may want to say that the population is A _____ 725,000.

APPROXIMATELY

119. While there are actually 5,280 feet in one mile, we may want to say that one mile is _____ 5000 feet in length.

> APPROXIMATELY

120. We shall use the method of ROUNDING OFF to approximate numbers. We round off a natural number by replacing all digits to the right of some place by zeros. Then 1,295,741 can be approximated by 1,296,000 which we obtain by _____ off the original number.

> ROUNDING

121. Let us illustrate the procedure for rounding off by considering the number 421,539.

Rounded off to tens, we obtain 421,540.

Rounded off to hundreds, we obtain 421,500.

Rounded off to _____, we obtain 422,000.

Rounded off to _____, we obtain 420,000.

Rounded off to _____, we obtain 400,000.

> THOUSANDS; TEN-THOUSANDS; HUNDRED-THOUSANDS

122. Consider the number 47,163.

Rounded off to tens, we obtain 47,160.

Rounded off to _____, we obtain 47,200.

Rounded off to _____, we obtain 47,000.

Rounded off to _____, we obtain 50,000.

> HUNDREDS; THOUSANDS; TEN-THOUSANDS

123. As these examples illustrate, when a natural number is rounded off to any place, all digits to the right of that place become _____.

> 0

124. 429177 rounded off to thousands becomes 429000.

5171 rounded off to _____ becomes 5000.

127450 rounded off to _____ becomes 130000.

5792 rounded off to _____ becomes 5800.

> THOUSANDS; TEN-THOUSANDS; HUNDREDS

125. All digits to the right of the place rounded off to become 0. As for the digit in that place, sometimes it is unchanged and sometimes it is increased by _____.

> 1

126. The number 2,186,312 becomes

2,186,310 rounded off to tens,

2,186,300 rounded off to hundreds,

and

2,186,000 rounded off to thousands.

In each of these cases, the tens, hundreds, and thousands digits were not changed. And note that the ones, tens, and hundreds digits are, respectively _____, _____, and _____.

> 2; 1; 3

127. The number 2,186,312 becomes

2,190,000 rounded off to ten-thousands,

and

2,200,000 rounded off to hundred-thousands.

Here the ten-thousands and hundred-thousands digits were increased by 1. And note that the thousands and ten-thousands digits are, respectively, _____ and _____.

6;   8

128. We shall use the following rule for deciding whether to leave a digit unchanged or increase it by 1 when rounding off. "Whenever the following digit is less than 5, we shall leave the digit in the place rounded off to _____."

UNCHANGED

129. Hence

45132 rounded off to thousands becomes 45000,

51723 rounded off to hundreds becomes 51700,

616353 rounded off to tens becomes _____,

and

4,747,172 rounded off to hundred-thousands becomes _____.

616350;   4,700,000

130. And

24391 rounded off to thousands becomes _____,

498,122 rounded off to tens becomes _____,

4444 rounded off to hundreds becomes _____,

380,123 rounded off to ten-thousands becomes _____.

24000;   498,120;   4400;   380,000

131. "But when the following digit is 5 or greater, the digit in the place rounded off to shall be increased by _____."

1

132. Hence

73152 rounded off to hundreds becomes 73200,

1,984,717 rounded off to thousands becomes 1,985,000,

275891 rounded off to ten-thousands becomes _____.

and

5,204,914 rounded off to thousands becomes _____.

280000;   5,205,000

133. And

201631 rounded off to thousands becomes

_____ ,

193,388 rounded off to hundreds becomes

_____ .

6,059,307 rounded off to ten-thousands becomes _____ .

21770 rounded off to tens becomes

_____ .

> 202000;   193,400;   6,060,000;   21770

134. 21770 rounded off to tens remains 21770, since the digit in the ones place is less than 5.

Round off each of the following to the place indicated.

429,717 (tens) _____

55,917 (ten-thousands) _____

2,123,115 (thousands) _____

2,700,516 (hundreds) _____

> 429,720;   60,000;   2,123,000;
> 2,700,500

135. Sometimes increasing a digit by 1 affects the digits to its left. Thus, rounded off to hundreds, 42971 becomes 43000, since increasing the hundreds digit, 9, by 1 causes an increase in the thousands digit.

Also,

5,619,843 rounded off to thousands becomes 5,620,000.

4896 rounded off to tens becomes 4900.

149789 rounded off to thousands becomes

_____ .

2,239,961 rounded off to hundreds becomes

_____ .

> 150000;   2,240,000

136. Round off each of the following to the place indicated.

69,123 (thousands) _____

175,396 (tens) _____

2,779,651 (ten-thousands) _____

1,569,953 (thousands) _____

> 69,000;   175,400;   2,780,000;
> 1,570,000

137. To round off a natural number to any place, then, requires:

1) that all digits to the right of that place become _____ , and

2) that the digit in the place rounded off to remains unchanged if the first digit to its _____ is 0, 1, 2, 3, or 4, or

3) that the digit in the place rounded off to is increased by 1 if the first digit to its right is _____ , 6, 7, 8, or 9.

> 0;   RIGHT;   5

138. The rules for rounding off a natural number are formulated so as to result in the smallest possible ERROR. That is, the original number and the approximation obtained by rounding off will differ by as little as possible using these rules.

For example, rounded off to thousands, 4,273,612 becomes _____ .

> 4,274,000

139. Now 4,274,000 ≠ 4,273,612. In fact,

4,274,000 − 4,273,612 = _____

> 388

140. 4,274,000 and 4,273,612 differ by 388. Our rounding off has resulted in an E _____ of 388.

> ERROR

141. 4,263,612 has been approximated by 4,274,000 resulting in an error of 388. Yet no other natural number, rounded off to thousands, will differ from 4,273,612 by less than 388. Hence 4,274,000 is the best approximation to thousands for this number.

Similarly, rounded off to hundreds, 397,451 becomes _____ .

> 397,500

142. Of course, 397,500 ≠ 397,451. In fact the error made in this approximation is

397,500 − 397,451 = _____

> 49

143. We have approximated 397,451 by 397,500 resulting in an error of 49. And yet no other natural number, rounded off to hundreds, is a better _____ .

> APPROXIMATION

144. Indeed, the rules we have given for rounding off a natural number result in an approximation which is as good as any we can obtain. Using these rules results in the smallest possible _____ .

> ERROR

145. In this chapter we have considered the system of numeration used to represent whole numbers. All of the numbers can be represented by means of the symbols

0, 1, 2, 3, 4, 5, 6, 7, 8, 9

which are called _____ .

> DIGITS

146. And since it requires only ten digits to express all whole numbers, we say that we have a _____ 10 system of numeration.

> BASE

147. The simplest form of any natural number uses the digits but no other operation symbols. This can be accomplished because the meaning of each digit depends on its _____ in the representation of the number.

> PLACE   or   POSITION

148. From right to left, we name the places in the simplest representation of a number:

_____ , _____ ,
_____ , _____

> ONES, TENS, HUNDREDS, THOUSANDS

149. Each natural number can be represented in an unlimited number of ways. The number 144, for example, can be represented as

$12 \cdot 12$

$142 + 2$

$432/3$

$160 - 20 + 4$

00144

150. However, we are seldom interested in these representations of the number 144. Instead, we prefer to express this number in its

a) simplest form: 144

b) complete factorization form:
$1 \cdot 2 \cdot 2 \cdot 2 \cdot 2 \cdot 3 \cdot 3$ or $1 \cdot 2^4 \cdot 3^2$

c) expanded digit form:

_____

$1 \cdot 100 + 4 \cdot 10 + 4 \cdot 1$

151. And the number represented by

$500 + 2 \cdot 45 - 5$

will usually be represented in one of the forms:

a) 585 which is its _____ form.

b) $1 \cdot 3^2 \cdot 5 \cdot 13$ which is its _____

_____ .

c) $5 \cdot 100 + 8 \cdot 10 + 5 \cdot 1$ which is its

_____ _____ representation.

SIMPLEST;   COMPLETE FACTORIZATION;   EXPANDED DIGIT

152. In fact, unless there are instructions to the contrary, all answers should be in simplest form.

Thus

$1 \cdot 2^3 \cdot 3 \cdot 5 = $ _____

$46 + \dfrac{24}{4} - 7(2 + 3) = $ _____

$2 \cdot 100000 + 7 \cdot 10000 + 3 \cdot 1000 + 8 \cdot 100 + 4 \cdot 10 + 9 \cdot 1 = $ _____

120;   17;   273,849

153. However, there are times when we seek only an approximation of a number. We obtain an approximation with a minimum error by _____ _____ the number.

ROUNDING OFF

Chapter 21

(Answers on page 511)

Give the name of the place of the underlined digit.

1. 5<u>4</u>26
2. 84<u>5</u>
3. <u>3</u>6
4. 5<u>4</u>,261
5. <u>9</u>00,000
6. 123,45<u>6</u>
7. <u>4</u>,444,444
8. 1<u>2</u>3,456

Write each of these in simplest form.

9. $3 \cdot 100 + 5 \cdot 10 + 7 \cdot 1$
10. $8 \cdot 10000 + 5 \cdot 1000 + 3 \cdot 100 + 9 \cdot 10 + 4 \cdot 1$
11. $5 \cdot 10 + 9 \cdot 100 + 2 \cdot 1$
12. $9 \cdot 1 + 8 \cdot 1000 + 5 \cdot 10 + 7 \cdot 100$
13. $3 \cdot 10 + 0 \cdot 100 + 5 \cdot 1 + 6 \cdot 1000$
14. $3 \cdot 1000000 + 3 \cdot 1$

Give the expanded digit representation of each number.

15. 345
16. 8142
17. 50
18. 92,001
19. 5,400,000
20. 900,999
21. $375 + 946$

Round off each number as indicated.

22. 8473   (tens)
23. 8473   (hundreds)
24. 8473   (thousands)
25. 89,316   (thousands)
26. 89,316   (ten-thousands)
27. 545,678   (thousands)
28. 545,678   (hundreds)
29. 545,678   (tens)
30. 545,678   (ten-thousands)
31. 545,678   (hundred-thousands)

Example: What is the error when 48,273 is rounded off to hundreds?

Answer: Rounded off to hundreds, 48,273 becomes 48,300. The error is 48,300 − 48,273 = 27.

Find the error when

32. 845   is rounded off to hundreds.
33. 9453   is rounded off to thousands.
34. 26,759   is rounded off to thousands.
35. 857,143   is rounded off to ten-thousands.
36. 8458   is rounded off to tens.

Answer the following:

37. In 1960 the population of a certain city was 273,512. What was the population, rounded off to the nearest thousand?

38. The distance by highway from San Francisco to Los Angeles is 423 miles. What is the distance rounded off to the nearest hundred miles?

39. In one small state one representative to the state assembly is allowed for each 10,000 citizens. How many representatives should be given to a county whose population is 177,259?

40. The population of a city increased from 173,212 to 351,619 during a 10-year period. Rounded off to the nearest thousand, what was the increase?

41. A politician estimated that during his 12 years in office he traveled a total of 853,000 miles. Rounded off to the nearest thousand miles, how far did he travel during an average year?

Problems B

Write each of these numbers in simplest form.

1. three thousand, four hundred twelve.

2. nine hundred sixteen.

3. eighty-five thousand, eighty-five.

4. seven thousand, seven.

5. six hundred forty-seven thousand, three hundred fifty-five.

6. five million, six hundred.

7. ninety-nine thousand, ninety-nine.

8. four hundred thousand, forty.

Write the expanded digit representation of each of these numbers.

9. 346

10. 50

11. 5,427

12. 82,000

13. 943,107

14. 7,001

15. 9,215,173

16. 800,072

Round off each number to the nearest (a) tens; (b) hundreds; (c) thousands.

17. 5614

18. 7387

19. 2696

20. 4499

21. 8888

22. 9876

Round off the numbers as indicated.

23. 575   (tens)

24. 94,215   (thousands)

25. 167,275   (hundreds)

26. 976,000   (ten-thousands)

27. 897,127   (ten-thousands)

28. 17,842,112   (millions)

What is the error when 5,673,956 is rounded off to the nearest

29. tens

30. hundreds

31. thousands

32. ten-thousands

33. hundred-thousands

34. millions

Answer the following:

35. The distance "around" the world is 23,892 miles. What is this distance rounded off to the nearest thousand miles?

36. A steamship traveled 3247 miles in 6 days. To the nearest 10 miles, how far did it travel per day?

37. An encyclopedia contains 24 volumes of 513 pages each. To the nearest hundred pages, what is the total number of pages?

38. An automobile traveled 28,789 miles on a set of tires. To the nearest thousand miles, what was the "mileage" for each tire?

39. A housing development which contains 47 houses is valued at $1,000,000. To the nearest $1,000 what is the average value of each house?

DECIMAL FORMS OF QUOTIENT NUMBERS

1. When two numbers are multiplied, the result is called their _____ .

   PRODUCT

2. The numbers multiplied are called _____ of the product.

   FACTORS

3. If a, b, and c represent numbers, and ab = c, then a and b are _____ of c; c is the _____ of a and b.

   FACTORS; PRODUCT

4. When one number is divided by another, the result is called their _____ .

   QUOTIENT

5. If a, b, and c represent numbers, a/b = c means _____ .

   c · b = a   or   b · c = a

6. If a/b = c,

   a is called the _____ and b the _____ in the division problem. c is called the _____ .

   DIVIDEND;   DIVISOR;   QUOTIENT

7. The expression 7^3 is read "the _____ power of _____ ."

   THIRD;   7

8. And 7^3 is defined to mean

   _____ · _____ · _____

   7 · 7 · 7

9. In the expression 7^3 we call 7 the _____ and 3 the _____ .

   BASE;   EXPONENT

10. $7^3 = 7 \cdot 7 \cdot 7$

Note that the _____ is used as a factor the number of times indicated by the _____.

11. For any number a, and any natural number n, we have defined the expression a^n.

If $n = 1$,

$$a^n = a^1 = \underline{\hspace{2cm}}$$

12. For any number a,

$$a^1 = a$$

For any other natural number, n,

$$a^n = a \cdot a \cdot a \cdot \cdot \cdot a$$

where the expression on the right contains _____ factors.

13. Let us investigate the powers of the number 10.

$10^1 = \underline{\hspace{2cm}}$

$10^2 = 10 \cdot 10 = \underline{\hspace{2cm}}$

$10^3 = \underline{\hspace{1cm}} \cdot \underline{\hspace{1cm}} \cdot \underline{\hspace{1cm}} = \underline{\hspace{1cm}}$

14. $10^1 = 10$

$10^2 = 10 \cdot 10 = 100$

$10^3 = 10 \cdot 10 \cdot 10 = 1000$

$10^4 = 10 \cdot 10 \cdot 10 \cdot 10 = \underline{\hspace{2cm}}$

$10^5 = 10 \cdot 10 \cdot 10 \cdot 10 \cdot 10 = \underline{\hspace{2cm}}$

$10^6 = 10 \cdot 10 \cdot 10 \cdot 10 \cdot 10 \cdot 10 = $

$\underline{\hspace{2cm}}$

15. $10^1 = 10$

$10^2 = 100$

$10^3 = 1000$

$10^4 = 10000$

$10^5 = 100000$

$10^6 = 1000000$

Every power of 10 is a natural number whose left-hand digit is _____ and whose remaining digits are all _____.

16. $10^1 = 10$

$10^2 = 100$

$10^3 = 1000$

$10^4 = 10000$

$10^5 = 100000$

$10^6 = 1000000$

And, in every power of 10, the number of times the digit 0 appears is equal to the _____ in the power expression.

17. A power of 10, then, can be found by writing the digit 1 and following it with the digit 0 written as many times as the exponent in the power expression. Thus

$$10^7 = \underline{\hspace{2cm}}$$

> 10000000

18. Every natural number can be represented in simplest form using the ten symbols

0, 1, 2, 3, 4, 5, 6, 7, 8, 9

We call these symbols _____ .

> · DIGITS

19. In representing a natural number in simplest form, not only the digits used, but their _____ in the representation, is important.

> PLACE ·

20. In fact, we give names to the places in the simplest form representation of a natural number. These are, from <u>right</u> to <u>left</u>:

_____, _____,
_____, _____,
_____,
_____, _____

> ONES, TENS, HUNDREDS, THOUSANDS, TEN-THOUSANDS, HUNDRED-THOU-SANDS, MILLIONS

21. Thus, the number

51,427

has the digit 7 in the _____ place,

the digit 2 in the _____ place,

the digit 4 in the _____ place,

and the digit 1 in the _____ place.

> ONES;   TENS;   HUNDREDS;
> THOUSANDS

22. Find the following products:

$$14 \cdot 10^1 = \quad 14 \cdot 10 = \underline{\hspace{2cm}}$$
$$627 \cdot 10^1 = \quad 627 \cdot 10 = \underline{\hspace{2cm}}$$
$$4316 \cdot 10^1 = 4316 \cdot 10 = \underline{\hspace{2cm}}$$
$$5599 \cdot 10^1 = 5599 \cdot 10 = \underline{\hspace{2cm}}$$

> 140;   6270;   43160;   55990

23. Find the following products:

$$8 \cdot 10^1 = \quad 8 \cdot 10 = \underline{\hspace{2cm}}$$
$$2400 \cdot 10^1 = \quad 2400 \cdot 10 = \underline{\hspace{2cm}}$$
$$71915 \cdot 10^1 = \quad 71915 \cdot 10 = \underline{\hspace{2cm}}$$
$$872461 \cdot 10^1 = 872461 \cdot 10 = \underline{\hspace{2cm}}$$

> 80;   24000;   719150;   8724610

24. $8 \cdot 10^1 = 80$

In the number 8, the digit 8 is in the _____ place.

After multiplying by 10^1, the product, 80, has the digit 8 in the _____ place.

> ONES;   TENS

25. $14 \cdot 10^1 = 140$

In the number 14, the digit 1 is in the tens place and the digit 4 is in the ones place. After multiplying by 10^1, the product, 140, has the digit 1 in the _____ place and the digit 4 in the _____ place.

HUNDREDS;   TENS

26. $627 \cdot 10^1 = 6270$

In 627, 6 is in the _____ place, 2 is in the _____ place, and 7 is in the _____ place.

After multiplying by 10^1, we have the product 6270. In it, 6 is in the thousands place, 2 is in the hundreds place, and 7 is in the tens place.

HUNDREDS;   TENS;   ONES

27. $4316 \cdot 10^1 = 43160$

Upon multiplying by 10^1, we see that the digit:

4 went from the thousands to the ten-thousands place.

3 went from the _____ to the _____ place.

1 went from the tens to the hundreds place.

6 went from the _____ to the _____ place.

HUNDREDS;   THOUSANDS;   ONES;
TENS

28. As these examples show, whenever a natural number is multiplied by 10^1, each digit is moved one place to the _____ and the digit 0 is placed in the _____ place.

LEFT;   ONES

29. That is, when a natural number is multiplied by the first power of ten, each digit in the number is moved _____ place to the _____, but the digits and their relative order do not change.

ONE;   LEFT

30. Find the following products:

$27 \cdot 10^2 = \quad 27 \cdot 100 = $ _____

$513 \cdot 10^2 = \quad 513 \cdot 100 = $ _____

$6 \cdot 10^2 = \quad 6 \cdot 100 = $ _____

$4970 \cdot 10^2 = \quad 4970 \cdot 100 = $ _____

2700;   51300;   600;   497000

31. $6 \cdot 10^2 = 600$

In the number 6, the digit 6 is in the _____ place. After multiplying by 10^2, we find the digit 6 in the _____ place.

ONES;   HUNDREDS

32. $27 \cdot 10^2 = 2700$

In 27, the digit 2 is in tens place and 7 is in the ones place. After multiplying by 10^2, we find the digit 2 in the _____ place and the digit 7 in the _____ place.

THOUSANDS;   HUNDREDS

33. $513 \cdot 10^2 = 51300$

In 513, _____ is in the hundreds place, _____ is in the tens place, and _____ is in the ones place.

After multiplying by 10^2, we have the product 51300. In it, 5 is in the ten-thousands place, 1 is in the thousands place, and 3 is in the hundreds place.

34. $4970 \cdot 10^2 = 497000$

Notice that as a result of multiplying by 10^2, the digit:

4 went from the thousands place to the hundred-thousands place.

9 went from the _____ place to the _____ place.

7 went from the _____ place to the _____ place.

35. $4970 \cdot 10^2 = 497000$

In 4970, the ones digit is 0. To what place in the product, 497000, did this 0 go?

_____

36. These examples show that when a natural number is multiplied by 10^2, each digit is moved _____ places to the _____, and the digit 0 is placed in the ones and tens places.

37. That is, when a natural number is multiplied by the _____ power of 10, each digit is moved to the _____ two places. The digits and their relative order remain the same.

38. $412 \cdot 10^3 = 412000$

$257 \cdot 10^4 =$ _____

$13 \cdot 10^5 = 1300000$

$7 \cdot 10^6 =$ _____

39. These examples, too, show that whenever a natural number is multiplied by a power of 10, each digit is moved to the _____. The number of places moved is equal to the E_____ in the power of 10.

40. If a natural number is multiplied by a power of 10, each digit is moved to the left. The relative order of the digits remains the same. The digit _____ is placed on the right as many times as the exponent in the power of 10.

41. Hence:

$142 \cdot 10^5 =$ _____

$7 \cdot 10^3 =$ _____

$220 \cdot 10^1 =$ _____

$6 \cdot 10^2 =$ _____

42. $6 \cdot 10^2 = 600$

The digit 6 is moved from the ones place to the hundreds place, and two digits 0 were placed on the right.

Could either of the 0 digits be omitted in 600? _____

> NO   (see next frame)

43. There is no convenient way to omit one of the digits 0 in the number 600. For if one writes 60, even though the 6 is intended to be in the hundreds place, it will appear as though the 6 is in the tens place! The digit 0, then, is included to indicate correctly the place the nonzero digit occupies.

We call a 0 used in this way a PLACE HOLDER.

44. Let n be any natural number. Then if a natural number is multiplied by 10^n, each of its digits is moved n places to the _____, and n digits 0 are inserted on the _____ as place _____.

> LEFT;   RIGHT;   HOLDERS

45. Find the following quotients:

$1420 \div 10^1 =$ $1420 \div 10 = 142$

$62000 \div 10^1 =$ $62000 \div 10 =$ _____

$567000 \div 10^1 = 567000 \div 10 =$ _____

> 6200;   56700

46. Find

$80 \div 10^1 =$ $80 \div 10 =$ _____

$980 \div 10^1 =$ $980 \div 10 =$ _____

$76300 \div 10^1 = 76300 \div 10 =$ _____

> 8;   98;   7630

47. $80 \div 10^1 = 8$

In the number 80, the digit 8 is in the _____ place. After dividing by 10^1, the quotient, 8, has the digit 8 in the _____ place.

> TENS;   ONES

48. $980 \div 10^1 = 98$

In the number 980, the digit 9 is in the hundreds place and the digit 8 is in the tens place. After dividing by 10^1, the quotient, 98, has the digit 9 in the _____ place and the digit 8 in the _____ place.

> TENS;   ONES

49. $1420 \div 10^1 = 142$

In 1420, 1 is in the _____ place, 4 is in the _____ place, and 2 is in the _____ place. After dividing by 10^1, in the quotient, 142, we have 1 in the _____ place, 4 in the _____ place, and 2 in the _____ place.

> THOUSANDS;   HUNDREDS;   TENS;
> HUNDREDS;   TENS;   ONES

50. In the division problems we have considered, the dividend had the digit 0 in the ones place and hence was divisible by 10^1. In dividing by 10^1, every digit (except the zero in the ones place) was moved _____ place to the _____.

> ONE;   RIGHT

51. Find the following quotients:

$$900 \div 10^2 = \quad 900 \div 100 = 9$$

$$52100 \div 10^2 = \quad 52100 \div 100 = \underline{\hspace{2cm}}$$

$$487000 \div 10^2 = 487000 \div 100$$

$$= \underline{\hspace{2cm}}$$

> 521;   4870

52. $900 \div 10^2 = 9$

In 900, the digit 9 is in the $\underline{\hspace{2cm}}$ place. In 9, the digit 9 is in the $\underline{\hspace{2cm}}$ place.

> HUNDREDS;   ONES

53. $52100 \div 10^2 = 521$

In 52100, the digit 5 is in the ten-thousands place, 2 is in the thousands place, and 1 is in the hundreds place. After dividing by 10^2, we find the digit 5 in the $\underline{\hspace{2cm}}$ place, 2 in the $\underline{\hspace{2cm}}$ place, and 1 in the $\underline{\hspace{2cm}}$ place.

> HUNDREDS;   TENS;   ONES

54. $487000 \div 10^2 = 4870$

As a result of dividing by 10^2, the digit

4 went from the hundred-thousands place to the thousands place;

8 went from the $\underline{\hspace{2cm}}$ place to the $\underline{\hspace{2cm}}$ place;

7 went from the $\underline{\hspace{2cm}}$ place to the $\underline{\hspace{2cm}}$ place.

> TEN-THOUSANDS;   HUNDREDS;
> THOUSANDS;   TENS

55. $487000 \div 10^2 = 4870$

In 487000, the hundreds digit is 0. To what place in the quotient, 4870, did this 0 go?

$$\underline{\hspace{3cm}}$$

> ONES

56. In the division problems of the last five frames, the dividend had the digit 0 in the ones and tens places and hence was divisible by 100. In dividing by $100 = 10^2$, every digit (except the two zeros in the ones and tens places) was moved $\underline{\hspace{2cm}}$ places to the $\underline{\hspace{2cm}}$.

> TWO;   RIGHT

57. Find

$$3000 \div 10^3 = 3$$

$$14270000 \div 10^4 = \underline{\hspace{2cm}}$$

$$52900000 \div 10^5 = \underline{\hspace{2cm}}$$

> 1427;   529

58. These examples, too, show that when a natural number is divisibly by a power of 10, the quotient can be obtained by moving digits to the $\underline{\hspace{2cm}}$. The number of places moved is equal to the $\underline{\hspace{2cm}}$ in the power of 10.

> RIGHT;   EXPONENT

59. But we have only considered dividends which were divisible by the power of 10 which was the divisor.

Now consider

$$1234 \div 10^1$$

Since we are dividing by 10^1, we might attempt to find the quotient by moving each digit _____ place to the _____ .

ONE;   RIGHT

60. $1234 \div 10^1$

In 1234, the digit 1 is in the thousands place. In the quotient, this digit would occur in the _____ place.

In 1234, the digit 2 is in the hundreds place. In the quotient, this digit would occur in the _____ place.

In 1234, the digit 3 is in the tens place. In the quotient, this digit would occur in the _____ place.

HUNDREDS;   TENS;   ONES

61. $1234 \div 10^1$

In 1234, the digit 4 is in the ones place. In dividing by 10^1, this digit should move one place to the right. Hence, in the quotient, the digit 4 will appear _____ place to the _____ of the ones place!

ONE;   RIGHT

62. But we cannot merely write

$$1234 \div 10^1 = 1234$$

since it would not be clear that in 1234, the digit 3 is in the ones place. We shall introduce the DECIMAL POINT to indicate the location of the ones place. Hence we shall write

$$1234 \div 10^1 = 123.4$$

63. $1234 \div 10^1 = 123.4$

In 123.4, the decimal point indicates that the digit at its left, 3, is in the _____ place.

ONES

64. Similarly, if we write

456.7

the decimal point indicates that the digit _____ is in the ones place.

6

65. In 13.29, the digit _____ is in the ones place. In 1.329, the digit _____ is in the ones place.

3;   1

66. We indicate the digit in the ones place by writing a _____ _____ immediately to its right.

DECIMAL POINT

67. We have written

$$1234 \div 10^1 = 123.4$$

We were led to this statement by following a pattern which was observed when dividing multiples of 10 by 10^1.

But 1234 is not divisible by 10^1, and there is a question as to just what 123.4 means!

68. Consider the problem

$$1 \div 10$$

Since there is no natural number whose product with 10 is 1, the number 1 is not _____ by 10.

69. However, there is a quotient number whose product with 10 is 1. It can be represented by the fraction _____.

70. $$\frac{1}{10} \cdot 10 = 1$$

and so we write

$$1 \div 10 = 1/10$$

But
$$10 = 10^1$$

and so

$$1 \div 10 = 1 \div 10^1.$$

Let us attempt to "perform" this division by moving digits. Since our divisor is 10^1, we should move each digit _____ place to the _____.

71. We are considering the problem $1 \div 10^1$.

But the dividend, 1, has only a single digit and it appears in the ones place. Hence, after division, this digit would appear one place to the right of the ones place. Thus

$$1 \div 10^1 = \text{_____}$$

72. We know that $1 \div 10 = 1 \div 10^1 = 1/10$ since $\frac{1}{10} \cdot 10 = 1$.

If we follow the pattern of moving digits, we must write

$$1 \div 10 = 1 \div 10^1 = .1$$

Hence, if we are to be consistent, we must agree that

$$.1 = \text{_____}$$

73. $$1 \div 10 = 1/10 \qquad 1 \div 10 = .1$$

To be consistent, we must have

$$1/10 = .1$$

The expression on the left is read "one tenth." Let us read the expression on the right in exactly the same way.

.1 will be read "_____ _____"

74. Similarly, since $\frac{3}{10} \cdot 10 = 3$, we must have

$$3 \div 10 = \text{_____}.$$

But, since
$$3 \div 10 = 3 \div 10^1,$$

we might wish to move digits and write

$$3 \div 10 = \text{_____}$$

75. $$3 \div 10 = 3/10 \qquad 3 \div 10 = .3$$

Again, for consistency, we must have

$$3/10 = .3$$

and either expression shall be read "_____ _____."

76. The division problems $4 \div 10$, $7 \div 10$, and $8 \div 10$ have quotients which can be represented by the fractions $4/10, 7/10$, and $8/10$.

We might also wish to move digits so that these quotients are represented by the expressions .4, .7, and .8.

Hence, again for consistency, we must have

.4 = 4/10 _____ = 7/10   and

.8 = _____

.7;   8/10

---

77. Since .4 = 4/10, we should read either as "four tenths."

Since .7 = 7/10, we should read either as "_____ tenths."

Since .8 = 8/10, we should read either as "_____ _____."

SEVEN;   EIGHT TENTHS

---

78. We have decided to call

.1 "one tenth"

.3 "three tenths"

.4 "four tenths"

.7 "seven tenths"

.8 "eight tenths"

If we are to name this first place to the right of the decimal point, it seems proper to call it the _____ place.

TENTHS

---

79. Then the expression .6 should be read "six _____," and .6 must be equal to the fraction _____.

TENTHS;   6/10

---

80. Similarly, the expression .9 will be read "_____ _____" and .9 must equal the fraction _____.

NINE TENTHS;   9/10

---

81. We have thus introduced a new place which a digit can occupy. It is one place to the right of the ones place and will be called the _____ place.

TENTHS   (not TENS!)

---

82. The meaning we give to a digit in the tenths place is dependent upon our desire for consistency and the definition of division.

The expression .2 must equal the fraction _____ and will be read "_____."

2/10;   TWO TENTHS

---

83. 2/10 is a fraction. There are many fractions which equal 2/10. The property shared by 2/10 and all fractions equal to it is called a _____ number.

QUOTIENT

---

84. But 2/10 is not the simplest representative of the quotient number determined by it. The simplest form of this number is _____.

1/5

---

85. Hence 2/10 represents the quotient number whose simplest form is 1/5. But 2/10 = .2, and so .2 also represents this same quotient number. We shall call .2 a DECIMAL DIGIT representation of this quotient number, although we often call this, simply, a DECIMAL representation, or decimal form.

86. .5 is the _____ digit form of the quotient number represented by the fraction 5/10. The simplest form of this number is _____.

DECIMAL;   1/2

---

87. Also, .9 is the _____ _____ representation of the quotient number whose simplest form is the fraction _____.

DECIMAL DIGIT;   9/10

---

88. Let us now return to the problem

$$1234 \div 10 = 1234 \div 10^1$$

We have written the result of this division as 123.4

Since 1234 is not divisible by 10, there is no _____ number which is their quotient.

NATURAL

---

89. We are considering the problem

$$1234 \div 10 = 1234 \div 10^1$$

While the quotient is not a natural number, we can express the result of the division by the quotient number represented by the fraction

1234/10

Note that this fraction is not in simplest form and is an _____ fraction.

IMPROPER

---

90. $1234 \div 10 = 1234/10$

Let us change the improper fraction to a mixed number. We could write

$$\frac{1234}{10} = 123\frac{4}{10}$$

But if $1234 \div 10^1 = 123.4$, then we must have

$$123.4 = 123\frac{4}{10}$$

Both expressions represent a quotient number and either should be read
" _____."

ONE HUNDRED TWENTY-THREE AND FOUR TENTHS

---

91. $123.4 = 123\frac{4}{10}$

Recall that $123\frac{4}{10}$ is an expression for $123 + \frac{4}{10}$, and $4/10 = .4$.

Hence

$$123 + \frac{4}{10} = 123 + .4$$

Then $123.4 = 123 + .4$. That is, the expression 123.4 is also a M_____ number.

MIXED

---

92. The expression 53.7 also represents a mixed number and

$$53.7 = 53 + .7 = 53 + \frac{7}{10} = 53\frac{7}{10}$$

Again, both expressions represent a quotient number and either expression will be read
" _____ - _____ and _____ _____."

FIFTY-THREE;   SEVEN TENTHS

---

93. The expression 4916.5 represents the mixed number _____, and either expression will be read "four thousand, nine hundred sixteen and five tenths."

$4916\frac{5}{10}$

94. Write as mixed numbers.

$327.2 = 327\frac{2}{10}$

$4.9 =$ _____

$7.8 =$ _____

$51.6 =$ _____

$4\frac{9}{10};\quad 7\frac{8}{10};\quad 51\frac{6}{10}$

95. $4.9 = 4\frac{9}{10}$

Both expressions represent a quotient number whose simplest form is $49/10$.

$7.8 = 7\frac{8}{10}$

Both expressions represent a quotient number whose simplest form is _____.

$39/5$

96. Now consider the problem

$1234 \div 10^2$

Since we are dividing by 10^2, we might attempt to form the quotient by moving each digit _____ places to the _____.

TWO; RIGHT

97. $1234 \div 10^2$

If each digit is moved two places to the right, the digit 1 will move to the _____ place and 2 will move to the _____ place.

TENS; ONES

98. $1234 \div 10^2$

But if each digit is moved two places to the right, the digit 3 will appear in the tenths place, and the digit 4 will appear two places to the right of the _____ place.

ONES

99. If we again use the decimal point to locate the ones place, we must write

$1234 \div 10^2 =$ _____

12.34

100. We write $1234 \div 10^2 = 12.34$ but, again, there is some question of the meaning of 12.34

Consider the problem

$1 \div 100$

While 1 is not divisible by 100, we can express the quotient $1 \div 100$ by the fraction _____.

$1/100$

101. $1 \div 100 = 1/100$

But $100 = 10^2$ and so

$1 \div 100 = 1 \div 10^2$

Again, let us attempt to "perform" this division by moving digits. Since our divisor is 10^2, we should move each digit _____ places to the _____.

TWO;   RIGHT

102. We are considering the problem $1 \div 10^2$

But the dividend, 1, has only a single digit and it appears in the ones place. Hence, after division this digit would appear two places to the right of the _____ place.

ONES

103. But we <u>cannot</u> write simply

$1 \div 10^2 = .\,1$

for this shows the digit 1 only one place to the right of the ones place. To indicate the proper location of the digit 1 in the result, we insert the digit 0 in the tenths place and write

$1 \div 10^2 =$ _____

.01

104. We shall write $1 \div 10^2 = .01$

Note that the digit 0 is necessary here. Without it, we would conclude the digit 1 was in the first place to the right of the ones place.

When it is used in this way, we again call 0 a _____ _____.

PLACE HOLDER

105. We know

$1 \div 100 = 1 \div 10^2 = 1/100.$

We wish to write

$1 \div 100 = 1 \div 10^2 = .01$

Therefore, the only meaning that we can give to .01 is to say that it is _____ to 1/100.

EQUAL

106. $.01 = 1/100$

and either expression will be read "one hundredth."

Next consider

$7 \div 100 = 7 \div 10^2.$

Of course the quotient $7 \div 100$ can be represented by the fraction _____ .

7/100

107. $7 \div 100 = 7/100$

On the other hand, $100 = 10^2$ and so we might move the digit 7 and write

$7 \div 10^2 =$ _____

.07

108. We have

$7 \div 10^2 = 7/100$

We want

$7 \div 10^2 = .07$

Hence we shall make

$.07 = 7/100$

and read either expression as " _____ _____ ."

SEVEN HUNDREDTHS

109. Similar appeals to the division operation could be used to define

$$.02 = 2/100 \qquad .03 = 3/100$$

$$.05 = \underline{\hspace{2cm}} \qquad .09 = \underline{\hspace{2cm}}$$

110. .02 = 2/100   We read either expression as "two hundredths."

.03 = 3/100   We read either expression as "three hundredths."

.05 = 5/100   Either expression is read "_____."

.09 = 9/100   Either expression is read "_____."

111. We now have another new place a digit can occupy. It is the second place to the right of the ones place, and it seems reasonable to call this the _____ place.

112. Consider

$$37 \div 100 = 37 \div 10^2$$

We know

$$37 \div 100 = 37/100$$

We would want

$$37 \div 10^2 = .37$$

Hence we define

$$.37 = 37/100$$

Also, we would define:

.53 = _____

.71 = _____

.99 = _____

113. And we should read

.53 as "_____ - _____ hundredths."

.71 as "seventy-one _____."

.99 as "_____ _____ _____."

114. The expressions .53, .71, and .99 are equal to the fractions 53/100, 71/100, and 99/100. Hence, like the fractions, they represent quotient numbers.

We say that .53, .71, and .99 are _____ forms of these quotient numbers.

115. We have introduced another new place which a digit can occupy. It is the second place to the right of the ones place and will be called the _____ place.

116. When an expression has a digit in the hundredths place and also in the tenths place, we include only the name of the hundredths place when we read the number. Thus, we read

.65   "sixty-five hundredths"

.14   "_____ _____"

.11   "_____ _____"

117. We have written

$$1234 \div 100 = 1234 \div 10^2 = 12.34$$

Since 1234 is not divisible by 100, there is no natural number which is the quotient. But we can express the result of the division by the quotient number represented by 1234/100, which can be written as the mixed number _____ .

$$12^{34}/_{100}$$

118. We have written

$$1234 \div 100 = 12.34$$

We know that

$$1234 \div 100 = 1234/100 = 12^{34}/_{100}$$

Hence

$$12.34 = 12^{34}/_{100}$$

Both expressions represent a quotient number and we should read either as
" _____ _____ _____ - _____ _____ . "

TWELVE AND THIRTY-FOUR HUNDREDTHS

119. $12.34 = 12^{34}/_{100}$

Each expression represents a quotient number whose simplest form is 617/50.

Similarly,

$$472.91 = 472 + .91 = 472 + \frac{91}{100} = 472^{91}/_{100}$$

Either expression will be read "four hundred seventy-two and ninety-one hundredths" and both 472.91 and $472^{91}/_{100}$ represent a quotient number whose simplest form is _____ .

47291/100

120. Write as mixed numbers.

$$5.88 = 5^{88}/_{100}$$

$$7.16 = \underline{\hspace{3cm}}$$

$$44.73 = \underline{\hspace{3cm}}$$

$$12.07 = \underline{\hspace{3cm}}$$

$7^{16}/_{100};\quad 44^{73}/_{100};\quad 12^{7}/_{100}$

121. Similar appeals to the definition of division and the desire for consistency would lead to the introduction of other places to the right on the ones digit.

Thus

$$7 \div 1000 = 7/1000$$

and

$$7 \div 1000 = 7 \div 10^3 = .007$$

Hence

$$.007 = 7/1000$$

Each will be read "seven thousandths," and we shall call the third place to the right of the ones place the _____ place.

THOUSANDTHS

122. Then .217 = 217/1000 and is read "two hundred seventeen thousandths,"

and .053 = _____ and is read "fifty-three thousandths,"

while .109 = 109/1000 and is read
" _____ _____ _____ _____ . "

53/1000;   ONE HUNDRED NINE THOUSANDTHS

123. Similarly $15.303 = 15{}^{303}\!/_{1000}$ and is read "fifteen and three hundred three thousandths," and $214.176 = $ _____ and is read "two hundred fourteen and one hundred seventy-six _____ ."

$214{}^{176}\!/_{1000};$ THOUSANDTHS

124. $9 \div 10000 = 9/10000$

   $9 \div 10^4 = .0009$

Hence $.0009 = $ _____ and each will be read " _____ - _____ ."

9/10000;   NINE TEN-THOUSANDTHS

125. Hence the fourth place to the right of the ones place is called the ten-thousandths place.

The expression

   $.1023 = 1023/10000$

and is read "one thousand twenty-three ten-thousandths." Also,

   $.0621 = $ _____

and is read " _____ _____ - _____ - _____ ."

621/10000;   SIX HUNDRED TWENTY-ONE TEN-THOUSANDTHS

126. Similarly, $17.7132 = 17{}^{7132}\!/_{10000}$ and is read "seventeen and seven thousand, one hundred thirty-two ten-thousandths," and $103.0281 = $ _____ and is read "one hundred three and two hundred eighty-one _____ - _____ ."

$103{}^{281}\!/_{10000};$ TEN-THOUSANDTHS

127. Write as a fraction or mixed number.

   $124.1007 = 124{}^{1007}\!/_{10000}$

   16.07   = _____

   .133   = _____

   7.019   = _____

   139.9   = _____

$16{}^{7}\!/_{100};$ ${}^{133}\!/_{1000};$ $7{}^{19}\!/_{1000};$ $139{}^{9}\!/_{10}$

128. Write as a fraction or mixed number.

   734.19   = _____

   7.005   = _____

   .1203   = _____

   1400.10 = _____

$734{}^{19}\!/_{100};$ $7{}^{5}\!/_{1000};$ ${}^{1203}\!/_{10000};$ $1400{}^{10}\!/_{100}$

129. Each natural number can be represented in expanded digit form. Thus

   $415 = 4 \cdot 100 + 1 \cdot 10 + 5 \cdot 1$

   $6293 = $ _____

   $77416 = $ _____

   $2009 = $ _____

$6 \cdot 1000 + 2 \cdot 100 + 9 \cdot 10 + 3 \cdot 1$
$7 \cdot 10000 + 7 \cdot 1000 + 4 \cdot 100 + 1 \cdot 10 + 6 \cdot 1$
$2 \cdot 1000 + 0 \cdot 100 + 0 \cdot 10 + 9 \cdot 1$

130. Now consider again the expression 123.4.

We have seen that $123.4 = 123 + .4$. If we write 123.4 in its expanded form, we obtain

   $123.4 = 123 + .4 = $ _____ $\cdot 100$

   $+ $ _____ $\cdot 10 + $ _____ $\cdot 1 + .4$

1;   2;   3

131. $123.4 = 1 \cdot 100 + 2 \cdot 10 + 3 \cdot 1 + .4$

Now
$$.4 = 4/10 = 4 \cdot \frac{1}{10}$$

and so we can write
$$123.4 = 1 \cdot 100 + 2 \cdot 10 + 3 \cdot 1 + \underline{\hspace{1cm}} \cdot \frac{1}{10}$$

> 4

132. Hence the expanded digit form of 123.4 is
$$1 \cdot 100 + 2 \cdot 10 + 3 \cdot 1 + 4 \cdot \frac{1}{10}$$

Similarly, the number
$$67.9 = 67 + .9$$

Since
$$.9 = \frac{9}{10} = 9 \cdot \frac{1}{10},$$

in expanded digit form we can write 67.9
= \underline{\hspace{4cm}}

> $6 \cdot 10 + 7 \cdot 1 + 9 \cdot \frac{1}{10}$

133. Write in expanded digit form:
$$447.6 = 4 \cdot 100 + 4 \cdot 10 + 7 \cdot 1 + 6 \cdot \frac{1}{10}$$
$$2017.8 = \underline{\hspace{3cm}}$$
$$5.5 = \underline{\hspace{3cm}}$$

> $2 \cdot 1000 + 0 \cdot 100 + 1 \cdot 10 + 7 \cdot 1 + 8 \cdot \frac{1}{10}$
>
> $5 \cdot 1 + 5 \cdot \frac{1}{10}$

134. The expanded digit representation of 123.4 is
$$1 \cdot 100 + 2 \cdot 10 + 3 \cdot 1 + 4 \cdot \frac{1}{10}$$

Note that the digit 4 is in the \underline{\hspace{2cm}}
place and that in the expanded digit form 4
multiplies the fraction \underline{\hspace{2cm}} .

> TENTHS;   1/10

135. Also, $12.34 = 12 + .34$

and so $12.34 = 1 \cdot 10 + 2 \cdot 1 + .34$

But $.34 = \frac{34}{100} = \frac{30+4}{100} = \frac{30}{100} + \frac{4}{100} = \frac{3}{10} + \frac{4}{100}$

and $\frac{3}{10} = \underline{\hspace{1.5cm}} \cdot \frac{1}{10}$ while

$\frac{4}{100} = \underline{\hspace{1.5cm}} \cdot \frac{1}{100}$

> 3;   4

136. So, in expanded digit form, we have:
$$12.34 = \underline{\hspace{1.5cm}} \cdot 10 + \underline{\hspace{1.5cm}} \cdot 1 +$$
$$\underline{\hspace{1.5cm}} \cdot \frac{1}{10} + \underline{\hspace{1.5cm}} \cdot \frac{1}{100}$$

> $12.34 = 1 \cdot 10 + 2 \cdot 1 + 3 \cdot \frac{1}{10} + 4 \cdot \frac{1}{100}$

137. $12.34 = 1 \cdot 10 + 2 \cdot 1 + 3 \cdot \frac{1}{10} + 4 \cdot \frac{1}{100}$

Similarly, the number $451.27 = 451 + .27$.
Since
$$.27 = \frac{27}{100} = \frac{20+7}{100} = \frac{20}{100} + \frac{7}{100} = \frac{2}{10} + \frac{7}{100}$$
$$= 2 \cdot \frac{1}{10} + 7 \cdot \frac{1}{100}$$

we can write in expanded digit form 451.27
= \underline{\hspace{3cm}}

> $4 \cdot 100 + 5 \cdot 10 + 1 \cdot 1 + 2 \cdot \frac{1}{10} + 7 \cdot \frac{1}{100}$

138. Write in expanded digit form.
$$216.18 = 2 \cdot 100 + 1 \cdot 10 + 6 \cdot 1 + 1 \cdot \frac{1}{10} + 8 \cdot \frac{1}{100}$$
$$23.63 = \underline{\hspace{3cm}}$$
$$4.89 = \underline{\hspace{3cm}}$$

> $23.63 = 2 \cdot 10 + 3 \cdot 1 + 6 \cdot \frac{1}{10} + 3 \cdot \frac{1}{100}$
>
> $4.89 = 4 \cdot 1 + 8 \cdot \frac{1}{10} + 9 \cdot \frac{1}{100}$

139. The expanded digit representation of 12.34 is

$$1 \cdot 10 + 2 \cdot 1 + 3 \cdot \frac{1}{10} + 4 \cdot \frac{1}{100}$$

Note that the digit 3 is in the tenths place and that in the expanded digit form, 3 multiplies the fraction 1/10. Note, too, that the digit 4 is in the _____ place and that in the expanded digit form, 4 multiplies the fraction _____ .

> HUNDREDTHS;   1/100

140. Consider next the number 123.456.

$$123.456 = 123 + .456$$

Certainly

$$123 = 1 \cdot 100 + 2 \cdot 10 + 3 \cdot 1$$

But

$$.456 = \frac{456}{1000} = \frac{400 + 50 + 6}{1000} = \frac{400}{1000} + \frac{50}{1000}$$

$$+ \frac{6}{1000} = \frac{4}{10} + \frac{5}{100} + \frac{6}{1000}$$

> 5;   6

141. $.456 = \dfrac{4}{10} + \dfrac{5}{100} + \dfrac{6}{1000} = 4 \cdot \dfrac{1}{10} + 5 \cdot \dfrac{1}{100}$

$$+ 6 \cdot \frac{1}{1000}$$

Thus, in expanded digit form,

$$123.456 = \underline{\hspace{1cm}} \cdot 100 + \underline{\hspace{1cm}} \cdot 10$$
$$+ \underline{\hspace{1cm}} \cdot 1 + \underline{\hspace{1cm}} \cdot \frac{1}{10} + \underline{\hspace{1cm}} \cdot \frac{1}{100}$$
$$+ \underline{\hspace{1cm}} \cdot \frac{1}{1000}.$$

> $123.456 = \underline{1} \cdot 100 + \underline{2} \cdot 10 + \underline{3} \cdot 1 + \underline{4} \cdot \dfrac{1}{10}$
>
> $+ \underline{5} \cdot \dfrac{1}{100} + \underline{6} \cdot \dfrac{1}{1000}$

142. $123.456 = 1 \cdot 100 + 2 \cdot 10 + 3 \cdot 1 + 4 \cdot \dfrac{1}{10}$

$$+ 5 \cdot \frac{1}{100} + 6 \cdot \frac{1}{1000}$$

Note that the digit 4 is in the tenths place and, in the expanded digit form, 4 multiplies the fraction 1/10.

The digit 5 is in the hundredths place and, in the expanded digit form, 5 multiplies the fraction 1/100.

Also, the digit 6 is in the _____ place and, in the expanded digit form, 6 multiplies the fraction _____ .

> THOUSANDTHS;   1/1000

143. $.3297 = \dfrac{3297}{10000} = \dfrac{3000 + 200 + 90 + 7}{10000} = \dfrac{3000}{10000}$

$$+ \frac{200}{10000} + \frac{90}{10000} + \frac{7}{10000} = \frac{3}{10} + \frac{2}{100} + \frac{9}{1000}$$

$$+ \frac{7}{10000}$$

> 3;   2;   9

144. $.3297 = \dfrac{3}{10} + \dfrac{2}{100} + \dfrac{9}{1000} + \dfrac{7}{10000}$

But

$$\frac{3}{10} = 3 \cdot \frac{1}{10} \qquad \frac{2}{100} = 2 \cdot \frac{1}{100} \qquad \frac{9}{1000} = 9 \cdot \frac{1}{1000}$$

$$\frac{7}{10000} = 7 \cdot \frac{1}{10000}$$

Hence .3297 has an expanded digit form

_____

> $3 \cdot \dfrac{1}{10} + 2 \cdot \dfrac{1}{100} + 9 \cdot \dfrac{1}{1000} + 7 \cdot \dfrac{1}{10000}$

145. Write in expanded digit form

$$483.54 = 4 \cdot 100 + 8 \cdot 10 + 3 \cdot 1 + 5 \cdot \frac{1}{10}$$
$$+ 4 \cdot \frac{1}{100}$$

$$2006.103 = \underline{\hspace{1cm}} \cdot 1000 + \underline{\hspace{1cm}} \cdot 100$$
$$+ \underline{\hspace{1cm}} \cdot 10 + \underline{\hspace{1cm}} \cdot 1 + \underline{\hspace{1cm}} \cdot \frac{1}{10}$$
$$+ \underline{\hspace{1cm}} \cdot \frac{1}{100} + \underline{\hspace{1cm}} \cdot \frac{1}{1000}$$

$$92.775 = \underline{\hspace{3cm}}$$

$$.0027 = \underline{\hspace{3cm}}$$

$$2006.103 = 2 \cdot 1000 + \underline{0} \cdot 100 + \underline{0} \cdot 10 + \underline{6} \cdot 1$$
$$+ \underline{1} \cdot \frac{1}{10} + \underline{0} \cdot \frac{1}{100} + \underline{3} \cdot \frac{1}{1000}$$
$$92.775 = 9 \cdot 10 + 2 \cdot 1 + 7 \cdot \frac{1}{10} + 7 \cdot \frac{1}{100}$$
$$+ 5 \cdot \frac{1}{1000}$$
$$.0027 = 0 \cdot \frac{1}{10} + 0 \cdot \frac{1}{100} + 2 \cdot \frac{1}{1000} + 7 \cdot \frac{1}{10000}$$

146. Write in expanded digit form.

$$1.0016 = \underline{\hspace{3cm}}$$
$$728.47 = \underline{\hspace{3cm}}$$
$$201.0 = \underline{\hspace{3cm}}$$
$$50.293 = \underline{\hspace{3cm}}$$

$$1.0016 = 1 \cdot 1 + 0 \cdot \frac{1}{10} + 0 \cdot \frac{1}{100} + 1 \cdot \frac{1}{1000}$$
$$+ 6 \cdot \frac{1}{10000}$$
$$728.47 = 7 \cdot 100 + 2 \cdot 10 + 8 \cdot 1 + 4 \cdot \frac{1}{10}$$
$$+ 7 \cdot \frac{1}{100}$$
$$201.0 = 2 \cdot 100 + 0 \cdot 10 + 1 \cdot 1 + 0 \cdot \frac{1}{10}$$
$$50.293 = 5 \cdot 10 + 0 \cdot 1 + 2 \cdot \frac{1}{10} + 9 \cdot \frac{1}{100}$$
$$+ 3 \cdot \frac{1}{1000}$$

147. Every decimal representation of a quotient number can be expressed in expanded digit form. A quotient number which can be represented by a proper fraction has no digits to the left of the decimal point. Its expanded digit representation involves the digits and the numbers

$$\frac{1}{10}, \frac{1}{100}, \frac{1}{1000}, \cdots$$

Thus, in expanded digit form,

$$.51927 = \underline{\hspace{3cm}}$$

$$.51927 = 5 \cdot \frac{1}{10} + 1 \cdot \frac{1}{100} + 9 \cdot \frac{1}{1000}$$
$$+ 2 \cdot \frac{1}{10000} + 7 \cdot \frac{1}{100000}$$

148. Every decimal representation of a quotient number can be expressed in expanded digit form. A quotient number which requires a mixed number for its representation contains digits both left and right of the decimal point. Write the expanded digit form:

$$38427.1956 = \underline{\hspace{3cm}}$$

$$38427.1956 = 3 \cdot 10000 + 8 \cdot 1000 + 4 \cdot 100$$
$$+ 2 \cdot 10 + 7 \cdot 1 + 1 \cdot \frac{1}{10} + 9 \cdot \frac{1}{100} + 5 \cdot \frac{1}{1000}$$
$$+ 6 \cdot \frac{1}{10000}$$

149.
$$42916 = 4 \cdot 10000 + 2 \cdot 1000 + 9 \cdot 100 + 1 \cdot 10$$
$$+ 6 \cdot 1$$

We call 4 the ten-thousands digit, and note that we have written $4 \cdot 10000$.

We call 2 the $\underline{\hspace{2cm}}$ digit, and note that we have written $2 \cdot 1000$.

We call 9 the $\underline{\hspace{2cm}}$ digit, and note that we have written $9 \cdot 100$.

We call 1 the $\underline{\hspace{2cm}}$ digit, and note that we have written $1 \cdot 10$.

And we call 6 the $\underline{\hspace{2cm}}$ digit and note that we have written $6 \cdot 1$.

THOUSANDS;   HUNDREDS;   TENS;   ONES

150. $.51927 = 5 \cdot \frac{1}{10} + 1 \cdot \frac{1}{100} + 9 \cdot \frac{1}{1000}$

$+ 2 \cdot \frac{1}{10000} + 7 \cdot \frac{1}{100000}$

We call 5 the tenths digit, and note that we have written $5 \cdot \frac{1}{10}$.

We call 1 the _____ digit, and note that we have written $1 \cdot \frac{1}{100}$.

We call 9 the _____ digit, and note that we have written $9 \cdot \frac{1}{1000}$.

We call 2 the _____ digit, and note that we have written $2 \cdot \frac{1}{10000}$.

> **HUNDREDTHS; THOUSANDTHS; TEN-THOUSANDTHS**

151. Each number expression containing a decimal point which we have considered is merely a representation of a quotient number. The decimal point marks the location of the ones digit. On the left, from <u>right</u> to <u>left</u>, we call the places

ones, _____, _____,
_____, · · ·

> **TENS; HUNDREDS; THOUSANDS**

152. Each number expression containing a decimal point which we have considered is merely a representative of a quotient number. The decimal point marks the location of the ones digit. On the right, from <u>left</u> to <u>right</u>, we call the places

tenths, _____,
_____,
_____, · · ·

> **HUNDREDTHS; THOUSANDTHS; TEN-THOUSANDTHS**

153. And those quotient numbers whose decimal forms we have considered can also be written in expanded digit form. In that form each digit multiplies a number whose name "agrees" with the _____ that digit occupies.

> **PLACE**

154. Each decimal digit expression represents a quotient number. In the next chapter we shall consider the problem of expressing such numbers in simplest form. As we shall see, however, not every quotient number has a decimal digit form.

155. Each decimal digit expression represents a quotient number whose product with, or quotient when divided by, a power of 10 is particularly easy to find. When multiplying by a power of 10, each digit is moved to the _____; when dividing by a power of 10, each digit is moved to the _____. In either case, the number of places moved is equal to the _____ of the power of 10.

> **LEFT; RIGHT; EXPONENT**

Chapter 22

Problems A (Answers on page 512)

Use the method of moving digits to give a decimal form for each of the following products and quotients.

Example: $(23.7) \div 100$.

Answer: $(23.7) \div 100 = .237$

1. $175 \div 100$
2. $(84.3) \div 10$
3. $(8.43) \cdot 10$
4. $(.502) \cdot 100$
5. $(7.3) \div 100$
6. $(.54) \div 10$
7. $(.83) \div 1000$
8. $314 \div 1000$
9. $(.9) \div 1$
10. $(.36) \cdot 100$
11. $(.23) \cdot 1000$
12. $(.03) \div 100$
13. $(3.5) \cdot 1000$
14. $(.0003) \cdot 10$
15. $21 \div 1000$

Give the name of the place in which the underlined digit occurs.

Example: 34.5<u>6</u>7. Answer: hundredths

16. 4.5<u>7</u>
17. 83.4<u>2</u>
18. 802.5<u>9</u>
19. .005<u>4</u>
20. .1234<u>5</u>
21. <u>8</u>14.12
22. <u>8</u>141.2
23. .814<u>1</u>2
24. .00000<u>5</u>
25. 814256.5

Write each of the following in decimal form.

26. seven tenths
27. forty-three hundredths
28. five hundred one thousandths
29. one hundred eleven and fifteen hundredths
30. sixteen thousandths
31. twelve and five thousandths
32. two hundred and six hundred four ten-thousandths
33. nine thousand, four and fourteen hundred-thousandths

34. $4 \cdot \dfrac{1}{10} + 3 \cdot \dfrac{1}{100}$

35. $8 \cdot \dfrac{1}{10} + 0 \cdot \dfrac{1}{100} + 6 \cdot \dfrac{1}{1000}$

36. $5 \cdot 10 + 3 \cdot 1 + 4 \cdot \dfrac{1}{10}$

37. $0 \cdot \dfrac{1}{10} + 0 \cdot \dfrac{1}{100} + 0 \cdot \dfrac{1}{1000} + 4 \cdot \dfrac{1}{10000}$

38. $3 \cdot \dfrac{1}{100} + 5 \cdot \dfrac{1}{10} + 4 \cdot \dfrac{1}{1000}$

39. $5 \cdot 1 + 8 \cdot \dfrac{1}{100} + 6 \cdot 10 + 4 \cdot \dfrac{1}{10}$

40. $1 \cdot 1 + 0 \cdot \dfrac{1}{10} + 0 \cdot \dfrac{1}{100} + 0 \cdot \dfrac{1}{1000} + 1 \cdot \dfrac{1}{10000}$

Write each of these in expanded digit form.

41. .375
42. 5.14
43. 23.05
44. .0003
45. 800.05001

Problems B

Write in decimal form.

1. eighteen hundredths

2. four hundred eleven thousandths

3. nine and seven tenths

4. two hundred one and seventy-five hundredths

5. four hundredths

6. nineteen ten-thousandths

7. fifty-three and twelve thousandths

8. one hundred forty-seven and twenty-three hundred-thousandths

9. two hundred eleven thousandths

10. two hundred and eleven thousandths

Write out the full name (as above) for each of these.

11. .251

12. .0075

13. 5.37

14. 200.3

15. 12.001

16. 5463.847

17. 400.075

18. .475

Write in expanded digit form.

19. .23

20. .476

21. 8.05

22. 23.002

23. 241.57

24. 8000.0002

25. .0000007

Move digits to give a decimal form for each product or quotient.

26. $(27.5) \div 100$

27. $(.275) \cdot 10$

28. $(.035) \cdot 1000$

29. $(3.5) \div 100$

30. $(.0035) \div 1000$

31. $84 \cdot 1000$

32. $84 \div 10000$

33. $(.084) \div 10$

34. $(23.5) \div 10^3$

35. $235 \div 10^2$

CHAPTER 23

FRACTIONS AND DECIMALS

1. In the number expression 73.192, the symbol between the digits 3 and 1 is called the _____ _____.

> DECIMAL POINT

2. In a number expression, the decimal point is used to indicate the location of the ones place. In 73.192, the digit _____ is in the ones place.

> 3

3. To represent a natural number in simplest form, the decimal point is <u>not</u> needed. The digit on the right is in the ones place and each digit, from right to left, is in one of the places:

ones, _____, _____, _____, ...

> TENS;   HUNDREDS;   THOUSANDS

4. Thus 129346 has the digit:

6 in the _____ place

4 in the _____ place

3 in the _____ place

9 in the _____ place

2 in the _____ place

1 in the _____ place.

> ONES;   TENS;   HUNDREDS; THOUSANDS;   TEN-THOUSANDS; HUNDRED-THOUSANDS

5. And the natural number 129,346 is read

" _____ _____ _____ - _____ _____, _____ _____ _____ "

> ONE HUNDRED TWENTY-NINE THOUSAND, THREE HUNDRED FORTY-SIX

6. But when a quotient number that is not a natural number is represented in decimal digit form, the decimal point is required. The digit to the right of the decimal point is in the tenths place and each digit thereafter, from left to right, is in one of the places:

tenths, _____,

_____,

_____, . . .

7. Thus .749105 has the digit:

7 in the _____ place

4 in the _____ place

9 in the _____ place

1 in the _____ place

0 in the _____ place

5 in the _____ place

8. And the quotient number .749105 is read:

" _____ _____

_____ - _____

_____, _____ _____

_____ millionths"

9. Mixed numbers, too, may be expressed in decimal form. The mixed number 107.528 is read

" _____ _____ _____

and _____ _____ _____

_____ - _____ _____ "

10. Every number expression we have written which contains a decimal point is a representation of a quotient number. Let us see how to obtain the simplest form of the quotient number a decimal expression represents.

If the decimal digit form contains no digits to the right of the decimal point, then the quotient number is also a _____ number.

11. Which of the following decimal forms represents a natural number?

a)   429.

b)   16531.

c)   .21

d)   5070. _____

12. If there are no digits to the right of the decimal point, the quotient number represented is also a natural number. To obtain the simplest form of this natural number we need only delete the _____.

13. Thus, 1492. = 1492 in simplest form.

Find the simplest form of

$$5073. = \underline{\hspace{3cm}}$$

$$61,717. = \underline{\hspace{3cm}}$$

$$370. = \underline{\hspace{3cm}}$$

$$99. = \underline{\hspace{3cm}}$$

14. If the decimal digit form of a quotient number contains any digit to the right of the decimal point, we cannot merely delete the decimal point to obtain its simplest form.

We can obtain the simplest form by the following rather involved procedure:

1) Write the number in expanded digit form.

2) Perform the multiplications and additions to obtain a fraction which represents the quotient number.

3) Reduce the fraction, if necessary, to obtain the simplest form.

15. Thus $6.82 = 6 \cdot 1 + 8 \cdot \dfrac{1}{10} + 2 \cdot \dfrac{1}{100}$

$$= 6 + \frac{8}{10} + \frac{2}{100}$$

$$= \frac{600}{100} + \frac{80}{100} + \frac{2}{100}$$

$$= \frac{682}{100}$$

and, in simplest form

$$682/100 = \underline{\hspace{3cm}}.$$

16. Also $17.609 = 1 \cdot 10 + 7 \cdot 1 + 6 \cdot \dfrac{1}{10} + 0 \cdot \dfrac{1}{100}$

$$+ 9 \cdot \frac{1}{1000}$$

$$= 10 + 7 + \frac{6}{10} + 0 + \frac{9}{1000}$$

$$= \frac{10000}{1000} + \frac{7000}{1000} + \frac{600}{1000} + \frac{9}{1000}$$

$$= \underline{\hspace{2cm}}, \quad \text{in simplest form.}$$

17. Find the simplest form.

$$4.2657 = 4 \cdot 1 + 2 \cdot \frac{1}{10} + 6 \cdot \frac{1}{100} + 5 \cdot \frac{1}{1000}$$

$$+ 7 \cdot \frac{1}{10000}$$

$$= 4 + \frac{2}{10} + \frac{6}{100} + \frac{5}{1000} + \frac{7}{10000}$$

$$= \frac{40000}{10000} + \frac{2000}{10000} + \frac{600}{10000} + \frac{50}{10000}$$

$$+ \frac{7}{10000}$$

$$= \underline{\hspace{3cm}}$$

18. Use the expanded digit representations to find the simplest form of each of the following:

$$75.01 = 7 \cdot 10 + 5 \cdot 1 + 0 \cdot \frac{1}{10} + 1 \cdot \frac{1}{100}$$

$$= 70 + 5 + 0 + \frac{1}{100}$$

$$= \frac{7000}{100} + \frac{500}{100} + \frac{1}{100} = \underline{\hspace{2cm}}$$

$$.423 = 4 \cdot \frac{1}{10} + 2 \cdot \frac{1}{100} + 3 \cdot \frac{1}{1000} = \frac{4}{10} + \frac{2}{100}$$

$$+ \frac{3}{1000} = \frac{400}{1000} + \frac{20}{1000} + \frac{3}{1000}$$

$$= \underline{\hspace{2cm}}$$

$$163.5 = 1 \cdot 100 + 6 \cdot 10 + 3 \cdot 1 + 5 \cdot \frac{1}{10}$$

$$= 100 + 60 + 3 + \frac{5}{10}$$

$$= \frac{1000}{10} + \frac{600}{10} + \frac{30}{10} + \frac{5}{10}$$

$$= \underline{\hspace{2cm}}$$

19. But the procedure for changing from a decimal form to simplest form can be considerably shortened. Let us use the examples of the last frame to illustrate a method by which this can be done.

20.   75.01 = 7501/100

Note that in the numerator of the simplest form of this quotient number we find the same digits, in the same order, as in the decimal form.

.423 = 423/1000

Again, note that in the numerator of the simplest form we find the same \underline{\hspace{2cm}}, in the same \underline{\hspace{2cm}}, as in the decimal form.

21. And, before we reduce to simplest form, we see that

163.5 = 1635/10

Again, the same digits occur in both forms.

This is a generally true fact about these two forms of such quotient numbers. The \underline{\hspace{2cm}} of a fraction which represents the quotient number will contain exactly those \underline{\hspace{2cm}} which occur in the decimal form of the number, arranged in the order of their appearance there.

22. Find the missing numerators:

$$16.113 = \frac{}{1000}$$

$$1.5574 = \frac{}{10000}$$

$$.362 = \frac{}{1000}$$

$$.0017 = \frac{}{10000}$$

23.   75.01 = 7501/100

Note that, in the denominator of the simplest form of this quotient number, we find the number 100, a power of 10. Note, too, that the right-hand digit of 75.01 occurs in the hundredths place.

.423 = 423/1000

Again, note that the denominator of the simplest form is \underline{\hspace{2cm}}, a power of 10, and the right-hand digit of .423 occurs in the \underline{\hspace{2cm}} place.

24. And, before we reduce to simplest form, we see that

$$163.5 = 1635/10$$

Again, the denominator is a power of 10 and "agrees" with the place in which the right-hand digit occurs.

This is a generally true result. A quotient number in decimal form can be represented by a fraction whose _____ is a power of 10 which "agrees" with the place of the _____-hand digit.

25. Find the missing denominators:

$$466.7 \quad = \frac{4667}{}$$

$$.5133 \quad = \frac{5133}{}$$

$$.00061 = \frac{61}{}$$

$$1.807 \quad = \frac{1807}{}$$

26. A quotient number in decimal form can be easily expressed in simplest form by:

1) Writing the digits in the decimal form, in order, in the _____ of a fraction.

2) Writing in the denominator of the fraction a power of _____ which "agrees" with the place of the right-hand digit.

3) Reducing the fraction, if necessary, so that the numerator and denominator are relatively _____ .

27. Find the simplest form of the quotient numbers represented by these decimals.

$$4.55 \quad = 455/100 = \underline{\hspace{2cm}}$$

$$21.860 = 21860/1000 = \underline{\hspace{2cm}}$$

$$774.3 \quad = \underline{\hspace{2cm}}$$

$$62.81 \quad = \underline{\hspace{2cm}}$$

28. Find the simplest form of the quotient numbers represented by these decimals.

$$127.333 = \underline{\hspace{2cm}}$$

$$.4191 = \underline{\hspace{2cm}}$$

$$6.012 = \underline{\hspace{2cm}}$$

$$41.0 = \underline{\hspace{2cm}}$$

29. Let us next consider the problem of obtaining a decimal digit representation of a quotient number.

If the quotient number is also a natural number, we can obtain a decimal form by simply inserting a decimal point in the simplest form of the number. We place the decimal point to the _____ of the ones place.

30. Thus $4271 = 4271.$

$$5170 = 5170.$$

$$65 = \underline{\hspace{1.5cm}}$$

$$42,718 = \underline{\hspace{2cm}}, \quad \text{in decimal}$$

form

31. Change the following to decimal form.

$$291 = \underline{\hspace{2cm}}$$

$$55{,}337 = \underline{\hspace{2cm}}$$

$$16 = \underline{\hspace{2cm}}$$

$$227{,}500 = \underline{\hspace{2cm}}$$

291.; 55,337.; 16.; 227,500.

32. If the quotient number is not a natural number, we must use another means of finding a decimal representation. Consider, first, a quotient number represented by a simple fraction whose denominator is a power of 10. We have already noted that division by a power of 10 can be accomplished by moving each digit to the _____ as many places as the _____ in the power of 10.

RIGHT; EXPONENT

33. Hence, treating such a fraction as a division problem, and expressing the denominator as a power of 10, we can change to decimal form. Thus

$$7/10 = 7/10^1 = .7$$

As before, the decimal point locates the digit 7 one place to the right of the ones place. Similarly

$$47/100 = 47/10^2 = \underline{\hspace{1.5cm}}$$

.47

34. Change to decimal form:

$$16/1000 = 16/10^3 = .016$$

$$729/10 = 729/10^1 = \underline{\hspace{2cm}}$$

$$5277/100 = 5277/10^2 = \underline{\hspace{2cm}}$$

$$64712/100 = 64712/10^2 = \underline{\hspace{2cm}}$$

72.9; 52.77; 647.12

35. Change to decimal form:

$$4702/10 = \underline{\hspace{2cm}}$$

$$6/10000 = \underline{\hspace{2cm}}$$

$$5296/1000 = \underline{\hspace{2cm}}$$

$$220/100 = \underline{\hspace{2cm}}$$

470.2; .0006; 5.296; 2.2

36. $5277/100 = 52.77$

Note that the digits in the decimal form, 52.77, are exactly the same, and in the same order, as in the numerator of the fraction, 5277/100.

$$4702/10 = 470.2$$

Again, the digits in the decimal form and those in the _____ of the fraction are the same and appear in the same _____.

NUMERATOR; ORDER

37. $64712/100 = 647.12$

Note that the right-hand digit in the decimal form, 2, is in the hundredths place, and the denominator of the fraction is 100.

$$6/10000 = .0006$$

Again, the right-hand digit in the simplest decimal form is in the _____- _____ place, and the denominator of the fraction is _____.

TEN-THOUSANDTHS; 10000

38. When a quotient number is represented by a fraction whose denominator is a power of 10, a decimal form is easily obtained. The digits in the decimal form are exactly those in the _____ of the fraction. The decimal point is inserted in the expression so that the right hand digit is in the place which "agrees" with the _____ of the fraction.

> NUMERATOR;   DENOMINATOR

39. Change to decimal form.

6/100 = _____

172/10 = _____

665/1000 = _____

7705/100 = _____

> .06;   17.2;   .665;   77.05

40. Change to decimal form.

162971/10000 = _____

76/1000 = _____

16/100 = _____

540/100 = _____

> 16.2971;   .076;   .16;   5.4

41. Next, consider a quotient number which is not a natural number and which is represented by a fraction whose denominator is not a power of 10.

It may be possible to represent such a quotient number by a fraction with a power of 10 as its denominator. Thus

1/2 = 5/10

3/4 = _____/100

1/8 = _____/1000

> 75;   125

42. But whenever a quotient number is represented by a fraction whose denominator is a power of 10, a decimal form can be easily obtained. Thus

1/2 = 5/10 = .5

3/4 = 75/100 = _____

1/8 = 125/1000 = _____

> .75;   .125

43. Change to decimal form:

7/20 = 35/100 = _____

29/25 = _____/100 = _____

1/40 = _____/1000 = _____

27/5 = _____/10 = _____

> 7/20 = 35/100 = .35;
> 29/25 = 116/100 = 1.16;
> 1/40 = 25/1000 = .025;
> 27/5 = 54/10 = 5.4

44. But for many quotient numbers it is not possible to find <u>any</u> representative fraction whose denominator is a power of 10. The fractions 1/3, 5/6, and 22/7 represent such numbers. These quotient numbers <u>do not have</u> a decimal digit form.

And even for quotient numbers which do have decimal forms, finding a representative fraction whose denominator is a power of 10 may not always be easy. Let us consider an alternative method of finding decimal forms.

45. Consider the division problem

45/9 = 5

In this problem we call 45 the _____, 9 the _____, and 5 the _____.

> DIVIDEND;   DIVISOR;   QUOTIENT

46. $45/9 = 5$

Let us multiply the dividend by 10.

$45 \cdot 10 = 450$

If we now divided this result by the original divisor, we obtain

$450/9 =$ _____

50

47. $45/9 = 5 \qquad 450/9 = 50$

Note that multiplying the dividend by 10 yields a result that is 10 times the original quotient. Hence, to obtain the original quotient, we must divide this last result by 10.

$50/10 =$ _____

5

48. $45/9 = 5 \qquad 450/9 = 50 \qquad 50/10 = 5$

We have taken a round-about way to arrive at a result we had at an earlier stage!

Similarly, $26/2 = 13$. If we multiply the dividend by 100 we obtain 2600, and

$2600/2 =$ _____

1300

49. $26/2 = 13 \qquad 2600/2 = 1300$

This time the result, 1300, is 100 times our original quotient and so, to obtain the original quotient, we must divide by _____.

100

50. $26/2 = 13 \qquad 2600/2 = 1300 \qquad 1300/100 = 13$

This is a general result. Whenever the dividend in a division problem is multiplied by a power of 10, the result must be _____ by that same power of 10 to obtain the original quotient.

DIVIDED

51. Thus

$145/5 = 29.$

If the dividend is multiplied by 1000, we have

$145000/5 = 29000$

and

$29000/1000 =$ _____

29

52. In the examples we have so far considered, the original dividend was divisible by the divisor and so there was little point in multiplying by a power of 10 and later dividing by that same number. But consider the problem $11/5$. 11 is not divisible by 5, but if we multiply the dividend by 10 we obtain 110, and

$110/5 =$ _____

22

53. 11 is not divisible by 5 and so $11/5$ does not represent a natural number. However,

$110/5 = 22$

To obtain the original quotient we must now divide by 10. Let us move digits to accomplish this division.

$22/10 =$ _____

2.2

54. 11/5 does not represent a natural number, although it does represent a quotient number.

$$110/5 = 22 \qquad 22/10 = 2.2$$

Note that 2.2 is a decimal form of the quotient number represented by _____ .

11/5

55. Hence we have found a decimal representation of the quotient number 11/5 by this process.

Consider the problem 7/4. 7 is not divisible by 4, but if we multiply 7 by 100 we obtain 700, and 700/4 = _____ .

175

56. 7/4 does not represent a natural number, but it does represent a quotient number.

$$700/4 = 175$$

To obtain our original quotient, we must divide 175 by 100. We do so by moving digits and thus obtain

$$175/100 = \rule{2cm}{0.4pt}$$

1.75

57. 7/4 represents a quotient number which is not a natural number.

$$700/4 = 175 \qquad 175/100 = 1.75$$

Thus 1.75 is a decimal form of this quotient number.

If we multiply and later divide by 1000, we obtain a decimal representative of 3/8.

$$3000/8 = 375 \qquad 375/1000 = \rule{2cm}{0.4pt}$$

.375

58. One way, then, to find a decimal form of a quotient number represented by a fraction is to _____ the numerator by a suitable power of 10 so that it will be divisible by the denominator. The resulting quotient is then _____ by this same power of 10 by moving digits.

MULTIPLY;   DIVIDED

59. But determining a "suitable" power of 10 to multiply and divide by is not always obvious. In actual practice, the entire procedure is made mechanical. Thus, to find a decimal form of 11/5, we divide:

$$\begin{array}{r} 2 \\ 5\overline{)11} \\ 10 \\ \hline 1 \end{array}$$

Since there is a remainder, we "continue" the division by placing a digit 0 to the right of the ones place.

$$\begin{array}{r} 2 \\ 5\overline{)110} \\ 10 \\ \hline 1 \end{array}$$

In effect, here we are multiplying the dividend by _____ .

10

60.
$$\begin{array}{r} 2 \\ 5\overline{)110} \\ \underline{10} \\ 1 \end{array}$$

We then continue the division to obtain

$$\begin{array}{r} 22 \\ 5\overline{)110} \\ \underline{10} \\ 10 \\ \underline{10} \end{array}$$

Finally, we divide the resulting quotient by 10. This is usually done by placing the decimal point in the quotient in the proper place. Thus, in decimal form,

11/5 = _____

2.2

61.   11/5 = 2.2

Even the placement of the decimal point can be mechanical if the original dividend, 11, is written as a decimal.

$$\begin{array}{r} 2.2 \\ 5\overline{)11.0} \\ \underline{10} \\ 1\ 0 \\ \underline{1\ 0} \end{array}$$

When this is done, the position of the decimal point in the result is just _____ that in the dividend.

ABOVE

62. In a similar way, we can obtain a decimal representation of 7/4 as follows:

$$\begin{array}{r} 1 \\ 4\overline{)7} \\ \underline{4} \\ 3 \end{array} \qquad \begin{array}{r} 1.7 \\ 4\overline{)7.0} \\ \underline{4} \\ 3\ 0 \\ \underline{2\ 8} \\ 2 \end{array} \qquad \begin{array}{r} 1.75 \\ 4\overline{)7.00} \\ \underline{4} \\ 3\ 0 \\ \underline{2\ 8} \\ 20 \\ \underline{20} \end{array}$$

Hence 7/4 = _____ , in decimal form.

1.75

63. To find a decimal representative of 3/8, we can again use this division method.

$$\begin{array}{r} .375 \\ 8\overline{)3.000} \\ \underline{2\ 4} \\ 60 \\ \underline{56} \\ 40 \\ \underline{40} \end{array}$$

Hence, in decimal form 3/8 = _____ .

.375

64. Use the division method to find a decimal representative of 3/16. _____

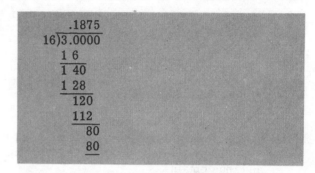

65. 3/16 = .1875, in decimal form.

When using the division method to find a decimal form of a quotient number, the division is continued until there is no remainder.

Use the division method to find a decimal representative of 5/32. _____

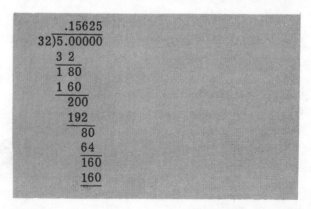

66. Hence 5/32 = .15625, in decimal form.

We have said that certain quotient numbers do not have decimal digit representations. Let us attempt to find a decimal form of such a quotient number, 1/3, by the division method. _____

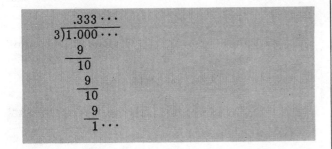

67.
```
     .333···
  3)1.000···
     9
     ──
     10
      9
     ──
     10
      9
     ──
      1···
```

It is clear that no matter how long the process is continued, there will always be a remainder of _____ .

> 1

68. Hence we cannot find a decimal form of 1/3.

We have also said that 5/6 has no decimal digit form. Let us use the division method to show that this is so. _____

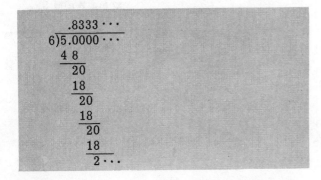

69.
```
     .8333···
  6)5.0000···
     4 8
     ───
      20
      18
     ───
      20
      18
     ───
      20
      18
     ───
       2···
```

It is clear that no matter how long the process is continued, there will always be a remainder of _____ .

> 2

70. To show that 22/7 has no decimal form requires more effort. The division process yields

```
      3.1428···
  7)22.0000···
     21
     ──
      1 0
        7
      ───
       30
       28
      ───
       20
       14
      ───
       60
       56
      ───
        4···
```

but it is not yet clear whether or not there will be some step at which there will be no remainder. However, there is a test which can be used to decide whether a quotient number has a decimal form.

71. The numbers 10, 100, 1000, 10000, ... are _____ of 10.

> POWERS

72. Let us write the complete factorizations of these powers of 10.

$$10 = 1 \cdot 2 \cdot 5$$
$$100 = 1 \cdot 2 \cdot 2 \cdot 5 \cdot 5$$
$$1000 = 1 \cdot 2 \cdot 2 \cdot 2 \cdot 5 \cdot 5 \cdot 5$$
$$10000 = 1 \cdot 2 \cdot 2 \cdot 2 \cdot 2 \cdot 5 \cdot 5 \cdot 5 \cdot 5$$

Note that, in each, the power of 10 has only two different prime factors, _____ and _____ .

2;   5   (either order)

73. We have seen that a decimal representation of any quotient number can be changed to a fraction whose denominator is a power of _____ .

10

74. Hence any quotient number which has a decimal form must have a representative fraction whose denominator is a power of 10. Therefore, the simplest form of such a quotient number is either

a natural number in simplest form,

a fraction whose denominator is a power of 10,

or a fraction which is <u>equal</u> to one whose _____ is a power of _____ .

DENOMINATOR;   10

75. Then 41 is the simplest form of a quotient number which has a decimal representative. A decimal form is merely _____ .

41.

76. And 17/1000 is the simplest form of a quotient number which has a decimal representation. A decimal form of 17/1000 is _____ .

.017

77. And since $5/8 = 625/1000$, the quotient number these fractions represent also has a decimal form. It is _____ .

.625

78. But the complete factorization of any power of 10 contains no prime factors except _____ and _____ .

2;   5   (either order)

79. Then if a fraction whose numerator and denominator are relatively prime is to equal one whose denominator is a power of 10, its _____ must not have a prime factor other than 2 or 5.

DENOMINATOR

80. Hence the simplest form of a quotient number which has a decimal representation must have no _____ factors in its _____ except 2 and 5.

PRIME;   DENOMINATOR

81. The fraction 22/7 is the simplest form of a quotient number. But the denominator is a prime number other than 2 or 5, and this fraction cannot equal one whose denominator is a power of 10. Hence this quotient number cannot have a _____ representation.

DECIMAL

82. The fraction 7/12 is the simplest form of a quotient number. But

$$\frac{7}{12} = \frac{1}{1 \cdot 2 \cdot 2 \cdot 3}$$

and since the denominator has a prime factor, 3, other than 2 or 5, this quotient number, too, has no _____ representation.

DECIMAL

83. Which of the following fractions have a decimal form?

a) $\frac{44}{500} = \frac{44}{1 \cdot 2 \cdot 2 \cdot 5 \cdot 5 \cdot 5}$

b) $\frac{17}{25} = \frac{17}{1 \cdot 5 \cdot 5}$

c) $\frac{5}{24} = \frac{5}{1 \cdot 2 \cdot 2 \cdot 2 \cdot 3}$ _____

a and b

84. $\frac{5}{24} = \frac{5}{1 \cdot 2 \cdot 2 \cdot 2 \cdot 3}$

cannot be changed to a decimal since 24 does not have only 2 and 5 as prime factors.

Which of the following fractions have a decimal form?

a) $\frac{71}{250} = \frac{71}{1 \cdot 2 \cdot 5 \cdot 5 \cdot 5}$

b) $\frac{1}{30} = \frac{1}{1 \cdot 2 \cdot 3 \cdot 5}$

c) $\frac{4}{143} = \frac{4}{1 \cdot 11 \cdot 13}$ _____

ONLY a

85. Then a quotient number which is not a natural number can be expressed in decimal form only if its denominator, in simplest form, has no prime factors other than 2 and 5.

Which of the following have a decimal form?

a) $\frac{3}{1 \cdot 2 \cdot 2 \cdot 5}$ b) $\frac{16}{1 \cdot 5 \cdot 5 \cdot 5}$

c) $\frac{27}{1 \cdot 2 \cdot 5 \cdot 5}$ d) $\frac{1}{1 \cdot 5 \cdot 5 \cdot 5 \cdot 5}$

_____

ALL DO

86. Which of the following have a decimal form?

a) $\frac{5}{1 \cdot 2 \cdot 3}$ b) $\frac{20}{1 \cdot 2 \cdot 2 \cdot 7}$

c) $\frac{100}{1 \cdot 11 \cdot 17}$ d) $\frac{1}{1 \cdot 5 \cdot 5 \cdot 13}$

_____

NONE HAS

87. And when a quotient number has a decimal form, this can be most easily obtained by "dividing" the _____ by the _____ .

> NUMERATOR; DENOMINATOR

88. Change to a decimal form, where possible.

$712/10$ = _____

$3/16$ = _____

$63/5$ = _____

$25/12$ = _____

> 71.2;   .1875;   12.6;   IMPOSSIBLE

89. But not every quotient number has a decimal form. Hence the set of quotient numbers which have a decimal representation is a _____ of the set of all quotient numbers.

> SUBSET

90. We have defined the simplest form of a natural number to be one of the symbols

  1, 2, 3, . . .

Which of the following are in simplest form?

a) 47,291

b) 17 + 5

c) 2^3

d) 1230   _____

> a and d

91. Which of the following are in simplest form?

a) 67-7

b) 10

c) $4 \cdot 100 + 3 \cdot 10 + 2 \cdot 1$

d) 056   _____

> ONLY b

92. 056 is not the simplest form of a natural number since the digit 0 appears to the left of every nonzero digit. The simplest form of this natural number is _____ .

> 56

93. Similarly, the simplest form of:

05070   is   5070

00771   is   _____

04545   is   _____

10005   is   _____

> 771;   4545;   10005

94. For a natural number, the simplest form may include the digit 0, but this digit will not occur to the _____ of every nonzero digit.

> LEFT

95. Let us define the SIMPLEST DECIMAL FORM of a quotient number which has a decimal digit representation. It is the decimal form in which the right-hand digit, if it occurs to the right of the decimal point, is not the digit 0. Thus 17.19 is in _____ decimal form, while 4.40 is not.

> SIMPLEST

96. And 16.309 is in simplest decimal form, but 2.3650 is not. Which of the following are in simplest decimal form?

a) 5029. b) 620.72 c) .0013
d) 7600. _____

97. Which of the following are in simplest decimal form?

a) .501 b) 6.0 c) .7950 d) 221.50

_____

98. If the decimal representation of a quotient number is not in simplest decimal form, it can easily be put in this form. All that is required is the deletion of any 0 that occurs to the right of the decimal point and to the right of every nonzero digit.

Thus, in simplest decimal form,

14.90 = 14.9

6.7200 = 6.72

.5030 = _____

147.020 = _____

99. 14.90 = 14.9 since both expressions represent the quotient number whose simplest form is 149/10.

6.7200 = 6.72 since both expressions represent the quotient number whose simplest form is 168/25.

.5030 = .503 since both expressions represent the quotient number whose simplest form is _____.

147.020 = 147.02 since both expressions represent the quotient number whose simplest form is _____.

100. Express each of the following in simplest decimal form.

147.20600 = _____

5.0030 = _____

.74080 = _____

16.02 = _____

101. Express each of the following in simplest decimal form.

675.60 = _____

1.09 = _____

.530000 = _____

290 = _____

102. Whenever a decimal representation of a quotient number is called for, we shall use the simplest decimal form unless otherwise indicated. And to obtain the simplest decimal form, we delete all digits _____ which occur to the _____ of the decimal point and to the right of every nonzero digit.

103. There are times when an approximation of a quotient number is required. For quotient numbers that are also natural numbers, an approximation is obtained by the method of _____ _____.

ROUNDING OFF

104. Thus,   4572 rounded off to tens is

_____ ,

31,729 rounded off to hundreds is

_____ ,

423,805 rounded off to thousands is

_____ ,

and 329,522 rounded off to thousands is

_____ .

4570;   31,700;   424,000;   330,000

105. When a natural number is rounded off to some place, all digits to the right of that place become _____ .

0

106. When a natural number is rounded off to some place, all digits to the right of that place become 0. The digit in the place rounded off to is either unchanged or is _____ by 1.

INCREASED

107. When a natural number is rounded off to some place, all digits to the right of that place become 0. The digit in the place rounded off to is _____ if the first digit to its right is

0, 1, 2, 3, or 4

and is _____ _____ if the first digit to its right is

5, 6, 7, 8, or 9

UNCHANGED;   INCREASED BY 1

108. Round off to the place indicated.

1,234,567 (millions)   _____

1,234,567 (hundreds)   _____

456,123 (thousands)   _____

456,123 (ten-thousands)   _____

1,000,000;   1,234,600;   456,000;
460,000

109. For quotient numbers that are not natural numbers we shall obtain an approximation by the same method of rounding off. But when such an approximation is obtained, we shall often express the result in simplest decimal form.

Thus, .43 rounded off to tenths shall be written .4,

and 1.57 rounded off to tenths shall be written _____ .

1.6

110. And   .627 rounded off to hundredths is .63

.5137 rounded off to hundredths is .51

.3456 rounded off to hundredths is

_____

4.872 rounded off to hundredths is

_____

.35;   4.87

111. While 41.7291 rounded off to thousandths is
41.729

5.0328 rounded off to thousandths is
5.033

.61479 rounded off to thousandths is

_____

42.655 rounded off to thousandths is

_____

.615;   42.655

112.   153.27   rounded off to ones is 153.

    47.831 rounded off to ones is _____

    625.9   rounded off to tens is 630.

    1471.66 rounded off to tens is _____

    7251.063 rounded off to hundreds is 7300.

    7251.063 rounded off to hundredths is

_____

> 48.;   1470.;   7251.06

113. To approximate a quotient number that is not a natural number we round off and express results in decimal form.

If we round off such a number to ones, tenths, hundredths, . . . , we simply delete all digits to the _____ of that place.

> RIGHT

114. Round off to the place indicated.

    773.4 (ones)   _____

    5.6913 (tenths)   _____

    .0727 (hundredths)   _____

    .71319 (thousandths)   _____

> 773.;   5.7;   .07;   .713

115. Round off to the place indicated.

    42.91 (hundredths)   42.91

    66.374 (tenths)   _____

    8.06 (ones)   _____

    .00073 (thousandths)   _____

    .0007 (hundredths)   _____

> 66.4;   8.;   .001;   .00

116. To approximate a quotient number that is not a natural number we round off and express results in decimal form.

If we round off such a number to tens, hundreds, thousands, . . . , we delete all digits to the right of the decimal point and replace with 0 all those to the left of the decimal point but to the _____ of the place rounded off to.

> RIGHT

117. Round off to the place indicated.

    54.97 (tens)   _____

    142.707 (hundreds)   _____

    284,717.3 (thousands)   _____

    69.49 (tens)   _____

> 50.;   100.;   285,000.;   70.

118. Round off to the place indicated.

    2745.0 (hundreds)   _____

    170.6 (tens)   _____

    271.00696 (ones)   _____

    5.0621 (tenths)   _____

> 2700.;   170.;   271.;   5.1

119. When a quotient number that is not a natural number is rounded off to tenths, we call the result a ONE-PLACE DECIMAL APPROXIMATION. Thus 5.3 is a _____-_____ decimal approximation of 5.283.

> ONE-PLACE

120. Find the one-place decimal approximations of:

14.305   14.3

8.87   _____

.62357   _____

74.510   _____

> 8.9; .6; 74.5

121. Find the one-place decimal approximations of:

39.45   _____

162.72   _____

56.88   _____

.3009   _____

> 39.5; 162.7; 56.9; .3

122. When a quotient number that is not a natural number is rounded off to hundredths, we call the result a TWO-PLACE DECIMAL AP-PROXIMATION. Thus 21.87 is a _____ _____ _____ approximation of 21.8739.

> TWO-PLACE DECIMAL

123. Find the two-place decimal approximations of:

3.6281   3.63

.553   _____

12.7044   _____

.296   _____

> .55; 12.70; .30

124. Find the two-place decimal approximations of:

47.222   _____

123.456   _____

.0777   _____

12.003   _____

> 47.22; 123.46; .08; 12.00

125. And .707 is a _____ - _____ _____ of .7071.

> THREE-PLACE DECIMAL APPROX-
> IMATION

126. Find the decimal approximation indicated.

21.77 (one-place)   _____

3.42416 (three-place)   _____

.000745 (four-place)   _____

19.195 (two-place)   _____

> 21.8; 3.424; .0007; 19.20

127. Find the decimal approximation called for

.99752 (four-place)   _____

16.0017 (two-place)   _____

9.775 (one-place)   _____

18.7625 (three-place)   _____

> .9975; 16.00; 9.8; 18.763

128. And when a quotient number that is not a natural number is rounded off to ones, we call the result a WHOLE NUMBER APPROXIMATION.

Thus 74. is a _____ _____ approximation of 73.905.

> WHOLE NUMBER

129. Find the whole number approximation of each of the following.

7.0139 _____
14.690 _____
70.3   _____
.821   _____

> 7.; 15.; 70.; 1.

130. Find the whole number approximation of each of the following.

129.3 _____
.791   _____
33.8   _____
.123   _____

> 129.; 1.; 34.; 0.

131. We have seen that the set of quotient numbers which have a decimal form is a subset of the set of all quotient numbers; not every quotient number has a decimal representation. Only those quotient numbers whose simplest forms do not have a prime factor other than _____ or _____ in the denominator can be expressed in decimal form.

> 2; 5 (either order)

132. Then

$$\frac{7}{16} = \frac{7}{1 \cdot 2 \cdot 2 \cdot 2 \cdot 2}$$

represents a quotient number which has a decimal form. The simplest way to obtain this form is by the division method. In simplest decimal form,

7/16 = _____

> .4375

133. But

$$\frac{1}{6} = \frac{1}{1 \cdot 2 \cdot 3}$$

represents a quotient number which does _not_ have a decimal form. Nevertheless, let us attempt to find a decimal form by the division method.

$$
\begin{array}{r}
.1666\cdots \\
6)\overline{1.0000\cdots} \\
\underline{6} \\
40 \\
\underline{36} \\
40 \\
\underline{36} \\
40 \\
\underline{36} \\
4\cdots
\end{array}
$$

It is clear that no matter how long the process is continued, there will always be a remainder of _____ .

> 4

134.
```
      .1666 ···
6)1.0000 ···
   6
  ──
   40
   36
  ──
    40
    36
   ──
     40
     36
    ──
      4 ···
```

If we attempt to use the division method to find a decimal form of 1/6, we find that the division problem never "ends" and we do not obtain a decimal representation. But we do obtain a kind of "perpetual" quotient

.1666 ···

which we shall call a REPEATING DECIMAL.

135. 1/6 represents a quotient number which does not have a decimal digit representation. However, we can write 1/6 as the _____ decimal .1666 ···.

136. 3/11 represents another quotient number which does not have a decimal form. But, using the division method, we obtain

```
        .272727 ···
11)3.000000 ···
   2 2
   ──
    80
    77
    ──
     30
     22
     ──
      80
      77
      ──
       30
       22
       ──
        80
        77
        ──
         3 ···
```

Hence, .272727 ··· represents 3/11 as a _____ _____.

137. 5/33 represents a quotient number which does not have a decimal form. Use the division method to express this number as a repeating decimal. _____

```
        .151515 ···
33)5.000000 ···
   3 3
   ──
   1 70
   1 65
   ────
     50
     33
     ──
      170
      165
      ───
       50
       33
       ──
        170
        165
        ───
          5 ···
```

138. Then .151515 ··· is the repeating decimal representation of 5/33. Use division to express each of the following as a repeating decimal.

2/3 _____

47/99 _____

7/12 _____

139. When using division to express a quotient number as a repeating decimal, it is important that the division be carried far enough to determine the result accurately. Find the repeating decimal which represents:

25/6 _____

61/750 _____

778/999 _____

140. Repeating decimals are not particularly useful, but they do enable us to easily approximate with a decimal expression quotient numbers which do not themselves have a decimal form.

The quotient number 1/6 can be represented by the repeating decimal .1666···, and we can obtain a decimal approximation of 1/6 from this by rounding off.

A one-place decimal approximation of 1/6 is _____.

A two-place decimal approximation of 1/6 is _____.

.2;   .17

141. 1/6 can be represented by .1666···.

A one-place decimal approximation of 1/6 is .2.

A two-place decimal approximation of 1/6 is .17.

A three-place decimal approximation of 1/6 is _____.

A four-place decimal approximation of 1/6 is _____.

.167;   .1667

142. The quotient number 3/11 can be represented by the repeating decimal .272727···, and we can obtain a decimal approximation of 3/11 by rounding off.

A one-place decimal approximation of 3/11 is _____.

A two-place decimal approximation of 3/11 is _____.

A three-place decimal approximation of 3/11 is _____.

A four-place decimal approximation of 3/11 is _____.

.3;   .27;   .273;   .2727

143. 5/33 can be represented by .151515···.

A three-place decimal approximation of 5/33 is _____.

2/3 can be represented by .666···

A two-place decimal approximation of 2/3 is _____.

47/99 can be represented by .474747···

A one-place decimal approximation of 47/99 is _____

7/12 can be represented by .58333···

A four-place decimal approximation of 7/12 is _____

.152;   .67;   .5;   .5833

144. 25/6 can be represented by 4.1666···

61/750 can be represented by .081333···

778/999 can be represented by .778778778···

Find a three-place decimal approximation of each.

_____ _____ _____

4.167;   .081;   .779

145. Find the three-place decimal approximation of

2/9 _____

22/7 _____

3⅓ = 10/3 _____

.222;   3.143;   3.333

146. We can even approximate quotient numbers which have a decimal representation. Thus

27/100 = .27

and a one-place decimal approximation of 27/100 is _____.

> .3

147. 27/100 = .27 in decimal digit form. However, .3 is the one-place decimal approximation of 27/100.

Find the decimal approximation called for.

5/8   _____ (two-place)

17/40   _____ (one-place)

217/1000   _____ (two-place)

> .63;   .4;   .22

148. Of course, if all that is required is a decimal approximation of a quotient number, there is no need to carry the division process more than one place beyond the last place required. Find the decimal approximations called for:

37/512 (three-place)   _____

22/7 (two-place)   _____

> .072;   3.14

149. In this chapter we have investigated the form quotient numbers can take. Every quotient number has a S_____ form, but not every quotient number has a _____ form.

> SIMPLEST;   DECIMAL

150. Only those quotient numbers which are natural numbers, or whose simplest form has a denominator whose only _____ factors are 2 and 5 have a decimal form. But for other quotient numbers, we can write a decimal _____ for the number.

> PRIME;   APPROXIMATION

151. When a quotient number has a decimal form, it can be easily found by _____ the _____ by the _____ of a representative fraction.

> DIVIDING;   NUMERATOR;   DENOMINATOR

152. And even when a quotient number does not have a decimal form, dividing the numerator by the denominator of a representative fraction yields a _____ _____ which can be rounded off to approximate the number.

> REPEATING DECIMAL

Problems A (Answers on page 512)

Write in simplest form.

Example: 1.28.

Answer: 1.28 = 128/100 = 32/25

1. .15

2. .06

3. .237

4. .225

5. .125

6. 3.9

7. 12.6

8. 1.005

9. .1875

10. 1.3125

Use the division method to find the simplest decimal form.

Example: 11/8. Answer:

```
         1.375
      8) 11.000
          8
          3 0
          2 4
            60
            56
            40
            40
```

11. 4/5

12. 7/2

13. 5/4

14. 3/25

15. 31/25

16. 3/8

17. 15/8

18. 1/20

19. 5/16

20. 7/625

Use the method of division to find a repeating decimal.

Example: 17/33. Answer:

```
          .5151 ...
      33) 17.0000 ...
          16 5
             50
             33
            170
            165
             50
             33
             17 ...
```

21. 7/12

22. 11/15

23. 19/24

24. 7/11

25. 6/7

Round off to the place indicated.

26. .63 (tenths)

27. .317 (hundredths)

28. 5.739 (tenths)

29. 21.059 (hundredths)

30. 21.059 (tenths)

31. 21.049 (tenths)

32. 17.385 (ones)

33. 8.3333 (thousandths)

34. 15.2727 (thousandths)

35. .00777 (thousandths)

36. .00777 (ten-thousandths)

37. .00777 (hundredths)

38. .00777 (tenths)

39. .75555 (thousandths)

40. .74999 (tenths)

Find a decimal approximation as indicated.

Example: 3/16 (two-place).

Answer:

```
          .187      .19
      16) 3.000
          1 6
          1 40
          1 28
            120
            112
```

41. 5/8 (one-place)

42. 2/3 (three-place)

43. 2/7 (four-place)

44. 22/7 (two-place)

45. 4/9 (three-place)

46. 10/11 (two-place)

47. $1\frac{3}{8}$ (one-place)

48. $17\frac{5}{9}$ (two-place)

49. 12/27 (two-place)

50. 83/84 (one-place)

Problems B

Write in simplest form.

1.	.83	6.	21.5
2.	.057	7.	1.375
3.	.75	8.	131.24
4.	.315	9.	5.55
5.	4.02	10.	.6875

Either find the decimal form or a repeating decimal.

11.	7/20	16.	9/16
12.	43/50	17.	9/11
13.	7/3	18.	19/22
14.	15/27	19.	11/37
15.	11/8	20.	3/7

Round off as indicated.

21. .1732 (two-place)

22. .00519 (ten-thousandths)

23. 15.73 (whole-number)

24. 275.21 (tens)

25. 5.1234 (three-place)

26. 91.055 (tenths)

27. 7.159 (two-place)

28. .195 (hundredths)

29. .7777 ··· (three-place)

30. .444 ··· (tenths)

31. .0135 (one-place)

32. 29.77 (tenths)

33. 100.499 (ones)

34. 1.0008 (two-place)

35. .373737 ··· (five-place)

Find a decimal approximation as indicated.

36. 3/8 (tenths)

37. 4/7 (two-place)

38. 9/13 (hundredths)

39. $3\frac{4}{21}$ (one-place)

40. 5/91 (one-place)

OPERATIONS WITH DECIMALS

1. Some, but not all, quotient numbers have a _____ digit representation.

   | DECIMAL |

2. Every quotient number that is also a _____ number has a decimal form.

   | NATURAL |

3. But, for quotient numbers that are not natural numbers, only those with a representative fraction whose _____ is a power of 10 have a decimal form.

   | DENOMINATOR |

4. We can call the set of quotient numbers that have a decimal form a _____ of the set of all quotient numbers.

   | SUBSET |

5. Every quotient number that has a decimal digit representation can be expressed in simplest decimal form. For natural numbers, the simplest decimal form is obtained by placing a _____ _____ to the right of the ones digit in the simplest form of the number.

   | DECIMAL POINT |

6. But for quotient numbers that are not natural numbers, their simplest decimal form is one that does not have a _____ as its right-hand digit.

   | 0 |

7. Which of the following are in simplest decimal form?

   a)   16.10

   b)   .0057

   c) 2370.

   d)   .70003 _____

   | b, c and d |

8. Which of the following are in simplest decimal form?

    a)   2.38

    b)   .62900

    c) 173.

    d) 179.0   _____

    a and c

9. Write each of the following in simplest decimal form.

    16.000 = _____

    .2790 = _____

    .0007 = _____

    5.220 = _____

    16.;   .279;   .0007;   5.22

10. Write each of the following in simplest decimal form.

    .050 = _____

    2.7700 = _____

    1492   = _____

    .6   = _____

    .05;   2.77;   1492.;   .6

11. As these examples illustrate, the simplest decimal form of a number can be obtained from any of its decimal representations. All that is necessary is the deletion of the digit _____ if it occurs to the right of the decimal point <u>and</u> to the right of every nonzero digit.

    0

12. We have seen that

    16.000 = 16.

That is, both symbols represent the same quotient number. Both are decimals although only 16. is in _____ decimal form.

    SIMPLEST

13. Similarly,

    2.7700 = 2.77

and so either symbol can be used to represent the quotient number whose simplest form is

_____ .

    277/100

14. Which of the following are true?

    a) 23.1   = 23.100

    b) 2.792 = 2.7920

    c) 16   = 16.000

    d) 3.5   = 3.50   _____

    ALL ARE TRUE

15. Which of the following are true?

    a)   41.6   =   41.600

    b) 120   = 120.000

    c)   .06   =   .060

    d) 17.1234 = 17.123   _____

    a, b, and c

16. Which of the following are true?

   a) $14.2 = 14.20$

   b) $14.2 = 14.200$

   c) $14.2 = 14.2000$

   d) $14.2 = 14.20000$ _____

ALL ARE TRUE

17. These examples show that an expression which is in simplest decimal form may also be written in other decimal forms. The digit 0 may be inserted on the right of the decimal point provided it is placed to the _____ of every nonzero digit.

RIGHT

18. Then $46.7 = 46.700$ since the two zero digits have been inserted to the right of the decimal point and to the right of every nonzero digit.

   But $46.7 \neq 46.070$, since one of the zero digits appears to the left of the digit _____.

7

19. And $657. = 657.0$ since the zero digit has been inserted to the right of the decimal point and to the right of every nonzero digit.

   But $657. \neq 6570.0$ since one of the zero digits has been inserted to the left of the

   _____ _____.

DECIMAL POINT

20. Insert either $=$ or $\neq$ between each pair of decimals so as to form a true statement.

45.6	_____	45.60
.570	_____	.5700
.61	_____	.614
923.	_____	92.30

$=$; $=$; $\neq$; $\neq$

21. Insert either $=$ or $\neq$ between each pair of decimals so as to form a true statement.

514.	_____	514.000
62.7	_____	62.07
.770	_____	.7700
.72	_____	0.720

$=$; $\neq$; $=$; $=$

22. $.72 = 0.720$

   The last example shows that it is also permissible to insert the digit 0 to the left of the decimal point provided it is placed to the _____ of every nonzero digit. (This will ordinarily not be done.)

LEFT

23. Then

   $$73.1 = 073.1$$

   since the digit 0 has been inserted to the left of the decimal point and to the left of every nonzero digit.

   But

   $$73.1 \neq 703.1$$

   since the zero digit has been inserted to the left of the decimal point and to the right of the digit _____.

7

24. And

.463 = 0.463

since the zero digit has been inserted to the left of the decimal point and to the left of every nonzero digit.

But

.463 ≠ 0.0463

since one of the zero digits has been inserted to the _____ of the decimal point and to the left of a nonzero digit.

25. Insert either = or ≠ between each pair of decimals so as to form a true statement.

5.7 _____ 5.700

.612 _____ 0.612

450. _____ 0450.0

.072 _____ 0.0072

26. We sometimes describe a decimal by a count of the number of digits to the right of the decimal point. Thus

17.32

is a TWO-PLACE decimal, while

167.30601

is a _____-PLACE decimal.

27. Classify each of the following decimals by the number of digits to the right of the decimal point.

17.01   two-place

.293   _____

45.6   _____

.7721   _____

28. Classify each decimal according to the number of places.

2935.01   _____

16.300   _____

.0010   _____

9.1077   _____

29. Express each of the following to the number of places indicated.

45   = 45.0   to one place

.82 = _____   to three places

7.8 = _____   to two places

5.3 = _____   to four places

30. Express each of the following to the number of places indicated.

320   = _____   to one place

.6927 = _____   to five places

15.000 = _____   to two places

1.773 = _____   to three places

31. Let a/b and c/d be any two fractions. Then each represents a quotient number. We have called the fractions equal and written

$$a/b = c/d$$

if _____ .

    ad = bc

32. $a/b = c/d$ if $ad = bc$

But in that case both fractions represent the _____ quotient number.

    SAME

33. We have said that the fraction a/b is less than the fraction c/d, and have written

$$a/b < c/d$$

if _____ .

    ad < bc

34. $a/b < c/d$ if $ad < bc$

In this case we say the quotient number represented by a/b is _____ the quotient number represented by c/d.

    LESS THAN

35. If a/b is neither equal to nor less than c/d, then we must have a/b _____ c/d, and we write

$$a/b \underline{\hspace{1cm}} c/d$$

Of course, then the quotient number represented by a/b is greater than the quotient number represented by c/d.

    GREATER THAN;   >

36. Thus, if two fractions are not equal, one must be less than the other. This fact concerning fractions makes it possible to say that the set of quotient numbers is _____ .

    ORDERED

37. But the set of quotient numbers which can be expressed in decimal form is a _____ of the set of all quotient numbers.

    SUBSET

38. Hence the set of all quotient numbers which have decimal representations must also be ordered. That is, if a and b represent quotient numbers in decimal form, then exactly one of the following statements is true:

$$a = b \qquad a \underline{\hspace{1cm}} b \qquad or \qquad a \underline{\hspace{1cm}} b$$

    <;   >;   (either order)

39. Consider the decimals .62 and .597. We could express each as a fraction and compare them by the method of common denominators.

$$.62 = 62/100 \qquad .597 = 597/1000$$

The LCM of 100 and 1000 is 1000, so we write each fraction with this denominator.

$$62/100 = \underline{\hspace{1cm}}/1000$$
$$597/1000 = 597/1000$$

    620

40. $.62 = 62/100 = 620/1000 \qquad .597 = 597/1000$

Then, since $597/1000 < 620/1000$, we know

$$.597 \underline{\hspace{1cm}} .62$$

    <

41.   .597 < .62

But there is an easier way to compare these decimals. First note that .597 is a _____-place decimal and .62 is a _____-place decimal.

42.   .597 is a three-place decimal.

.62 is a two-place decimal.

It is possible to express both numbers as three-place decimals. To do so we write

.62 = _____

43.   .597 is a three-place decimal.

.620 is also a three-place decimal.

If we now ignore the decimal points, we have the _____ numbers 597 and 620.

44. But

597 < 620

And we have already seen that

.597 < .62

or

.597 < .620

Notice that, except for the decimal points, the statements

597 < 620   and   .597 < .620

are similar.

45. In fact, quotient numbers in decimal form can always be compared in this way:

1) Each is expressed to the same number of decimal places, without rounding off either number.

2) Decimal points are ignored and the resulting natural numbers are compared.

3) If the quotient numbers are unequal, the natural numbers that are compared will also be unequal. And the smaller of the two natural numbers will have been derived from the _____ quotient number.

46. Thus, to compare 7.720 and 15.3, we can first write each in simplest decimal form:

7.72   and   15.3

and then

1) Express each as a two-place decimal:

7.72   and   _____

47. To compare 7.720 and 15.3, we can

1) Express each as a two-place decimal:

7.72   and   15.30

2) Ignore decimal points and compare the resulting natural numbers:

772   and   1530

Of course 772 _____ 1530.

48. To compare 7.720 and 15.3 we can

   1) Express each as a two-place decimal:

       7.72   and   15.30

   2) Compare the natural numbers that result when the decimal points are ignored:

       772 < 1530

   3) And, finally, compare the original numbers:

       7.720 _____ 15.3

49. Between each of the following pairs of decimals, insert one of the symbols <, =, >, so as to form a true statement.

   62.77   >   49.03

   .789   _____   .777

   5.0038   _____   5.2

   11.86   _____   8.10034

>;   <;   >

50. Between each of the following pairs of decimals, insert one of the symbols <, =, >, so as to form a true statement.

   147.6   _____   147.0

   62.1   _____   62.1000

   .7001   _____   .7010

   .333   _____   .3333

>;   =;   <;   <

51. The primary reason for introducing the decimal digit representation of quotient numbers is the ease with which computations can be carried out when numbers are in decimal form. We shall examine each of the operations, beginning with addition.

52. To add two quotient numbers in decimal form we

   1) Express each term to the same number of decimal places, without rounding off either number.

   2) Ignore the decimal points and add the numbers as if they were natural numbers in simplest form.

   3) Insert the decimal point in the result so that the sum also has the same number of decimal places as do the terms.

53. Thus, to add 6.042 and 17.3, we can:

   1) Write 17.3 = _____

17.300

54. To add 6.042 and 17.3, we can:

   1) Write 17.3 = 17.300

   2) Find the sum of 6042 and 17300:

      6042 + 17300 = _____

23342

55. To add 6.042 and 17.3 we can:

   1) Write 17.3 = 17.300

   2) Find the sum of 6042 and 17300:

      6042 + 17300 = 23342

   3) Insert a decimal point in the expression 23342 so it will be a three-place decimal:

      _____

23.342

56. Hence $6.042 + 17.3 = 23.342$

It is interesting to arrange the numbers vertically:

$$\begin{array}{r} 6.042 \\ 17.300 \\ \hline 23.342 \end{array}$$

Note that the digits in each place are written under one another and that in every number the _____ _____ locates the ones place.

DECIMAL POINT

57. Let us next find $29.634 + 7.7581$

First we write $29.634 = 29.6340$.

Then we add 296340 and 77581.

Finally, we insert a decimal point in the result so it will be a four-place decimal.

The sum is _____.

37.3921

58. $29.634 + 7.7581 = 37.3921$

Again, note that when arranged vertically,

$$\begin{array}{r} 29.6340 \\ 7.7581 \\ \hline 37.3921 \end{array}$$

the sum can be determined by adding the digits in each place. The "carrying" of a digit from one column to the next is done without regard to the decimal point. Let us verify that this procedure yields the correct result.

59. $29.634 + 7.7581$

We shall find the sum of these quotient numbers by expressing the terms as fractions.

$29.634 = 29634/1000$

$7.7581 = $ _____

77581/10000

60. $$29.634 + 7.7581 = \frac{29634}{1000} + \frac{77581}{10000}$$

We shall not simplify these fractions but shall use the method of common denominators to find their sum.

The LCM of 1000 and 10000 is _____, and so we change the fractions so that both have that number for their

_____.

10000;   DENOMINATOR

61. $$29.634 + 7.7581 = \frac{29634}{1000} + \frac{77581}{10000}$$
$$= \frac{296340}{10000} + \frac{77581}{10000}$$
$$= \underline{\hspace{2cm}},$$

when added.

373921/10000

62. $29.634 + 7.7581 = 373921/10000$

But, changing the sum to decimal form, we get

$373921/10000 = 37.3921$

That is, of course, precisely what we had already obtained.

By adding decimal forms, find

$12.73 + 4.588 = $ _____

$$\begin{array}{r} 12.730 \\ 4.588 \\ \hline 17.318 \end{array}$$

63. When three or more numbers are to be added, we have seen that they can be combined in any order, two at a time. But to find the sum of 7.299, 16.5, .012, and .673 it is better to re-write them vertically, after expressing each as a three-place decimal. Find the sum:

$$\begin{array}{r} 7.299 \\ 16.500 \\ .012 \\ .673 \\ \hline \end{array}$$

24.484

64. Indeed, in adding numbers in decimal form, any number of terms can be combined in this way. All that is necessary is that the digits in any place are added to the other digits in that place. And this is most simply accomplished by aligning the _____

_____ .

DECIMAL POINTS

65. Find the sum:

$$6.2915 + 451.3 + 72 + .0016 + 7.7$$

_____

$$\begin{array}{r} 6.2915 \\ 451.3000 \\ 72.0000 \\ .0016 \\ 7.7000 \\ \hline 537.2931 \end{array}$$

66. Of course, the digit 0 need not actually be written in every case. If a number is expressed in simplest decimal form, zeros inserted so that each term will have the same number of decimal places need not be written. Find the sum:

$$40.26 + 607 + .0723 + 5.9 \quad \rule{2cm}{0.4pt}$$

$$\begin{array}{r} 40.26 \\ 607. \\ .0723 \\ 5.9 \\ \hline 653.2323 \end{array}$$

67. Note that the sum of two decimals is also a decimal. Hence, the set of all quotient numbers that can be represented in decimal form is _____ with respect to the operation of addition.

CLOSED

68. To subtract one quotient number in decimal form from another, we proceed much as in addition. We:

1) Express the subtrahend and the minuend to the same number of decimal places.

2) Ignore the decimal points and subtract the numbers as if they were natural numbers in simplest form.

3) Insert the decimal point in the result so that the difference also has the same number of decimal places.

69. Thus, to subtract 45.31 from 59.876, we can

1) Write 45.31 = _____

45.310

70. To subtract 45.31 from 59.876, we can:

1) Write 45.31 = 45.310

2) Find the difference of 59876 and 45310:

59876 − 45310 = _____

14566

71. To subtract 45.31 from 59.876, we can:

1) Write 45.31 = 45.310

2) Find the difference of 59876 and 45310:

59876 − 45310 = 14566

3) Insert a decimal point in the expression 14566 so that it will be a three-place decimal: _____

14.566

72. Hence

59.876 − 45.31 = 14.566

It is again interesting to arrange the numbers vertically,

59.876
45.310
14.566

and note that aligning the _____
_____ assures that the digits in each place are under one another.

DECIMAL POINTS

73. Let us next find 341.62 − 77.593

First we write 341.62 = _____

Then we subtract 341620 − 77593.

Finally, we insert a decimal point in the result so it will be a _____-place decimal.

The difference is _____.

341.620;   THREE;   264.027

74. 341.62 − 77.593 = 264.027

Again, we arrange the numbers vertically.

341.620
77.593
264.027

Note that the difference can be determined by subtracting digits in each place and that "borrowing" from one column to another is done as in subtraction of natural numbers.

75. Let us verify that 341.62 − 77.593 = 264.027

Changing to fractions,

341.62 = 34162/100

77.593 = 77593/1000

The LCM of the denominators is 1000, so the first fraction is changed to one with this denominator.

$34162/100 = $ _____ $/1000$

341620

76. $341.62 - 77.593 = \dfrac{341620}{1000} - \dfrac{77593}{1000}$

= _____, by the method of common denominators.

264027/1000

77. $341.62 - 77.593 = \dfrac{341620}{1000} - \dfrac{77593}{1000} = \dfrac{264027}{1000}$

and changing to a decimal gives

264027/1000 = 264.027

thus verifying the result.

By subtracting decimal forms, find

22.067 − 5.4732 = _____

22.0670
5.4732
16.5938

78. In subtraction, it is not considered a good idea to avoid writing the digit 0. In the last problem, if this were done, we would have

$$\begin{array}{r} 22.067 \\ \underline{5.4732} \end{array}$$

which leaves some doubt as to what the digit 2 is to be subtracted from. Find

7.152 − .66673 = _____

$$\begin{array}{r} 7.15200 \\ \underline{.66673} \\ 6.48527 \end{array}$$

79. Can you find

7.96327 − 16.1? _____

NO

80. The problem 7.96327 − 16.1 has no solution because

7.96327 _____ 16.1

<

81. As we have seen, the set of quotient numbers is not closed with respect to subtraction. In fact, subtraction of quotient numbers only is possible when the subtrahend is _____ than or _____ to the minuend.

LESS;   EQUAL

82. The set of quotient numbers that have a decimal representation is a subset of the set of quotient numbers. In this subset, too, we see that subtraction is not _____.

CLOSED

83. Find the following sum:

4.931 + .767 + .012 = _____

5.710

84. 4.931 + .767 + .012 = 5.710

Notice that each of the terms is a three-place decimal and each is in simplest decimal form. But, in simplest decimal form, the sum is a _____-place decimal. Of course, it is correct to write the sum as 5.710, but the simplest decimal form is _____.

TWO;   5.71

85. Use a vertical arrangement to find the following sums and differences in simplest decimal form:

.7935 + .621 = _____
3.1416 − .142 = _____
50 − 37.50 = _____
3 − 2.178 = _____

1.4145;   2.9996;   12.5;   .822

86. To multiply two quotient numbers in decimal form we:

1) Ignore the decimal points and multiply the numbers as if they were natural numbers in simplest form.

2) Insert the decimal point in the result so that the product has a number of decimal places equal to the sum of the number of places in each factor.

87. Thus, to multiply 6.4 and .73 we can

1) Find the product of 64 and 73.

(64)(73) = _____

4672

88. To multiply 6.4 and .73 we can:

1) Find the product of 64 and 73.

$$(64)(73) = 4672$$

2) 6.4 is a one-place decimal and .73 is a two-place decimal. Hence we insert a decimal point in 4672 so as to form a three-place decimal: _____

> 4.672

89. Therefore,

$$(6.4)(.73) = 4.672$$

To find the product $(653.1)(3.27)$ we first find

$$(6531)(327) = \underline{\hspace{2cm}}$$

Then, since 653.1 is a one-place decimal and 3.27 is a two-place decimal, we insert a decimal point so the product will be a _____-place decimal.

> 2135637;   THREE

90. Hence

$$(653.1)(3.27) = \underline{\hspace{2cm}}$$

We can again verify this result by changing to fractional representatives of these numbers.

> 2135.637

91. $653.1 = 6531/10$ and $3.27 = 327/100$
Then

$$(653.1)(3.27) = \frac{6531}{10} \cdot \frac{327}{100} = \frac{(6531)(327)}{(10)(100)}$$
$$= \underline{\hspace{2cm}}$$

> 2135637/1000

92. But

$$2135637/1000 = 2135.637$$

Hence we have shown that, for this example, our procedure yields the correct result:

$$(653.1)(3.27) = 2135.637$$

Find the following product by multiplying decimal forms.

$$(.00735)(49) = \underline{\hspace{2cm}}$$

> .36015

93. $(.00735)(49) = .36015$

Note that .00735 is a five-place decimal. In simplest decimal form, 49. is a "zero-place" decimal. Hence the product must be a five-place decimal.

Find the following product:

$$(.43)(.01278) = \underline{\hspace{2cm}}$$

> .0054954

94. $(.43)(.01278) = .0054954$

Note that .43 is a two-place decimal and .01278 is a five-place decimal. Hence the product must be a seven-place decimal. But $(43)(1278) = 54954$, a five-digit number. Therefore it is necessary to insert two digits 0 on the left as _____ _____ so that we can write the product as a seven-place decimal.

> PLACE HOLDERS

95. Find the following product in simplest decimal form:

$$(5.6)(.135) = \underline{\hspace{2cm}}$$

> .756

96. (5.6)(.135) = .756

This is not an exception to our rule for multiplying decimals. The product obtained by that rule is .7560, but the result was to be found in simplest decimal form.

Find the following products in simplest decimal form:

(4.9)(.625) = _____

(2.254)(12) = _____

(.378)(2.5) = _____

3.0625;   27.048;   .945

97. Note that the product of two decimals is also a decimal. Then the set of all quotient numbers that can be represented in decimal form is _____ with respect to the operation of multiplication.

CLOSED

98. Of course, when one of the factors is a power of 10, we already know how to find the product. Each digit in the other factor is moved to the _____ as many places as the _____ in the power of 10.

LEFT;   EXPONENT

99. Thus, in simplest decimal form:

(49.7)(100) = (49.7)(10^2)   = 4970.

(.7192)(100) = (.7192)(10^2) = _____

(16.821)(10) = (16.821)(10^1) = _____

(.0583)(1000) = (.0583)(10^3) = _____

71.92;   168.21;   58.3

100. Consider the decimal 3.092. If this number is multiplied by 10^3, the result, 3092., is a natural number. No smaller power of 10 than the third will accomplish this.

In each of the following, what is the smallest power of 10 the given number can be multiplied by to yield a product which is a natural number?

.707   third

684.3   _____

3.14   _____

.002   _____

FIRST;   SECOND;   THIRD

101. In each of the following, what is the smallest power of 10 the given number can be multiplied by to yield a product which is a natural number?

55.07   _____

.1234   _____

44.4   _____

SECOND;   FOURTH;   FIRST

102. In fact, if a quotient number is expressed in simplest decimal form, the smallest power of 10 it can be multiplied by to yield a natural number is one in which the _____ equals the number of digits to the _____ of the decimal point.

EXPONENT;   RIGHT

103. To divide one quotient number in decimal form by another we:

    1) Determine the smallest power of 10 the divisor must be multiplied by to yield a natural number.

    2) Multiply both the dividend and the divisor by this power of 10 and note the number of decimal places in the modified dividend.

    3) Ignore the decimal points and divide the dividend by the divisor as if they were natural numbers in simplest form.

    4) Insert the decimal point in the result so that the quotient will have the same number of decimal places as the modified dividend.

104. Thus, to divide .42 by 1.4 we can:

    1) Determine the smallest power of 10 that 1.4 must be multiplied by to yield a natural number. It is _____.

10^1

105. To divide .42 by 1.4 we can:

    1) Determine the smallest power of 10 that 1.4 must be multiplied by to yield a natural number: 10^1.

    2) Multiply .42 and 1.4 by 10^1.

       $.42 \cdot 10^1 = 4.2$ $1.4 \cdot 10^1 = 14$

    and note that 4.2 is a _____-place decimal.

ONE

106. To divide .42 by 1.4 we can:

    1) Determine the smallest power of 10 that 1.4 must be multiplied by to yield a natural number: 10^1.

    2) Multiply

       $.42 \cdot 10^1 = 4.2$ $1.4 \cdot 10^1 = 14$

    and note that 4.2 is a one-place decimal.

    3) Divide 42 by 14.

       $42 \div 14 =$ _____

3

107. To divide .42 by 1.4 we can:

    1) Determine the smallest power of 10 that 1.4 must be multiplied by to yield a natural number: 10^1.

    2) Multiply

       $.42 \cdot 10^1 = 4.2$ $1.4 \cdot 10^1 = 14$

    and note that 4.2 is a one-place decimal.

    3) Divide 42 by 14.

       $42 \div 14 = 3$

    4) Insert a decimal point in the result, 3, so it will be a one-place decimal:

    _____

.3

108. Hence .42 ÷ 1.4 = .3

It is interesting to observe the four steps when a different notation for division is used.

$$1.4)\overline{.42}$$

is a statement of the original problem.

$$14.)\overline{4.2}$$

shows the dividend and divisor each multiplied by 10^1.

$$\begin{array}{r} 3 \\ 14)\overline{42} \\ \underline{42} \end{array}$$

shows the division of natural numbers carried out.

$$\begin{array}{r} .3 \\ 14)\overline{4.2} \\ \underline{4\ 2} \end{array}$$

is the result of the previous step in which decimal points have been inserted.

Note that the decimal point in the quotient is just above that in the modified _____.

109. Let us next find 2.6112 ÷ 8.16.

We first note that $8.16 \cdot 10^2 = 816$.

We then multiply $2.6112 \cdot 10^2 = 261.12$ and note that the result is a two-place decimal.

We divide 26112 by 816. The result is 32.

Finally, we insert a decimal point in the result so that it will be a two-place decimal.

Then

$$2.6112 ÷ 8.16 = \underline{\hspace{2cm}}$$

110. 2.6112 ÷ 8.16 = .32

Again, by using a different notation for division the steps become mechanical.

$$8.16)\overline{2.6112} \qquad 816.)\overline{261.12} \qquad \begin{array}{r} .32 \\ 816.)\overline{261.12} \\ \underline{244\ 8} \\ 16\ 32 \\ \underline{16\ 32} \end{array}$$

All we need to do is "move" the decimal point in the divisor and in the dividend and write it in the _____ above its new location in the dividend.

111. 2.6112 ÷ 8.16 = .32

We can verify this result by expressing the original quotient numbers as fractions.

2.6112 = 26112/10000

8.16 = _____

112. $$2.6112 ÷ 8.16 = \frac{26112}{10000} ÷ \frac{816}{100} = \frac{(26112)(100)}{(10000)(816)}$$

by the cross product rule for division.

But

10000 = (100)(100)

and so we can write

$$2.6112 ÷ 8.16 = \frac{(26112)(100)}{(10000)(816)} = \frac{(26112)(100)}{(100)(100)(816)}$$

Upon cancelling the common factor 100, we obtain _____

113. Hence

$$2.6112 \div 8.16 = \frac{26112}{(100)(816)}$$

Now

$$\frac{26112}{(100)(816)} = \frac{1}{100} \cdot \frac{26112}{816} = \frac{26112}{816} \cdot \frac{1}{100}$$

We can find 26112/816 by division:

26112/816 = _____

> **32**

114.
$$2.6112 \div 8.16 = \frac{26112}{816} \cdot \frac{1}{100} = 32 \cdot \frac{1}{100}$$

$$= 32 \div 100$$

And, moving digits, we obtain

$$2.6112 \div 8.16 = .32$$

Hence we have shown, for this example, that our procedure yields the correct result.

Find the following quotient by dividing decimal forms.

.04144 ÷ .07 = _____

> $$\begin{array}{r} .592 \\ .07)\overline{.04144} \qquad 07.)\overline{04.144} \\ 3\ 5 \\ \hline 64 \\ 63 \\ \hline 14 \\ 14 \\ \hline \end{array}$$

115.   .04144 ÷ .07 = .592

Find the following quotient:

.3381 ÷ 14.7 = _____

> **.023**

116.   .3381 ÷ 14.7 = .023

Note that the digit 0 has been inserted in the quotient as a _____
so that it will be a three-place decimal.

> **PLACE HOLDER**

117. Now let us return to the general problem of division of quotient numbers. We have seen that the quotient of two fractions can be found by several methods. One of these is a cross product method for division.

If a/b and c/d are fractions, then

$$\frac{a}{b} \div \frac{c}{d} = \text{\underline{\hspace{2cm}}}$$

> **ad/bc**

118. To find the quotient of two quotient numbers, we divide their representative fractions. Since the quotient of two fractions is also a fraction, we see that the set of all quotient numbers is _____ with respect to the operation of division.

> **CLOSED**

119. The set of quotient numbers that have a decimal representation is a subset of the set of all quotient numbers. Let us show that this subset is _not_ closed with respect to division.

Consider the quotient numbers represented by .5 and .9. The simplest forms of these numbers are

.5 = _____   .9 = _____

> **1/2;   9/10**

120. Let us find the quotient of .5 and .9.

$$.5 \div .9 = \frac{1}{2} \div \frac{9}{10} = \frac{1 \cdot 10}{2 \cdot 9} = \underline{\hspace{2cm}},$$

in simplest form.

> 5/9

121. But 5/9 has the prime factor 3 in its denominator and, hence, does not have a _____ representation.

> DECIMAL

122. This example shows that the quotient of two numbers in decimal form need not have a decimal form. Indeed, the case for decimal forms of quotient numbers is rather like that of natural numbers. Dividing the decimal representation of one quotient number by that of another usually results in a quotient number which has no _____ form.

> DECIMAL

123. Of course, even if a quotient number has no decimal form, it can be represented by a repeating decimal.

Thus, we can write

$$.5 \div .9 = \frac{5}{9}$$

as a repeating decimal _____ and from this form any desired decimal approximation.

> .555 ⋯

124. Since the quotient of two decimals is usually a repeating decimal, we often seek an approximation for the result.

Find a two-place decimal approximation for the quotient

$$\frac{.4773}{.062} \qquad \underline{\hspace{2cm}}$$

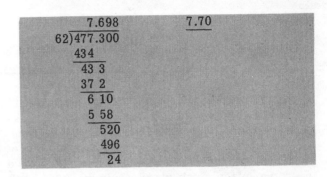

125. Even when the quotient has a decimal form, we may seek only an approximation for the result.

Find a three-place decimal approximation for

$$\frac{.140857}{7.9} \qquad \underline{\hspace{2cm}}$$

```
       .0178           .018
    79)1.40857
       79
       618
       553
        655
        632
         23
```

126. The primary reason for introducing decimals is the ease with which computations can be carried out with numbers in this form. Yet for one operation, division, the computation cannot usually be done in decimal form unless only an approximate result is acceptable. And, since many quotient numbers do not even have decimal representations at all, there may be some question as to how useful decimals are.

127. Indeed, decimals are widely used in computations simply because most numbers in a problem are usually only approximations. Thus, the fact that one can only write approximate decimal forms for most quotient numbers, or that division problems have only approximate results, causes no difficulty. And, for the most part, we are interested in results that are also only

_____.

APPROXIMATIONS

128. Thus if we read that a can contains 46 ounces of juice, and are told it will serve 8 persons, then we can find an approximate number of ounces per serving by division. In fact, a one-place decimal approximation of each serving is _____ ounces.

5.8

129. Or if we are told that the cost of pouring concrete is 26.40 dollars a "yard" and we estimate that 12.4 "yards" will be required, then we can find an approximate number of dollars total cost by multiplication. In fact, the whole number approximation of this cost is _____ dollars.

327

130. Of course, when only approximate numbers are used, or approximate results are desired, the degree of approximation must be indicated or clearly understood. A number of conventions are used for this purpose, but we shall be specific whenever an approximate result is called for.

Find a two-place decimal approximation for the sum:

162.93 + 58.773 + 41.2 + 6.60

_____

269.50

131. Find a one-place decimal approximation for the difference:

49.7 − 26.98 _____

22.7

132. Find a four-place decimal approximation for the product:

(.0062)(5.91) _____

.0366

133. Find a three-place decimal approximation for the quotient:

$\dfrac{.0162}{.047}$ _____

.345

Chapter 24

Problems A (Answers on page 513)

Find the simplest decimal form.

1. (3.42) + (41.6)
2. (15.9) + (.345)
3. (.0041) + (7.639)
4. (14.96) − (8.47)
5. (9.36) − (.8)
6. (15.2) − (3.74)
7. (84.4) − (76.913)
8. (12) + (.316)
9. (12) − (.316)
10. (3.6)(8.4)
11. (15.1)(8.63)
12. (.91)(.84)
13. (.36)(.2)
14. (.051)(.016)
15. (9)(.42)
16. (3.41) + (82.7) + (.482)
17. (.041) + (14) + (1.46)
18. (19.3) + (.113) + (5.2) + (9.44)
19. (12.6) − (8.9) + (1.75)
20. (83.14) − (.86) − (1.3)

Find a two-place decimal approximation.

21. (.36)(4.57)
22. (1.428) − (.87)
23. (.07)(.42)
24. (7.81) ÷ 11
25. (4.213) ÷ 7.8
26. (.148) ÷ (.23)
27. (.087) ÷ (17.4)
28. (15.7) ÷ (.07)
29. (1.738) + (.05) + (63.4)
30. 1.63/5.8

Problems B

Find the simplest decimal form.

1. (1.73) + (.5)
2. (.375) + (5.71)
3. (15.12) + (7.03)
4. (48) + (9.03)
5. (3.47) − (.02)
6. (.07) − (.043)
7. (.7) − (.043)
8. (12) − (.35)
9. (.12) − (.035)
10. (41.3)(1.8)
11. (2.6)(40.4)
12. (.61)(50.3)
13. (.048)(.23)
14. (.081)(.007)
15. (48)(9.03)
16. 4.678 + 34.26 + 4.57248
17. 27.43 + 6.847 + 135 + 26.1
18. .38 − .002 − .049
19. 6 − .06 + .60
20. .0013 + .042 − .009

Find a one-place decimal approximation.

21. (.85)(3.46)
22. (16.07) ÷ (2.9)
23. (3.674) ÷ (.589)
24. (13.7) ÷ (20.9)
25. (2.67)(.067)
26. (47.21) ÷ (.836)
27. (2.056) ÷ (36.12)
28. (3.197) + (51.7) − (5.8177)
29. (.816) − (.07) − (.3)
30. .12/2.47

PERCENT

1. A quotient number is a property shared by _____ fractions.

> **EQUAL**

2. Every quotient number can be expressed in simplest form.

   For a quotient number that is also a natural number, its simplest form is one of the symbols

   _____, _____, _____, . . .

   > **1;   2;   3**

3. Every quotient number can be expressed in simplest form.

   For a quotient number that is not a natural number, its simplest form is a fraction whose numerator and denominator are _____ _____.

   > **RELATIVELY PRIME**

4. Some, but not all, quotient numbers also have a decimal form.

   Every quotient number that is also a natural number has a decimal representation. It can be obtained from the simplest form of the number by inserting a decimal point to the right of the _____ digit.

   > **ONES**

5. Thus, in simplest decimal form,

   142 = _____

   5,280 = _____

   216,000 = _____

   7 = _____

   > **142.;   5,280.;   216,000.;   7.**

6. Some, but not all, quotient numbers also have a decimal form.

   A quotient number that is not a natural number has a decimal representation only if the denominator in its simplest form does not contain a prime factor other than _____ or _____.

   > **2;   5   (either order)**

7. When a quotient number is represented by a fraction whose denominator is a power of 10, its simplest decimal form is easily obtained. The digits in the _____ of the fraction are written in order and the decimal point is placed so that the right-hand digit appears in a place which "agrees" with the _____ of the fraction.

NUMERATOR;   DENOMINATOR

8. Then, in simplest decimal form,

7/10 = _____

53/100 = _____

39/1000 = _____

127/100 = _____

.7;   .53;   .039;   1.27

9. But when a quotient number that has a decimal representation is expressed as a fraction whose denominator is not a power of 10, its decimal form can be more easily obtained by dividing the _____ of the fraction by the _____.

NUMERATOR;   DENOMINATOR

10. Use division to change each of the following to simplest decimal form:

5/16 = _____

64/25 = _____

7/125 = _____

.3125;   2.56;   .056

11. If a quotient number does not have a decimal representation, the denominator of its simplest form has a prime factor other than 2 or 5.

Nevertheless, if the numerator of a representative fraction is divided by the denominator, we obtain an expression for the quotient number as a _____ decimal.

REPEATING

12. Use division to express each of the following as a repeating decimal.

2/3 = _____

47/99 = _____

7/12 = _____

.666...;   .474747...;   .58333...

13. Sometimes we seek only a decimal approximation of a quotient number. Whether the quotient number has a decimal representation or not, such an approximation can always be obtained by _____ off.

ROUNDING

14. The following fractions represent quotient numbers that have decimal representations. Use division to find their simplest decimal forms and round off to find the required approximation.

277/625 (three-place) _____

158147/5000 (two-place) _____

277/625 = .4432 → .443;
158147/5000 = 31.6294 → 31.63

15. The following fractions represent quotient numbers that do <u>not</u> have decimal representations. Use divi<u>sion</u> to express them as repeating decimals and round off to obtain the required decimal approximation.

7/15 (three-place) _____

31/24 (two-place) _____

.4666 . . . → .467;   1.291666 . . . → 1.29

16. When a quotient number is expressed in decimal form, a fractional representative is easily obtained. The digits in the decimal form become the _____ of the fraction and a power of 10 which "agrees" with the place of the right-hand digit becomes the _____ of the fraction.

NUMERATOR;   DENOMINATOR

17. Express each of the following as a fraction.

.73   = _____

6.171 = _____

42.9   = _____

.0313 = _____

73/100;   6171/1000;   429/10;
313/10000

18. When a quotient number is expressed in decimal form, its simplest form can be obtained by first finding a fractional representative and then reducing.

Express each of the following in simplest form.

.405 = _____

.72   = _____

1.6   = _____

6.010 = _____

81/200;   18/25;   8/5;   601/100

19. Recall that "percent," or the symbol "%," means

"_____ by 100"

DIVIDED

20. Thus, 7% means 7 ÷ 100, which we can write, in simplest form, as 7/100.

And 47% means 47 ÷ 100, which we can write, in simplest form, as _____.

47/100

21. Express each of the following "percents" in simplest form.

86% = _____

133% = _____

400% = _____

1% = _____

43/50;   133/100;   4;   1/100

22. And $3\frac{1}{2}\%$ means $3\frac{1}{2} \div 100$ which we can write as

$\frac{3\frac{1}{2}}{100}$ or, in simplest form, $\frac{7}{200}$.

Also, 7/10% means $\frac{7}{10} \div 100$ which we can write as $\frac{7/10}{100}$ or, in simplest form,

_____.

7/1000

23. Express each of the following "percents" in simplest form.

$3/4\% =$ _____

$2/3\% =$ _____

$5\frac{1}{4}\% =$ _____

$4\frac{4}{5}\% =$ _____

> 3/400;   2/300;   21/400;   6/125

24. It is also possible to begin with the simplest form of a quotient number and express it as "percent."

Thus

$$5 = 500/100 = 500 \div 100 = 500\%$$

and

$$13 = 1300/100 = 1300 \div 100 = \underline{\hspace{2cm}}\%.$$

> 1300

25. Also

$$\frac{7}{8} = \frac{7 \cdot \frac{100}{8}}{8 \cdot \frac{100}{8}} = \frac{700/8}{100} = \frac{87\frac{1}{2}}{100} = 87\frac{1}{2}\%$$

and

$$\frac{13}{4} = \frac{13 \cdot \frac{100}{4}}{4 \cdot \frac{100}{4}} = \frac{1300/4}{100} = \frac{325}{100} = \underline{\hspace{1.5cm}}\%$$

> 325

26. But expressions involving percent are most easily handled when quotient numbers are expressed in decimal forms.

Thus, 15.7% means $15.7 \div 100$ which we can write as $15.7/10^2$, and the quotient is easily obtained by moving digits:

$$15.7\% = .157$$

And 86.15% means $86.15 \div 100$ which can be written as $86.15/10^2$. Moving digits, we obtain $86.15\% = \underline{\hspace{2cm}}$.

> .8615

27. Express each of the following in simplest decimal form.

$83.3\% =$ _____

$1.67\% =$ _____

$102.9\% =$ _____

$4.\% =$ _____

> .833;   .0167;   1.029;   .04

28. Express each of the following in simplest decimal form.

$16.4\% =$ _____

$.56\% =$ _____

$88\% =$ _____

$164.5\% =$ _____

> .164;   .0056;   .88;   1.645

29. Thus, when an expression in decimal form is followed by a percent symbol, its simplest decimal form can be obtained by deleting the percent symbol and moving each digit _____ places to the _____.

> TWO;   RIGHT

30. Express in simplest decimal form.

$$4.85\% = \underline{\hspace{3cm}}$$
$$99.44\% = \underline{\hspace{3cm}}$$
$$121.2\% = \underline{\hspace{3cm}}$$
$$200\% = \underline{\hspace{3cm}}$$

.0485;   .9944;   1.212;   2.

31. And for numbers that are not in decimal form, we may first express them as decimals. Thus, in simplest decimal form,

$$44\tfrac{1}{2}\% = 44.5\% = \underline{\hspace{3cm}}$$
$$19/20\% = .95\% = \underline{\hspace{3cm}}$$
$$4\tfrac{4}{5}\% = 4.8\% = \underline{\hspace{3cm}}$$
$$455/4\% = 113.75\% = \underline{\hspace{3cm}}$$

.445;   .0095;   .048;   1.1375

32. Find each of the following in simplest decimal form.

$$37\tfrac{1}{2}\% = 37.5\% = \underline{\hspace{3cm}}$$
$$5\tfrac{3}{4}\% = \underline{\hspace{3cm}}$$
$$125\tfrac{2}{5}\% = \underline{\hspace{3cm}}$$
$$99\tfrac{44}{100}\% = \underline{\hspace{3cm}}$$

.375;   .0575;   1.254;   .9944

33. We can begin with a decimal form of a quotient number and express it as a "percent" by simply reversing the procedure. Thus

$$1.42 = 142.\%$$
$$.075 = 7.5\%$$
$$.12 = \underline{\hspace{2cm}}\%$$
$$.808 = \underline{\hspace{2cm}}\%$$

12;   80.8

34. Express each of the following as a "percent."

$$.078 = \underline{\hspace{2.5cm}}\%$$
$$5.3 = \underline{\hspace{2.5cm}}\%$$
$$.0016 = \underline{\hspace{2.5cm}}\%$$
$$21.3 = \underline{\hspace{2.5cm}}\%$$

7.8;   530.;   .16;   2130.

35. Hence to express a quotient number in decimal form as a "percent" we merely move each digit _____ places to the _____ and annex a percent symbol.

TWO;   LEFT

36. Express each of the following as a "percent."

$$.0493 = \underline{\hspace{3cm}}$$
$$.88 = \underline{\hspace{3cm}}$$
$$1.05 = \underline{\hspace{3cm}}$$
$$.101 = \underline{\hspace{3cm}}$$

4.93%;   88.%;   105.%;   10.1%

37. Indeed, to change a fraction or mixed number representation to a "percent," it is usually easier to first express the quotient number in decimal form. This can then be changed to a "percent" by moving digits.

Thus,

$$3/8 = .375 = 37.5\%$$

and

$$2\tfrac{7}{20} = 2.35 = \underline{\hspace{3cm}}\%$$

235.

38. First change each fraction or mixed number expression to decimal form, and then write as a "percent."

1/2	= _____	= _____	%
6¼	= _____	= _____	%
5/2	= _____	= _____	%
3/125	= _____	= _____	%

> 1/2   = .5 = 50.%
> 6¼   = 6.25 = 625.%
> 5/2   = 2.5 = 250.%
> 3/125 = .024 = 2.4%

39. But when a fraction or mixed number represents a quotient number that has no decimal form, we cannot use this procedure. In such cases we shall often seek an approximate result.

Thus 2/3 can be approximated by the three-place decimal .667, and so 2/3 is approximately 66.7%.

Similarly, 5/6 can be approximated by the three-place decimal .833, and so 5/6 is approximately _____ %.

> 83.3

40. Find a three-place decimal approximation of each of the following and then express the result as a "percent."

1/6	.167	= 16.7%
7/12	_____	= _____	%
9/14	_____	= _____	%

> .583 = 58.3%;   .643 = 64.3%

41. Approximations are also useful when writing certain "percents" in decimal form. Thus, since 7.333 is a three-place decimal approximation of $7\frac{1}{3}$, a three-place decimal approximation of $7\frac{1}{3}\%$ is .073.

And, since 16.667 is a three-place decimal approximation of $16\frac{2}{3}$, a three-place decimal approximation of $16\frac{2}{3}\%$ is _____ .

> .167   (not .166!)

42. Find the required decimal approximation.

$6\frac{1}{6}\%$ (three-place)	_____
$33\frac{1}{3}\%$ (three-place)	_____
$1/12\%$ (four-place)	_____
$83\frac{1}{3}\%$ (two-place)	_____

> .062;   .333;   .0008;   .83

43. Let us consider the general problem in which percent is encountered. In such problems the word "of" replaces the conventional multiplication symbol. Thus, the expression 7% of 12 simply means

$(.07) \cdot (12)$

and the expression 4% of 16 means

_____ .

> $(.04) \cdot (16)$

44. Express each of the following as a product.

5% of 255	_____
88% of 1,620	_____
.12% of 45	_____
33.3% of 100	_____

> (.05)(255);   (.88)(1,620);   (.0012)(45);
> (.333)(100)

45. To find what number is 7% of 12, we need only write 7% of 12 as a product and compute the result.

7% of 12 = (.07)(12) = .84

To find what number is 4% of 16, we write 4% of 16 as a product and compute the result.

4% of 16 = (.04)(16) = _____

.64

46. What number is 5% of 255?

_____

What number is 88% of 1620?

_____

What number is .12% of 45?

_____

What number is 33.3% of 100?

_____

5% of 255 = (.05)(255) = 12.75
88% of 1,620 = (.88)(1,620) = 1425.6
.12% of 45 = (.0012)(45) = .054
33.3% of 100 = (.333)(100) = 33.3

47. "A class has 25 members. 40% of the students will receive a grade of 'C'. How many students in the class will receive a 'C' grade?"

This problem, too, can be solved by the same method. The number of students who will receive a 'C' is

40% of 25 = _____

10.

48. "In one county, 78% of the taxpayers paid their property taxes on time. If the total number of taxpayers was 30,400, how many paid their tax bill promptly?" _____

23,712

49. Now consider the problem: "5.6 is 16% of what number?"

If we again interpret "of" as a symbol for multiplication, this problem can be written

5.6 = (16%)[   ]   or   5.6 = (.16)[   ]

The number we seek is one factor in a multiplication problem whose product and one of whose factors are known. The missing factor is found by _____ the product by the known factor.

DIVIDING

50. "5.6 is 16% of what number?"

is equivalent to

5.6 = (.16)[   ]

and the missing factor is _____.

35.

51. Similarly, the problem "20 is 6.25% of what number?" can be written

20 = (6.25%)[   ]   or   20 = (.0625)[   ]

and the missing factor is _____.

320.

52. 2.756 is 52% of what number? _____

2.756 = (.52)[   ]

1.452 is 3.3% of what number? _____

1.452 = (.033)[   ]

5.3;   44.

53. 10.25 is 125% of what number? _____

9.425 is 6½% of what number? _____

8.2;   145.

54. "In a mixture of flower bulbs, only 3% yield red blossoms. How many bulbs should be planted to 'insure' that 12 plants yield red blossoms?"

This problem is another example in which we seek a missing factor.

12 = (.03)[   ]

The number of bulbs that should be planted is _____ .

400.

55. "Only 2.3% of the balls hit into the grandstand at one major league ball park fall back onto the playing field. If, in one year, 69 balls were recovered from the field, how many balls in all were hit into the grandstand?"

_____

3000.

56. Finally, consider the problem: "12 is what percent of 48?"

Again interpreting "of" as a symbol for multiplication, the problem can be written

12 = [   ](48)

The missing factor can be found by division. It is _____ .

.25

57. "12 is what percent of 48?"

is equivalent to

12 = [   ](48)

and the missing factor is .25.

But, to answer the original question, we must express .25 as a "percent."

.25 = _____%

25.

58. Hence, 12 is 25 percent of 48.

Similarly, the problem "3.608 is what percent of 16.4?" can be written

3.608 = [   ](16.4)

and the missing factor is _____ .

.22

59. "3.608 is what percent of 16.4?"

can be written

3.608 = [   ](16.4)

and the missing factor is .22.

To answer the original question we must express the result as a "percent."

.22 = _____

22%

60. 48 is what percent of 15? _____

48 = [   ](15)

.02442 is what percent of .814? _____

.02442 = [   ](.814)

320.%;   3.%

61. 20.4 is what percent of 480? _____

.2256 is what percent of 1.88? _____

4.25%;   12.%

62. "Of the 248 weather forecasts made so far this year, 186 have proved correct. What percent of the forecasts have been reliable?"

This problem is another in which we seek a missing factor, expressed as a "percent."

$186 = [\quad](248)$

The weather man has been correct _____ of the time.

75.%

63. "In a recent city election, only 7,748 of the registered 23,840 voters cast a ballot. What percent of those eligible actually voted?"

_____

32.5%

64. Sometimes only an approximation is desired or possible.

What number is 47.3% of 16.7? (Find a two-place decimal approximation of the answer.)

_____

7.90

65. Sometimes only an approximation is desired or possible.

22 is 35% of what number? (Find a one-place decimal approximation of the answer.)

_____

62.9

66. Sometimes only an approximation is desired or possible.

7.26 is what percent of 427.1? (Find a one-place decimal approximation of the answer.)

_____

1.7%

67. A monthly service charge is $1\frac{1}{2}$% of the unpaid balance. If this balance is 124.72 dollars, find a two-place decimal approximation of the number of dollars service charge.

_____

1.87

68. An insurance company awards a dividend which is 3.2% of the reserve value of its policies. What is the reserve value of a policy on which it pays a dividend of 24.75 dollars? Find a two-place decimal approximation of your answer. $ _____

773.44

69. The regular price for a carton of detergent is 89 cents. The carton is marked "7 cents off." What percent of the normal price is this reduction? Express your answer as a one-place decimal approximation. _____

7.9%

70. In this chapter we have considered the idea of percent and certain problems that frequently occur in connection with it.

Any expression that contains the percent symbol represents a quotient number which can be expressed in fraction or decimal form by recalling that "percent" means " _____ _____ _____ ."

DIVIDED BY 100

71. However, it will be most convenient to work with decimal forms or approximations when considering the percent idea.

To write a decimal as a "percent" one merely moves each digit two places to the _____ and includes a percent symbol; to change a "percent" to a decimal, each digit is moved two places to the _____ and the percent sign is dropped.

LEFT;   RIGHT

72. In expressions in which percent occurs, the word "of" is used as a symbol for the operation of _____.

MULTIPLICATION

73. What number is 24% of 18? _____

18 is 40% of what number? _____

48 is what percent of 15? _____

4.32;   45.;   320.%

74. Find a one-place decimal approximation in answer to each of the following.

16 is what percent of 56? _____

What number is 112% of 24? _____

5.8 is 12% of what number? _____

28.6%;   26.9;   48.3

Problems A   (Answers on page 513)

Change each decimal form to a "percent."

1. .37

2. .05

3. 1.35

4. 4.3

5. .237

6. .0372

7. .003

8. 2.345

9. 3.

10. 100.

Change each "percent" to simplest decimal form.

11. 17%

12. 9%

13. 115%

14. 205%

15. 400%

16. 93.7%

17. 8.42%

18. .31%

19. .05%

20. 1.05%

Find a three-place decimal approximation for each quotient number, and change this decimal approximation to a "percent."

Example: 2³/₇. Answer: Decimal approximation of 2³/₇ is 2.429 = 242.9%.

21. 1/6

22. 4/11

23. 1²/₃

24. 12/17

25. 174/89

Find a three-place decimal approximation for each "percent."

Example: 7⁵/₁₃%. Answer: 7⁵/₁₃% is approximately 7.4% and 7.4% = .074.

26. 39¹/₈%

27. 2²/₇%

28. 135³/₈%

29. 5/8%

30. 1/3%

For each of the following find a one-place decimal approximation, unless otherwise directed.

31. What number is 17% of 83?

32. What number is 143% of 12?

33. What number is 3.7% of 8.9?

34. 73 is 21% of what number?

35. 8.35 is 261% of what number?

36. 3.9 is .5% of what number?

37. 49 is what percent of 91?

38. 2.3 is what percent of .85?

39. .017 is what percent of .03?

40. A 7.5% raise is granted to workers after a lengthy strike. If the hourly wage before the strike was $2.93, how much (to the nearest cent) was the hourly raise in wages?

41. 87% of those eligible to vote actually voted in a Presidential election. If a total of 21,141 in one county voted, what was the total eligible vote in that county?

42. Willie Mays collected 142 hits in 407 official times at bat. What percent of the time did he hit safely?

43. During one year a blue chip stock whose average price was $243.00 per share paid a dividend of $9.85 per share. What was the "percent" paid?

44. In one year the annual rainfall was 23.6 inches. If this was 74% of the normal rainfall, what was the normal rainfall?

45. During a sale, goods are offered at 20% off the regular price. If the sale price of an item is $59.16, what was its regular price?

Following is a partial tax table for computing federal income tax for 1964.

Taxable income	Tax
$2,000 - 4,000	$340 plus 20% of excess over $2,000
$4,000 - 6,000	$740 plus 23.5% of excess over $4,000
$6,000 - 8,000	$1,210 plus 27% of excess over $6,000
$8,000 - 10,000	$1,750 plus 30.5% of excess over $8,000

Example: Compute the tax, rounded off to the nearest cent, on $5,424 taxable income.

Answer: $5,424 is between $4,000 and $6,000. Then the tax is $740, plus 23.5% of the excess over $4,000.

$$\begin{array}{r} \$1,424 \\ .235 \\ \hline 7120 \\ 4272 \\ 2848 \\ \hline 334.460 \end{array}$$

$5,424
−4,000
Excess is 1,424   Tax on excess is 334.460

$ 740.00
   334.64
Tax is $1,074.64

Compute the tax, rounded off to the nearest cent, if the taxable income is as given.

46. $2,970

47. $6,475

48. $5,315

49. $8,075

50. $7,890

Problems B

Find a three-place decimal approximation for each "percent."

1. 93.48%

2. 15¼%

3. 5.234%

4. 1/2%

5. .02%

Find a two-place decimal approximation for each of these.

6. 21.7 is 9% of what number?

7. What number is 143% of 18.7?

8. 16.9 is what percent of 70?

9. The difference of 17.5 and 12.8 is what percent of the subtrahend?

10. What is the sum of 18.3 and 54% of 18.3?

11. A worker is granted a 3.5% raise in pay. If his salary was $2.42 per hour, what is his hourly increase in pay?

12. A bank pays 4.25% interest per year on a savings account. How much interest will an account of $840 earn in one year?

13. Last year the annual snowfall in Presque-Isle, Maine, was 137.5 inches. This year the snowfall increased by 11%. What was the snowfall this year?

14. Only .2% of the ball bearings made in a certain factory fail to meet production specifications. If 286 ball bearings are rejected for failing to meet the standards, how many ball bearings were produced in all?

15. Unemployment decreased this year from 4.8% to 4.5%. If the total work force was 83,000,000 throughout the year, how many additional people were employed during the year?

16. Last year the enrollment at a certain college was 4250. This year there are 950 more students attending. What was the percent of increase in enrollment?

17. Improved production methods have cut the cost of manufacturing a certain item from $9 each to only $7 each. The decrease in cost is what percent of the former cost?

18. During a sale, a suit marked "20% OFF THE REGULAR PRICE" sells for $44. What is the "regular price" of this suit?

Use the tax table in Problems A to compute the tax to the nearest cent, if the taxable income is as given.

19. $3,495

20. $2,750

21. $5,175

22. $7,840

23. $9,840

24. $10,000

25. $2,800

ADDITION OF INTEGERS

1. The numbers represented by the symbols, 1, 2, 3, 4, ..., are called _____ numbers.

NATURAL

2. Multiplication of natural numbers is defined in such a way that the product of any two natural numbers is a natural number. Hence, we say that the natural numbers are _____ with respect to the operation of multiplication.

CLOSED

3. And the multiplication of natural numbers is defined in such a way that some very interesting properties are true. In fact, for any natural numbers a, b, and c it is true that

ab = ba

a(bc) = _____

(ab)c

4. We call the property illustrated by

ab = ba

the _____ property of multiplication, and that illustrated by

a(bc) = (ab)c

the _____ property of multiplication.

COMMUTATIVE;   ASSOCIATIVE

5. There is a very special natural number, represented by the symbol _____, which has the unique property that its product with any given natural number is that given number.

1

6. Since

a · 1 = 1 · a = a

for any number a, we call 1 the multiplicative _____.

IDENTITY

7. Addition of natural numbers is also defined in such a way that the sum of two natural numbers is a natural number. Hence, the natural numbers are also _____ with respect to addition.

CLOSED

8. And addition is defined in such a way that the commutative property, illustrated by

$a + b =$ _____

and the associative property, illustrated by

$a + (b + c) =$ _____

are true for all natural numbers a, b, and c.

$b + a;$ $(a + b) + c$

9. There is a useful property which involves both multiplication and addition, called the _____ property, which is illustrated by

$a(b + c) =$ _____

DISTRIBUTIVE; $ab + ac$

10. However, the additive identity, a number whose sum with any number is that same number, is not a natural number. We represent the additive identity by the symbol _____.

0

11. We enlarge our set of numbers to include the number, 0, and we define addition and multiplication with zero in such a way that the commutative, associative, and distributive properties are still true for all such whole numbers. In fact, we define the operations with zero as follows:

$a + 0 = 0 + a =$ _____

$a \cdot 0 = 0 \cdot a \quad =$ _____

a;   0

12. Division of natural numbers is defined to be the inverse of _____.

MULTIPLICATION

13. We say that the quotient of two numbers is a number whose product with the _____ equals the dividend.

DIVISOR

14. But it is not always possible to find a natural number whose product with the divisor equals the dividend, and thus we say that the natural numbers are not closed with respect to _____.

DIVISION

15. The fact that the set of natural numbers is not closed with respect to division seems unsatisfactory, and so we enlarge the set to form a new set that includes not only the natural numbers, but also those numbers which are represented by fractions. This enlarged set is called the set of _____ numbers.

QUOTIENT

16. Addition and multiplication of quotient numbers are defined in such a way that they do not contradict the rules already established for those quotient numbers which are also natural numbers. And since the addition and multiplication of natural numbers are defined in such a way that the associative, commutative, and distributive properties are true, we define addition and multiplication of _____ numbers in such a way that these properties are true for them also.

QUOTIENT

17. The definitions for addition and multiplication for quotient numbers are made in such a way that the sum of any two quotient numbers is a quotient number and the product of any two quotient numbers is a quotient number. Hence, the quotient numbers are closed with respect to both _____ and _____.

ADDITION; MULTIPLICATION
(either order)

18. And corresponding to each quotient number is another quotient number such that the product of the two numbers is one. When the product of two numbers is one, we say that each is the _____ _____ or reciprocal of the other.

MULTIPLICATIVE INVERSE

19. Division of quotient numbers is defined the same way as for the natural numbers. The quotient is a number whose _____ with the divisor equals the dividend.

PRODUCT

20. But we can also show that the quotient of two quotient numbers is the product of the _____ and the multiplicative inverse of the _____.

DIVIDEND; DIVISOR

21. And thus we can show that the quotient of two quotient numbers is always a quotient number. Hence the quotient numbers are _____ with respect to _____.

CLOSED; DIVISION

22. Subtraction is defined to be the inverse of _____.

ADDITION

23. That is, the difference of any two numbers is a number whose _____ with the subtrahend equals the minuend.

SUM

24. But given any two natural numbers it is not always possible to find another natural number whose sum with the subtrahend equals the minuend, and hence the natural numbers are not closed with respect to _____.

SUBTRACTION

25. In fact, even the larger set of quotient numbers is not closed with respect to subtraction. That is, the difference of two quotient numbers is not always a _____ number.

QUOTIENT

26. We now further enlarge the set of numbers in such a way that this enlarged set will be closed with respect to subtraction. We assign to each natural number a number called its ADDITIVE INVERSE, a number whose sum with the original natural number is _____, the additive identity.

> 0

27. We represent the additive inverse of 3 by −3, and, by definition, the sum of 3 and −3 is _____.

> 0

28. Similarly, the additive inverse of 4 is −4, the additive inverse of 5 is _____, and the additive inverse of 2 is _____.

> −5;   −2

29. −2 is the additive _____ of 2, and the sum of 2 and −2 is _____.

> INVERSE;   0

30. We represent the sum of 1 and its additive inverse, −1, by writing

$$1 + (-1)$$

Since the sum of any number and its additive inverse is _____, we can write

$$1 + (-1) = \text{_____}$$ •

> 0;   0

31. Similarly,

$$2 + (-2) = 0$$
$$3 + (-3) = 0$$
$$4 + (-4) = \text{_____}$$
$$5 + (-5) = \text{_____}$$
$$6 + (-6) = \text{_____}$$

> 0;   0;   0

32. The sum of any number and its _____ _____ is zero.

> ADDITIVE INVERSE

33. And if the sum of two numbers is zero, we say that each number is the _____ _____ of the other.

> ADDITIVE INVERSE

34. Then 1 is the additive inverse of −1, and _____ is the additive inverse of −2.

> 2

35. Give the additive inverse of each number.

−3	3
10	−10
7	_____
−4	_____
25	_____
−9	_____

> −7;   4;   −25;   9

36. Let N = {1, 2, 3, 4, ...}

Then N is the set of all _____ numbers.

NATURAL

37. N = {1, 2, 3, 4, ...}

The natural number 12 is a _____ of N, even though 12 is not listed above. The three dots indicate that the rest of the natural numbers after 4 are understood to be _____ of N.

MEMBER;   MEMBERS

38. Consider the set that contains all the natural numbers, their additive inverses, and zero. We represent this set by

I = {..., −3, −2, −1, 0, 1, 2, 3, ...}

and although they are not listed above, both 7 and −365 are understood to be _____ of I.

MEMBERS

39. N = {1, 2, 3, 4, ...}

I = {..., −3, −2, −1, 0, 1, 2, 3, ...}

Since every member of N is also a member of I, we say that N is a _____ of I.

SUBSET

40. N = {1, 2, 3, 4, ...}

I = {..., −3, −2, −1, 0, 1, 2, 3, ...}

N is a subset of I.

We call the members of I INTEGERS.

Hence every natural number is also an I _____.

INTEGER

41. I = {..., −3, −2, −1, 0, 1, 2, 3, ...}

The numbers 4, −12, 0, −5, 263 are _____.

INTEGERS

42. I = {..., −3, −2, −1, 0, 1, 2, 3, ...}

Which of these are integers?

$$100, \quad -75, \quad 1/2, \quad 0, \quad -\frac{2}{3}$$

_____

100,   −75,   0

43. N = {1, 2, 3, 4, ...}

I = {..., −3, −2, −1, 0, 1, 2, 3, ...}

Every natural number, and its additive _____, is an _____.

INVERSE;   INTEGER

44. I = {..., −3, −2, −1, 0, 1, 2, 3, ...}

But quotient numbers that are not natural numbers are not _____.

INTEGERS

45. Since every _____ number is an integer, we say that the set of _____ numbers is a subset of the set of integers.

NATURAL;   NATURAL

46. Every natural number is also an integer. We shall call every natural number a POSITIVE integer. And the additive inverse of a natural number will be called a N _____ integer.

NEGATIVE

47. Then 3, 12, 50, 275 are all _____ integers, while −4, −9, −173 are all _____ integers.

POSITIVE;   NEGATIVE

48. Zero is neither a positive nor a negative integer. Then the integers are divided into three groups, the positive integers, also called _____ _____, the negative integers, and zero.

NATURAL NUMBERS

49. The additive inverse of a positive integer is a negative integer, while the additive inverse of a negative integer is a _____ _____.

POSITIVE INTEGER

50. We want to define the operations on integers in such a way that these definitions do not contradict the operations already established for the natural numbers, and in such a way that (hopefully) the integers are closed with respect to these operations, and the commutative, associative, and distributive properties are true.

51. Since the positive integers are also _____ numbers, we accept the rules already established for adding _____ numbers, and say that these same rules are used for adding positive integers.

NATURAL;   NATURAL

52. And we assume that zero is the additive identity for all the integers, both positive and negative. Then

$0 + 3 \quad = 3 + 0 \quad = 3$

$0 + (−4) = (−4) + 0 = $ _____

−4

53. We have already assumed that

$1 + (−1) = 0$

$2 + (−2) = 0$

$3 + (−3) = 0$

$4 + (−4) = 0$

In order that the commutative property of addition will be true, we also define

$(−1) + 1 = 0$

$(−2) + 2 = 0$

$(−3) + 3 = $ _____

$(−4) + 4 = $ _____

0;   0

54. We may also indicate the sum of a negative integer and its additive inverse without using parentheses. Then the sum of −4 and 4 can be written

$$-4 + 4$$

and

$$-4 + 4 = 0$$
$$-5 + 5 = \underline{\hspace{2cm}}$$
$$-6 + 6 = \underline{\hspace{2cm}}$$

0;   0

55. Similarly, the sum of two negative integers may be indicated in two ways. The sum of −2 and −3 may be written either

$$(-2) + (-3) \quad \text{or} \quad -2 + (-3)$$

Indicate the sum of −5 and −7 in two ways.

\underline{\hspace{3cm}} \underline{\hspace{3cm}}

(−5) + (−7);   −5 + (−7)   (either order)

56. −2 and −3 are the additive inverses of \underline{\hspace{2cm}} and \underline{\hspace{2cm}}, respectively.

2;   3

57. Since −2 and −3 are the additive inverses of 2 and 3, we might think that the sum of −2 and −3 is the additive inverse of \underline{\hspace{2cm}}.

5

58. In fact, we will show that if the associative and commutative properties are assumed for addition of negative integers, then the sum of −2 and −3 must be \underline{\hspace{2cm}}, the additive inverse of 5.

−5

59. The sum of any number and its additive inverse is \underline{\hspace{2cm}}. And, if the sum of two numbers is \underline{\hspace{2cm}}, each number is the additive inverse of the other.

0;   0

60. Then if we show that the sum of two numbers is zero, we know that the numbers are additive inverses. We will show that the sum of 5 and (−2) + (−3) is zero. This will mean that (−2) + (−3) is the additive inverse of \underline{\hspace{2cm}}, which we represent by \underline{\hspace{2cm}}.

5;   −5

61. We represent the sum of 5 and (−2) + (−3) by writing

$$5 + [(-2) + (-3)]$$

The brackets here are used as a symbol of grouping and mean \underline{\hspace{3cm}} just as do the parentheses in the expression

$$7 + (3 + 5)$$

FIRST

62. Now 5 = 2 + 3, so we may write

$$5 + [(-2) + (-3)]$$
$$= [2 + \underline{\hspace{1.5cm}}] + [(-2) + (-3)]$$

3

63. If we assume the commutative and associative properties of addition, we may change the order and grouping of the terms in this sum and write

$$[2 + 3] + [(-2) + (-3)]$$
$$= [2 + (-2)] + [3 + \underline{\hspace{1.5cm}}]$$

(−3)

64. But $2 + (-2) =$ _____

   $3 + (-3) =$ _____

   0; 0

65. Then repeating the results of the last few frames,

   $$5 + [(-2) + (-3)] = [2 + 3] + [(-2) + (-3)]$$
   $$= [2 + (-2)] + [3 + (-3)]$$
   $$= 0 + 0$$
   $$= \underline{\hspace{1cm}}$$

   0

66. We have shown that

   $$5 + [(-2) + (-3)] = 0$$

   And since the sum of 5 and $(-2) + (-3)$ is 0, we can say that $(-2) + (-3)$ is _____, the additive inverse of 5.

   -5

67. Then

   $$(-2) + (-3) = -5$$

   In a similar way we can show that

   $$(-5) + (-3) = -8$$
   $$(-2) + (-9) = \underline{\hspace{1cm}}$$
   $$-6 + (-3) = \underline{\hspace{1cm}}$$

   -11; -9

68. Find the sum of the following integers.

   $$(-12) + (-3) = \underline{\hspace{1cm}}$$
   $$(-5) + (-10) = \underline{\hspace{1cm}}$$
   $$(-1) + (-1) = \underline{\hspace{1cm}}$$
   $$(-8) + 8 = \underline{\hspace{1cm}}$$
   $$5 + 9 = \underline{\hspace{1cm}}$$

   -15; -15; -2;   0;   14

69. The sum of two <u>negative</u> integers is a _____ integer, and the sum of two positive integers is a _____ integer.

   NEGATIVE;   POSITIVE

70. Next, we consider the sum of a positive integer and a negative integer.

   $$8 + (-3)$$

   Since $8 = 5 + 3$, we may write

   $$8 + (-3) = [5 + 3] + \underline{\hspace{1cm}}$$

   (-3)

71. Then

   $$8 + (-3) = [5 + 3] + (-3)$$
   $$= 5 + [3 + \underline{\hspace{1cm}}]$$

   Notice that the last step is justified by the associative property of addition, which we assume for integers.

   (-3)

72. But then combining the previous results, we have

$$8 + (-3) = [5 + 3] + (-3)$$
$$= 5 + [3 + (-3)]$$
$$= 5 + \underline{\hspace{1.5cm}}$$
$$= 5$$

0

73. Similarly,

$$10 + (-4) = [6 + 4] + (-4)$$
$$= 6 + [4 + (-4)]$$
$$= \underline{\hspace{1.5cm}}$$

6

74. And $12 + (-4) = [8 + \underline{\hspace{1.5cm}}] + (-4)$
$$= 8$$

4

75. Notice,

$$25 + (-5) = [20 + 5] + (-5) \qquad = 20$$
$$17 + (-8) = [\underline{\hspace{1.5cm}} + 8] + (-8) = \underline{\hspace{1.5cm}}$$

9; 9

76. In the last few frames we have shown that

$$8 + (-3) = 5$$
$$10 + (-4) = 6$$
$$12 + (-4) = 8$$
$$25 + (-5) = 20$$
$$17 + (-8) = 9$$

Before reaching any hasty conclusions, we must now consider a sum such as

$$3 + (-5)$$

77. Now we have already shown that

$$(-3) + (-2) = -5$$

Then

$$3 + (-5) = 3 + [(-3) + \underline{\hspace{1.5cm}}]$$

(-2)

78. $3 + (-5) = 3 + [(-3) + (-2)]$
$$= [3 + (-3)] + \underline{\hspace{1.5cm}}$$

The last step is justified by the
\underline{\hspace{3cm}} property of addition.

(-2);   ASSOCIATIVE

79. Then $3 + (-5) = 3 + [(-3) + (-2)]$
$$= [3 + (-3)] + (-2)$$
$$= \underline{\hspace{1.5cm}} + (-2)$$
$$= -2$$

0

80. Similarly,

$$4 + (-9) = 4 + [(-4) + (-5)]$$
$$= [4 + (-4)] + (-5)$$
$$= \underline{\hspace{1.5cm}} + (-5)$$
$$= \underline{\hspace{1.5cm}}$$

0;   -5

81. And $3 + (-12) = 3 + [(-3) + \underline{\hspace{1.5cm}}]$
$$= \underline{\hspace{1.5cm}}$$

(-9);   -9

82. $7 + (-15) = 7 + [\text{_____} + (-8)]$
        $= \text{_____}$

> (−7);   −8

83. In the last several frames we have shown

$8 + (-3) = 5$	$3 + (-5) = -2$
$10 + (-4) = 6$	$4 + (-9) = -5$
$12 + (-4) = 8$	$3 + (-12) = -9$
$25 + (-5) = 20$	$7 + (-15) = -8$
$17 + (-8) = 9$	

   It is obvious that the sum of a positive integer and a negative integer is sometimes _____ and sometimes _____.

> POSITIVE;   NEGATIVE   (either order)

84. The sum of two positive integers is positive. The sum of two negative integers is _____. But the sum of a positive integer and a negative integer may be either positive or negative.

> NEGATIVE

85. The method used in the several frames preceding this one may always be used to find the sum of a positive and a negative integer, but it is an awkward one. In order to simplify the rule for addition of integers we define the ABSOLUTE VALUE of an integer. The absolute value of −3 is 3, and the absolute value of −4 is _____.

> 4

86. Also, the absolute value of 3 is 3, and the absolute value of 4 is _____.

> 4

87. Both 5 and −5 have an absolute value of _____.

> 5

88. Both 6 and −6 have an _____ value of 6. And 7 and −7 have an _____ value of 7.

> ABSOLUTE;   ABSOLUTE

89. Each number and its additive inverse have the same _____ _____.

> ABSOLUTE VALUE

90. Then the absolute value of both:
   8 and −8 is 8
   9 and −9 is _____
   10 and −10 is _____
   11 and −11 is _____

> 9;   10;   11

91. We also use the symbol
   $|-3|$
   to represent the absolute value of −3 and write
   $|-3| = 3$
   $|-4| = \text{_____}$
   $|-5| = \text{_____}$
   $|-6| = \text{_____}$

> 4;   5;   6

92. Similarly, we may represent the absolute value of 3 with the symbol

$$|3|$$

and we may write

$$|3| = 3$$
$$|4| = \underline{\hspace{2cm}}$$
$$|5| = \underline{\hspace{2cm}}$$
$$|6| = \underline{\hspace{2cm}}$$

93. Find each of the following absolute values.

$$|25| = 25$$
$$|17| = \underline{\hspace{2cm}}$$
$$|-8| = 8$$
$$|-9| = \underline{\hspace{2cm}}$$
$$|-12| = \underline{\hspace{2cm}}$$
$$|7| = \underline{\hspace{2cm}}$$

94. Since the absolute value of −9 is 9, and the absolute value of 3 is 3, we say that −9 has a larger absolute value than 3. Similarly, 8 has a _____ absolute value than −3.

95. −5 has a larger absolute value than 3. And 15 has a larger absolute value than −7. Which number in each pair below has the larger absolute value?

   −7 or 5   −7   (has the larger absolute value)

   3 or −2   _____

   −8 or 7   _____

96. We consider again the sums which have been found previously.

$$8 + (-3) = 5 \qquad 3 + (-5) = -2$$
$$10 + (-4) = 6 \qquad 4 + (-9) = -5$$
$$12 + (-4) = 8 \qquad 3 + (-12) = -9$$
$$25 + (-5) = 20 \qquad 7 + (-15) = -8$$
$$17 + (-8) = 9$$

Each is the sum of a positive integer and a negative integer. If the term with larger absolute value is positive, the sum is _____, and if the term with larger absolute value is negative, the sum is _____.

97. Then the sum of a positive integer and a negative integer is either positive or negative, depending on which term has the larger _____ _____.

98. $8 + (-3) = 5$

The sum here is also the _____ of 8 and 3, the absolute values of the terms.

99. $$8 + (-3) = 5$$
$$10 + (-4) = 6$$
$$12 + (-4) = 8$$
$$25 + (-5) = 20$$
$$17 + (-8) = 9$$

In each case the sum is positive, since the positive term has the larger absolute value. And in each case the sum is also the difference of the _____ _____ of the terms.

100. $3 + (-5) = -2$

In this example the sum is negative, since the negative term, -5, has the larger absolute value, and the absolute value of the sum is also the _____ of 5 and 3.

DIFFERENCE

101. $3 + (-5) = -2$
        $4 + (-9) = -5$
        $3 + (-12) = -9$
        $7 + (-15) = -8$

In each case the sum is negative, since the negative term has the larger absolute value, and the absolute value of the sum is the difference of the _____ _____ of the terms. (But the smaller absolute value must be subtracted from the larger absolute value.)

ABSOLUTE VALUES

102.   To find the absolute value of the sum of a positive integer and a negative integer, we must _____ the smaller absolute value from the larger.

SUBTRACT

103.   And the sum of a positive integer and a negative integer will be either positive or negative. If the positive term has the larger absolute value, the sum is _____. If the negative term has the larger absolute value, the sum is _____.

POSITIVE;   NEGATIVE

104.   Determine whether each of these sums is positive or negative.

$(-12) + 5$	negative (since -12 has the larger absolute value)
$8 + (-2)$	positive
$(-5) + 10$	_____
$9 + (-10)$	_____
$(-211) + 175$	_____

POSITIVE;   NEGATIVE;   NEGATIVE

105.   Is the sum positive or negative?

$-36 + 10$	_____
$3 + (-100)$	_____
$(-2) + (-12)$	_____
$5 + 2$	_____

NEGATIVE;   NEGATIVE;   NEGATIVE; POSITIVE

106.   We have established the sums:

$3 + 5 \qquad\qquad = 8$
$(-2) + (-9) \qquad = -11$
$(-6) + (-3) \qquad = _____$
$(-136) + (-95) = _____$

-9; -231

107. $3 + 5 \qquad\qquad = 8$
        $(-2) + (-9) \qquad = -11$
        $(-6) + (-3) \qquad = -9$
        $(-136) + (-95) = -231$

To find the absolute value of the sum of two positive integers or two negative integers we _____ the absolute values of the terms.

ADD

108. $(-3) + 12 = 9$

$6 + (-11) = -5$

$-3 + 10 = 7$

$(-8) + 5 = -3$

To find the absolute value of the sum of a positive and a negative integer (in either order) we _____ the absolute values of the terms.

SUBTRACT

109. In each case determine whether the absolute values of the terms should be added or subtracted.

$(-4) + (-9)$ Add the absolute values.

$9 + (-3)$ Subtract the absolute values.

$(-15) + 6$ _____ the absolute values.

$-5 + (-12)$ _____ the absolute values.

SUBTRACT; ADD

110. Should the absolute values of the terms be added or subtracted?

$-2 + (-10)$ _____

$8 + (-12)$ _____

$-6 + 2$ _____

$5 + 9$ _____

ADDED; SUBTRACTED;
SUBTRACTED; ADDED

111. If both terms are positive or both terms are negative, we _____ their absolute values to find the absolute value of the sum. If one term is positive and the other is negative, we _____ their absolute values to find the absolute value of the sum.

ADD; SUBTRACT

112. The sum of two negative integers is always a _____ integer, and the sum of two positive integers is always a _____ integer.

NEGATIVE; POSITIVE

113. But the sum of a positive and a negative integer may be either positive or negative. When the positive term has the larger _____ _____, the sum is positive. When the negative term has the larger _____ _____, the sum is negative.

ABSOLUTE VALUE; ABSOLUTE VALUE

114. Find the sum. First determine whether the sum is positive or negative, and then determine whether the absolute values of the terms should be added or subtracted.

$(-3) + (-11) =$ _____

$(-8) + 2$ $=$ _____

$7 + (-1)$ $=$ _____

-14; -6; 6

115. Find each sum.

$-4 + 9$ $=$ _____

$-12 + 2$ $=$ _____

$-5 + (-3)$ $=$ _____

$-8 + (-15) =$ _____

5; -10; -8; -23

116. $127 + (-86) =$ _____
      $(-251) + (-77) =$ _____
      $-315 + 109 =$ _____
      $-914 + (-96) =$ _____
      $-735 + 735 =$ _____

      41;   −328;   −206;   −1010;   0

117. We have defined the sum of two integers in such a way that the sum is always another integer, and hence the integers are _____ with respect to addition.

      CLOSED

118. And the commutative property is true for the addition of integers. Thus

      $(-2) + (-9) = (-9) +$ _____ $=$ _____

      $(-2);$ -11

119. We could illustrate the associative property of addition of integers by writing

      $(-3) + [(-2) + 7] = [(-3) +$ _____ $] + 7$

      (-2)

120. And we illustrate the truth of

      $(-3) + [(-2) + 7] = [(-3) + (-2)] + 7$

      by computing each side. Remember, the brackets mean "first." Hence

      $(-3) + [(-2) + 7] = (-3) +$ _____
      $=$ _____

      $[(-3) + (-2)] + 7 =$ _____ $+ 7 =$ _____

      $(-3) + [(-2) + 7] = (-3) + \underline{5} = \underline{2};$
      $[(-3) + (-2)] + 7 = (\underline{-5}) + 7 = \underline{2}$

121. The additive identity, namely _____, is an integer.

      0

122. And corresponding to each integer is an integer called its additive _____, whose sum with the former integer is _____.

      INVERSE;   ZERO

123. To summarize: The integers have five important characteristics with respect to addition.

      1) Addition is closed.

      2) The commutative property applies:
         $a + b = b + a$

      3) The associative property applies:
         $a + (b + c) = (a + b) + c$

      4) There is an additive identity, 0, such that $a + 0 = 0 + a = a$, for any integer a.

      5) For each integer a, there is an additive inverse −a such that
         $a + (-a) = (-a) + a = 0$

Chapter 26

Problems A   (Answers on page 513)

The simplest form of an integer is one of the symbols, 0, 1, –1, 2, –2, 3, –3, ... Find the simplest form of each of the following:

1. |–14|
2. |–516|
3. |21|
4. |0|
5. |15–2|

Which number, in each pair below, has the larger absolute value?

6. –12 or 5
7. 15 or –9
8. –42 or –35
9. –16 or 0
10. –846 or 847

For each of the following sums, indicate:

a) whether the absolute values of the terms should be added or subtracted.

b) whether the sum is a positive integer or a negative integer.

c) the simplest form of the integer.

11. (–3) + (–7)
12. (–9) + (–12)
13. –14 + (–5)
14. –46 + (–18)
15. 9 + (–11)
16. 14 + (–8)
17. 26 + (–45)
18. –14 + 8
19. –31 + 56
20. –52 + 39
21. 544 + (–612)
22. –319 + 514
23. –643 + (–819)
24. 562 + (–98)
25. –8216 + (–599)

26. The elevation of a certain point in Death Valley, California, is –194 feet above sea level (i.e., 194 feet below sea level). If a 45-foot tower is built on that spot, what is the elevation above sea level of the top of the tower?

27. The low temperature in Fargo, North Dakota, one morning was –33°F. If the low temperature the next morning was 4° colder, what was the new temperature?

28. "Absolute zero" is considered to be –273°C. If a substance at absolute zero is heated until its temperature rises 184°C, what is its new temperature?

29. A housewife overdrew her checking account by $12. If she then deposited $50, and the bank did not charge her for the overdraft, what was the condition of her account?

30. At a certain point off the shore of Texas the bottom of the Gulf of Mexico is 143 feet below the surface of the water. An oil company finds oil by drilling 375 feet beneath the bottom of the gulf. What is the elevation (expressed as feet above sea level) of the surface of the oil?

Problems B

Find the simplest form of each of these integers.

1. (–2) + (–7)
2. (–5) + (–9)
3. –8 + (–2)
4. –15 + (–9)
5. 5 + (–2)
6. 12 + (–9)
7. 15 + (–23)
8. 5 + (–14)
9. 2 + (–3)
10. (–4) + 5
11. (–9) + 3
12. –13 + 2
13. –25 + 7
14. –33 + 33
15. 42 + (–42)
16. (–17) + (–17)
17. (–3) + 0
18. 0 + (–5)
19. |–15|
20. |4|
21. |5 + 2|
22. |5 –7|
23. |–3 + 1|
24. |6 + (–9)|
25. |–2| + |–5|
26. |12| + |–2|
27. |12 + (–2)|
28. 243 + (–175)
29. –814 + 167
30. –914 + (–842)
31. (–159) + (–642)
32. 137 + (–215)
33. (–544) + (–544)
34. –842 + 842
35. (–153) + 165

The sum of three or more integers may be indicated in a manner similar to that used for the sum of three or more natural numbers. Thus

$$(-2) + 5 + (-9) + 12$$

represents the sum of the four integers

$$-2, \ 5, \ -9, \ 12$$

Adding from left to right, we have

$$(-2) + 5 + (-9) + 12 = 3 + (-9) + 12$$
$$= (-6) + 12$$
$$= 6$$

Find the simplest form by adding from left to right.

36. $(-8) + (-2) + (-19)$

37. $(-12) + (-5) + 11$

38. $5 + (-19) + (-2)$

39. $(-5) + 15 + 3 + (-19)$

40. $214 + (-312) + (-136) + 305$

SUBTRACTION OF INTEGERS

1. A member of the set $\{\ldots, -3, -2, -1, 0, 1, 2, 3, \ldots\}$ is called an _____.

   INTEGER

2. Every natural number and its _____ _____ is an integer.

   ADDITIVE INVERSE

3. The natural numbers are called _____ integers, while their additive inverses are called _____ integers.

   POSITIVE;   NEGATIVE

4. Each integer and its additive inverse have the same _____ value.

   ABSOLUTE

5. The absolute value of an integer is never a _____ integer.

   NEGATIVE

6. $|-12| = $ _____

   $|12| = $ _____

   For completeness we also define

   $|0| = $ _____

   12;   12;   0

7. The sum of two positive integers is a _____ _____.

   The sum of two negative integers is a _____ _____.

   POSITIVE INTEGER;   NEGATIVE INTEGER

8. But the sum of a positive and a negative integer may be either positive, negative or zero.

   When the positive term has the larger _____ _____, the sum is positive, but when the negative term has the larger _____ _____ the sum is negative.

   ABSOLUTE VALUE;   ABSOLUTE VALUE

9. If the sum of a positive and a negative integer is zero, then the terms have the same absolute value, and in fact each term must be the _____ _____ of the other.

ADDITIVE INVERSE

10. The absolute value of the sum of two positive integers is the _____ of the absolute values of the terms, and the absolute value of the sum of two negative integers is the _____ of the absolute values of the terms.

SUM;   SUM

11. But the absolute value of the sum of a positive and a negative integer is the _____ of the larger absolute value and the smaller.

DIFFERENCE

12. Find the sums indicated below.

    $(-2) + (-5) =$ _____

    $4 + 9$ $=$ _____

    $(-12) + 6$ $=$ _____

    $15 + (-8)$ $=$ _____

    $(-18) + 18$ $=$ _____

    −7;   13;   −6;   7;   0

13. Find the sums.

    $-35 + 15$ $=$ _____

    $-5 + 40$ $=$ _____

    $-8 + 8$ $=$ _____

    $-17 + (-9)$ $=$ _____

    −20;   35;   0;   −26

14. Add as indicated.

    $(-376) + 409$ $=$ _____

    $(-843) + (-575)$ $=$ _____

    $-9377 + 9375$ $=$ _____

    $4653 + (-4650)$ $=$ _____

    33;   −1418;   −2;   3

15. Supply the missing integer.

    $5 +$ _____ $= 12$

    $5 +$ _____ $= 2$

    7;   (−3)

16. Find an integer that makes each of these a true statement.

    $(-3) +$ _____ $= -12$

    $(-9) +$ _____ $= -7$

    (−9);   2

17. Complete each statement with an integer.

    $-9 + 4 =$ _____

    _____ $+ (-3) = -8$

    _____ $+ (-5) = -2$

    −5;   −5;   3

18. Complete each statement:

    $5 +$ _____ $= 100$

    $12 +$ _____ $= -4$

    $-30 +$ _____ $= -12$

    $-42 +$ _____ $= -50$

    95;   (−16);   18;   (−8)

19.　　$-4 +$ _____ $= -4$

　　　　$-4 +$ _____ $= -8$

　　　　$-4 +$ _____ $= 8$

　　　　$-4 +$ _____ $= 0$

0;　　(−4);　　12;　　4

20.　It seems that, given any two integers, we may always find an integer which is their sum. And given any two integers we may always find an integer whose sum with the first integer equals the second integer.

21.　But this is not the case with natural numbers. Given any two natural numbers, we may always find a natural number which is their sum.

But it is possible to find a natural number whose sum with the first number equals the second number only when the first number is _____ than the second.

LESS

22.　In fact this is how the relation "less than" is defined. We say

$a < b$

if there is some natural number d such that

$a + d =$ _____

b

23.　And subtraction of natural numbers is defined only when the subtrahend is _____ than the minuend.

LESS

24.　That is, if $a < b$, then we may subtract a from b and indicate this difference by writing

_____ $-$ _____

b − a

25.　And the difference of b and a, b − a, is exactly that natural number d whose _____ with a equals b.

SUM

26.　If a and b are natural numbers with $a < b$, then b − a is the natural number whose sum with _____ equals _____.

a;　　b

27.　Hence

$b - a = d$

means that

$a +$ _____ $=$ _____

a + d = b

28.　The difference of two natural numbers is the natural number whose _____ with the subtrahend equals the minuend, provided such a natural number can be found.

SUM

29.　And since it is not always possible to find such a natural number, we say that the natural numbers are not closed with respect to the operation of _____.

SUBTRACTION

30. We will define the subtraction of integers in much the same way as for natural numbers. Then the difference of two integers is an integer whose sum with the subtrahend equals the _____.

MINUEND

31. We have already observed that addition of integers is such that given <u>any</u> two integers it is <u>always</u> possible to find an integer whose sum with one of the integers equals the other integer. Then _____ of integers is always possible.

SUBTRACTION

32. Consider the subtraction

$15 - 7$

The subtrahend is _____, and the minuend is _____.

7;   15

33. $15 - 7 = 8$

The difference is _____, a number whose sum with _____ equals _____.

8;   7;   15

34. We indicate the difference of the negative integers -4 and -7 by writing either

$(-4) - (-7)$ or $-4 - (-7)$

Indicate the difference of -2 and -9 in two ways.

_____   _____

$(-2) - (-9)$; $-2 - (-9)$ (either order)

35. $(-4) - (-7)$

The minuend is -4, and the subtrahend is _____.

-7

36. $(-4) - (-7)$

The difference is an integer whose sum with the subtrahend equals the minuend, or whose sum with _____ equals _____.

-7; -4

37. $(-4) - (-7)$

We want a number whose _____ with -7 equals -4.

SUM

38. $(-4) - (-7)$

Then we want a number which makes the following true:

$(-7) + [\quad] = -4$

And we see that the integer which makes the above true is _____.

3

39. Since

$$(-7) + 3 = -4$$

we say that 3 is the _____ of −4 and −7.

DIFFERENCE

40. $(-7) + 3 = -4$

Then 3 is the difference of −4 and −7, or

$$(-4) - (-7) = \underline{\hspace{1cm}}$$

3

41. Consider

$$4 - (-9)$$

This represents the _____ of 4 and −9.

DIFFERENCE

42. $4 - (-9)$

The difference of 4 and −9 is an integer whose sum with the subtrahend, _____, equals the minuend, _____.

−9;   4

43. Then

$$4 - (-9)$$

is an integer which makes true the statement

$$(-9) + [\quad] = 4$$

The missing integer is _____.

13

44. Then since

$$(-9) + 13 = 4$$

$$4 - (-9) = \underline{\hspace{1cm}}$$

13

45. To find

$$(-8) - (-5)$$

we want an integer whose sum with _____ equals _____.

−5;   −8

46. Then since the sum

$$(-5) + \underline{\hspace{1cm}} = -8$$

we see that the difference

$$(-8) - (-5) = \underline{\hspace{1cm}}$$

(−3);   −3

47. And $(-7) - (-2) = \underline{\hspace{1cm}}$

since $(-2) + (-5) = -7$

Remember, the difference is an integer whose sum with the subtrahend equals the minuend.

−5

48. We may indicate the difference of −2 and 5 by either

$$(-2) - 5 \quad \text{or} \quad -2 - 5$$

Similarly, we indicate the difference of −8 and 3 by _____ or _____.

(−8) −3;   −8 − 3   (either order)

49. For the difference

$$-2 - 5$$

the minuend is -2 and the subtrahend is
_____ .

    5 (not -5)

50. Identify the subtrahend for each difference:

    $-8 - (-3)$:   The subtrahend is _____ .

    $8 - 3$:   The subtrahend is _____ .

    $8 - (-3)$:   The subtrahend is _____ .

    $-8 - 3$:   The subtrahend is _____ .

    -3;   3; -3;   3

51. The difference of two integers is an integer
whose sum with the _____ equals
the _____ .

    SUBTRAHEND;   MINUEND

52. Then

    $-8 - (-3) =$ _____

since the sum of -3 and _____ equals -8.

    -5; -5

53. Similarly,

    $8 - 3 =$ _____ ,   since $3 +$ _____ $= 8$

    $8 - (-3) =$ _____ ,   since

    $(-3) +$ _____ $= 8$

    5;   5;   11;   11

54. And

    $-8 - 3 =$ _____   since

    $3 +$ _____ $= -8$

    -11; (-11)

55. In the last several frames we have shown that

    $(-4) - (-7) = 3$ $-8 - (-3) = -5$

    $4 - (-9) = 13$ $8 - 3 = 5$

    $(-8) - (-5) = -3$ $8 - (-3) = 11$

    $(-7) - (-2) = -5$ $-8 - 3 = -11$

These examples illustrate that the difference
of two integers is sometimes a _____
integer and sometimes a _____ integer.

    POSITIVE;   NEGATIVE   (either order)

56. $(-4) - (-7) = 3$ $-8 - (-3) = -5$

    $4 - (-9) = 13$ $8 - 3 = 5$

    $-8 - (-5) = -3$ $8 - (-3) = 11$

    $-7 - (-2) = -5$ $-8 - 3 = -11$

Sometimes the difference is positive and
sometimes negative, but this does not seem
to depend on which number has the larger
absolute value, as is the case in addition of
integers. Also, the absolute value of the difference is obtained by sometimes adding and
sometimes subtracting the absolute value of
the numbers. We must look for some rule
which will give an easier way to find the difference of two integers. Consider the difference

    $(-4) - (-7) = 3$

The subtrahend is _____ , and the additive
inverse of this subtrahend is _____ .

    -7;   7

57. $(-4) - (-7) = 3$

The subtrahend is −7, and its additive inverse is 7.

Now consider the sum of the minuend and the additive inverse of the subtrahend. We indicate this sum by writing

$(-4) + $ _____

> **7**

58. $(-4) - (-7) = 3$

And the sum of the minuend and the additive inverse of the subtrahend is

$(-4) + 7 = $ _____

> **3**

59. The second difference we earlier considered was

$4 - (-9) = 13$

The sum of the minuend and the additive inverse of the subtrahend is

$4 + $ _____ $ = 13$

> **9**

60. And we earlier showed that

$-8 - (-5) = -3$

Again the sum of the _____ and the _____ _____ of the subtrahend is

$-8 + 5 = -3$

> **MINUEND;   ADDITIVE INVERSE**

61. The next example was

$-7 - (-2) = -5$

The sum of the minuend and the additive inverse of the subtrahend is

_____ + _____ = −5

> **−7 + 2 = −5**

62. Consider the other examples.

$-8 - (-3) = -5$

Again the sum of the _____ and the additive inverse of the _____ equals the _____.

That is,

$-8 + 3 = -5$

> **MINUEND;   SUBTRAHEND;**
> **DIFFERENCE**

63. $8 - 3 = 5$

The subtrahend is _____, and the sum of the minuend and the additive inverse of the subtrahend is

_____ + _____ = _____

> **3;   8 + (−3) = 5**

64. a) $8 - (-3) = 11$ The subtrahend is −3.

b) $-8 - 3 = -11$ The subtrahend is 3.

Find the sum of the minuend and the additive inverse of the subtrahend for each example.

a) $8 + $ _____ = _____

b) $-8 + $ _____ = _____

> **a) 8 + 3 = 11;   b) −8 + (−3) = −11**

65. These examples illustrate that the difference of two integers is also the _____ of the minuend and the _____ _____ of the subtrahend.

66. We can prove the statement of the previous frame.

Let a and b be any integers, either positive or negative. We indicate the difference of a and b by

a – b

where the minuend is _____ and the subtrahend is _____.

67. a – b

The subtrahend is b, and we represent the additive inverse of the subtrahend by –b. Then the sum of the minuend and the additive inverse of the subtrahend is indicated by

a + _____

68. The difference of a and b is represented by

a – b

The sum of the minuend and the additive inverse of the subtrahend is represented by

_____

69. We want to show that

a – b = a + (–b)

That is, we want to show that the _____ of two integers is equal to the sum of the minuend and the _____ _____ of the subtrahend.

70. Now we have defined the difference of two integers to be an integer whose sum with the _____ equals the _____.

71. Then to show that

a – b = a + (–b)

we must show that the sum of the subtrahend, _____, and a + (–b) equals the minuend, a.

72. We want to show that

a – b = a + (–b)

We must show that the sum of b and a + (–b) is a.

We indicate the sum of b and a + (–b) by

b + [a + _____]

73. Now   b + [a + (–b)] = b + [(–b) + _____]

by the commutative property of addition.

74. Hence

$$b + [a + (-b)] = b + [(-b) + a]$$
$$= [b + (-b)] + a$$

The last result is justified by the _____ property of addition.

ASSOCIATIVE

75. But $b + [a + (-b)] = b + [(-b) + a]$
$$= [b + (-b)] + a$$
$$= \underline{\hspace{1cm}} + a$$
$$= \underline{\hspace{1cm}}$$

0;   a

76. We have shown that

$$b + [a + (-b)] = a$$

Then since the sum of b and a + (-b) is a, we know that a + (-b) is the _____ of a and b.

DIFFERENCE

77. Then for any integers a and b it is true that

$$a - b = a + (-b)$$

That is, the difference of two integers is also the _____ of the minuend and the additive inverse of the _____.

SUM;   SUBTRAHEND

78. Recall that a similar result was proved for the quotient of two quotient numbers. We originally defined the quotient to be a number whose _____ with the divisor equals the dividend, but later we showed that the quotient is also the product of the dividend and the multiplicative _____ of the divisor.

PRODUCT;   INVERSE

79. And now we have first defined the difference of two integers to be an integer whose _____ with the subtrahend equals the minuend, but we have later shown that the difference is also the sum of the minuend and the _____ _____ of the subtrahend.

SUM;   ADDITIVE INVERSE

80. Then to subtract two integers we may instead add the _____ and the additive inverse of the _____.

MINUEND;   SUBTRAHEND

81. For the difference

$$(-8) - (-4)$$

the minuend is _____ and the subtrahend is _____.

−8;   −4

82. $(-8) - (-4)$

The sum of the minuend and the additive inverse of the subtrahend is

$$-8 + 4 = \underline{\hspace{1cm}}$$

−4

83. Then $(-8) - (-4) = -8 + 4 = -4$

Also $(-3) - (-12) = -3 + \underline{\hspace{1.5cm}} = 9$

> 12

84. Similarly,

$-4 - (-9) = -4 + \underline{\hspace{1.5cm}} = \underline{\hspace{1.5cm}}$

$-6 - (-6) = -6 + \underline{\hspace{1.5cm}} = \underline{\hspace{1.5cm}}$

$-4 - (-9) = -4 + \underline{9} = \underline{5};$

$-6 - (-6) = -6 + \underline{6} = \underline{0}$

85. Subtract by adding the minuend and the additive inverse of the subtrahend.

$-9 - (-3) = \underline{\hspace{1.5cm}} + \underline{\hspace{1.5cm}} = \underline{\hspace{1.5cm}}$

$-17 - (-20) = \underline{\hspace{1.5cm}} + \underline{\hspace{1.5cm}} = \underline{\hspace{1.5cm}}$

> $-9 - (-3) = \underline{-9} + \underline{3} = \underline{-6}$
>
> $-17 - (-20) = \underline{-17} + \underline{20} = \underline{3}$

86. $-8 - 9$

The minuend is $\underline{\hspace{1.5cm}}$ and the subtrahend is $\underline{\hspace{1.5cm}}$.

> $-8;$ 9

87. $-8 - 9 = \underline{\hspace{1.5cm}} + \underline{\hspace{1.5cm}} = \underline{\hspace{1.5cm}}$

Remember, add the minuend and the additive inverse of the subtrahend.

> $-8 = 9 = \underline{-8} + \underline{(-9)} = \underline{-17}$

88. Find the difference by adding the minuend and the additive inverse of the subtrahend.

$-3 - 8 = \underline{\hspace{1.5cm}} + \underline{\hspace{1.5cm}} = \underline{\hspace{1.5cm}}$

$-475 - 263 = \underline{\hspace{1.5cm}} + \underline{\hspace{1.5cm}} = \underline{\hspace{1.5cm}}$

$-3 - 8 = \underline{-3} + \underline{(-8)} = \underline{-11};$

$-475 - 263 = \underline{-475} + \underline{(-263)} = \underline{-738}$

89. Find the difference:

$4 - (-8) = \underline{\hspace{1.5cm}} + \underline{\hspace{1.5cm}} = \underline{\hspace{1.5cm}}$

$-4 - (-8) = \underline{\hspace{1.5cm}} + \underline{\hspace{1.5cm}} = \underline{\hspace{1.5cm}}$

$4 - 8 = \underline{\hspace{1.5cm}} + \underline{\hspace{1.5cm}} = \underline{\hspace{1.5cm}}$

$-4 - 8 = \underline{\hspace{1.5cm}} + \underline{\hspace{1.5cm}} = \underline{\hspace{1.5cm}}$

$4 - (-8) = \underline{4} + \underline{8} = \underline{12}$

$-4 - (-8) = \underline{-4} + \underline{8} = \underline{4}$

$4 - 8 = \underline{4} + \underline{(-8)} = \underline{-4}$

$-4 - 8 = \underline{-4} + \underline{(-8)} = \underline{-12}$

90. The difference is the sum of the $\underline{\hspace{2cm}}$ and the $\underline{\hspace{2cm}}$ $\underline{\hspace{2cm}}$ of the $\underline{\hspace{2cm}}$.

> MINUEND;   ADDITIVE INVERSE;
> SUBTRAHEND

91. Find the difference:

$(-8) - (-2) = -8 + 2 = \underline{\hspace{1.5cm}}$

$-9 - (-3) = \underline{\hspace{1.5cm}}$

$-4 - 12 = \underline{\hspace{1.5cm}}$

$4 - 17 = \underline{\hspace{1.5cm}}$

$3 - (-11) = \underline{\hspace{1.5cm}}$

> $-6;$ $-6;$ $-16;$ $-13;$ 14

92. Identify each of these as either a sum or a difference.

−3 + 6:   sum of −3 and 6

−3 − 6:   difference of −3 and 6

−12 + 8:   _____ of −12 and 8

−12 − 8:   _____ of −12 and 8

SUM;   DIFFERENCE

93. We have said that

−3 − 6

is the difference of −3 and 6.

But to find this difference, we may instead find the sum of the minuend and the additive inverse of the subtrahend; that is, the sum of −3 and _____ .

−6

94. Then, although the expression

−3 − 6

represents the difference of −3 and 6, it may also be considered as the _____ of −3 and −6.

SUM

95. And we may think of the expression

−12 − 8

as representing either the difference of −12 and _____ , or the sum of −12 and _____ , since each result is the same, namely, _____ .

8;   −8;   −20

96. And   4 − 17

represents either the difference of _____ and _____ , or the sum of _____ and _____ , since each result is _____ .

4;   17;   4;   −17;   −13

97. Every difference with integers is equivalent to a certain _____ , namely the _____ of the minuend and the additive inverse of the subtrahend.

SUM;   SUM

98. Then to find the difference of two integers we will instead find the sum of the _____ and the _____ _____ of the _____ .

MINUEND;   ADDITIVE INVERSE;
SUBTRAHEND

99. And to find the resulting sum, we will use the rules for adding integers. To add two integers, we sometimes add their _____ values, and sometimes subtract their _____ values.

ABSOLUTE;   ABSOLUTE

100. When finding the sum of a positive and a negative integer, we _____ their absolute values, but when finding the sum of two positive or two negative integers, we _____ their absolute values. In each case we obtain only the _____ _____ of the sum.

SUBTRACT;   ADD;   ABSOLUTE
VALUE

101. The absolute value of the sum of a positive and a negative integer is found by _____ the absolute values of the terms, and the sum is either P_____ or _____, depending on whether the term with larger absolute value is _____ or _____.

> SUBTRACTING;   POSITIVE;
> NEGATIVE;   POSITIVE;   NEGATIVE

102. The absolute value of the sum of two positive or two negative integers is found by _____ the absolute values of the terms, and the sum is _____ when adding two positive integers, but _____ when adding two negative integers.

> ADDING;   POSITIVE;   NEGATIVE

103. Find the indicated sum or difference.

$$-8 + 14 = \underline{\hspace{1.5cm}}$$
$$-3 - 12 = \underline{\hspace{1.5cm}}$$
$$4 - (-9) = \underline{\hspace{1.5cm}}$$
$$-8 + (-2) = \underline{\hspace{1.5cm}}$$
$$(-2) - 4 = \underline{\hspace{1.5cm}}$$

> 6;   −15;   13;   −10;   −6

104. Compute the sum or difference as indicated.

$$-375 - 496 = \underline{\hspace{2cm}}$$
$$849 - 1153 = \underline{\hspace{2cm}}$$
$$-490 + 831 = \underline{\hspace{2cm}}$$
$$356 - (-214) = \underline{\hspace{2cm}}$$
$$-975 + (-117) = \underline{\hspace{2cm}}$$

> −871;   −304;   341;   570;   −1092

105. For addition of integers we know that

$$a + b = b + a$$

and we call this the _____ property of _____.

> COMMUTATIVE;   ADDITION

106. Consider the difference

$$(-2) - (-9)$$

If the subtrahend and minuend are interchanged, the resulting difference is indicated by

$$(-9) - \underline{\hspace{1.5cm}}$$

> (−2)

107. And

$$(-2) - (-9) = \underline{\hspace{1.5cm}}$$

While

$$(-9) - (-2) = \underline{\hspace{1.5cm}}$$

> 7;   −7

108.
$$(-2) - (-9) = 7$$
$$(-9) - (-2) = -7$$

It is interesting to observe that when the minuend and the subtrahend are interchanged in this example, the resulting differences are additive _____.

> INVERSES

109. Consider

$$9 - 4 = \underline{\hspace{2cm}}$$

$$4 - 9 = \underline{\hspace{2cm}}$$

Again, when the minuend and the subtrahend are interchanged, one difference is the _____ _____ of the other.

110. It can be shown that whenever the minuend and subtrahend are interchanged, one difference is the additive inverse of the other. Then since

$$12 - 4 = 8$$

we know at once that

$$4 - 12 = \underline{\hspace{2cm}}$$

111. And if

$$a - b = 5$$

it follows that

$$b - a = \underline{\hspace{2cm}}$$

112. If $x - y = -4$

then $y - x = \underline{\hspace{2cm}}$

113. Then in general $a - b$ and $b - a$ are not equal, and hence, there is no _____ property of subtraction of integers.

114. Consider the example

$$(-2) - [(-3) - 5]$$

Here the brackets mean "first," and the difference within the brackets is

$$(-3) - 5 = \underline{\hspace{2cm}}$$

115. Then

$$(-2) - [(-3) - 5] = (-2) - (-8) = \underline{\hspace{2cm}}$$

But

$$[(-2) - (-3)] - 5 = \underline{\hspace{2cm}} - 5 = \underline{\hspace{2cm}}$$

116. $(-2) - [(-3) - 5] = (-2) - (-8) = 6$

$$[(-2) - (-3)] - 5 = 1 - 5 = -4$$

Notice that these two problems involve the differences of the same integers, $-2, -3$, and 5, but that they are grouped differently. And the differences are not the same. This example shows that there is no _____ property of subtraction of integers.

117. Then while the addition of integers is defined in such a way that both the _____ and _____ properties are always true, the subtraction of integers enjoys neither of these two properties.

118. The sum of two integers is always an integer, so we say that addition of integers is closed. Also, the difference of two integers has been shown to be the sum of the minuend and the additive inverse of the subtrahend. Since this latter sum must always exist and be an integer, the integers are also closed with respect to _____.

SUBTRACTION

119. To summarize: Subtraction of integers has been defined in such a way that:

1) Subtraction is closed.

2) There is no commutative property. In fact, $a - b$ is the additive inverse of $b - a$.

3) There is no associative property: $a - (b - c)$ does not equal $(a - b) - c$.

Chapter 27

Problems A (Answers on page 513)

For each of the following:

a) identify the subtrahend,

b) indicate the sum of the minuend and the additive inverse of the subtrahend,

c) find the simplest form of the number.

Example: $-8 - (-3)$.

Answer: a) subtrahend is -3
   b) $-8 + 3$
   c) -5

1. $18 - 12$
2. $5 - 8$
3. $6 - (-3)$
4. $8 - (-4)$
5. $-5 - 6$
6. $-4 - 12$
7. $-5 - (-8)$
8. $-9 - (-4)$
9. $-4 - (-4)$
10. $6 - (-6)$
11. $-6 - 6$
12. $(-15) - 15$
13. $(-8) - (-8)$
14. $0 - (-5)$
15. $0 - 5$
16. $214 - (-183)$
17. $-841 - (513)$
18. $-314 - (-512)$
19. $473 - (-185)$
20. $-532 - (-532)$

Find the simplest form.

21. $-12 - 9$
22. $45 - (-19)$
23. $-15 - (-16)$
24. $19 + (-12)$
25. $-18 + 4$
26. $-25 + (-12)$
27. $814 - 716$
28. $-541 - 97$
29. $-56 + (-173)$
30. $-841 - (-914)$
31. $636 - (-914)$
32. $-514 + 619$
33. $-842 - (-842)$
34. $-842 + (-842)$
35. $-842 - 842$
36. $0 + (-842)$
37. $0 - (-842)$
38. $-842 + 0$
39. $-842 - 0$
40. $0 - 842$

Problems B

Find the simplest form for each integer.

1. $-8 - 12$
2. $5 - 17$
3. $-3 + (-9)$
4. $-15 - 3$
5. $(-12) - (-6)$
6. $-19 + 3$
7. $-9 - 2$
8. $0 - 7$
9. $-4 + 4$
10. $-9 + 0$
11. $-18 - (-18)$
12. $4 + (-19)$
13. $-5 - (5)$
14. $0 - (-5)$
15. $-15 - 0$
16. $(-14) + (-14)$
17. $15 - 41$
18. $(-5) - (-12)$
19. $3 - (-5)$
20. $-9 + (-2)$
21. $175 - 314$
22. $-814 - 512$
23. $-436 + (-215)$
24. $-534 - (-317)$
25. $-173 - (-842)$
26. $976 + (-215)$
27. $317 - (-214)$
28. $-317 + (-214)$
29. $-642 - (-642)$
30. $-642 + (-642)$
31. $215 + (-317)$
32. $-317 - (-215)$
33. $-275 + (-85)$
34. $275 - (-85)$
35. $-412 - 516$

36. A diving bell is 2315 feet below the surface of the ocean. How far must it be raised to be only 1850 feet below the surface?

37. The elevation of death valley, California is -282 feet above sea level, and the elevation of nearby Mt. Whitney is 14,495 feet above sea level. What is the difference in elevation between Death Valley and Mt. Whitney?

38. On two successive days the low temperature in Caribou, Maine, was $-27°F$ and $-12°F$. How much did the temperature rise?

39. If the temperature at dusk is $5°F$ and during the night it drops by $23°F$, what is the temperature in the morning?

40. A checking account contains $87.50. If a check for $126.00 is written, what is the new balance?

MULTIPLICATION AND DIVISION OF INTEGERS; RATIONAL NUMBERS

1. Any member of the set I = $\{\ldots, -3, -2, -1, 0, 1, 2, 3, \ldots\}$ is called an _____.

> INTEGER

2. The set of integers contains each _____ number, its additive _____, and zero.

> NATURAL;   INVERSE

3. The natural numbers are also called _____ integers, while the additive inverse of a natural number is called a _____ integer.

> POSITIVE;   NEGATIVE

4. Given any two integers, we may always find an integer which is their sum, and hence, the integers are _____ with respect to _____.

> CLOSED;   ADDITION

5. Find the indicated sums.

   $-4 + 3$ = _____

   $5 + (-9)$ = _____

   $-3 + (-3)$ = _____

   $-9 + 9$ = _____

> −1;   −4;   −6;   0

6. Addition of integers is a binary operation. That is, we may add only _____ integers at a time.

> TWO

7. For natural numbers addition was also a _____ operation, since only two natural numbers may be added at once. But because of the associative property of addition, we were able to define the expression

   $a + b + c$

   to mean either

   $a + (b + c)$ or $(a + b) + c$

   since both sums are equal.

> BINARY

8. Since the associative property of addition is also true for integers, we may give meaning to the expression

$$(-2) + (-5) + (-3)$$

It means either

$$[(-2) + (-5)] + (-3) \quad \text{or}$$
$$(-2) + [(-5) + (-3)]$$

and in either case the sum is _____ .

> **−10**

9. We shall agree that for a sum of the form

$$(-2) + (-4) + (-2) + (-9)$$

we add the terms, two at a time, from left to right. Then the sum

$$(-2) + (-4) + (-2) + (-9) = \text{\_\_\_\_\_}$$

> **−17**

10. Find each of the following sums by adding from left to right.

$$(-4) + (-3) + (-5) \qquad = \text{\_\_\_\_\_}$$
$$2 + (-8) + (-1) \qquad = \text{\_\_\_\_\_}$$
$$(-2) + (-2) + (-2) \qquad = \text{\_\_\_\_\_}$$
$$(-2) + (-2) + (-2) + (-2) = \text{\_\_\_\_\_}$$

> **−12;   −7;   −6;   −8**

11. For natural numbers we defined the product

$$4 \cdot 2$$

to be the sum

$$2 + 2 + 2 + 2 = 8$$

And the product $5 \cdot 3$ is defined to be the sum

$$\text{\_\_\_\_\_} + \text{\_\_\_\_\_} + \text{\_\_\_\_\_} + \text{\_\_\_\_\_}$$
$$+ \text{\_\_\_\_\_} = \text{\_\_\_\_\_}$$

> **3 + 3 + 3 + 3 + 3 = 15**

12. Since the positive integers are also _____ numbers, we accept these same definitions for the multiplication of positive integers. Then the product of the integers 3 and 4, indicated by either

$$3 \cdot 4 \quad \text{or} \quad (3)(4)$$

means the sum

$$\text{\_\_\_\_\_} + \text{\_\_\_\_\_} + \text{\_\_\_\_\_} = \text{\_\_\_\_\_}$$

> **NATURAL;   4 + 4 + 4 = 12**

13. We want to define multiplication for negative integers in such a way that the commutative and associative properties are true, the distributive property is true, and the integers are closed with respect to multiplication.

First we consider the product of a positive integer and a negative integer. The product of 3 and −2 is indicated by writing either

$$(3)(-2) \quad \text{or} \quad 3(-2)$$

Similarly, the product of 5 and −4 is written either

$$\text{_____} \quad \text{or} \quad \text{_____}$$

> **(5)(−4);   5(−4)   (either order)**

14. We define the product

$$(3)(-2)$$

to be the sum of three terms, each of which is −2. Then

$$(3)(-2) = (-2) + (-2) + (-2) = \text{\_\_\_\_\_}$$

> **−6**

15. Similarly,

$$(5)(-4) = (-4) + (-4) + (-4) + (-4) + (-4)$$
$$= \text{\_\_\_\_\_}$$

> **−20**

16. The product of any positive and any negative integer is defined similarly.

$$(2)(-8) = (-8) + (-8) = \underline{\hspace{2cm}}$$

$$4(-3) = (-3) + (-3) + (-3) + (-3) = \underline{\hspace{2cm}}$$

-16;   -12

17. For natural numbers we call _____ the multiplicative identity, since the product of _____ and any natural number is that same number.

1;   1

18. And we define multiplication of integers in such a way that 1 is still the multiplicative identity. Then

$$(1)(-2) = \underline{\hspace{2cm}}$$

$$(1)(-3) = \underline{\hspace{2cm}}$$

$$(1)(-10) = \underline{\hspace{2cm}}$$

-2;   -3;   -10

19. Represent each product as a sum and add:

$$(3)(-1) = (-1) + (-1) + (-1) = -3$$

$$(4)(-3) = \underline{\hspace{1.5cm}} + \underline{\hspace{1.5cm}} + \underline{\hspace{1.5cm}}$$
$$+ \underline{\hspace{1.5cm}} = \underline{\hspace{1.5cm}}$$

$$(2)(-5) = \underline{\hspace{1.5cm}} + \underline{\hspace{1.5cm}} = \underline{\hspace{1.5cm}}$$

(-3) + (-3) + (-3) + (-3) = -12;
(-5) + (-5) = -10

20. The product of a positive and a negative integer is always the sum of negative integers. But the sum of negative integers is a _____ integer, and hence the product of a positive and a negative integer is always a _____ integer.

NEGATIVE;   NEGATIVE

21. We have shown that

$$(3)(-2) = -6$$

$$(5)(-4) = -20$$

$$(2)(-8) = -16$$

$$(3)(-1) = -3$$

$$(4)(-3) = -12$$

$$(2)(-5) = -10$$

In each case the product is negative. Note that the _____ value of each product is the product of the _____ values of the factors.

ABSOLUTE;   ABSOLUTE

22. In fact, the product of any positive integer and any negative integer will be a _____ integer, whose absolute value is the _____ of the absolute values of the factors.

NEGATIVE;   PRODUCT

23. Hence $(5)(-9) = -45$

$$(7)(-8) = \underline{\hspace{2cm}}$$

$$(12)(-10) = \underline{\hspace{2cm}}$$

$$(9)(-7) = \underline{\hspace{2cm}}$$

$$(236)(-849) = \underline{\hspace{2cm}}$$

-56;   -120;   -63;   -200364

24. If we define multiplication so that the commutative property is valid, then the product of a negative integer and a positive integer is determined. Thus

$$(-3)(4) = (4)(-3) = \underline{\hspace{2cm}}$$

$$(-8)(3) = (3)(-8) = \underline{\hspace{2cm}}$$

$$(-215)(73) = (73)(-215) = \underline{\hspace{2cm}}$$

-12;   -24;   -15695

25. Then the product of a positive and a negative integer in either order is always a _____ integer whose _____ value is the _____ of the _____ values of the factors.

NEGATIVE; ABSOLUTE; PRODUCT; ABSOLUTE

26. The number zero has a very special property of multiplication. If a is any natural number, we define

$$a \cdot 0 = 0 \cdot a = \underline{\hspace{2cm}}$$

0

27. To avoid contradiction we also define the product of zero and any integer, positive or negative, to be _____ .

0

28. Then

$$(4)(0) = \underline{\hspace{1.5cm}}$$
$$(0)(-7) = \underline{\hspace{1.5cm}}$$
$$(-2)(0) = \underline{\hspace{1.5cm}}$$
$$(0)(0) = \underline{\hspace{1.5cm}}$$

0;   0;   0;   0

29. Find the indicated product.

$$(-9)(2) = \underline{\hspace{1.5cm}}$$
$$(4)(3) = \underline{\hspace{1.5cm}}$$
$$(5)(-7) = \underline{\hspace{1.5cm}}$$
$$(-273)(0) = \underline{\hspace{1.5cm}}$$
$$(-53)(1) = \underline{\hspace{1.5cm}}$$

-18;   12;   -35;   0;   -53

30. If the distributive property for integers is valid, then we must have

$$(7)[(-2) + (-3)] = (7)(-2) + \underline{\hspace{2cm}}$$

(7)(-3)

31. Notice that there is no contradiction.

$$(7)[(-2) + (-3)] = (7)(-5) = -35$$

while

$$(7)(-2) + (7)(-3) = (-14) + (-21)$$
$$= \underline{\hspace{1.5cm}}$$

-35

32. It remains to define the product of two negative integers. Consider the product of -3 and -4, indicated by

$$(-3)(-4) \quad \text{or} \quad -3(-4)$$

There is no obvious way to define this product. Let us first consider the expression

$$4 + (-4) = 0$$

Then

$$(-3)[4 + (-4)] = (-3)(0) = \underline{\hspace{1.5cm}}$$

0

33. We have just observed that

$$(-3)[4 + (-4)] = 0$$

But if the distributive property is valid, then

$$(-3)[4 + (-4)] = (-3)(4) + \underline{\hspace{2cm}}$$

(-3)(-4)

34. By the distributive property

$$(-3)[4 + (-4)] = (-3)(4) + (-3)(-4)$$

But we know that

$$(-3)(4) = \underline{\hspace{1cm}}$$

And hence

$$(-3)[4 + (-4)] = \underline{\hspace{1cm}} + (-3)(-4)$$

—12;   —12

35. In the previous frame we established

$$(-12) + (-3)(-4) = -3[4 + (-4)]$$

But also we have that

$$-3[4 + (-4)] = (-3)(0) = 0$$

Then it follows that in simplest form

$$(-12) + (-3)(-4) = \underline{\hspace{1cm}}$$

0

36. $(-12) + (-3)(-4) = 0$

The sum of —12 and (—3)(—4) is zero, and hence (—3)(—4) is the $\underline{\hspace{2cm}}$ $\underline{\hspace{2cm}}$ of —12.

ADDITIVE INVERSE

37. Since $(-12) + (-3)(-4) = 0$, we say that $(-3)(-4)$ is the additive inverse of —12. But the additive inverse of —12 is $\underline{\hspace{1cm}}$. Then we can conclude that

$$(-3)(-4) = \underline{\hspace{1cm}}$$

12;   12

38. To review the argument

$$(-3)[4 + (-4)] = (-3)(0) = 0$$

$$(-3)[4 + (-4)] = (-12) + (-3)(-4)$$

Hence

$$(-12) + (-3)(-4) = 0$$

Then (—3)(—4) is the additive inverse of —12, so

$$(-3)(-4) = \underline{\hspace{1cm}}$$

12

39. In a similar way we can show that

$$(-4)(-5)\ = 20$$
$$(-2)(-9)\ = 18$$
$$(-7)(-5)\ = 35$$
$$(-3)(-20) = 60$$
$$(-8)(-7)\ = \underline{\hspace{1cm}}$$

56

40. In fact, the product of two negative integers is always a $\underline{\hspace{2cm}}$ integer, whose absolute value is the product of the absolute values of the factors.

POSITIVE

41. Then to find the absolute value of the product of any two integers, positive or negative, we $\underline{\hspace{2cm}}$ the absolute values of the factors.

MULTIPLY

42. The product of a positive and a negative integer is a _____ integer.

The product of two positive or two negative integers is a _____ integer.

> NEGATIVE;   POSITIVE

43. Find each product.

$(-3)(-9)$ = _____

$(4)(-7)$ = _____

$(-8)(3)$ = _____

$(5)(6)$ = _____

> 27;   −28;   −24;   30

44. Multiply

$(-215)(87)$ = _____

$(53)(-413)$ = _____

$(-711)(-296)$ = _____

> −18705;   −21889;   210456

45. We have defined multiplication of integers in such a way that the product of two integers is always an integer, and so the integers are _____ with respect to _____.

> CLOSED;   MULTIPLICATION

46. Also, the multiplication of integers is defined in such a way that the commutative and _____ properties are true. And even the _____ property, which involves both multiplication and addition, is true for integers.

> ASSOCIATIVE;   DISTRIBUTIVE

47. We are now ready to consider the division of integers. Recall that for natural numbers, we said the quotient of two natural numbers is a natural number whose _____ with the divisor equals the dividend, if such a natural number can be found.

> PRODUCT

48. Then, for natural numbers, division is the inverse of _____.

> MULTIPLICATION

49. We indicate the quotient of the natural numbers 8 and 2 by writing

$8/2$ or $\dfrac{8}{2}$

and we say that

$8/2 =$ _____,   since _____ $\cdot 2 = 8$

> 4;   4

50. We will define the quotient of two integers in exactly the same way. The quotient of two integers is an integer whose _____ with the divisor equals the _____, provided such an integer can be found.

> PRODUCT;   DIVIDEND

51. The quotient of the integers −12 and 3 is indicated by writing

$(-12)/3$

And we see that

$(-12)/3 =$ _____,   since

$(-4)(3) = -12$

> −4

52. Similarly,

$$(-15)/5 = \underline{}, \quad \text{since}$$
$$(-3)(5) = -15$$

$$(-20)/4 = \underline{}, \quad \text{since}$$
$$\underline{}(4) = -20$$

-3;   -5;   (-5)

53. $30/(-6) = \underline{}, \quad \text{since}$
$$\underline{} \cdot (-6) = 30$$

$$(-16)/(-8) = \underline{}, \quad \text{since}$$
$$\underline{} \cdot (-8) = -16$$

-5;   -5;   2;   2

54. $12/4 = 3, \quad \text{since} \quad 3 \cdot 4 = 12$

$$12/(-4) = \underline{}, \quad \text{since}$$
$$\underline{}(-4) = 12$$

$$(-12)/4 = \underline{}, \quad \text{since}$$
$$\underline{}(4) = -12$$

$$(-12)/(-4) = \underline{}, \quad \text{since}$$
$$\underline{}(-4) = -12$$

-3;   -3;   -3;   -3;   3;   3

55. $12/4 = 3 \qquad 12/(-4) = -3$

$(-12)/(-4) = 3 \qquad (-12)/4 = -3$

We see that the quotient of two positive integers is positive, the quotient of two negative integers is \underline{}, while the quotient of a positive and a negative integer, or a negative and a positive integer, is \underline{}.

POSITIVE;   NEGATIVE

56. But it is not always possible to find an integer whose product with the divisor equals the dividend. Consider

$$5/(-2) = []$$

There is no integer whose product with \underline{} equals \underline{}, and hence the quotient of 5 and -2 is not an integer.

-2;   5

57. Then since the quotient of two integers is not always an integer, we say that the integers are not \underline{} with respect to \underline{}.

CLOSED;   DIVISION

58. This is an unhappy result! Our reason for introducing the negative integers is to ensure that subtraction is always possible. We carefully defined addition and multiplication in such a way that these operations are always possible, and in such a way that the commutative, associative, and distributive properties are true. But still the set of integers is not large enough to ensure that \underline{} is always possible.

DIVISION

59. Let us enlarge the set of numbers again. This same problem of impossible divisions with natural numbers was solved by introducing the \underline{} numbers, which are represented by fractions.

QUOTIENT

60. And this larger set of quotient numbers is closed with respect to addition, multiplication and division. But the quotient numbers are not closed with respect to _____ .

SUBTRACTION

61. Let us assume that corresponding to each quotient number there is another number, called its additive inverse, with the property that the sum of these two numbers is 0. We represent the additive inverse of 2/3 by −(2/3), and the additive inverse of 3/4 by _____ .

−(3/4)

62. The set which contains all the quotient numbers, each of their additive inverses, and zero is called the set of RATIONAL NUMBERS. Then 2/3, −(2/3), and 0 are all members of the set of _____ numbers.

RATIONAL

63. It is impossible to list all the members of this set, and it is even impossible to indicate the set by listing a few members and using three dots, but we can describe the set of rational numbers by saying that it consists of all the _____ numbers, their additive inverses, and _____ .

QUOTIENT;   ZERO

64. Every quotient number is also a _____ number, and the additive inverse of every quotient number is a _____ number.

RATIONAL;   RATIONAL

65. Since

2/3,   4,   5/3

are all quotient numbers, then they are also _____ numbers.

RATIONAL

66. Which of these are rational numbers?

2/5,   −4,   9,   −(3/7),   0

ALL ARE

67. Every quotient number is a rational number, but some of the rational numbers are not also _____ _____ .

QUOTIENT NUMBERS

68. While

2/5,   −4,   9,   −(3/7),   0

are all rational numbers, only _____ and _____ from among these are also quotient numbers.

2/5;   9   (either order)

69. We call those rational numbers which are also quotient numbers the positive rational numbers, and we call the additive inverses of the positive rational numbers the _____ rational numbers.

NEGATIVE

70. Then 3,   4/7,   9,   12/5 are all _____ rational numbers, while –3, –(4/7), –9, –(12/5) are all _____ rational numbers.

POSITIVE;   NEGATIVE

71. There is one rational number which is neither a quotient number nor the additive inverse of a quotient number, and hence it is neither positive nor negative. It is the number _____ .

ZERO

72. Since every positive integer is a natural number, and hence a quotient number, we can say that every positive integer is also a R_____ number.

RATIONAL

73. And the negative integers, being the additive inverses of quotient numbers, are also R_____ numbers.

RATIONAL

74. In fact, every integer, positive, negative, or zero, is also a _____ number.

RATIONAL

75. Then we have the three sets: the natural numbers, the integers, and the rational numbers. Every natural number is both an _____ and a _____ number. Every integer is a _____ number.

INTEGER;   RATIONAL;   RATIONAL

76. Like the integers, every rational number and its additive inverse have the same _____ value.

ABSOLUTE

77. And we indicate the absolute value of the rational numbers with the same symbol we used before.

$|-(3/4)| = 3/4$

$|-(7/8)| = $ _____

$|5/3| = $ _____

7/8;   5/3

78. We now agree that the word number will mean rational number, the most inclusive of the sets of numbers so far considered. And we define the addition, subtraction, and multiplication of rational numbers in exactly the same way as for the integers. Then the sum of two negative numbers is a _____ number.

NEGATIVE

79. But the sum of a positive and a negative number may be either positive or negative, depending on which term has the larger _____ _____ .

ABSOLUTE VALUE

80. We indicate sums with rational numbers in the same way as for integers.

$(-\frac{1}{5}) + (-\frac{2}{5}) = $ _____

$(-\frac{3}{7}) + \frac{1}{7} = $ _____

–(3/5);   –(2/7)

81. The associative and commutative properties of addition are valid for the rational numbers, and since the sum of any two rational numbers is also a rational number, we say that the set of _____ numbers is _____ with respect to _____.

RATIONAL; CLOSED; ADDITION

82. Subtraction of rational numbers is defined in the usual way. The difference of two rational numbers is a number whose _____ with the subtrahend equals the _____.

SUM; MINUEND

83. And we can show that the difference of two rational numbers is also the sum of the minuend and the _____ _____ of the subtrahend, as we did for the integers.

ADDITIVE INVERSE

84. Then since every rational number has an additive inverse, and subtraction is merely the addition of the minuend and the additive inverse of the subtrahend, and addition is always possible, it follows that _____ is always possible, or that the rational numbers are closed with respect to _____.

SUBTRACTION; SUBTRACTION

85. The product of two rational numbers is _____ if both factors are positive or both factors are negative. But the product is _____ when one factor is positive and the other is negative, just as for the integers.

POSITIVE; NEGATIVE

86. Hence
$$\left(-\frac{2}{3}\right)\left(\frac{4}{5}\right) = -\frac{8}{15}$$
$$\left(-\frac{1}{2}\right)\left(-\frac{3}{4}\right) = \underline{\hspace{3cm}}$$
$$\left(\frac{5}{3}\right)\left(-\frac{2}{7}\right) = \underline{\hspace{3cm}}$$

3/8;   −(10/21)

87. The product of two rational numbers is always a rational number, so the rational numbers are closed with respect to _____. And the commutative and associative properties of multiplication are true for the rational numbers, as is the distributive property.

MULTIPLICATION

88. In fact the rational numbers have all the properties of the integers with respect to addition, subtraction, and multiplication. We will next show how the rational numbers are also closed with respect to division (except for division by _____).

ZERO

89. Consider the quotient of the integers −5 and 2. We indicate this quotient by

(−5)/2

It is not possible to find an integer whose product with the divisor, _____, equals the dividend, _____.

2;   −5

90. $(-5)/2 = [\quad]$

But there is a rational number whose product with 2 equals −5. It is the rational number −(5/2), the additive inverse of the quotient number _____.

$$\frac{5}{2}$$

91. Then

$(-5)/2 = -(5/2)$

Here the divisor is 2, the dividend is −5, and the quotient is − (5/2). We shall show that the product of the quotient and the _____ equals the _____.

DIVISOR;   DIVIDEND

92. $(-5)/2 = -(5/2)$

We must show that the product of −(5/2), the quotient, and 2, the divisor, equals −5, the dividend, and

$$\left(-\frac{5}{2}\right)(2) = \left(-\frac{5}{2}\right)\left(\frac{2}{1}\right) = -\frac{10}{2} = \underline{\quad}$$

−5

93. We have shown that the quotient of −5 and 2 is the rational number − (5/2). Similarly, we could show that the quotient of −7 and 3 is the rational number _____.

−(7/3)

94. Consider the quotient of 3 and −4, which we indicate by

$3/(-4)$

Since $-\frac{3}{4}(-4) = 3$, we see that −(3/4) is a number whose product with the divisor, −4, equals the dividend, 3, and hence −(3/4) is the _____ of 3 and −4.

QUOTIENT

95. Then

$3/(-4) = -(3/4)$

Similarly we can show that

$6/(-7) = \underline{\quad}$

And this result is just the additive inverse of the quotient number _____.

−(6/7);   6/7

96. $(-3)/(-8)$ represents the quotient of −3 and −8, and since $(3/8)(-8) = -3$, we see that

$(-3)/(-8) = \underline{\quad}$

3/8

97. $(-3)(-8) = 3/8$

We can also show that

$(-2)/(-9) = \underline{\quad}$

2/9

98. Consider the quotient of the rational numbers $-(3/4)$ and $1/2$.

We represent this quotient by $\left(-\frac{3}{4}\right) \div \frac{1}{2}$.

And the quotient must be a number whose product with the divisor $1/2$ equals the dividend, $-(3/4)$.

But

$$\left(-\frac{3}{2}\right)\left(\frac{1}{2}\right) = -\frac{3}{4},$$

and so $-(3/2)$ is such a number, and

$$\left(-\frac{3}{4}\right) \div \left(\frac{1}{2}\right) = \underline{\hspace{3cm}}.$$

> $-(3/2)$

99. In a similar way we can find the quotient of other rational numbers, unless the divisor is zero. Recall that when the product of two quotient numbers is 1, we say that each is the multiplicative _____ of the other.

> INVERSE

100. Then the multiplicative inverse of $2/3$ is $3/2$, since

$$\frac{2}{3} \cdot \frac{3}{2} = 1.$$

Every rational number, except zero, also has a multiplicative inverse. Since

$$\left(-\frac{2}{3}\right) \cdot \left(-\frac{3}{2}\right) = 1,$$

we see that _____ is the multiplicative inverse of $-(2/3)$.

> $-(3/2)$

101. And the multiplicative inverse of -4 is _____.

> $-(1/4)$

102. We showed that the quotient of two quotient numbers is also the _____ of the dividend and the multiplicative inverse of the divisor.

> PRODUCT

103. The same result can be shown for rational numbers. The quotient of two rational numbers is also the product of the _____ and the multiplicative inverse of the _____.

> DIVIDEND;   DIVISOR

104. And since every rational number, except zero, has a multiplicative inverse, and multiplication of rational numbers is always possible, we see that _____ of rational numbers is also possible, unless the _____ is zero.

> DIVISION;   DIVISOR

105. Then the rational numbers are also _____ with respect to _____ except for _____ by zero.

> CLOSED;   DIVISION;   DIVISION

106. Then we may always add, subtract, multiply, or divide with _____ numbers (with the exception of division by zero).

> RATIONAL

107. Add, subtract, multiply, or divide as indicated.

a) $\left(-\dfrac{3}{10}\right) + \left(-\dfrac{4}{10}\right) = $ _____

b) $\left(\dfrac{5}{9}\right) - \left(-\dfrac{2}{9}\right) = $ _____

c) $\left(-\dfrac{2}{5}\right)\left(\dfrac{3}{7}\right) = $ _____

d) $\left(-\dfrac{3}{8}\right) \div \left(-\dfrac{1}{3}\right) = $ _____

$-(7/10); \quad 7/9; \quad -(6/35); \quad 9/8$

108. We have defined the set of rational numbers to be the set containing every _____ number, its additive inverse, and zero.

QUOTIENT

109. And a positive rational number is what we have also called a _____ number.

QUOTIENT

110. And we have seen that the quotient of any two integers is always a _____ number, unless the divisor is zero.

RATIONAL

111. In fact, the rational numbers can be defined to be all those numbers which are the _____ of two integers (provided the _____ is not zero).

QUOTIENT;   DIVISOR

112. Since each of the symbols

$1/2, \quad 3, \quad -4, \quad -(5/6), \quad 0$

represents either zero, a quotient number, or the additive inverse of a quotient number, each represents a _____ number.

RATIONAL

113. And since each of the symbols

$(-2)/3, \quad 4/(-9), \quad (-5)/1, \quad -5$

represents the quotient of two integers, each is a _____ number.

RATIONAL

114. 1) A rational number is any quotient number, its additive inverse, or zero, or

2) A rational number is any number which is the quotient of two _____, provided the divisor is not zero.

INTEGERS

115. The symbol

3.71

is called a decimal form for the quotient number which can also be represented by the fraction

371/100

Then 3.71 is not only a quotient number, but also a _____ number.

RATIONAL

116. And other decimal forms of quotient numbers, such as

.3,   2.5,   9.22,   10.05

and their additive inverses, represented by

−.3,   −2.5,   −9.22,   −10.05

are also _____ numbers.

RATIONAL

117. We have seen that many quotient numbers do not have decimal representations. But even those which have no decimal form can be represented by a repeating decimal. Such repeating decimals represent quotient numbers, and also _____ numbers.

RATIONAL

118. Which of these represent rational numbers?

3/4, −(9/5), 4, 0, 1.5, −3.6, 5.222 · · ·

_____

ALL DO

119. We will see in the next chapter that not every number is a rational number. But every number which is a _____ number or its additive inverse, or every number which is the quotient of two _____ (divisor not zero) is a rational number.

QUOTIENT;   INTEGERS

120. Since every integer is a rational number, the set of integers is a _____ of the set of rational numbers. And since every _____ number is also an integer, the set of _____ numbers is a _____ of the set of integers.

SUBSET;   NATURAL;   NATURAL;   SUBSET

121. The natural numbers are the numbers in the set N = _____.

The integers are the numbers in the set I = _____.

$\{1, 2, 3, \ldots\}$; $\{\ldots, -3, -2, -1, 0, 1, 2, 3, \ldots\}$

122. The rational numbers cannot be listed in any logical order as can the natural numbers and the integers, but we may describe the rational numbers as being all those numbers which are _____ of two _____ (divisor not zero).

QUOTIENTS;   INTEGERS

123. The quotient numbers are not widely known as "quotient numbers." In fact, most people call them the positive _____ numbers.

RATIONAL

124. The symbol 7 represents a number which we describe as being a natural number, an integer, and also a rational number. But the symbol −12 is described as being only an _____ and a _____.

INTEGER;   RATIONAL NUMBER

125. While –(3/4) is neither an integer nor a natural number, it is a _____ .

126. From this set of numbers identify the natural numbers, integers, and rational numbers.

$\{-4, 0, 2, 1/2, -(2/3), 1.5\}$

The natural numbers are _____ .

The integers are _____ .

The rational numbers are _____ .

127. Every number in the set $\{1, 2, 3, \ldots\}$ is called a _____ _____ .

Every number in the set $\{\ldots, -3, -2, -1, 0, 1, 2, 3, \ldots\}$ is called an _____ .

128. Every number which is the quotient of two integers (divisor not zero) is called a _____ _____ .

129. The positive rational numbers are also called _____ _____ .

130. The _____ _____ are closed with respect to addition, subtraction, multiplication, and division (except for division by zero).

131. The _____ are closed with respect to addition, subtraction and multiplication, but not division.

132. The _____ _____ are closed with respect to addition, multiplication, and division, but not subtraction.

133. The _____ _____ are closed with respect to addition and multiplication only.

Chapter 28

Problems A (Answers on page 514)

The simplest form for a quotient number has already been defined. The simplest form for the additive inverse of a quotient number is indicated by writing a minus sign before the simplest form of the quotient number. Thus the simplest forms for 4/6 and its additive inverse are 2/3 and $-(2/3)$.

Write each of these rational numbers in simplest form.

1. $(-4)(-12)$
2. $(15)(-7)$
3. $(-3)(52)$
4. $5(-34)$
5. $-6(21)$
6. $-7(-4)$
7. $-3(0)$
8. $(-8) + (-2)$
9. $(-12) - (-4)$
10. $0 - (-8)$
11. $(-15)/5$
12. $(-20)/(-4)$
13. $(-36)/(-12)$
14. $0/(-3)$
15. $(-8)/6$
16. $(-12)/(-8)$
17. $6/(-20)$
18. $10/(-45)$
19. $-[10/(-2)]$
20. $-[(-8)/(-4)]$

21. $\left(-\dfrac{1}{9}\right) + \left(-\dfrac{4}{9}\right)$
22. $\left(-\dfrac{2}{7}\right) - \left(-\dfrac{1}{7}\right)$
23. $\dfrac{5}{11} + \left(-\dfrac{3}{11}\right)$
24. $\left(-\dfrac{2}{3}\right)\left(-\dfrac{5}{9}\right)$
25. $\left(-\dfrac{1}{2}\right)\left(\dfrac{5}{7}\right)$
26. $\left(\dfrac{3}{8}\right)\left(-\dfrac{2}{5}\right)$
27. $\dfrac{2}{3} \div \left(-\dfrac{5}{4}\right)$
28. $\left(-\dfrac{3}{7}\right) \div \left(-\dfrac{2}{3}\right)$
29. $5 \div \left(-\dfrac{2}{3}\right)$
30. $\left(-\dfrac{3}{5}\right) \div (3)$

For the following problems consider the four sets

a) natural numbers
b) integers
c) quotient numbers
d) rational numbers

Indicate which of these sets contain the given number.

Example: -3. Answer: b and d.

31. $2/3$
32. -2
33. 5
34. 1.3
35. $-(3/4)$
36. $.333 \cdots$
37. -5.24

Which of the sets above:

38. Are closed with respect to subtraction?
39. Are closed with respect to division (except for division by zero)?
40. Are subsets of the integers?
41. Are subsets of the quotient numbers?
42. Contain the additive identity?
43. Contain the additive inverse of each of their members?

Problems B

Write each of these in simplest form.

1. $(-3)(-9)$
2. $(5)(-8)$
3. $(-7)(4)$
4. $4(-9)$
5. $-3(12)$
6. $(-8) + (-9)$
7. $5 - (-3)$
8. $-8 - (-8)$
9. $(-15)/3$
10. $12/(-6)$
11. $(-18)/(-3)$
12. $(-6)/4$
13. $9/(-12)$
14. $0/(-5)$

15. $\left(-\dfrac{2}{3}\right) + \left(-\dfrac{2}{3}\right)$
16. $\dfrac{3}{8} + \left(-\dfrac{6}{8}\right)$
17. $\left(-\dfrac{1}{5}\right) - \left(-\dfrac{2}{5}\right)$
18. $-\dfrac{2}{9} - \dfrac{5}{9}$
19. $\left(-\dfrac{3}{7}\right)\left(\dfrac{5}{8}\right)$
20. $\left(-\dfrac{5}{9}\right)\left(-\dfrac{2}{7}\right)$
21. $\left(\dfrac{3}{11}\right) \div \left(-\dfrac{2}{5}\right)$
22. $\left(-\dfrac{5}{12}\right) \div \left(-\dfrac{7}{5}\right)$

The simplest decimal form for quotient numbers has been defined for those numbers which have decimal forms. The simplest decimal form for the additive inverse of a quotient number which has a decimal form is indicated by using the minus sign before the simplest decimal form of the quotient number. Thus the simplest decimal forms for 3/2 and its additive inverse are 1.5 and −1.5.

Find the simplest decimal form for each of these.

23. (2.6) + (−.9)

24. (−8.26) + (−5.4)

25. (−5.6) − (−1.87)

26. (−2.5)(3.1)

27. (−16.8) ÷ (−4)

For the following problems consider the sets:

a) natural numbers

b) integers

c) quotient numbers

d) rational numbers

Which of these sets contain

28. 3/2

29. −(4/9)

30. 6

31. −9

32. 1.3

33. −8.7

34. 0

35. .6666 ⋯

36. −.454545 ⋯

Which of these sets

37. Are closed with respect to addition, subtraction, and multiplication, but not division?

38. Is closed with respect to addition, multiplication, and division, but not subtraction?

39. Is closed with respect to addition, subtraction, multiplication, and division (except for division by zero)?

40. Is closed with respect to addition and multiplication, but not subtraction and division?

41. Is a subset of the set of natural numbers?

42. Contain every integer?

43. Contains every quotient number and its additive inverse?

44. Are subsets of the set of rational numbers?

45. Contain only positive numbers?

46. Contain both positive and negative numbers?

47. Contains the multiplicative inverse of each of its members?

CHAPTER 29

REAL NUMBERS AND THE NUMBER LINE

1. The property shared by all sets of the same size is called a _____

   _____.

   NATURAL NUMBER

2. The set of natural numbers can be represented by

   $\{1, 2, 3, \ldots\}$.

   The number we represent by

   0

   is called _____ and is the size of the _____ set.

   ZERO;   EMPTY

3. Zero and the natural numbers are ordered. That is, if a and b represent such numbers, exactly one of the following is true:

   a _____ b
   a _____ b
   a _____ b

   =;   <;   >   (any order)

4. If a and b represent natural numbers or zero, then by

   $a < b$

   we mean there is a natural number, d, such that

   _____

   $a + d = b$ or $d + a = b$

5. The property shared by all fractions equal to any given fraction is called a _____

   _____.

   QUOTIENT NUMBER

6. And since every natural number may be represented by a fraction, the set of natural numbers is a subset of the set of _____ numbers.

   QUOTIENT

7. The quotient numbers, too, are ordered. If a/b and c/d represent quotient numbers, then

   a/b = c/d   if   _____

   a/b < c/d   if   _____

   a/b > c/d   if   _____

   ad = bc;   ad < bc;   ad > bc

8. The additive inverse of 0 is _____ .

   0

9. And every natural number also has an additive inverse. If a is a natural number, its additive inverse is represented by the symbol (–a), and

   a + (–a) = (–a) + a = _____

   0

10. Zero, the natural numbers, and their additive inverses are referred to as _____ .

    INTEGERS

11. The set of integers has, as two subsets, the set of natural numbers and the set of additive inverses of the natural numbers. On occasion the natural numbers are called the _____ integers and their additive inverses the _____ integers.

    POSITIVE;   NEGATIVE

12. But _____ is neither positive nor negative, although it is an integer.

    ZERO

13. The set of natural numbers, but not the set of quotient numbers, is a _____ of the set of integers.

    SUBSET

14. In fact the set of integers can be thought of as the _____ of the set of zero and the natural numbers and the set of their additive inverses.

    UNION

15. Zero and the natural numbers are ordered. But we have not yet ordered the integers. Let us do so now, but let us do so in such a way that the resulting ordering does not conflict with the order already established for natural numbers. One way to insure that this will happen is to use the same definition of "less than."

    That is, if x and y represent integers, then we shall say x < y if there is a _____ number d such that

    x + d = y

    NATURAL

16. We know that

    4 < 9   since   4 + 5 = 9

    Also

    –2 < 5   since   –2 + _____ = 5

    7

17. –3 < 7   since   (–3) + 10 = 7

    –4 < 4   since   (–4) + _____ = 4

    –13 < –2   since   (–13) + _____ = –2

    8;   11

18. And $-3 < 1$ since   _____

while $-100 < 0$ since   _____

> $(-3) + 4 = 1;$ $(-100) + 100 = 0$

19. Is $1 < -10$?   _____

> NO   (see next frame)

20. $1 + (-11) = -10$, but since -11 is not a <u>natural</u> number, 1 is not less than -10. In fact $(-10) + 11 = 1$ and so we <u>can</u> write

_____ .

> $-10 < 1$

21. Since $-10 < 1$ is true, we shall again say that -10 is less than 1 or that 1 is _____ than -10, and we shall write this fact, in symbols, as 1 _____ -10.

> GREATER; $>$

22. Insert either $<$ or $>$ so as to form a true statement:

-4 _____ 13

-6 _____ -9

4 _____ -8

-17 _____ -2

> $<;$ $>;$ $>;$ $<$

23. We have assumed that every quotient number has an additive inverse. If a/b represents a quotient number, then its additive inverse can be represented by $-(a/b)$ and

$$\frac{a}{b} + \left(-\frac{a}{b}\right) = \underline{\hspace{2cm}}$$

> 0

24. The set which contains every quotient number, its additive inverse, and zero is called the set of _____ numbers.

> RATIONAL

25. The quotient numbers are also called the _____ rational numbers, while their additive inverses are called the _____ rational numbers.

> POSITIVE;   NEGATIVE

26. But zero, while a rational number, is neither _____ nor _____ .

> POSITIVE;   NEGATIVE
> (either order)

27. The rational numbers, then, may be described as being the union of a set which contains zero and all the _____ numbers with a set which contains the additive inverses of the _____ numbers.

> QUOTIENT;   QUOTIENT

28. And the set of natural numbers, the set of quotient numbers, and the set of integers are all _____ of the set of rational numbers.

> **SUBSETS**

29. The set of quotient numbers is ordered. But we have not yet ordered the set of rational numbers. We shall soon do so, but let us first recall an alternate definition of a rational number. A rational number is one which may be written as a quotient of _____ (the divisor not zero).

> **INTEGERS**

30. Then

$$(-7)/3, \quad 6/(-13), \quad 0/21, \quad \text{and} \quad (-4)/(-9)$$

are all quotients of integers and so each represents a _____ number.

> **RATIONAL**

31. $4/(-12)$ and $(-2)/6$ each represents a rational number, since each is a quotient of integers. But both $4/(-12)$ and $(-2)/6$ are ways of writing the rational number $-(1/3)$ which is the _____ _____ of $1/3$. Hence we can write

$$4/(-12) \quad \underline{} \quad (-2)/6$$

> **ADDITIVE INVERSE; =**

32. Similarly, both $(-35)/(-10)$ and $(-42)/(-12)$ represent the rational number $7/2$ and so we could write

$$(-35)/\underline{} = \underline{}/(-12)$$

> $(-35)/(\underline{-10}) = (\underline{-42})/(-12)$

33. Every quotient number can be represented by a fraction, and we have seen that the same quotient number can be represented by many different fractions. However, all such fractions are _____.

> **EQUAL**

34. For rational numbers, too, the same number can be expressed as a quotient of integers in many ways. We shall, of course, want to call all such representations " _____."

> **EQUAL**

35. One way to determine whether two such representations of rational numbers are equal is to see if they each represent the same quotient number or additive inverse of the same quotient number.

Thus, $(-84)/7$ and $120/(-10)$ are equal since each represents the integer _____.

> **−12**

36. Hence we would write

$$(-84)/7 = 120/(-10)$$

But the cross product test for equality, which we used to determine whether two representatives of quotient numbers were equal, is also valid for rational numbers.

$$(-84)(-10) = 840 = (7)(120)$$

Use the cross product test to show that

$$3/(-17) = 12/(-68)$$

> $(3)(-68) = -204 = (-17)(12)$

37. Then $(-5)/(-4) = 35/28$ since
$(-5)(28) = -140 = (-4)(35)$

and $(-22)/7 = (-176)/56$ since

_____

But $4/(-13) \neq (-28)/78$ since
$(4)(78) = 312 \neq 364 = (-13)(-28)$

and $15/8 \neq (-30)/16$ since

_____

> $(-22)(56) = -1232 = (7)(-176)$
> $(15)(16) = 240 \neq -240 = (8)(-30)$

38. Insert = or $\neq$ between each pair of rational number representations so as to form a true statement. Use the cross product test.

$5/(-6)$ _____ $40/(-45)$

$(-13)/3$ _____ $65/(-15)$

$(-3)/(-22)$ _____ $27/198$

> $\neq$;   =;   =

39. Let us now establish an order for the rational numbers. But let us do so in such a way that the order we have defined for the subset of the rational numbers which is the quotient numbers is not changed.

Recall, again, that if a/b and c/d represent quotient numbers,

$a/b < c/d$ means _____ .

> $ad < bc$

40. We might be tempted to use this definition to order the rational numbers. After all, we know it is valid for the subset of the rational numbers which is the quotient numbers.

But consider the rational numbers $(-12)/4$ and $20/(-2)$. Taking cross products,

$(-12)(-2) = 24$ and $(4)(20) = 80$,

and certainly $24 < 80$. We might, then, wish to conclude that

$(-12)/4 < 20/(-2)$

But this cannot be correct!

41. $(-12)/4 = -3$ and $20/(-2) = -10$

From our ordering of the integers, which we also wish to preserve,

-3 _____ -10

and so we must conclude that

$(-12)/4$ _____ $20/(-2)$

> >;   >

42. $(-12)/4 > 20/(-2)$

Now we can write

$20/(-2) = (-20)/2$

since _____

> $(20)(2) = 40 = (-2)(-20)$

43. If we now compare $(-12)/4$ and $(-20)/2$ by their cross products we obtain

$(-12)(2) = -24$ and $(4)(-20) = -40$

Observe that

$-24 > -40$ and $(-12)/4 > (-20)/2$

The cross products now indicate the correct order of these rational numbers. Note that both $(-12)/4$ and $(-20)/2$ have positive _____ .

> DIVISORS

44. Let us use this observation to define the ordering of the rational numbers. If x and y represent rational numbers, then $x < y$ if there are representations of x and y as quotients of integers with _____ divisors

$x = p/q, \quad y = r/s$

such that

$ps < qr$

> POSITIVE

45. Then to compare $-(3/8)$ and $-(5/11)$, we can write

$$-(3/8) = (-3)/8 \quad \text{and} \quad -(5/11) = (-5)/11$$

Then,

$$(-5)/11 < (-3)/8$$

since

$$(-5)(8) = -40 \underline{\hspace{1cm}} -33 = (11)(-3)$$

and so

$$-(5/11) \underline{\hspace{1cm}} -(3/8)$$

<;   <

46. And to compare $-(5/3)$ and $2/7$, we can write

$$-(5/3) = (-5)/3$$

and compare this with $2/7$.

Then $\quad (-5)/3 < 2/7 \quad$ since

$$\underline{\hspace{5cm}}$$

$(-5)(7) = -35 < 6 = (3)(2)$

47. If x and y represent rational numbers, then by the statement $x > y$ we shall mean that $y < x$.

Thus, $\quad -(4/9) > -(8/3)$

since $\quad -(8/3) < -(4/9)$

which can be seen by writing

$$-(8/3) = (-8)/3 \text{ and } -(4/9) = (-4)/9$$

and comparing $(-8)(9)$ and $(3)(-4)$.

Is $\quad -(21/2) > -(40/3)$? $\quad \underline{\hspace{1.5cm}}$

YES; $\left(-\dfrac{21}{2} = \dfrac{-21}{2}; \quad -\dfrac{40}{3} = \dfrac{-40}{3} \text{ and } \dfrac{-40}{3} < \dfrac{-21}{2} \text{ since } -80 < -63 \right)$

48. Insert one of the symbols $=, <, >$ so as to form a true statement.

$$2/3 \underline{\hspace{2cm}} -4$$
$$-(5/8) \underline{\hspace{2cm}} -(10/15)$$
$$17/(-4) \underline{\hspace{2cm}} -(85/20)$$
$$(-6)/(-11) \underline{\hspace{2cm}} 7/12$$

>;   >;   =;   <

49. Insert one of the symbols $=, <, >$ so as to form a true statement.

$$-3 \underline{\hspace{2cm}} -(12/5)$$
$$-(8/9) \underline{\hspace{2cm}} -(7/8)$$
$$(-15)/4 \underline{\hspace{2cm}} -(27/7)$$
$$0 \underline{\hspace{2cm}} -(5/6)$$

<;   <;   >;   >

50. The concept of a STRAIGHT LINE is familiar to you. Which of the following represent a straight line? $\underline{\hspace{1.5cm}}$

a) 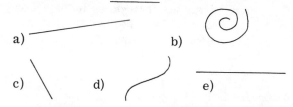 b)

c) d) e)

a, c, and e

51. Every straight line will be considered as a set of POINTS. Thus, the line below includes the points marked A, B, and C as well as other points not named.

Is point D on this straight line? $\quad \underline{\hspace{1.5cm}}$

Is point E? $\quad \underline{\hspace{2cm}}$

NO;   YES

52. Since we shall usually be concerned with straight lines only, we will often refer to them simply as LINES. We shall name a line by naming any two points on it. Then "line XY" refers to which line below? _____

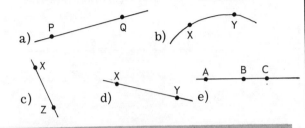

a) ___
b) ___
c) ___
d) ___
e) ___

d

53. Any two points determine a line. It is the line that contains the two points. We shall assume that only _____ such line exists.

ONE

54. That is, if the points marked A and B, below, are given, then only _____ line can be found which contains these points. Draw it.

ONE;

55. If your answer to the last frame was

you were not quite correct! A line does not have a beginning or an end. The line containing A and B does not B _____ at A and E _____ at B.

BEGIN;   END

56. Of course, this means that we can never really draw any line completely. Since each line should continue forever in both directions, we might use dots:

Often we shall not do so, but we must remember that a straight line has no

_____ or _____ .

BEGINNING;   END   (either order)

57. When three distinct points lie on the same line, one of the points is BETWEEN the other two. On the line below, point _____ is between points A and _____ .

A ·   C B

C;   B

58. On the line below, point Q is _____ points P and R.

P   Q   R

BETWEEN

59. But we only speak of a point as being between two points if all three lie on the same

_____ _____ .

STRAIGHT LINE

60.

·C
A   D   B

Then point _____ is between A and B, but point _____ is not between A and B.

D;   C

61. Is point X between points W and Y? _____

X ——— W ——————————— Y

Is point G between points F and H? _____

Is point R between points S and T? _____

S — R ————— T

62. The line below contains the points X and Y.

X Y

We shall call the set of points whose members are X, Y, and all points between them a LINE SEGMENT. We shall represent this line segment by

X ——————————— Y

63. Then F ———— G ———— represents a
_____ _____ , while

F •————————————• G represents a _____
_____.

64. A line has no beginning or end, but a line segment has two END POINTS. The line segment

R •———————————————• S

has _____ and _____ as end points.

65. We shall often use number symbols, rather than letters, to name points on a line.

Thus points 3, 5, and –(7/2) lie on the line shown below and point _____ is between points _____ and –(7/2) on this line.

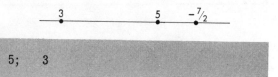

66. Let us consider a horizontal line and a single point on it.

_____

We shall call this point the ORIGIN, and use the number zero to label it.

0

67.
_____•_____
0

Let us also consider a line segment XY of some fixed length:

X •———————• Y

By placing XY on the line so that X is at the origin and Y is to the right of X, we obtain a new point, which we label 1.

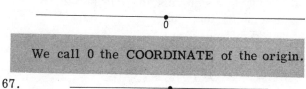

Again, we call 1 the _____ of this point.

68.

If we again place the line segment XY on the line so that, this time, X is at the point 1 and Y is to the right of X, we obtain a third point which we label 2.

We call 2 the _____ of this new point.

COORDINATE

69.

```
 _____
   0   1   2
```

The process can be repeated indefinitely. Each time we place the segment XY on the line we obtain a new point which we label with the next _____ number. And in this way we obtain

```
 _____
   0   1   2   3   4   5
```

NATURAL

70.

```
 _____ ...
   0   1   2   3   4   5
```

We have determined, for each natural number, one point on our original line. Let us next place the segment XY so that X is at the origin, but point Y is to the left of X.

```
   Y   X
 _____
   0   1   2   3   4   5
```

We shall use the number _____ as the co-ordinate of the point thus determined.

−1

71.

```
 _____
  -1   0   1   2   3   4   5
```

And, again, placing the line segment XY as shown below

```
   Y   X
 _____
   1   0   1   2   3   4   5
```

We obtain another point whose coordinate is _____.

−2

72.

```
 _____
  -2  -1   0   1   2   3   4   5
```

Continuing in this way we can find a new point on the line for each negative integer.

```
... _____ ...
   -5  -4  -3  -2  -1   0   1   2   3   4   5
```

Thus we have determined one point on our line for each _____. But many points still have no _____.

INTEGER;   COORDINATE

73.

```
 _____
  -5  -4  -3  -2  -1   0   1   2   3   4   5
```

We have determined one point on the line for each integer in such a way that no two integers correspond to the same point. We shall find it useful, on occasion, to refer to the points on the line corresponding to integers when we wish to make a statement about those integers.

For example, we have seen that −2 < 3. Note that the point corresponding to −2 is to the _____ of the point corresponding to 3.

LEFT

74.

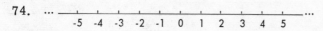

We have also seen that −4 < −1. Note that the point corresponding to −4 is to the _____ of the point corresponding to −1.

The point whose coordinate is −5 is to the left of the point whose coordinate is 4. Is −5 < 4? _____

LEFT;   YES

75.

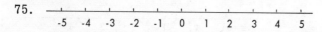

It is generally true that if one integer is less than a second, the point on our line corresponding to the first integer will be to the _____ of the point corresponding to the second. In fact, this furnishes us with a handy means of deciding which of two integers is the S _____.

LEFT;   SMALLER

76.

It is a line with −5 −4 −3 −2 −1 0 1 2 3 4 5

Then, even though our line is not drawn completely, we see from it that

$$-6 < -2;$$
$$-3 \underline{\hspace{1cm}} 7;$$
$$-2 \underline{\hspace{1cm}} 1;$$
$$4 \underline{\hspace{1cm}} -4$$

<;   <;   >

77.

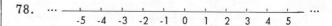

$$4 > -4 \quad \text{since} \quad -4 < 4$$

Also, we have seen that 3 is between 2 and 4. That is,

$$2 < 3 < 4$$

Observe that on our line the point whose coordinate is 3 lies _____ the points with coordinates 2 and 4.

BETWEEN

78.

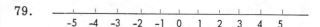

Again, we can use our line to see at a glance whether one integer is between two others.

Is   −2 between   −3 and 1?   _____
Is   0 between   −7 and −3?   _____
Is   3 between   −1 and 5?   _____
Is   2 between   1 and 2?   _____

YES;   NO;   YES;   NO

79.

−5 −4 −3 −2 −1 0 1 2 3 4 5

We have constructed a line on which each integer has exactly one corresponding point. Let us "extend" this process so that

1) Every rational number will correspond to one, and only one, point.

2) Those rational numbers which are also integers will correspond to the points already determined.

3) The _____ of two rational numbers will correspond to a point to the left of that which the _____ number corresponds to.

SMALLER;   LARGER

80.

Consider the segment RS

R⌞____⌟S

When RS is placed on our line so that R is at 0 and S is to the right of R, a new point T on our line is determined.

81.

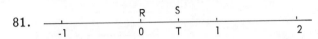

Now suppose that when RS is again placed on our line, this time so that R is at T and S is to the right of R, point S falls on the point whose coordinate is 1.

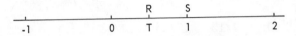

Then segment RS is said to SPAN segment 01 exactly twice. Let us use the rational number _____ as the coordinate of T.

82.

Let us also place segment RS so that R is at 1 and S is to the right of R.

The point where S now falls will be given the coordinate _____ .

83.

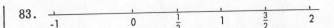

Similar placements of RS would give points whose coordinates would also be rational numbers.

Indeed, the coordinate of A would be _____ and the coordinate of B would be _____ .

84.

Suppose that segment TU spans segment 01 exactly four times.

T_⌞_⌟U

Then, if we place TU on our line so that T falls at 0 and U is to the right of T, we get a point whose coordinate will be the rational number _____ .

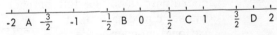

85.

Segment TU can also be used to locate other points whose coordinates are rational numbers.

Give the coordinates of points

A _____   B _____
C _____   D _____

86. In fact, using the segment TU in all possible ways will give coordinates to many points.

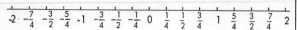

Using segment VW, which spans segment 01 exactly five times, we could give coordinates to other points on our line.

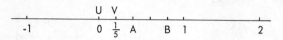

Point A has coordinate _____ and B has coordinate _____ .

2/5;   4/5

87. Indeed, we can find a line segment that will exactly span segment 01 any natural number of times, and each such segment can be used to give coordinates to many points on our line.

We shall not do so, but continuing in this way would eventually result in determining one point on our line for each _____ number.

RATIONAL

88. The following facts about the line we have constructed in this way will be assumed:

1) Our line has one, and only one, point corresponding to each rational number.

2) Every rational number which is an integer corresponds to a point whose coordinate is the integer previously assigned it.

3) Every point which has a rational number coordinate is to the left of each point whose coordinate is a _____ rational number.

LARGER

89. We have previously shown that between every two quotient numbers there is another quotient number. For example, between the quotient numbers represented by 2/3 and 3/4 is the quotient number represented by

$$\frac{2+3}{3+4} = \frac{5}{7}$$

Find such a quotient number between:

7/12 and 10/13 _____

19/3 and 17/2 _____

$$\frac{7+10}{12+13} = \frac{17}{25}; \quad \frac{19+17}{3+2} = \frac{36}{5}$$

90. $7/12 < 17/25 < 10/13$

$19/3 < 36/5 < 17/2$

Our line shows these facts, too.

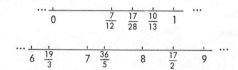

This process can be continued endlessly. There is no limit to the number of quotient numbers we can find between any given two. We say that there are an _____ number of quotient numbers between any two.

INFINITE

91. The same statement can also be made for rational numbers, although the method for finding a rational number between the given rational numbers is more complicated than for quotient numbers. Between any two rational numbers there is an infinite number of other rational numbers.

But each rational number corresponds to one point on our line. Hence between any two points with rational number coordinates is an _____ number of other points with _____ number coordinates.

INFINITE;   RATIONAL

92.

Hence our line has one and only one point for each rational number, but between any two such points are an infinite number of other points with rational number coordinates!

No matter how close together two points with rational coordinates may be, there are an infinite number of points with rational coordinates _____ them.

BETWEEN

93.

Between any two points with rational coordinates there are an infinite number of other such points. It would surely seem then that every point on our line has a rational number coordinate. But this is <u>not</u> the case. There are points on the line which do not have any rational number as their coordinate!

We have not named all the points on our line!!

94. A simple way to locate a point whose coordinate is not a rational number is to take the circle shown below

and place it on the line at the origin.

95.

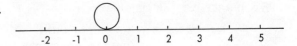

If the circle is now rolled to the right along the line until the point initially at 0 is again on the line

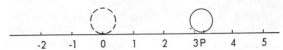

the point P has a _____ which is not a rational number.

COORDINATE

96.

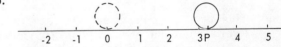

The point P determined in this way does not have a rational number for its coordinate. We shall introduce a new kind of number, an IRRATIONAL number, as a coordinate for P.

Using other circles, or using the same circle starting at other points, we can find many other points whose coordinates are _____ numbers.

IRRATIONAL

97. Indeed, between any two points whose coordinates are irrational numbers there is an infinite number of other points whose coordinates are also <u>irrational</u> numbers.

But this same statement was made for the rational numbers! How can this be? Only if the points with rational and irrational numbers occur _____ one another.

BETWEEN

98. In fact, we can conclude:

   1) Between any two points with
      _____ number coordinates there
      are an infinite number of points which
      have rational number coordinates and
      also an infinite number of points which
      have irrational number coordinates!

   2) Between any two points with
      _____ number coordinates there
      are, again, an infinite number of points
      which have rational number coordinates
      and also an infinite number of points
      which have irrational number co-
      ordinates!!

   RATIONAL;   IRRATIONAL   (either
   order)

99. This is a difficult state of affairs to picture.
    Every point on our line has a coordinate
    which is either a rational or an irrational
    number, but the points are so close together
    that between any two are an infinite number
    of other points of both kinds.

    The set of all irrational numbers determined
    in this way is interesting but we shall not in-
    vestigate it in this text.

100. We shall call the union of the set of rational
     numbers and the set of irrational numbers
     the set of REAL numbers. The set of real
     numbers, then, has both the set of rational
     numbers and the set of irrational numbers
     as _____ .

   SUBSETS

101.
   ```
   ────┼────┼────┼────┼────┼────┼────
      -2   -1   0    1    2    3
   ```

   And every point on our line corresponds to
   one, and only one, _____ number.

   REAL

102.
   ```
   ────┼────┼────┼────┼────┼────┼────
      -2   -1   0    1    2    3
   ```

   In fact, we shall refer to our line as the REAL
   NUMBER LINE or, simply, as the "number
   line."

   Every point on the real number line has a
   coordinate which is either a _____
   or an _____ number.

   RATIONAL;   IRRATIONAL

103. Every rational number except zero is either
     a _____ number or the additive in-
     verse of a _____ number.

   QUOTIENT;   QUOTIENT

104. Some quotient numbers also have a decimal
     representation. Thus we can write

     $5/8 = .625$

     $7/20 =$ _____

     $15/16 =$ _____

   .35;   .9375

105. Then certain rational numbers also have a
     decimal representation.

     $-(14/5) = -2.8$

     $-(3/25) =$ _____

     $-(117/40) =$ _____

   $-.12;$ -2.925

480   STRUCTURE OF ARITHMETIC

[29:98]

106. But most quotient numbers do not have a decimal representation and so most rational numbers cannot be expressed in decimal form.

However, we can find a repeating decimal to represent quotient numbers which have no decimal form.

Thus, we can write

2/3 = .666···

5/6 = _____

1/7 = _____

107. And so we can also represent certain rational numbers with no decimal form by repeating decimals.

−(2/9) = −.222···

−(19/3) = _____

−(5/12) = _____

108. For purposes of computation we often use suitable decimal approximations of quotient numbers. Thus

.67 is a two-place decimal approximation of 2/3.

_____ is a three-place decimal approximation of 5/6.

_____ is a two-place decimal approximation of 1/7.

109. And for rational numbers, too, we can form decimal approximations.

−.2 is a one-place decimal approximation for −(2/9)

_____ is a two-place decimal approximation for −(19/3)

_____ is a three-place decimal approximation for −(5/12)

110. But an irrational number is one which is not rational. Hence an irrational number cannot have a decimal form nor can it be expressed as a repeating decimal. Indeed, one of the difficulties with irrational numbers is that we <u>cannot</u> write them <u>at all</u> using only the digits and the decimal point!

111. One way to represent an irrational number is to use a letter symbol rather than one involving digits. Thus the Greek letter _____ is often used to name the coordinate of the point P determined by rolling our circle along the number line.

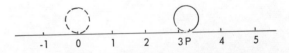

112. But for computational purposes we must resort to approximations. Fortunately, we have an infinite number of rational numbers between any two irrational numbers and so can use these to approximate any irrational number.

Thus, a two-place decimal approximation for the number π is

3.14

and a one-place decimal approximation for this number is

_____

113. A three-place decimal approximation for π is 3.142 and 3.1416 is a _____ - _____ decimal approximation for π.

114. Decimal approximations for π with still more places are possible, but we should point out that:

    1) No matter how many places are used, only a rational approximation for the irrational number π is possible.

    2) No matter how many places are considered, no sequence of digits is repeated. π cannot be represented as a repeating decimal.

    3) For computation purposes, as we shall see in the next chapter, an approximation is not only acceptable, but desired.

115. π is only one example of an irrational number, but the statements made for it apply to every irrational number.

To summarize, every point on the number line

has a coordinate which is a _____ number.

116. Every real number is either a _____ or an _____ number.

117. And the set of rational numbers has the sets of _____ numbers, _____ numbers, and integers as subsets.

Problems A   (Answers on page 514)

Each of the following integers is the coordinate of a point on the number line. For each pair of points tell which point is on the left on the number line, and insert the symbol < or > between the integers.

Example: −4 and −9.

Answer: −9 is on the left; −4 > −9.

1. 3 and 8

2. −1 and 5

3. 2 and −10

4. 5 and −1

5. −9 and −3

6. −4 and −10

7. 0 and 7

8. 0 and −3

9. −5 and 5

10. −12 and −13

11. −435 and 2

12. 157 and −812

13. −814 and 0

14. −543 and −175

15. −316 and −519

For each pair of rational numbers insert the symbol <, >, or =.

16. −(3/2) _____ −(1/2)

17. 7 _____ −(5/3)

18. −(4/5) _____ −(3/5)

19. −(3/7) _____ −(2/5)

20. −(8/13) _____ −(5/8)

21. 0 _____ −(7/10)

22. −(5/7) _____ −(7/10)

23. 1.65 _____ 1.64

24. −1.65 _____ −1.64

25. 3.2 _____ −4.9

26. −3.2 _____ 4.9

27. 275.42 _____ 275.4

28. −275.42 _____ −275.4

29. 1/3 _____ .3

30. −1/3 _____ −.3

For the following problems consider the sets

    a) natural numbers

    b) integers

    c) quotient numbers

    d) rational numbers

    e) irrational numbers

    f) real numbers

    g) empty set

Exactly one of the above sets is described by each of the expressions. Tell which set is described.

Example: A set which contains 3 and −2, but not 1.5. Answer: b

Example: The intersection of the natural numbers and the integers. Answer: a

31. A set which contains 2/3, but not −1.

32. A set which contains −2.3, but not π.

33. A set which contains π, but not 1.

34. A set which contains both π and 1.

35. A set which contains neither π nor 1.

36. The union of the rational and irrational numbers.

37. The intersection of the quotient numbers and the rational numbers.

38. The intersection of the irrational numbers and the real numbers.

39. A subset of the real numbers which is not a subset of the rational numbers, and is not the set of real numbers.

40. A subset of the integers which contains 0.

Problems B

Insert the symbol $<$, $>$, or $=$ between each of the following pairs of rational numbers.

1. -4 _____ 10

2. 12 _____ -6

3. 3 _____ -15

4. -21 _____ 3

5. 0 _____ -9

6. -5 _____ 0

7. -7 _____ -2

8. -1 _____ -9

9. -436 _____ 9

10. -275 _____ -375

11. 342 _____ -751

12. $-(7/8)$ _____ $-(1/8)$

13. $-(4/3)$ _____ $1/2$

14. $-(3/8)$ _____ $-(5/13)$

15. $-(9/10)$ _____ $3/5$

16. 1.75 _____ 1.79

17. -1.75 _____ -1.79

18. 16.53 _____ 16.5

19. -16.53 _____ -16.5

20. $1/3$ _____ $.33$

21. $-(1/3)$ _____ $-.33$

22. $-(2/5)$ _____ $-.5$

23. -1.8 _____ $9/5$

24. 0 _____ -175.4

25. -83.42 _____ -834.2

For the following problems consider the seven sets

a) natural numbers
b) integers
c) quotient numbers
d) rational numbers
e) irrational numbers
f) real numbers
g) empty set

Each description corresponds to exactly one of the above sets. Identify the sets.

26. A set which contains 3.7 but not -3.7.

27. A set which contains both 1/2 and π.

28. A set which contains -1, but not $-(1/2)$.

29. A set which contains 1, but neither 1/2 nor -2.

30. A set which contains $-(1/2)$, but not π.

31. The union of the natural numbers and the integers.

32. The intersection of the integers and the quotient numbers.

33. The union of the quotient numbers and the rational numbers.

34. The intersection of the rational and the irrational numbers.

35. The union of the irrational numbers and the real numbers.

36. A subset of the quotient numbers which contains 1 but not 1/2.

37. A subset of the rational numbers which contains -1 but not $-(1/2)$.

38. A subset of the real numbers which does not contain 1, but which is not the empty set.

39. A subset of the irrational numbers which does not contain π.

40. A set which is disjoint from the natural numbers and which is not a subset of the integers.

CHAPTER 30

MEASUREMENT

1. We have constructed the real number line. We began by choosing a line and one point on it. We called this point the _____.

> ORIGIN

2.

```
..._____...
         0
```

The origin was labeled with the number zero, and we called zero the _____ of the origin.

> COORDINATE

3.

```
..._____...
         0
```

We next chose a line segment

```
X       Y
•———————•
```

and used it to locate other points both to the left and right of the origin.

```
...___|___|___|___|___|___|___|___|___|___...
     -2  -1   0   1   2   3   4   5   6
```

The points thus determined had coordinates which are numbers that form a set called the _____.

> INTEGERS

4.

```
...___|___|___|___|___|___|___|___...
     -2  -1   0   1   2   3   4
```

But some points on the line had not been given coordinates. The rational numbers enabled us to give coordinates to many other points.

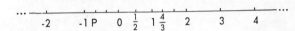

```
...___|___|___|___|___|___|___|___...
     -2  -1 P  0  ½  1⅓  2   3   4
```

What coordinate is given to the point labeled P?

> – (2/3)

5.

```
...___⬭___|___|___⭕|___...
     -2  -1   0   1   2   3 Q  4
```

But there were still points on our line to which no rational number could be assigned as a coordinate. The point Q, above, was such a point. We used an _____ number as a coordinate for Q.

> IRRATIONAL

6.

Many other points on our line had coordinates which were irrational numbers. Indeed, between any two points with rational number coordinates are an _____ number of points with rational number coordinates and an _____ number of points with irrational number coordinates.

INFINITE;   INFINITE

7. And between any two points with irrational number coordinates were an infinite number of points with _____ number coordinates and an infinite number of points with _____ number coordinates.

RATIONAL;   IRRATIONAL
(either order)

8. The union of the set of rational numbers and the set of irrational numbers is the set of _____ numbers.

REAL

9. Hence every point on our line had a coordinate which was a real number, and we called our line the _____ _____ line.

REAL NUMBER

10.

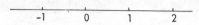

The segment

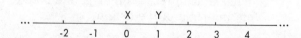

which we used to construct our real number line played a very important part. The coordinate of every point (other than the origin) depended on our choice of segment XY. We shall call XY a UNIT SEGMENT, or simply a "unit."

11. It would have been quite correct to construct our real number line using a <u>different</u> unit segment. Thus, if our choice of unit had been

we could still have constructed a real number line

and each point on this line would still have had a _____ number for its coordinate.

REAL

12.

But the coordinate of every point (other than the origin) on the number line which uses segment WZ as a unit is _____ _____ the coordinate of that point on the number line which uses segment XY as a unit.

DIFFERENT FROM   (not LESS THAN!)

13. Thus, the point Q has coordinate _____ if segment XY is our unit segment, but Q has coordinate 9/5 if segment WZ is the unit used.

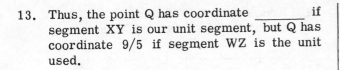

4

14. Another segment which could be used as a unit is UV.

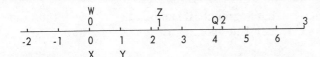

The number line thus determined,

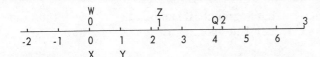

still has one, and only one, _____ number as a coordinate for every point on it. But the coordinates of all points (other than the _____) are different from what they would be if some other unit segment were chosen.

REAL;   ORIGIN

15. In fact, any line segment may be used as a unit segment when constructing the real number line. Each choice of unit determines a real number _____ for every point on the line.

COORDINATE

16. Consider again the number line formed using segment XY as a unit.

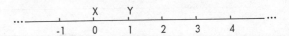

Let AB be any line segment

If we place segment AB on the number line so that A is at the origin and B is to the right of A, then B falls on some point on the line. The coordinate of this point is called the LENGTH of segment AB.

17.

The coordinate of point B is called the _____ of segment AB.

LENGTH

18. To find the length of segment CD

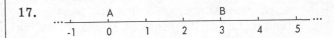

we place this segment so that point C is at the origin of our number line and point D is to the right of C. Then the _____ of the point where D falls is the _____ of segment CD.

COORDINATE;   LENGTH

19.

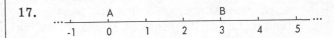

And, since the length of segment CD is the coordinate of point D above, the length must be a positive, _____ number.

REAL

20. The length of segment EF is _____ .

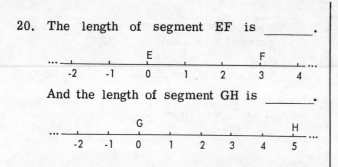

And the length of segment GH is _____ .

```
      G                        H
...___|___|___|___|___|___|___|___|___...
      -2  -1   0   1   2   3   4   5
```

> 3;   5

21. Indeed, every line segment has a length which is a real number. To find the length, one end point of the segment is placed at the _____ and the other end point to the _____ of the origin.

> ORIGIN;   RIGHT

22. And the length of the segment is the _____ of the right end point. Since this point lies to the right of the origin, the length of any segment will always be a _____ real number.

> COORDINATE;   POSITIVE

23. But the coordinate of any point (other than the origin) of the number line depends on the unit segment used. Hence the length of a segment, too, depends on the _____ used.

> UNIT

24. Thus, segment JK has length _____ if the number line has segment XY as a unit

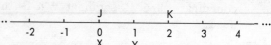

but segment JK has length _____ if the number line has segment WZ as a unit.

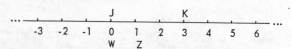

> 2;   3

25. Segment JK has length 2 if XY is the unit segment, but length 3 if WZ is the unit segment. Of course, the segment JK

```
J                 K
|_____|
```

is the same segment, no matter which unit is used. But the _____ of segment JK depends on our choice of unit.

> LENGTH

26.
```
L                M
|_____|

X Y
|_|

W   Z
|___|
```

The length of the segment LM will depend on the unit segment. If XY is the unit segment, then the length of LM is _____ , but if WZ is the unit segment, the length of LM is _____ . Finally, if LM is itself chosen as the unit segment, then the length of LM is _____ .

> 6;   3;   1

27. The length of any line segment depends on the unit segment chosen as well as the original line segment. But in every case, the length will be some _____, _____ number.

POSITIVE;   REAL   (either order)

28. We shall often wish to know the length of a line segment. Since this involves placing the segment so that one end point is at the origin and the other is to the _____ of the origin, only _____ real numbers will occur as lengths.

RIGHT;   POSITIVE

29. Then we need no longer consider that portion of the number line to the left of the origin when determining the length of a segment. We shall no longer write it.

N
0   1   2   3   4   5   6   7   8
P

The length of segment NP is _____.

7

30. The length of any segment depends on the unit chosen. In actual practice, several units have been accepted as standard. The common "ruler" found in the home and at school is simply part of a number line where the unit segment is called an _____.

1   2   3   4   5   6   7   8   9   10   11

INCH

31. Using such a ruler, one would say that the length of segment QR is 8 _____.

Q   R
1   2   3   4   5   6   7   8   9   10   11

INCHES

32. But for expressing the length of other segments we might prefer a different unit. Thus, on a football field

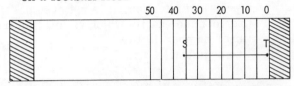

the unit used is called a "yard." In the sketch above, the segment ST has length _____ yards.

35

33. Another unit we commonly use is the "foot." In fact, what we commonly call a "yardstick" can be considered a line segment whose length can be described as 1 yard, _____ feet, or _____ inches.

3;   36

34. Other units are also encountered. In many parts of the world the "meter," "kilometer," and "centimeter" are common. In addition to the "inch," "foot," and "yard," the "mile" is often used in this country as a unit. In laboratories one can meet the "micron," "Angstrom," and "light year." We shall not consider the difficulties of problems involving a change of unit. Instead, we shall continue to use an arbitrary, unspecified unit when stating a length.

35. The length of a line segment is the coordinate of its right end point when its left end point is placed at the origin of a number line. Then the length of a segment is some real number. But every real number is either a _____ or an _____ number.

36. Every length is either a rational or an irrational number. But it is not possible to write down any irrational number using only the digits and the decimal point. Indeed, in a practical situation, it is not even <u>possible</u> to determine exactly which rational or irrational number is the _____ of <u>any</u> line segment.

37. We shall avoid this difficulty be writing only a decimal approximation for <u>all</u> lengths. In fact, when we MEASURE any line segment, we merely find a decimal A_____ of its length.

38. We will not continue to say that the decimal form which measures the length of a line segment is only approximate. But when we say that a particular segment, AB, is 4.7 units long, it will be understood that 4.7 is a one-place decimal _____ of its length.

39.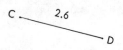

The picture above indicates that AB is approximately _____ units long.

40.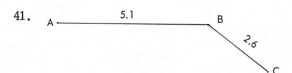

Segment AB is approximately 5.1 units long. We shall call 5.1 the DISTANCE from A to B or from B to A.

What is the distance from C to D? _____

41.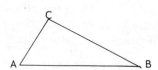

The sum of the distances from A to B and from B to C is _____.

42.

When three line segments are joined end to end as shown above, the resulting figure, which may be designated by ABC, is called a _____, and we say that it has three sides, AB, AC, and CB.

43.

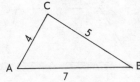

The sum of the lengths of the three sides AB, BC, and AC, is _____, and we will call this number the PERIMETER of the triangle ABC.

16

44.

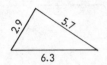

The perimeter of this triangle is _____.

14.9

45. The horizontal and vertical lines in the left-hand figure are said to be PERPENDICULAR to one another.

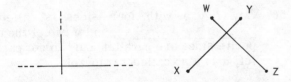

Are segments XY and WZ perpendicular to one another? _____

YES   (Turn the book until one of the segments is horizontal.)

46.

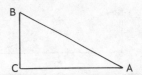

In this figure we say that segment BC is _____ to CA, but segment BC is not _____ to segment BA.

PERPENDICULAR;   PERPENDICULAR

47.

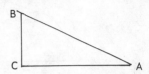

Since BC is _____ to CA, we call triangle ABC a RIGHT TRIANGLE.

PERPENDICULAR

48. When one side of a triangle is perpendicular to another, we call the triangle a _____ triangle.

RIGHT

49.

This triangle is not a right triangle, but its _____ is 18.

PERIMETER

50.

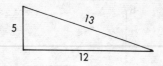

The length of the longest side is 13, and the length of the shortest side is _____.

The perimeter is _____. Is this a right triangle? _____

> 5;   30;   YES

51.

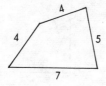

This figure is called a QUADRILATERAL since it has _____ sides. Its perimeter is the sum of the length of the sides, and equals _____.

> FOUR;   20

52.

--- ——————— ---

--- ——————— ---

These two lines are said to be PARALLEL, since they never meet.

If we think of them as being sets of points, the intersection of these two sets is _____.

> φ   (they do not intersect)

53.

--- ——A——————B—— ---

--- ——C——————D—— ---

The points A, B, C, and D are on parallel lines. We call the line segments AB and CD _____ line segments.

> PARALLEL

54.

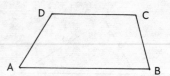

This is a quadrilateral, since it has four sides. Sides AB and DC are _____, but AD and BC are not _____.

> PARALLEL;   PARALLEL

55.

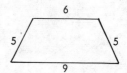

This quadrilateral has two opposite sides parallel and two opposite sides not parallel. We call this special type of quadrilateral a TRAPEZOID. The perimeter of this trapezoid is _____, and the longest side has length _____.

> 25;   9

56. Any figure with four sides is called a _____, and if two of the opposite sides are parallel and two not parallel, it is also called a trapezoid.

> QUADRILATERAL

57.

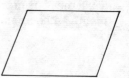

This is a quadrilateral, since it has four sides. But since both pairs of opposite sides are _____, it is not a trapezoid. We call this figure a PARALLELOGRAM.

> PARALLEL

58.

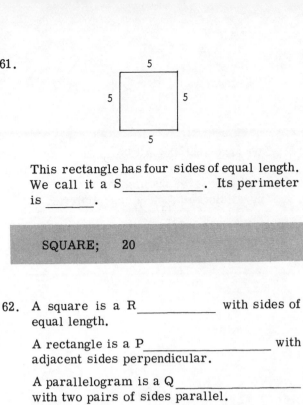

Figure ABCD is a _____, since it has only one pair of parallel sides, but EFGH is a parallelogram, since it has two pairs of parallel sides.

> TRAPEZOID

59.

Since this figure has two pairs of parallel sides, it is a _____. But since the adjacent sides are perpendicular, it is also called a RECTANGLE. The _____ of this rectangle is 20.

> PARALLELOGRAM;   PERIMETER

60.

This figure has four sides, so it is a Q_____. It has two pairs of parallel sides, so it is a P_____. And since its adjacent sides are perpendicular, it is a R_____.

> QUADRILATERAL;   PARALLELOGRAM; RECTANGLE

61.

This rectangle has four sides of equal length. We call it a S_____. Its perimeter is _____.

> SQUARE;   20

62. A square is a R_____ with sides of equal length.

A rectangle is a P_____ with adjacent sides perpendicular.

A parallelogram is a Q_____ with two pairs of sides parallel.

A trapezoid is a _____ with only one pair of sides parallel.

> RECTANGLE;   PARALLELOGRAM;
> QUADRILATERAL;   QUADRILATERAL

63.

This square has sides of length 1 unit. We call it a SQUARE UNIT. Its perimeter is _____ units.

> 4

64.

We say that the AREA of this figure is 1 square unit, or simply 1. The figure is not only a square, but also a _____, a parallelogram, and a quadrilateral.

RECTANGLE

65.

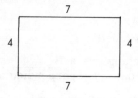

We call 7 the LENGTH of this rectangle and _____ its WIDTH. The perimeter of this rectangle is _____.

4;   22

66.

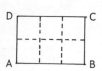

If AB has length 3, and BC has length 2, we see that rectangle ABCD could contain _____ square units. We say that its area is _____ square units, or simply _____.

6;   6;   6

67.

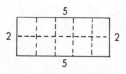

This rectangle could contain 10 square units, and we say that its area is 10. Its length is _____, and its width is _____.

5;   2

68.

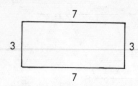

The area of this rectangle is _____, the product of its length and width.

But its _____ is 20.

21;   PERIMETER

69. We define the area of any rectangle to be the product of its _____ and its _____.

LENGTH;   WIDTH   (either order)

70. If the length of a rectangle is 2.5 and its width is 4, then its area is _____.

10

71. Let x be the length of a rectangle and y its width. Find its area, A, if

1) x = 3
    y = 9   A = 3·9 = 27
2) x = 5.9
    y = 2.1   A = _____

12.39

72. If x and y are the length and width of any rectangle, then its area, A, is given by

A = _____

xy

73.

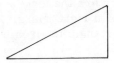

Since two sides of this triangle are perpendicular, we call it a _____ triangle.

RIGHT

74.

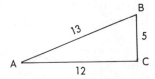

For this right triangle we call side AC the BASE and side BC the ALTITUDE. The length of the altitude of this triangle is _____.

5

75.

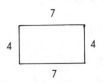

This figure is called a R _____, and its area is _____.

RECTANGLE; 28

76.

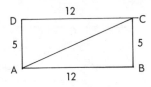

The segment AC is called a DIAGONAL of the rectangle. The area of the rectangle ABCD is _____.

60

77.

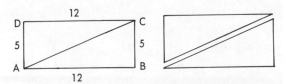

We may think of the diagonal AC as dividing the rectangle ABCD into two equal _____ triangles as shown. What is the length of the base of triangle ABC?

RIGHT; 12

78.

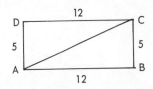

The diagonal divides the rectangle ABCD into two equal right triangles. The area of the rectangle is 60, so the area of each of the equal triangles is _____.

30

79. The area of each right triangle in the previous frame is only 1/2 the area of the rectangle. Suppose ABC is another right triangle.

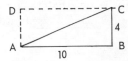

The figure ABCD is a rectangle whose area is _____, so the area of the triangle ABC is only _____.

40; 20

80.

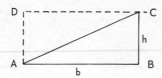

Let ABC be <u>any</u> triangle whose base is b units long, and whose altitude is h units long. Then b and h are also the length and width of a rectangle whose area is _____ .

> bh

81.

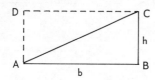

Since the area of rectangle ABCD is bh, then the area of triangle ABC is _____ .

> bh/2

82. For any right triangle the area is one-half the area of a rectangle whose length and width are the lengths of the base and altitude of the triangle. Then the area of any right triangle is one-half the product of the lengths of its _____ and its _____ .

> BASE;   ALTITUDE   (either order)

83. If the base of a right triangle is 10, and its altitude is 7, then its area is _____ .

> $\frac{7 \cdot 10}{2} = \underline{35}$

84. If b and h are the lengths of the base and altitude of a right triangle, then the area, A, of this triangle is given by

> A = _____

> bh/2

85.   A = bh/2

This gives the _____ of a right triangle whose base is _____ units long and whose altitude is _____ units long.

> AREA;   b;   h

86.   A = bh/2

If b = 7 and h = 4, then A = _____ .

If b = 3.5 and h = 4.6, then A = _____ .

> 14;   8.05

87.

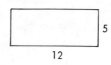

The area of the rectangle is _____ .

The area of the triangle is _____ .

> 60;   10

88.

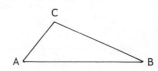

This is not a right triangle since no two of the sides are _____ .

> PERPENDICULAR

89.

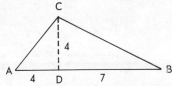

Triangle ABC is not a right triangle, but both triangle ADC and CDB are right triangles. For right triangle ADC, the base is 4 units long and the altitude is also 4 units long. The area of triangle ADC is _____. The area of triangle CDB is _____.

$$\frac{4 \cdot 4}{2} = \underline{8}; \qquad \frac{4 \cdot 7}{2} = \underline{14}$$

90.

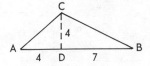

Area of ADC = 8

Area of CDB = 14

But the area of triangle ABC is the sum of the areas of the other two smaller triangles, and hence the area of ABC is _____.

22

91.

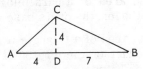

Area of ADC = 8; Area of CDB is 14; Area of ABC = 22

The sum of the distances AD and DB equals _____, and we call this the length of the base of triangle ABC. And we call the length CD, which is _____, the length of the altitude of triangle ABC.

11;   4

92.

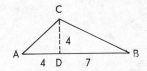

The area of ABC was found to be 22 square units.

The base of ABC is _____ units long.

The altitude of ABC is _____ units long.

One-half the product of the base and the altitude is _____.

11;   4; $\frac{11 \cdot 4}{2} = \underline{22}$

93.

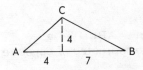

Then even for this triangle, which is not a right triangle, its area is one-half the product of the lengths of its _____ and its _____.

BASE;   ALTITUDE   (either order)

94.

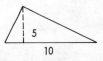

The area of this triangle is _____.

25

95.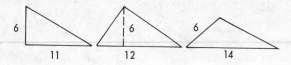

The area of the first triangle is _____.

The area of the second triangle is _____.

The area of the third triangle is _____.

33;   36;   impossible to tell since the length of the altitude is not known

96.

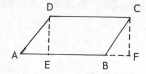

Figure ABCD is a _____, since both pairs of opposite sides are parallel.

Figure EFCD is a _____, since it is a parallelogram with sides perpendicular.

Since triangle ADE and triangle BCF are of equal area, the area of the parallelogram and the rectangle are equal.

PARALLELOGRAM;   RECTANGLE

97.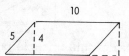

The parallelogram and the rectangle have equal area. The length of the rectangle is 10, and its width is _____. Then the area of the rectangle and the area of the parallelogram are each _____.

4;   40

98.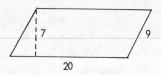

We call 20 the length of the base of the parallelogram, 7 the length of its altitude, and 9 the slant height. The area of this parallelogram is the same as for a rectangle whose length and width are the lengths of the base and altitude of the parallelogram. The area of the parallelogram is _____.

$7 \cdot 20 = \underline{140}$

99.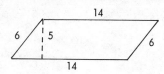

The area of the parallelogram is _____.

The perimeter of the parallelogram is _____.

$5 \cdot 14 = \underline{70}$; $6 + 14 + 6 + 14 = \underline{40}$

100. The area of a rectangle is the product of its length and _____.

The area of a parallelogram is the product of the lengths of its base and _____.

The area of a triangle is _____ the product of the lengths of its _____ and altitude.

WIDTH;   ALTITUDE;   1/2;   BASE

101.

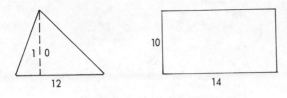

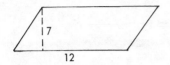

The area of the triangle is _____ .

The area of the rectangle is _____ .

The area of the parallelogram is _____ .

60;   140;   84

102.

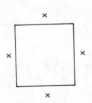

This rectangle is also a S_____ , and its area is _____ . Its perimeter is _____ .

SQUARE;   100;   40

103.

The length and width of this rectangle are both _____ , so its area is given by the formula

A = _____

x;   A = xx or A = x²

104.   a)   A = xy

b)   A = $\frac{1}{2}$ bh

c)   A = bh

d)   A = x²

If x and y represent length and width, and b and h represent lengths of base and altitude, then a) gives the area of a rectangle, b) the area of a _____ , c) the area of a parallelogram, and d) the area of a _____ .

TRIANGLE;   SQUARE

105.

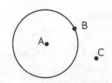

This is a picture of a CIRCLE and three points, A, B, and C. Point B is on the circle, but neither point A nor C is on the circle. Point _____ is at the center of the circle.

A

106.

Every point on the circle is at the same _____ from the point C, and we call C the _____ of the circle.

DISTANCE;   CENTER

107.

The length of CA is called the RADIUS of the circle. If CA has length 5, then the length of CB is _____.

5

108.

The _____ of this circle is 6, which if the distance from its center to any _____ on the circle.

RADIUS;   POINT

109.

The length of AB is called the DIAMETER of the circle. We see that the diameter of this circle is two times its radius, so the diameter is _____.

4

110. The diameter of any circle is two times its _____.

RADIUS

111.

The diameter of this circle is _____.
Its _____ is 6.

12;   RADIUS

112.

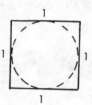

This is a square whose perimeter is _____.

We see that the perimeter of the circle inside the square is less that that of the square.

4

113.

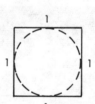

The _____ of the circle is the same as the length of a side for the square. The diameter of the circle is _____.

DIAMETER;   1

114.

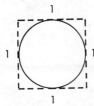

The diameter of the circle is 1. The perimeter of the square is 4. What is the perimeter of the circle? Clearly, it is a real number which is less than 4. In fact, we can determine the perimeter by resorting to a device we used before.

115. Let us place the circle on a number line at the origin.

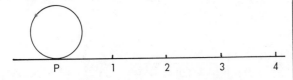

If we now allow the circle to roll to the right until point P again lies on the line,

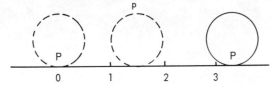

we see that the perimeter of the circle is the irrational number _____.

π

116.

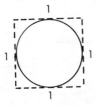

The perimeter of this circle is an irrational number which we represent by π. A five-place decimal _____ for this number is 3.14159.

APPROXIMATION

117.

The perimeter of this circle is approximately 3.14159. Give a two-place decimal approximation of the perimeter. _____.

3.14

118. For most cases we can say that the _____ of a circle whose diameter is 1 is approximately 3.14.

PERIMETER

119. But if we wish to be quite precise, we shall use the Greek letter π to represent the irrational number which is the perimeter of a circle whose diameter is _____.

1

120. π is irrational, but a two-place decimal approximation of π is _____.

3.14

121.

The circle has diameter _____, and its perimeter is _____ times the perimeter of the circle with the diameter only 1.

2;   2

122. Then a circle whose diameter is 2 has _____ equal to 2π. And _____ is approximately 3.14.

> PERIMETER;   π

123. If the _____ of a circle is 3, then its perimeter is 3π.

> DIAMETER

124. In general, if the diameter of a circle is d, then its _____ is dπ or πd.

> PERIMETER   .

125. Then a circle whose diameter is 17 has a perimeter we can indicate by _____.

> 17π

126. Another word for the perimeter of a circle is CIRCUMFERENCE. Then the circumference of a circle whose diameter is 9 is indicated by _____.

> 9π

127. If C is the circumference of a circle, and d is its diameter, then

$$C = \text{_____}$$

> πd   (or dπ)

128.   C = πd

This gives the _____ or perimeter of a circle as the product of π and the _____ of the circle.

> CIRCUMFERENCE;   DIAMETER

129.   C = πd

If the diameter is 14, then the circumference is _____.

> 14π

130. The _____ of a circle is twice the radius. Then if the radius of a circle is 3, its diameter is _____, and hence its circumference is _____.

> DIAMETER;   6;   6π

131.   d = 2r

This says that the _____ of a circle is _____ times its _____.

> DIAMETER;   2;   RADIUS

132. Since

d = 2r   and   C = πd

we may also write

_____ = π(2r) = 2πr

> C

133. $C = \pi d$
$C = 2\pi r$

Both give the circumference of a circle. Use the first rule if the _____ is given. Use the second if the _____ is given.

DIAMETER;   RADIUS

134. $C = \pi d$
$C = 2\pi r$

Find C if

a) $r = 8$ $C =$ _____

b) $d = 5$ $C =$ _____

16π; 5π

135. The symbol _____ is used to represent the circumference of a circle whose diameter is 1. And a two-place decimal approximation of this irrational number is _____.

π;   3.14

136. π is approximately 3.14, and

$C = \pi d$

Then if $d = 5$, approximately $C = (3.14)(5) =$ _____.

Similarly, if $d = 2.1$, then approximately $C =$ _____.

15.7;   6.594 or 6.6

137. We have defined the length of a line segment to be the _____ of a point on the number line.

COORDINATE

138. The perimeter of a figure is the _____ around the figure. For figures like a triangle or a quadrilateral it is the _____ of the lengths of the sides.

DISTANCE;   SUM

139. But for a circle the perimeter or _____ is the product of π and the _____ of the circle.

CIRCUMFERENCE;   DIAMETER

140. The area of a rectangle, triangle, or parallelogram is the _____ of the lengths of two line segments. And we describe the area as being a certain number of square units.

PRODUCT

141. a) $C = \pi d$

b) $A = xy$

c) $A = \frac{1}{2} bh$

d) $P = x + y + x + y$

Rule c gives the area of a triangle.

Rule _____ gives the area of a rectangle.

Rule _____ gives the perimeter of a rectangle.

Rule _____ gives the circumference of a circle.

b;   d;   a

Chapter 30

Problems A   (Answers on page 514)

For each of the following figures, find
a) the perimeter
b) the area

1.
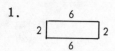

2.
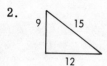

3.
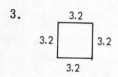

4.
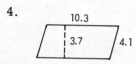

Give a one-place decimal approximation for each of the following.

5. The area of a rectangle whose width is 4.62 and whose length is 7.81.

6. The perimeter of a square whose sides are 3.651.

7. The area of a triangle whose base has length 4.71 and whose altitude has length 3.45.

8. The perimeter of a rectangle whose length is 7/2 and whose width is 5/4.

9. The area of a square whose sides are 3/4.

10. The circumference of a circle whose diameter is 5.

11. The circumference of a circle whose radius is 3.4.

12. The length of a rectangle whose area is 12.63 and whose width is 4. (Hint: What operation involves finding a factor when the other factor and the product are known?)

13. The area of a square whose perimeter is 16.4. (Hint: Find the length of a side first.)

14. The diameter of a circle whose circumference is 12.

Use any method to solve the following problems.

15. The triangle below has a perimeter of 15. Find its area.

16. A room is 14.2 feet long and 11.6 feet wide. Find a one-place decimal approximation for its area.

17. If carpet costs $1.25 per square foot, how much will it cost to carpet the room in problem 16 from wall to wall?

18. A hallway is 4 feet wide, 12 feet long, and 9 feet from floor to ceiling.
    a) What is the area of the ceiling?
    b) What is the area of one of the "long" walls?

19. One can of paint will cover approximately 40 square feet. Find a one-place decimal approximation of the number of cans required to paint the ceiling and one of the "long" walls of the hallway in problem 18. (Hint: The product of the number of cans and 40 will equal the total area painted.)

20. A circular flower bed is to be bordered by a single row of bricks which are each one-half of a foot long. If the radius of the bed is 5 feet, what is the smallest number of bricks needed to make the border?

Problems B

For each of the following find
a) the perimeter
b) the area

1.
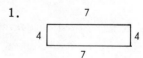

2.
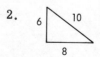

3.

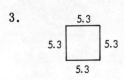

4.

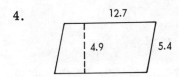

Find a one-place decimal approximation for each of the following.

5. The area of a rectangle whose sides are 12.7 and 9.6.

6. The perimeter of a square whose sides are 9.4.

7. The area of a right triangle whose perpendicular sides are 9.3 and 5.8.

8. The circumference of a circle whose diameter is 7.3.

9. The circumference of a circle whose radius is 3.4.

10. The area of a square whose sides are 2/5.

11. The length of a rectangle whose area is 27.5 and whose width is 4.

12. The altitude of a triangle whose base is 14.4 and whose area is 25.2.

13. The perimeter of a square whose area is 25.

14. The diameter of a circle whose circumference is 15.5.

15. The radius of a circle whose circumference is 37.

16. A company charges $.17 per square foot to install tile squares on a floor. If a kitchen measures 12 feet by 7 feet, what is the cost of tile for this room?

17. A Rembrandt masterpiece measures 42 in. by 29 in. and recently sold for $890,000 at an auction. What is the cost per square inch of this painting?

18. What is the cost of fencing a rectangular lot which is 87 feet by 103 feet, if fencing costs $1.45 per foot?

19. The diameter of a circular race track is 1/2 mile. How far does a car travel if it makes exactly 53 trips around the track?

20. The average diameter of the playing surface of a phonograph record is 3/4 foot. If the record turns at $33\frac{1}{3}$ revolutions per minute for 27 minutes, over how many feet of record surface does the needle travel?

ANSWERS TO PROBLEMS

Chapter 1: Answers A (Problems on page 20).

1. =
2. ≠
3. ≠
4. ≠
5. =
6. Do
7. Do
8. Do
9. Do Not
10. Do Not
11. A, B, C, F
12. {1, 2, 3, 4, 5, 6, 7}
13. {2, 3, 5, 6}
14. {1, 2, 3, 4, 5} or A
15. {5, 6}
16. φ
17. {1, 2, 3, 4, 5} or A or F
18. B and C; C and E
19. A and F
20. B and E; A and F
21. True
22. True
23. False
24. False
25. True
26. The set of all persons living in California.
27. The set of all people living in Cincinnati.
28. The set of all girls under five years of age.
29. The empty set.
30. The set of all persons whose income last year was under $10,000.

Chapter 2: Answers A (Problems on page 35)

1. The natural number two.
2. The natural number three is that property shared by all sets of the same size as {x, y, z}.

3. A, E, F
4. 3
5. 2
6. 4
7. 1
8. 5
9. 4
10. 1
11. Could not be used. Has size 3 but is not disjoint with A.
12. Could be used. Has size 3 and is disjoint with A.
13. Could not be used. Is disjoint with A but has the wrong size, 4.
14. Could not be used. Is disjoint with A but has the wrong size, 2.
15. Could not be used. Is disjoint with A but has the wrong size, 1.
16. Could be used. Has size 3 and is disjoint with A.
17. A ∪ B = B ∪ A
    A ∩ B = B ∩ A
18. d
19. 5
20. 9
21. The natural number two.
22. a, c
23. One cannot say. If no one on the basketball team is also on the football team, the size is 16. But if any man stars in both football and basketball, the size will be less than 16.
24. 1

Chapter 3: Answers A (Problems on page 51)

1. 13
2. 11
3. 22
4. 52
5. 116
6. 6181
7. 17 + 6 = 23
8. 19 + 100 = 119
9. 83 + 56 = 139
10. 13 + 3 = 16
11. 15 + 7 = 22
12. 45 + 10 = 55
13. 51
14. 314

15. 20
16. 5694
17. 7067
18. 7330
19. 164
20. 735
21. 212
22. 1367
23. 5354
24. 14300
25. 1584

26. 2825
27. 5 + 9
28. 26 + 27
29. 12 + 12
30. 0 + 0
31. 493
32. 10535
33. 11
34. 18560 feet
35. 2519

Chapter 4: Answers A (Problems on page 69)

1. 63
2. 48
3. 72
4. 121
5. 594
6. 2646
7. $56 \cdot 9 = 504$
8. $4 \cdot 100 = 400$
9. $300 \cdot 2 = 600$
10. $35 \cdot 2 = 70$
11. $675 \cdot 4 = 2700$
12. $10 \cdot 8 \cdot 9 = 80 \cdot 9 = 720$
13. 720
14. 1120
15. 36,750
16. 4576
17. 15,133
18. 9750
19. 70,595
20. 471,016
21. $12 \cdot 2$
22. $21 \cdot 3$
23. $6 \cdot 6$
24. 0
25. 1
26. Commutative property of multiplication
27. Associative property of multiplication
28. Associative property of addition
29. Commutative property of addition
30. Commutative property of multiplication
31. 2112
32. 1152
33. 1,920,000
34. 252
35. 26400

Chapter 5: Answers A (Problems on page 86)

1. 37
2. 17
3. 28
4. 28
5. 13
6. 12
7. 72
8. 21
9. 45
10. 19
11. Product; $7 \cdot 3 + 7 \cdot 5$
12. Product; $4 \cdot 1 + 5 \cdot 11$
13. Sum; $2(5 + 7)$
14. Sum; $(9 + 8)4$
15. Sum; $12(6 + 4)$
16. Product; $12 \cdot 13 + 12 \cdot 20$
17. Product; $41 \cdot 27 + 9 \cdot 27$
18. Sum; $(64 + 36) \cdot 18$
19. Sum; $2(3 + 1)$
20. Sum; $2(3 + 1)$
21. Distributive property
22. Commutative property of addition
23. Commutative property of multiplication
24. Associative property of multiplication
25. Distributive property
26. Distributive property
27. Associative property of addition
28. Commutative property of multiplication
29. Commutative property of multiplication
30. Commutative property of multiplication

Chapter 6: Answers A (Problems on page 101)

1. $5 < 11; 11 > 5; 6 < 11; 11 > 6$
2. $17 < 20; 20 > 17; 3 < 20; 20 > 3$
3. $0 < 8; 8 > 0$
4. $4 < 8; 8 > 4$
5. $6 < 25; 25 > 6; 19 < 25; 25 > 19$
6. $10 < 30; 30 > 10; 20 < 30; 30 > 20$
7. $6 < 17; 17 > 6; 11 < 17; 17 > 11$
8. $0 < 4; 4 > 0$
9. $12 < 19; 19 > 12; 7 < 19; 19 > 7$
10. $13 < 63; 63 > 13; 50 < 63; 63 > 50$
11. $<$
12. $>$
13. $=$
14. $<$
15. $=$
16. $<$
17. $=$
18. $>$
19. $<$
20. $=$
21. 1, 6, 7, 19
22. 0, 4, 5, 8, 12, 101
23. 0, 1, 2, 3, 4, 5, 6, 7, 9
24. 13, 15, 16, 18, 23, 25, 26, 28, 36
25. 0, 1, 2, 6, 7, 8, 9, 10, 90, 100
26. $<$
27. $>$

28. >   30. <
29. <

Chapter 7: Answers A   (Problems on page 117)

1. Addition	21. 86
2. Subtraction	22. 308
3. Multiplication	23. 27
4. Subtraction	24. 22
5. Division	25. Impossible
6. Division	26. 29
7. Addition	27. 136
8. Multiplication	28. Impossible
9. Division	29. 1328
10. Subtraction	30. 37
11. 21	31. Yes
12. 11	32. No
13. 117	33. Yes
14. 6	34. 1560
15. 34	35. 14 dollars
16. 13	36. 901,968 dollars
17. 45	37. 47
18. 12	38. 16,616
19. 124	39. 7721
20. 16	40. 14,219

Chapter 8: Answers A   (Problems on page 133)

1. Multiple
2. Factor
3. Neither
4. Multiple
5. Factor
6. Multiple
7. Neither
8. Factor
9. Multiple
10. Multiple
11. Multiple
12. Factor
13. Multiple
14. Factor
15. Neither
16. Multiple
17. Factor
18. Multiple or factor
19. Multiple
20. Multiple or factor
21. Divisible by
22. An exact divisor of
23. An exact divisor of
24. Divisible by
25. An exact divisor of
26. Neither
27. An exact divisor of
28. An exact divisor of
29. An exact divisor of or divisible by
30. An exact divisor of
31. 8; 3
32. 5; 5
33. 1; 222
34. 0; 86
35. 205; 0
36. 73 boxes; 4 feet
37. 6 days
38. 168 engines; 64 pounds
39. 104 dollars
40. 242 reels; 122 feet

Chapter 9: Answers A   (Problems on page 151)

1. Complete factorization of 45
2. Complete factorization of 24
3. Not a complete factorization; 4 is composite.
4. Not a complete factorization; factor 1 is missing.
5. Not a complete factorization; 9 is composite.
6. Complete factorization of 231
7. Not a complete factorization; factor 1 is missing.
8. Complete factorization of 125.
9. Complete factorization of 39.
10. Not a complete factorization; 18 is composite.
11. $1 \cdot 2 \cdot 2 \cdot 2$
12. $1 \cdot 2 \cdot 2 \cdot 3 \cdot 3$
13. $1 \cdot 2 \cdot 2 \cdot 2 \cdot 5$
14. $1 \cdot 2 \cdot 2 \cdot 11$
15. $1 \cdot 2 \cdot 5 \cdot 5$
16. $1 \cdot 2 \cdot 3 \cdot 3$
17. $1 \cdot 3 \cdot 23$
18. $1 \cdot 2 \cdot 2 \cdot 5 \cdot 5$
19. $1 \cdot 2 \cdot 2 \cdot 5 \cdot 13$
20. $1 \cdot 2 \cdot 2 \cdot 3 \cdot 5 \cdot 5 \cdot 7 \cdot 11$
21. 6; 14; 21; 42
22. 2; 3; 6
23. 9; 15; 49
24. 6; 10; 14; 15; 21; 35; 30; 42; 70; 105; 210
25. 4; 8; 16; 32
26. 1, 3, 4, 15
27. 1, 2, 3, 6, 7, 14, 21, 42
28. 1, 2, 7, 14, 49, 98
29. 1, 2, 4, 8, 16, 32, 64
30. 1, 2, 3, 4, 5, 6, 10, 12, 15, 20, 25, 30, 50, 60, 75, 100, 150, 300

Chapter 10: Answers A   (Problems on page 170)

1. 4, 8, 12, 16, 20, 24, 28, 32, 36, 40
   6, 12, 18, 24, 30, 36, 42, 48, 54, 60   LCM: 12

2. 10, 20, 30, 40, 50, 60, 70, 80, 90, 100
   14, 28, 42, 56, 70, 84, 98, 112, 126, 140   LCM: 70

3. 8, 16, 24, 32, 40, 48, 56, 64, 72, 80
   12, 24, 36, 48, 60, 72, 84, 96, 108, 120   LCM: 24

4. 7, 14, 21, 28, 35, 42, 49, 56, 63, 70
   10, 20, 30, 40, 50, 60, 70, 80, 90, 100   LCM: 70

5. 6, 12, 18, 24, 30, 36, 42, 48, 54, 60   LCM: 18
   18, 36, 54, 72, 90, 108, 126, 144, 162, 180

6. 1, 2, 4
   1, 2, 3, 6   GCD: 2

7. 1, 2, 7, 14
   1, 2, 3, 7, 21   GCD: 7

8. 1, 3, 9
   1, 2, 3, 4, 6, 12   GCD: 3

9. 1, 3, 5, 15
   1, 2, 4, 8, 16   GCD: 1

10. 1, 7
    1, 3, 7, 21   GCD: 7

11. LCM: $1 \cdot 2 \cdot 3 \cdot 5$,   GCD: $1 \cdot 2 \cdot 3$

12. LCM: $1 \cdot 2 \cdot 2 \cdot 2 \cdot 3 \cdot 5$,   GCD: $1 \cdot 2$

13. LCM: $1 \cdot 2 \cdot 3 \cdot 5 \cdot 5$,   GCD: $1 \cdot 3 \cdot 5 \cdot 5$

14. LCM: $1 \cdot 2 \cdot 3 \cdot 3 \cdot 5 \cdot 7$,   GCD: 1

15. LCM: $1 \cdot 2 \cdot 2 \cdot 3 \cdot 7$,   GCD: $1 \cdot 2 \cdot 3 \cdot 7$

16. LCM: 12,   GCD: 4

17. LCM: 25,   GCD: 5

18. LCM: 11,   GCD: 1

19. LCM: 36,   GCD: 3

20. LCM: 56,   GCD: 7

21. LCM: 144,   GCD: 4

22. LCM: 440,   GCD: 4

23. LCM: 1350,   GCD: 2

24. LCM: 6900,   GCD: 1

25. LCM: 1300,   GCD: 20

18. $1 \cdot 2^3 \cdot 3^2$

19. $1 \cdot 2^2 \cdot 11$

20. $1 \cdot 2 \cdot 5^2$

21. $1 \cdot 2 \cdot 3^3$

22. $1 \cdot 3 \cdot 23$

23. $1 \cdot 2^2 \cdot 5^2$

24. $1 \cdot 2^2 \cdot 5 \cdot 13$

25. $1 \cdot 2^2 \cdot 3 \cdot 5^2 \cdot 7 \cdot 11$

26. LCM: $1 \cdot 2^3 \cdot 3^2$,   GCD: $1 \cdot 2^2 \cdot 3$

27. LCM: $1 \cdot 2 \cdot 3^3 \cdot 5^2$,   GCD: $1 \cdot 3^2 \cdot 5$

28. LCM: $1 \cdot 5^2 \cdot 7^3$,   GCD: $1 \cdot 5 \cdot 7^2$

29. LCM: $1 \cdot 2^3 \cdot 3^2 \cdot 5^2 \cdot 7^2$,   GCD: $1 \cdot 2 \cdot 3$

30. LCM: $1 \cdot 2^2 \cdot 3^2 \cdot 5 \cdot 7^2$,   GCD: 1

31. 1, 3, 5, 7, 9, 11, 13

32. 1, 2, 4, 5, 7, 8, 10, 11, 13, 14

33. 1, 5, 7, 11, 13

34. 1, 2, 4, 7, 8, 11, 13, 14

35. 1, 5, 11, 13

36. 18

37. 124

38. 46

39. 0

40. 66

41. 7

42. 33

43. 151

44. 216

45. 156

Chapter 11: Answers A   (Problems on page 188)

1. $2 \cdot 2 \cdot 2 \cdot 2$

2. $2 \cdot 3 \cdot 3 \cdot 3$

3. $2 \cdot 2 \cdot 3 \cdot 3 \cdot 3 \cdot 5$

4. $3 \cdot 3 \cdot 3 \cdot 3 \cdot 5 \cdot 5 \cdot 5 \cdot 7$

5. $2 \cdot 2 \cdot 3 \cdot 3 \cdot 3 \cdot 5 \cdot 5 \cdot 5 \cdot 5 \cdot 7 \cdot 7 \cdot 7 \cdot 7 \cdot 7$

6. $2^3 \cdot 3^2$

7. $2 \cdot 3^4 \cdot 5^2$

8. $3^2 \cdot 5^3 \cdot 7 \cdot 11^4$

9. $2^2 \cdot 3^2 \cdot 5^2 \cdot 7^3 \cdot 11$

10. $5^3 \cdot 11^2 \cdot 13 \cdot 17^4$

11. 81

12. 90

13. 675

14. 5250

15. 29,700

16. $1 \cdot 2^4$

17. $1 \cdot 2^2 \cdot 3^2$

Chapter 12: Answers A   (Problems on page 203)

1. $=$

2. $=$

3. $=$

4. $\neq$

5. $\neq$

6. 5/8

7. 12/7

8. 3/5

9. 7/10

10. 4/3

11. 1/2

12. 12/5

13. 4

14. 1

15. 3

16. 9/5

17. 7/11

18. 17/31

19. 11/7

20. 7

Chapter 13: Answers A   (Problems on page 217)

1. 15/14

2. 3/2

3. 3/20

4. 52/77

5. 4

6. 11/12

7. 6/5

8. 19/24

9. 1/6
10. 35/12
11. 16/3
12. 2
13. 19/3
14. 6
15. 77/5
16. 3/4
17. 7/4
18. 7/4
19. 0
20. 3/4
21. $\left(\dfrac{3}{5}+\dfrac{1}{4}\right)+\dfrac{1}{3}=\dfrac{17}{20}+\dfrac{1}{3}=\dfrac{71}{60}$
22. $\dfrac{3}{5}+\left(\dfrac{1}{4}+\dfrac{1}{3}\right)=\dfrac{3}{5}+\dfrac{7}{12}=\dfrac{71}{60}$
23. Associative property of addition.
24. $\dfrac{1}{2}\left(\dfrac{2}{3}+\dfrac{1}{5}\right)=\dfrac{1}{2}\left(\dfrac{13}{15}\right)=\dfrac{13}{30}$
    $\left(\dfrac{1}{2}\cdot\dfrac{2}{3}\right)+\left(\dfrac{1}{2}\cdot\dfrac{1}{5}\right)=\dfrac{1}{3}+\dfrac{1}{10}=\dfrac{13}{30}$
    Distributive property.
25. $\dfrac{a}{b}\cdot\dfrac{c}{d}=\dfrac{a\cdot c}{b\cdot d}$ by definition of multiplication of fractions.
    $=\dfrac{c\cdot a}{d\cdot b}$ since a, b, c, and d are natural numbers and multiplication of such numbers is commutative.
    $=\dfrac{c}{d}\cdot\dfrac{a}{b}$ by definition of multiplication of fractions.

5. $<$
6. $\dfrac{3}{8}<\dfrac{4}{9}<\dfrac{4}{7}$
7. $\dfrac{3}{7}<\dfrac{4}{9}<\dfrac{5}{11}$
8. $\dfrac{9}{4}<\dfrac{7}{3}<\dfrac{12}{5}$
9. $\dfrac{8}{17}<\dfrac{9}{17}<\dfrac{10}{17}<\dfrac{11}{17}<\dfrac{12}{17}$
10. $\dfrac{11}{9}<\dfrac{11}{8}<\dfrac{11}{7}<\dfrac{11}{6}<\dfrac{11}{5}$
11. 2 and 3
12. 5 and 6
13. 4 and 5
14. 11 and 12
15. 3 and 4
16. 3, 4, 5, 6, 7
17. 1, 2
18. 2
19. 1
20. 11, 12
21. Jane $(436/10 > 473/11)$
22. The history class $(27/31 > 20/23)$
23. The second automobile $(173/9 < 98/5)$
24. Yes $(7/600 > 9/800)$
25. Florida $(2,000,000/3,000,000 > 6,000,000/11,000,000)$

Chapter 14: Answers A   (Problems on page 231)

1. 7
2. 84
3. 65
4. 8
5. 50
6. 16
7. 20
8. 57/28
9. 19/12
10. 11/3
11. 7/5
12. 23/18
13. 31/14
14. 19/16
15. 57/40
16. 199/46
17. 2
18. 38/9
19. 0
20. 19/7
21. 261
22. 290
23. 1432
24. 9/20
25. $3600

Chapter 16: Answers A   (Problems on page 257)

1. 34/9
2. 273/5
3. 9
4. 1568/3
5. 55/7
6. 61/24
7. 21
8. 443/3
9. 1789/5
10. 896
11. False
12. True
13. False
14. True
15. True
16. False
17. True
18. False
19. 26
20. 63
21. Yes (total gain was $10\frac{1}{4}$ yards)
22. 479/12 yards (or $39\frac{11}{12}$ yards)
23. 105/2 ounces (or $52\frac{1}{2}$ ounces)
24. 15/8 cups (or $1\frac{7}{8}$ cups)
25. 4732/15 miles (or $315\frac{7}{15}$ miles)

Chapter 15: Answers A   (Problems on page 245)

1. $<$
2. $>$
3. $<$
4. $>$

Chapter 17: Answers A   (Problems on page 273)

1. $\dfrac{17}{60} + \dfrac{3}{10} = \dfrac{7}{12}$

2. $\dfrac{56}{3} + 5\frac{1}{3} = 24$

3. $\dfrac{47}{42} - \dfrac{2}{7} = \dfrac{5}{6}$; $\dfrac{47}{42} - \dfrac{5}{6} = \dfrac{2}{7}$

4. $\dfrac{535}{12} - \dfrac{100}{3} = \dfrac{45}{4}$; $\dfrac{535}{12} - \dfrac{45}{4} = \dfrac{100}{3}$

5. $\dfrac{261}{16} + 6\frac{3}{16} = 22\frac{1}{2}$

6. $6\frac{1}{56} - 3\frac{1}{7} = 2\frac{7}{8}$; $6\frac{1}{56} - 2\frac{7}{8} = 3\frac{1}{7}$

7. $1 + 6\frac{5}{12} = \dfrac{89}{12}$

8. 3/2
9. 3/31
10. 25/3
11. 7/30
12. 47/105
13. 1/84
14. 21/40
15. 13/12
16. 1/5
17. 5/18
18. 22/3
19. 85/3
20. 25/6
21. 3092/15
22. 53/60
23. 145/6
24. 43/8
25. 11/3

Chapter 18: Answers A (Problems on page 286)

1. 7/10
2. 66/7
3. 32/21
4. 35/6
5. 1
6. 9/4
7. 21/2
8. 4/9
9. 5/3
10. 7/24
11. 833/24
12. 63/32
13. 2
14. 13/5
15. 0
16. 13/7
17. 128
18. 34/9
19. 151/122
20. 0
21. True
22. True
23. False
24. True
25. False
26. True
27. False
28. True
29. False
30. False

Chapter 19: Answers A (Problems on page 301)

1. 8/3
2. 4/9
3. 1/12
4. 9
5. 1
6. 2/3
7. 3/14
8. 4/701
9. 27/40
10. 8/25
11. 2
12. 49/2
13. 5/8
14. 10/3
15. 144/25
16. 3/32
17. 2/3
18. 2/5
19. 2/15
20. 2/3
21. 4/5
22. 9/28
23. 33/20
24. 40/3
25. 2/55
26. 5/24
27. 100/13
28. 63/10
29. 101/60
30. 185/44

Chapter 20: Answers A   (Problems on page 317)

1. 23/12
2. 7/12
3. 9/20
4. 19/8
5. 61/12
6. 7/8
7. 13/3
8. 65/6
9. 18
10. 199/30
11. 87/100
12. 14/25
13. 3/8
14. 1/300
15. 13/6
16. 40%
17. 35%
18. 225%
19. $41\frac{2}{3}\%$
20. $18\frac{3}{4}\%$
21. $22\frac{7}{8}$ or 183/8
22. 85 cents
23. 16
24. The store offering "1/3 off"
25. 350

Chapter 21: Answers A (Problems on page 339)

1. Hundreds
2. Ones
3. Tens
4. Thousands
5. Hundred-thousands
6. Ones
7. Millions
8. Ten-thousands
9. 357
10. 85,394
11. 952

12. 8759
13. 6035
14. 300,003
15. $3 \cdot 100 + 4 \cdot 10 + 5 \cdot 1$
16. $8 \cdot 1000 + 1 \cdot 100 + 4 \cdot 10 + 2 \cdot 1$
17. $5 \cdot 10 + 0 \cdot 1$
18. $9 \cdot 10000 + 2 \cdot 1000 + 0 \cdot 100 + 0 \cdot 10 + 1 \cdot 1$
19. $5 \cdot 1000000 + 4 \cdot 100000 + 0 \cdot 10000 + 0 \cdot 1000$
    $+ 0 \cdot 100 + 0 \cdot 10 + 0 \cdot 1$
20. $9 \cdot 100000 + 0 \cdot 10000 + 0 \cdot 1000 + 9 \cdot 100 + 9 \cdot 10$
    $+ 9 \cdot 1$
21. $1 \cdot 1000 + 3 \cdot 100 + 2 \cdot 10 + 1 \cdot 1$
22. 8470
23. 8500
24. 8000
25. 89,000
26. 90,000
27. 546,000
28. 545,700
29. 545,680
30. 550,000
31. 500,000
32. 45
33. 453
34. 241
35. 2857
36. 2
37. 274,000
38. 400 miles
39. 18
40. 178,000
41. 71,000 miles

21. hundreds
22. thousands
23. ten-thousandths
24. millionths
25. hundred-thousands
26. .7
27. .43
28. .501
29. 111.15
30. .016
31. 12.005
32. 200.0604
33. 9004.00014
34. .43
35. .806
36. 53.4
37. .0004
38. .534
39. 65.48
40. 1.0001
41. $3 \cdot \dfrac{1}{10} + 7 \cdot \dfrac{1}{100} + 5 \cdot \dfrac{1}{1000}$
42. $5 \cdot 1 + 1 \cdot \dfrac{1}{10} + 4 \cdot \dfrac{1}{100}$
43. $2 \cdot 10 + 3 \cdot 1 + 0 \cdot \dfrac{1}{10} + 5 \cdot \dfrac{1}{100}$
44. $0 \cdot \dfrac{1}{10} + 0 \cdot \dfrac{1}{100} + 0 \cdot \dfrac{1}{1000} + 3 \cdot \dfrac{1}{10,000}$
45. $8 \cdot 100 + 0 \cdot 10 + 0 \cdot 1 + 0 \cdot \dfrac{1}{10} + 5 \cdot \dfrac{1}{100} + 0 \cdot \dfrac{1}{1000}$
    $+ 0 \cdot \dfrac{1}{10,000} + 1 \cdot \dfrac{1}{100,000}$

Chapter 22: Answers A (Problems on page 361)

1. 1.75
2. 8.43
3. 84.3
4. 50.2
5. .073
6. .054
7. .00083
8. .314
9. .9
10. 36.
11. 230.
12. .0003
13. 3500.
14. .003
15. .021
16. tenths
17. ones
18. hundredths
19. thousandths
20. hundred-thousandths

Chapter 23: Answers A (Problems on page 385)

1. 3/20
2. 3/50
3. 237/1000
4. 9/40
5. 1/8
6. 39/10
7. 63/5
8. 201/200
9. 3/16
10. 21/16
11. .8
12. 3.5
13. 1.25
14. .12
15. 1.24
16. .375
17. 1.875
18. .05
19. .3125
20. .0112
21. .58333 $\cdots$
22. .7333 $\cdots$
23. .791666 $\cdots$
24. .636363 $\cdots$
25. .857142857142857142 $\cdots$
26. .6
27. .32
28. 5.7
29. 21.06
30. 21.1
31. 21.0
32. 17.
33. 8.333
34. 15.273
35. .008
36. .0078
37. .01
38. .0
39. .756
40. .7
41. .6
42. .667
43. .2857
44. 3.14

45. .444
46. .91
47. 1.4
48. 17.56
49. .44
50. 1.0

Chapter 24: Answers A (Problems on page 405)

1. 45.02
2. 16.245
3. 7.6431
4. 6.49
5. 8.56
6. 11.46
7. 7.487
8. 12.316
9. 11.684
10. 30.24
11. 130.313
12. .7644
13. .072
14. .000816
15. 3.78
16. 86.592
17. 15.501
18. 34.053
19. 5.45
20. 80.98
21. 1.65
22. .56
23. .03
24. .71
25. .54
26. .64
27. .01
28. 224.29
29. 65.19
30. .28

Chapter 25: Answers A (Problems on page 416)

1. 37%
2. 5%
3. 135%
4. 430%
5. 23.7%
6. 3.72%
7. .3%
8. 234.5%
9. 300%
10. 10,000%
11. .17
12. .09
13. 1.15
14. 2.05
15. 4.
16. .937
17. .0842
18. .0031
19. .0005
20. .0105
21. 16.7%
22. 36.4%
23. 166.7%
24. 70.6%
25. 195.5%
26. .393
27. .023
28. 1.354
29. .006
30. .003
31. 14.1
32. 17.2
33. .3
34. 347.6
35. 3.2
36. 780.0
37. 53.8%
38. 270.6%
39. 56.7%
40. $.22
41. 24,300
42. 34.9%
43. 4.1%
44. 31.9 inches
45. $73.95
46. $534.00
47. $1338.25
48. $1049.03
49. $1772.88
50. $1720.30

Chapter 26: Answers A (Problems on page 433)

1. 14
2. 516
3. 21
4. 0
5. 13
6. −12
7. 15
8. −42
9. −16
10. 847
11. a) added
    b) negative
    c) −10
12. a) added
    b) negative
    c) −21
13. a) added
    b) negative
    c) −19
14. a) added
    b) negative
    c) −64
15. a) subtracted
    b) negative
    c) −2
16. a) subtracted
    b) positive
    c) 6
17. a) subtracted
    b) negative
    c) −19
18. a) subtracted
    b) negative
    c) −6
19. a) subtracted
    b) positive
    c) 25
20. a) subtracted
    b) negative
    c) −13
21. a) subtracted
    b) negative
    c) −68
22. a) subtracted
    b) positive
    c) 195
23. a) added
    b) negative
    c) −1462
24. a) subtracted
    b) positive
    c) 464
25. a) added
    b) negative
    c) −8815
26. −149 feet
27. −37°F
28. −89°C
29. $38
30. −518 feet

Chapter 27: Answers A (Problems on page 449)

1. a) 12
   b) 18 + (−12)
   c) 6
2. a) 8
   b) 5 + (−8)
   c) −3
3. a) −3
   b) 6 + 3
   c) 9
4. a) −4
   b) 8 + 4
   c) 12
5. a) 6
   b) −5 + (−6)
   c) −11
6. a) 12
   b) − 4 + (−12)
   c) −16
7. a) − 8
   b) − 5 + 8
   c) 3
8. a) − 4
   b) − 9 + 4
   c) − 5
9. a) − 4
   b) − 4 + 4
   c) 0
10. a) − 6
    b) 6 + 6
    c) 12
11. a) 6
    b) − 6 + (−6)
    c) −12
12. a) 15
    b) (−15) + (−15)
    c) −30
13. a) − 8
    b) (−8) + 8
    c) 0
14. a) − 5
    b) 0 + 5
    c) 5
15. a) 5
    b) 0 + (−5)

       c) − 5
16. a) −183
    b) 214 + 183
    c) 397
17. a) 513
    b) −841 + (−513)
    c) −1354
18. a) −512
    b) −314 + 512
    c) 198
19. a) −185
    b) 473 + 185
    c) 658
20. a) −532
    b) −532 + 532
    c) 0
21. −21
22. 64

23. 1
24. 7
25. −14
26. −37
27. 98
28. −638
29. −229
30. 73
31. 1550
32. 105
33. 0
34. −1684
35. −1684
36. −842
37. 842
38. −842
39. −842
40. −842

Chapter 28: Answers A   (Problems on page 465)

1. 48
2. −105
3. −156
4. −170
5. −126
6. 28
7. 0
8. −10
9. −8
10. 8
11. −3
12. 5
13. 3
14. 0
15. −(4/3)
16. 3/2
17. −(3/10)
18. −(2/9)
19. 5
20. −2
21. −(5/9)
22. −(1/7)

23. 2/11
24. 10/27
25. −(5/14)
26. −(3/20)
27. −(8/15)
28. 9/14
29. −(15/2)
30. −(1/5)
31. c and d
32. b and d
33. a, b, c, d
34. c and d
35. d
36. c and d
37. d
38. b and d
39. c and d
40. a and b
41. a and c
42. b and d
43. b and d

Chapter 29: Answers A   (Problems on page 483)

1. 3 is on the left
   3 < 8
2. −1 is on the left
   −1 < 5

3. −10 is on the left
   2 > −10
4. −1 is on the left
   5 > −1
5. −9 is on the left
   −9 < −3
6. −10 is on the left
   −4 > −10
7. 0 is on the left
   0 < 7
8. −3 is on the left
   0 > −3
9. −5 is on the left
   −5 < 5
10. −13 is on the left
   −12 > −13
11. −435 is on the left
   −435 < 2
12. −812 is on the left
   157 > −812
13. −814 is on the left
   −814 < 0
14. −543 is on the left
   −543 < −175
15. −519 is on the left
   −316 > −519

16. <
17. >
18. <
19. <
20. >
21. >
22. <
23. >
24. <
25. >
26. <
27. >
28. <
29. >
30. <
31. (c)
32. (d)
33. (e)
34. (f)
35. (g)
36. (f)
37. (c)
38. (e)
39. (e)
40. (b)

Chapter 30: Answers A   (Problems on page 504)

1. a) 16   b) 12
2. a) 36   b) 54
3. a) 12.8   b) 10.24
4. a) 28.8   b) 38.11
5. 36.1
6. 14.6
7. 8.1
8. 9.5
9. .6
10. 15.7
11. 21.4
12. 3.2
13. 16.8
14. 3.8
15. 7.5
16. 164.7
17. $205.88
18. a) 48   b) 108
19. 3.9
20. 63

GLOSSARY

ABSOLUTE VALUE
The absolute value of a positive number is the number itself.

The absolute value of a negative number is the additive inverse of the number.

ADDITIVE INVERSE
See inverse.

ASSOCIATIVE
The associative property of addition states that for a sum involving three terms either the first two terms may be added first or the last two terms may be added first without changing the result.

The associative property of multiplication states that for a product involving three factors either the first two factors may be multiplied first or the last two factors may be multiplied first without changing the result.

Thus,
$$(a + b) + c = a + (b + c)$$
$$(a \cdot b) \cdot c = a \cdot (b \cdot c)$$

BASE
The base of our system of numeration is 10.
The base of a triangle is any one of the sides.
In the expression 6^3, 6 is called the base.

BETWEEN
If $a < b$ and $b < c$, then b is said to be between a and c.

We often write $a < b < c$ in this case.

If point R is on the line segment that joins P and Q, then R is said to be between P and Q.

BINARY
A binary operation is an operation that associates with each pair of objects a third object. The operations of addition, multiplica-

tion, subtraction, and division of numbers, and union and intersection of sets are all binary operations.

BRACES
The symbols $\{ \ \}$ are called braces and are used to designate a set.

BRACKETS
The symbols $[\ ]$ are called brackets and may be used in exactly the same way as parentheses. They are also used in this text to indicate a missing number which is not to be found by the reader.

CANCEL
To cancel is to delete a factor which is common to both the numerator and denominator of a fraction. Thus, in the fraction

$$\frac{7 \cdot 5}{4 \cdot 5}$$

the 5 can be cancelled.

$$\frac{7 \cdot 5}{4 \cdot 5} = \frac{7}{4}$$

CIRCUMFERENCE
The circumference of a circle is its perimeter, or length of its "side."

CLOSED
If a set has the property that the result of a particular operation with any of its members is always a member of the set, then the set is said to be closed with respect to that operation, or that operation is closed with the set. Thus since the sum of two natural numbers is always a natural number, the set of natural numbers is said to be closed with respect to addition, or addition is closed with natural numbers. A set that does not have

the property of being closed with respect to an operation is said to be "not closed." Thus, since the difference of two natural numbers is sometimes not a natural number, the set of natural numbers is not closed with respect to subtraction; or, subtraction is not closed with natural numbers.

COMMON DENOMINATOR
When two fractions have the same denominator, they are said to have a common denominator.

COMMON DIVISOR
If the natural number a is an exact divisor of the natural number b and also an exact divisor of the natural number c, then a is a common divisor of b and c.

COMMON FACTOR
If the natural number a is a factor of the natural number b and also a factor of the natural number c, then a is a common factor of b and c.

COMMON MULTIPLE
If the natural number a is a multiple of the natural number b and also a multiple of the natural number c, then a is a common multiple of b and c.

COMMUTATIVE
The commutative property of addition states that two terms in a sum may be interchanged without changing the result.

The commutative property of multiplication states that two factors in a product may be interchanged without changing the result.

Thus,
$$a + b = b + a$$
$$a \cdot b = b \cdot a$$

COMPLEX FRACTION
A complex fraction is an expression of the form x/y, which is not a simple fraction, but where both x and y represent quotient numbers.

COMPOSITE
A natural number greater than one which is not a prime number is called a composite number.

CONSECUTIVE
If a and b are natural numbers, a is less than b, and there are no natural numbers between a and b, then a and b are said to be consecutive natural numbers.

COORDINATE
The number assigned to a point on the number line is called the coordinate of the point.

CROSS PRODUCT
If a/b and c/d are any two fractions, ad and bc are called their cross products.

CUBE
The cube of a number is the third power of that number.

DECIMAL DIGIT REPRESENTATION
The decimal digit representation of a number is a representation that uses only the digits 0, 1, 2, 3, 4, 5, 6, 7, 8, 9 and the decimal point.

DENOMINATOR
In the fraction a/b, b is called the denominator.

DIAMETER
The diameter of a circle is the length of the line segment connecting two points on the circle and passing through the center. It is two times the radius.

DIFFERENCE
The difference of two numbers is the result of subtracting the second number from the first. The difference is a number whose sum with the subtrahend equals the minuend. The minus sign, $-$, represents difference.

Thus $a - b$ represents the difference of a and b and $a - b = d$ only if $b + d = a$.

DIGIT
A digit is any one of the symbols 0, 1, 2, 3, 4, 5, 6, 7, 8, 9.

DISJOINT
Two sets are disjoint if their intersection is the empty set.

DISTANCE
The coordinate of a point to the right of the origin on the number line is called its distance from the origin.

DISTRIBUTIVE
The distributive property states that certain products are the same as certain sums.
Thus $a(b + c) = a \cdot b + a \cdot c$

DIVIDEND
By a/b we mean a number whose product with b is a. We call a the product of the implied multiplication and the dividend of the division problem.

DIVISIBLE

If the quotient of the natural numbers a and b is a natural number, then a is divisible by b. Every multiple of a natural number is divisible by the natural number.

DIVISOR

By a/b we mean a number whose product with b is a. We call b a factor in the implied multiplication and the divisor of the division problem.

If the quotient of the natural numbers a and b, that is, a/b, is a natural number, then b is called an exact divisor of a. Every factor of a is an exact divisor of a.

EMPTY SET

The empty set is the set that contains no members.

The symbol ϕ represents the empty set.

EQUAL

Two sets are equal if they contain exactly the same members.

Two number symbols are equal if they represent the same number.

The symbol = represents equal.

EXPONENT

In the expression 6^3, 3 is called the exponent of 6. The exponent indicates how many times 6 is used as a factor.

FACTOR

The numbers that are multiplied in a product are called the factors of that product.

A factor of a given natural number is any natural number whose product with some natural number is the given one. Then if the product of a and b, both natural numbers, is c, both a and b are said to be factors of c.

FACTORIZATION

The complete factorization of a number is that number expressed as a product of 1 and prime factors.

FRACTION

A fraction is a symbol of the form a/b, where both a and b are symbols which represent natural numbers.

GCD

The greatest common divisor of two natural numbers, abbreviated as GCD, is the largest number which is an exact divisor of the first number and also an exact divisor of the second number.

GREATER THAN

If a first number is less than a second, then the second is said to be greater than the first. The symbol > represents greater than.

Thus, a > b means that b < a.

HCF

The highest common factor of two natural numbers, abbreviated as HCF, is their GCD.

IDENTITY

The additive identity is the number whose sum with each number is that same number. The additive identity is represented by the symbol 0.

The multiplicative identity is the number whose product with each number is that same number. The multiplicative identity is indicated by the symbol 1.

IMPROPER

An improper fraction is a fraction whose numerator is greater than or equal to its denominator.

INTEGER

An integer is a member of the set that contains every natural number, the additive inverse of every natural number, and zero.

Thus an integer is a member of the set $\{\ldots, -3, -2, -1, 0, 1, 2, 3, \ldots\}$.

INTERSECTION

The intersection of two sets is the set that contains all the members of the first set which are also members of the second set. The symbol $\cap$ represents intersection.

INVERSE

The additive inverse of a number is a number whose sum with that number is zero, the additive identity.

The multiplicative inverse of a number is a number whose product with that number is one, the multiplicative identity.

IRRATIONAL

If the coordinate of a point on the number line is not a rational number, then it is an irrational number.

LCM

The least common multiple of two natural numbers, abbreviated as LCM, is the smallest number which is a multiple of the first and also a multiple of the second number.

LENGTH

The length of a segment is the coordinate of its right end point when its left end point is placed at the origin of the number line.

LESS THAN

One natural number is less than another if there is some natural number whose sum with the first equals the second. The symbol $<$ represents less than. Thus $a < b$ if there is a natural number, d, such that $a + d = b$.

One quotient number is less than another if, for representative fractions, the first cross product is less than the second. Thus $a/b < c/d$ if, and only if, $ad < bc$.

One rational number is less than another if, for representative fractions with positive denominators, the first cross product is less than the second.

One real number is less than another if the point on the real number line whose coordinate is the first number is to the left of the point on the number line whose coordinate is the second number.

MEMBER

Each of the things which together form a set is called a member of that set.

MINUEND

In the subtraction problem $a - b$ the number a is called the minuend.

MIXED NUMBER

When the sum of a natural number and a fraction is indicated without using the plus sign, it is called a mixed number.

Thus, $3\frac{1}{2}$, which represents the sum of 3 and $1/2$, is a mixed number.

MULTIPLE

A multiple of a natural number is the product of that number with any natural number.

MULTIPLICATIVE INVERSE

See inverse.

NATURAL NUMBER

A natural number is the property shared by all sets that have the same size as some particular set.

NEGATIVE

The additive inverse of a positive number is a negative number. The negative numbers are coordinates of points to the left of the origin on the number line.

NUMERATOR

For the fraction a/b, a is called the numerator.

ORDERED

A set is ordered if it is possible to decide, for any two members, whether or not the first is less than the second. The set of real numbers is ordered since for any two of its members, a and b, either $a < b$ or a is not less than b ($a = b$ or $a > b$).

ORIGIN

The origin is the point on the number line whose coordinate is zero.

PARALLELOGRAM

A quadrilateral with both pairs of opposite sides parallel is called a parallelogram.

PARENTHESES

The symbols ( ) are parentheses and are used to indicate grouping of number symbols. They indicate that the operation within them is to be performed first.

PARTIAL QUOTIENT

See remainder.

PERCENT

Percent means "divided by 100" and is represented by the symbol, %.

PERIMETER

The length of the boundary of a closed figure is called the perimeter.

POSITIVE

A positive number is the coordinate of a point which is to the right of the origin on the number line.

POWER

The product of n factors each of which is b is called the nth power of b. The nth power of b is represented by b^n.

PRIME

A natural number greater than one whose only factors are itself and one is called a prime number.

When the GCD of two numbers is 1, the numbers are said to be relatively prime.

PRODUCT

The product of two numbers is the result of multiplying the numbers.

A product may be indicated by the dot, $\cdot$, or by

the omission of any symbol in certain contexts. Thus both a · b and ab represent the product of a and b.

The product of two natural numbers a and b is a sum with a terms each of which is the number b. (When a is one, the product of a and b is b.)

PROPER

A proper fraction is a fraction whose numerator is less than its denominator.

QUADRILATERAL

A quadrilateral is a closed figure with four line segments as sides.

QUOTIENT

The quotient of two numbers is the result of dividing the numbers. The bar −, the shilling/, and the symbol ÷ are all used to represent division.

Thus $\frac{a}{b}$, a/b, and a ÷ b all represent the quotient of a and b.

The quotient of two numbers is a number whose product with the divisor equals the dividend.

Thus a/b = q, such that qb = a.

For partial quotient, see remainder.

QUOTIENT NUMBER

A quotient number is the property shared by all fractions which are equal to some particular fraction.

RADIUS

The radius of a circle is the distance from its center to any point on the circle.

RATIONAL NUMBER

A rational number is any member of the set which is the union of the set of quotient numbers and the set of additive inverses of the quotient numbers and zero.

REAL NUMBER

A real number is a member of the set which is the union of the rational numbers and the irrational numbers. The coordinate of every point on the number line is a real number.

RECIPROCAL

The reciprocal of a number is the multiplicative inverse of that number.

RECTANGLE

A parallelogram with two sides perpendicular is called a rectangle.

RELATIVELY PRIME

See prime.

REMAINDER

If a = q · b + r, where a, q, b, and r are all natural numbers or zero, and r is less than b, then r is called the remainder when a is divided by b. If r is not zero, q is called the partial quotient of a and b. If r is zero, then q is called the quotient of a and b.

REPRESENTATIVE FRACTION

A representative of a quotient number is any one of the equal fractions that share a property which is called that quotient number.

RIGHT TRIANGLE

A triangle with two sides perpendicular is called a right triangle.

ROUNDING OFF

The process of approximating a decimal form with another decimal form which may use fewer digits is called rounding off.

SET

Any collection of things is called a set.

SIMPLE FRACTION

A simple fraction is a symbol of the form a/b where both a and b are the simplest forms of natural numbers.

SIMPLEST FORM

The simplest form of a natural number is one of the symbols 1, 2, 3, 4, ...

The simplest form of a quotient number which is not a natural number is a fraction whose numerator and denominator are relatively prime.

The simplest form of zero is 0. The simplest form of a number is often the easiest to write or the most commonly used form.

SIZE

Two sets have the same size if the members of the first can be paired exactly with the members of the second.

The size of a set is the natural number which this set and all other sets with the same size determine.

SUBSET

One set is a subset of another if every member of the first set is also a member of the second.

SUBTRAHEND

In a − b, the number b is called the subtrahend.

SUM

The sum of two numbers is the result of adding the numbers.

The sum of two natural numbers is the size of the union of two disjoint sets whose sizes are the natural numbers.

A sum may be indicated by the plus sign, +. Thus a + b represents the sum of a and b.

SQUARE

The square of a number is the second power of that number.

A square is a rectangle with equal sides.

TERM

The numbers that are added in a sum are called the terms of that sum. In the expression a + b, a and b are called terms.

TRAPEZOID

A quadrilateral with one pair of opposite sides parallel and one pair of opposite sides not parallel is called a trapezoid.

TRIANGLE

A triangle is a closed figure with three line segments as sides.

UNION

The union of two sets is the set which contains all the members which are either in the first set or the second set or in both sets. The symbol $\cup$ represents union.

UNIT

The distance between the origin and the point whose coordinate is one on the number line is called a unit distance. Any convenient segment may be chosen as the unit.

INDEX